HBJ GEOMETRY

James F. Ulrich

Harcourt Brace Jovanovich, Publishers

Orlando   New York   Chicago   San Diego   Atlanta   Dallas

ABOUT THE AUTHOR

JAMES F. ULRICH
Chairman of Department of Mathematics
Arlington High School
Arlington Heights, Illinois

EDITORIAL ADVISORS

Wayne Eacker
Former Mathematics Department Chairman
and Mathematics Teacher
Shadle Park High School
Spokane, Washington

Sara L. Harrigan
Department Head, Mathematics
Wethersfield Public Schools
Wethersfield, Connecticut

James McCormack
Mathematics Teacher
Castle Park Junior High School
Chula Vista, California

Gloria Becker Pettit
Former Mathematics Teacher
Westside High School
Omaha, Nebraska

Mrs. Beverly Williams
Mathematics Coordinator
Pulaski County Special School District
Little Rock, Arkansas

ISBN 0-15-353872-4

Contents

UNIT I   PROOF AND CONGRUENCE

Chapter 1:   Introduction to Geometry   1

Basic Ideas

1-1	Introduction to Geometry	2
1-2	Definitions and Logical Order	7
1-3	Postulates and Theorems	10

Segments and Angles

1-4	Segments	17
	Applications: *Using Segments*	22
1-5	Angles	23
1-6	Important Angle Pairs	29
	Applications: *Using Angle Pairs*	35

Features

Career Application: *Geometry and Design Engineering* 14
Computer Application: *Angles* 36
Calculator Application: *Checking Equations* 28
Puzzles 13, 28

Review and Testing

Algebra Review Capsules 16, 28
Review: *Sections 1–1—1–3* 16
Review: *Sections 1– 4—1–6* 37
Chapter Summary 37
Chapter Objectives and Review 38
Chapter Test 42

Chapter 2:   Introduction to Proof   43

Two-Column Proofs
    2-1   Algebraic Properties and Proof   44
    2-2   Conditionals and Deductive Reasoning   49
    2-3   Deductive Reasoning and Proof   51
    2-4   Two-Column Proofs   57

Proofs and Polygons
    2-5   Theorems About Perpendicular Lines   66
    2-6   Polygons   71
          Applications: *Using Polygons*   75
    2-7   Inductive Reasoning   76
          Applications: *Using Inductive Reasoning*   79

Features
Consumer Application: *Geometric Figures and Driving* 81
Computer Application: *Perimeter* 82
Puzzle 69

Review and Testing
Geometry Review Capsule 71
Review: *Sections 2–1—2–4* 64
Review: *Sections 2–5—2–7* 80
Chapter Summary 83
Chapter Objectives and Review 84 ● Chapter Test 87

Chapter 3:   Congruent Triangles   89

Congruence and Triangles
    3-1   Congruence   90
    3-2   Congruent Triangles: SAS Postulate   94
    3-3   Congruent Triangles: ASA and SSS Postulates   100
          Applications: *Using Triangles*   106

Congruence and Isosceles Triangles
    3-4   Isosceles Triangle Theorems   108
    3-5   More Isosceles Triangle Theorems   114
          Applications: *Using Isosceles Triangles*   120
    3-6   Congruence and Overlapping Triangles   121

Indirect Proof and Logic
    3-7   Indirect Proof in Geometry   127
    3-8   Congruence in Right Triangles   132
    3-9   Contrapositives and Biconditionals   140

Features
Consumer Application: *Logical Reasoning and Advertising* 144
Puzzles 137, 139

Review and Testing
Geometry Review Capsules 93, 99, 107, 113, 121, 132, 139
Review: *Sections 3–1—3–3* 107
Review: *Sections 3–4—3–6* 126
Review: *Sections 3–4—3–9* 143
Chapter Summary 146
Chapter Objectives and Review 146 ● Chapter Test 150
Cumulative Review: Chapters 1-3 151
Preparing for College Entrance Tests 153, 154

UNIT II QUADRILATERALS AND SIMILAR POLYGONS

Chapter 4: Parallel Lines   155

Parallel Lines and Angles
4-1	Interior and Exterior Angles	156
4-2	Parallel Lines and Angles	162
4-3	More Angle Relationships	168
4-4	Corresponding Angles and Parallel Lines	173
	Applications: *Using Parallel Lines*	179

Angle Sums in Polygons
4-5	Triangle-Sum Theorem	182
4-6	Triangle-Sum Corollaries	187
4-7	Angles of a Polygon	193
4-8	Exterior Angles of a Polygon	197
	Applications: *Using Angles in Polygons*	200

Features
Career Application: *Geometry and Optometry* 167
Computer Application: *Angles in Triangles and Polygons* 201
Calculator Application: *Evaluating Formulas* 196
Puzzle 186

Review and Testing
Algebra Review Capsules 181, 192
Geometry Review Capsules 161, 166, 173, 187, 196
Review: *Sections 4–1—4–4* 180
Review: *Sections 4–5—4–8* 199
Chapter Summary 202 ● Chapter Objectives and Review 203 ● Chapter Test 206

Chapter 5: Using Parallel Lines   207

Parallelograms
5-1	Parallelograms and their Properties	208
5-2	Proving that a Quadrilateral is a Parallelogram	213
5-3	Rectangles, Rhombuses, and Squares	220
5-4	Midpoints and Parallel Lines	225
5-5	Parallel Lines and Congruent Segments	228
	Applications: *Using Quadrilaterals*	234

Inequalities and Triangles
5-6	Inequalities in Triangles	236
5-7	More Inequalities in Triangles	243
5-8	Dihedral Angles	248
	Applications: *Using Inequalities and Dihedral Angles*	252

Features
Career Application: *Geometry and Chemistry* 219
Computer Application: *Triangles* 253
Puzzles 218, 223, 242

Review and Testing
Algebra Review Capsules 224, 228, 242
Geometry Review Capsules 218, 236
Review: *Sections 5–1—5–5* 233
Review: *Sections 5–6—5–8* 254
Chapter Summary 254 ● Chapter Objectives and Review 255 ● Chapter Test 258

Chapter 6:   Similarity   259

Proportions and Segments

6-1	Ratio and Proportion	260
	Applications: Using Ratio and Proportion	264
6-2	Other Properties of Proportions	265
	Applications: *Using the Geometric Mean*	270
6-3	Proportional Segments	271
6-4	Other Corollaries on Proportional Segments	274

Similar Figures

6-5	Similar Polygons	280
6-6	Similar Triangles	283
6-7	More on Similar Triangles	288
	Applications: *Using Similar Polygons*	294

Features

Consumer Application: *Ratios and Banking* 279
Computer Application: *Similarity* 296
Calculator Application: *Finding the Geometric Mean* 269
Calculator Application: *Similar Polygons* 282
Puzzle 263

Review and Testing

Algebra Review Capsule 265
Geometry Review Capsules 271, 283, 287
Review: *Sections 6-1—6-4* 278
Review: *Sections 6-5—6-7* 293
Chapter Summary 297 ● Chapter Objectives and Review 297 ● Chapter Test 300
Cumulative Review: Chapters 1-6 301
Preparing for College Entrance Tests 303, 304

UNIT III   RIGHT TRIANGLES/CIRCLES/CONSTRUCTIONS

Chapter 7:   Right Triangles   305

Properties of Right Triangles

7-1	Similarity Properties in Right Triangles	306
7-2	The Pythagorean Theorem	310
	Applications: *Using the Pythagorean Theorem*	315
7-3	Special Right Triangles	316

Trigonometric Ratios

7-4	The Tangent Ratio	322
	Applications: *Using the Tangent Ratio*	327
7-5	The Sine and Cosine Ratios	328
	Applications: *Using the Sine and Cosine Ratios*	332
7-6	Angle of Elevation/Angle of Depression	333

Features

Career Application: *Geometry and Astronomy* 320
Computer Application: *Right Triangles* 338
Calculator Application: *Trigonometric Functions* 331

Review and Testing

Algebra Review Capsules 309, 316, 322
Review: *Sections 7-1—7-3* 321
Review: *Sections 7-4—7-6* 337
Chapter Summary 339 ● Chapter Objectives and Review 339 ● Chapter Test 342

Chapter 8:   Circles   **343**

Properties of Circles
8-1	The Circle: Related Lines and Segments	344
8-2	Central Angles and Arcs	348
	Applications: *Using Angles and Arcs*	353
8-3	Congruent Chords and Arcs	354

Chords and Tangents
8-4	Chords and Inscribed Polygons	360
8-5	Tangents to a Circle	364
8-6	Inscribed Angles	369

Angles and Segments
8-7	Inscribed Angle Corollaries	375
8-8	More Angles and Arcs	378
8-9	Lengths of Segments	383
	Applications: *Using Chords and Arcs*	388
8-10	The Sphere	389

Features
Career Application: *Other Geometries and Mathematics* 394
Computer Application: *Angles in Circles* 374
Puzzles 368, 373, 393

Review and Testing
Algebra Review Capsule 360
Geometry Review Capsules 347, 354, 364, 368, 378, 383
Review: *Sections 8–1—8–3* 359
Review: *Sections 8–4—8–6* 373
Review: *Sections 8–7—8–10* 392
Chapter Summary 395 ● Chapter Objectives and Review 396 ● Chapter Test 399

Chapter 9:   Constructions and Loci   **401**

Construction Applications
9-1	Congruent Segments, Angles, and Triangles	402
9-2	Perpendicular and Parallel Lines	405
9-3	Circles	409
9-4	Special Segments	413

Introduction to Locus
9-5	Meaning of Locus	418
9-6	Intersection of Loci	422
9-7	Constructions and Loci	425
	Applications: *Constructions and Loci*	428

Features
Career Application: *Geometry and Geology* 416
Puzzles 417, 427

Review and Testing
Geometry Review Capsules 404, 408
Review: *Sections 9–1—9–4* 417
Review: *Sections 9–5—9–7* 429
Chapter Summary 429
Chapter Objectives and Review 430
Chapter Test 432
Cumulative Review: Chapters 1-9 433
Preparing for College Entrance Tests 435, 436

UNIT IV   AREA AND VOLUME

Chapter 10: Area   437

Quadrilaterals and Triangles
10-1	Area: Rectangles and Squares	438
10-2	Area: Parallelograms and Triangles	442
10-3	Area: Rhombuses and Trapezoids	447
	Applications: *Using Area*	451
10-4	Circumscribed and Inscribed Polygons	452

Regular Polygons and Circles
10-5	Area: Regular Polygons	458
10-6	Similarity and Polygons	462
10-7	Circumference and Arc Length	466
10-8	Area: Circles, Sectors, and Segments	470
	Applications: *Using Area, Perimeter, and Circumference*	474

Features

Consumer Application: *Geometry and Wallpapering* 465
Computer Application: *Area* 475
Calculator Application: *Hero's Formula* 450

Review and Testing

Geometry Review Capsules 447, 452, 458, 464
Review: *Sections 10–1—10–4* 457
Review: *Sections 10–5—10–8* 476
Chapter Summary 476
Chapter Objectives and Review 477
Chapter Test 479

Chapter 11: Surface Area and Volume   481

Surface Area
11-1	Surface Area: Prisms	482
11-2	Surface Area: Pyramids	486
11-3	Surface Area: Cylinders and Cones	490
	Applications: *Using Surface Area*	494

Volume
11-4	Volume: Prisms and Pyramids	496
11-5	Volume: Cylinders and Cones	500
11-6	Surface Area and Volume: Spheres	505
	Applications: *Using Volume*	508

Features

Consumer Application: *Volume and Air Conditioning* 504
Computer Application: *Surface Area and Volume* 511
Puzzles 499, 510

Review and Testing

Geometry Review Capsules 486, 505
Review: *Sections 11–1—11–3* 495
Review: *Sections 11–4—11–6* 510
Chapter Summary 512
Chapter Objectives and Review 512
Chapter Test 514
Cumulative Review: Chapters 1-11 515
Preparing for College Entrance Tests 517, 518

UNIT V   OTHER METHODS OF PROOF

Chapter 12: Coordinate Geometry   **519**

Lines and Linear Equations
12-1	The Coordinate Plane	520
12-2	Midpoint Formula	523
12-3	Slope of a Line	526
12-4	Slope and Linear Equations	528

Lines, Circles, and Proof
12-5	Parallel and Perpendicular Lines	532
12-6	Distance Formula	536
12-7	Equations of Circles	539
12-8	Coordinate Proofs	541

Features
Calculator Application: *Distance Formula* 538
Puzzle 544

Review and Testing
Algebra Review Capsules 525, 528, 531
Geometry Review Capsule 536
Review: *Sections 12–1—12– 4* 530
Review: *Sections 12–5—12–8* 545
Chapter Summary 545
Chapter Objectives and Review 546
Chapter Test 548

Chapter 13: Introduction to Transformations   **549**

Reflections
13-1	Reflections	550
13-2	Special Reflections	553

Other Transformations
13-3	Rotations	557
13-4	Dilations	560

Review and Testing
Chapter Summary 563
Chapter Objectives and Review 563
Chapter Test 565
Cumulative Review: Chapters 12-13   566

Table of Squares and Square Roots	568
Table of Sines, Cosines, and Tangents	569
Postulates and Theorems	570
Symbols	583
Glossary	584
Index	590
Answers to Selected Exercises	596

PICTURE CREDITS

CHAPTER **1**

Introduction to Geometry

Sections
1-1 Introduction to Geometry
1-2 Definitions and Logical Order
1-3 Postulates and Theorems
1-4 Segments
     Applications: Using Segments
1-5 Angles
1-6 Important Angle Pairs
     Applications: Using Angle Pairs

Features
Career Application: Geometry and Design Engineering
Computer Application: Angles
Calculator Application: Checking Equations
Puzzles

Review and Testing
Algebra Review Capsules
Review: Sections 1–1 through 1–3
Review: Sections 1–4 through 1–6
Chapter Summary
Chapter Objectives and Review
Chapter Test

1–1 Introduction to Geometry

You are familiar with sets of points such as lines and angles. **Space** is the set of all points. **Geometry** is the study of sets of points in space.

Figure	Name	Description
A •	Point *A*	Indicates position; has no size. Points are *in* or *on* lines and planes.
B C (line)	Line *BC* or Line *CB*	Extends without end in two opposite directions. Lines are *in* or *on* planes.
I, Q, P, R (plane figure)	Plane *PQR* or Plane I	A flat surface that extends without end in all directions. A plane is usually represented by a four–sided figure.

Points that are on the same line are **collinear**.

D   E   F (line)

For any three distinct (different) points on a line, one is **between** the other two. Point *E* is *between D* and *F* on line *DF*.

Figure	Name	Description
G, K (segment)	Segment *GK* or Segment *KG*	Consists of two endpoints, *G* and *K*, and all the points between them.
M, N (ray)	Ray *MN*	Extends without end in one direction from its one endpoint, *M*.

Symbols are often used to name lines, line segments, and rays.

Line *BC*: $\overleftrightarrow{BC}$

Segment *BC*: $\overline{BC}$

Ray *BC*: $\overrightarrow{BC}$

EXAMPLE 1   Use symbols and the given line to name each of the following.

        a. Three different segments   **b.** Three different rays

        c. Ray AB in two other ways   **d.** The line in three ways

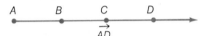

Solutions: **a.** Segments: $\overline{AB}, \overline{AC}, \overline{BC}$ **b.** Rays: $\overrightarrow{AD}, \overrightarrow{DA}, \overrightarrow{BD}$

        c. Other names for ray AB: $\overrightarrow{AC}, \overrightarrow{AD}$ **d.** The line: $\overleftrightarrow{AD}, \overleftrightarrow{BC}, \overleftrightarrow{BD}$

        NOTE: Other answers are possible.

NOTE: $\overline{AD}$ and $\overline{DA}$ are the same segment. However, $\overrightarrow{AD}$ and $\overrightarrow{DA}$ are different rays.

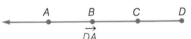

Many familiar geometric figures are made up of segments and rays.

Figure	Name	Description
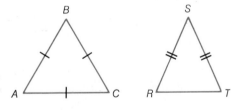	Angle ABC ($\angle ABC$) or Angle CBA ($\angle CBA$)	$\overrightarrow{BA}$ and $\overrightarrow{BC}$ are the sides of the angle. The common point of the sides is the **vertex** (plural: vertices) of the angle. It is the middle letter in the name.
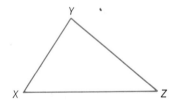	Triangle DEF ($\triangle DEF$) or Triangle FDE ($\triangle FDE$) or Triangle FED ($\triangle FED$)	$\overline{DE}, \overline{EF}$, and $\overline{FD}$ are the three sides of the triangle. $\angle DEF$ ($\angle E$), $\angle EFD$ ($\angle F$), and $\angle FDE$ ($\angle D$) are the three angles.

Triangles are classified according to the lengths of their sides. Thus, triangles are *equilateral, isosceles,* or *scalene.*

Triangle	Name	Description
$\triangle ABC$	**Equilateral**	All sides are equal.
$\triangle RST$	**Isosceles**	Two sides are equal.
$\triangle XYZ$	**Scalene**	No sides are equal.

The marks on $\triangle ABC$ and $\triangle RST$ indicate the equal sides.

The *parts* (sides and angles) of an isosceles triangle have special names.

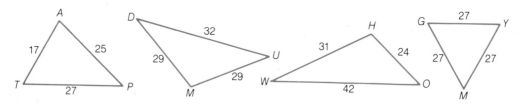

Part(s)	Name	Description
$\overline{SR}$, $\overline{ST}$	**Legs**	The two equal sides
$\overline{RT}$	**Base**	The other side
$\angle S$	**Vertex angle**	The angle opposite the base
$\angle R$, $\angle T$	**Base angles**	The angles opposite the equal sides

EXAMPLE 2 a. Name each given triangle according to the lengths of its sides.
   b. Identify the legs, vertex angle, and the base of the isosceles triangle.

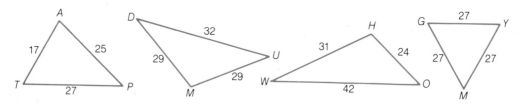

Solutions: a. Equilateral: $\triangle GYM$ Isosceles: $\triangle MUD$ Scalene: $\triangle TAP$ and $\triangle WHO$
   b. The legs of isosceles triangle MUD are $\overline{MU}$ and $\overline{MD}$; the vertex angle is $\angle DMU$, or $\angle M$; the base is $\overline{DU}$.

CLASSROOM EXERCISES

Replace the __?__ with the missing symbol or name.

1. Name: __?__
   Symbol: $\overrightarrow{TU}$

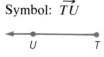

2. Name: Triangle HAP
   Symbol: __?__

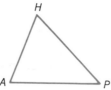

3. Name: __?__
   Symbol: $\angle WHY$

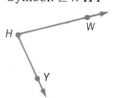

In Exercises 4–7, refer to the line below.

4. Use the point G to name the line in three different ways.

5. Name two rays that have H as an endpoint.

6. Name three segments.

7. Name $\overrightarrow{GJ}$ in a different way.

Classify each triangle as *equilateral, isosceles,* or *scalene.*

8. The triangle has no two sides equal.

9. The lengths of the sides of the triangle are 15, 18, and 15.

10. Each side of the triangle is 100 millimeters long.

In every triangle, there is a side opposite each angle. Exercises 11–12 refer to an isosceles triangle.

11. What is the name of the angle opposite the base?

12. What are the sides opposite the base angles called?

WRITTEN EXERCISES

A Match one or more names in Column A with each figure in Exercises 1–6.

1.

2.

3.

4.

5.

6.

Column A

a. △ *BCA*

b. $\overline{PQ}$

c. $\overrightarrow{RT}$

d. ∠ *FED*

e. $\overrightarrow{OS}$

f. $\overleftrightarrow{XY}$

g. ∠ *DEF*

h. $\overline{QP}$

i. $\overrightarrow{NS}$

j. △ *CAB*

k. ∠ *E*

l. $\overleftrightarrow{YX}$

Classify each statement as true, *T,* or false, *F.* Refer to lines *MR* and *HK* which intersect at *E.*

7. Point *E* is between points *M* and *R.*

8. Point *E* is on $\overleftrightarrow{MR}$.

9. Point *E* is on $\overleftrightarrow{HK}$.

10. Points *M, H,* and *E* are collinear.

11. $\overline{EM}$ has two endpoints.

13. $\overleftrightarrow{EM}$ has no endpoints.

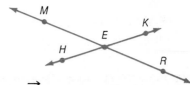

12. $\overrightarrow{EM}$ has one endpoint.

14. Another name for $\overrightarrow{EM}$ is $\overrightarrow{ME}$.

In Exercises 15–19, refer to the figures below to name each side and angle in the given triangle.

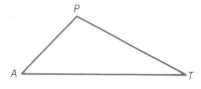
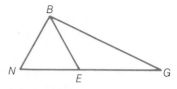

15. $\triangle PAT$ **16.** $\triangle BNG$ **17.** $\triangle BNE$ **18.** $\triangle BEG$ **19.** $\triangle GNB$

Refer to isosceles triangle *HJK* at the right for Exercises 20–23.

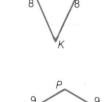

20. Name the legs of the triangle.

21. Name the base of the triangle.

22. Name the vertex angle.

23. Name the base angles in two ways.

Refer to the figure at the right for Exercises 24–26.

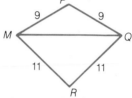

24. Name two isosceles triangles.

25. Name the base, the base angles, the legs, and the vertex angle for each of the triangles you named in Exercise 24.

26. Name the segment in the figure that is the common base of two triangles.

27. Triangle *RST* is equilateral. Name each side and each angle. Is it true that $RS = RT$? that $RS = ST$? that $ST = RT$?

B

28. How many segments are formed by three different collinear points?

29. How many rays are formed by three different collinear points?

30. How many lines are formed by three different collinear points?

31. How many segments, rays, and lines are formed by three different non-collinear points?

32. Name every segment in the figure at the right.

33. Name every ray with endpoint *A* in the figure.

34. Name four triangles in the figure at the right.

35. Name six segments in the figure for Exercise 34.

36. Triangle *TAN* is isosceles with vertex angle *N*. Name the base angles, the legs, and base of the triangle.

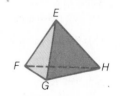

C

37. Copy the figure for Exercise 32 and add a fifth point, *E*, to the line so that *D* is between *C* and *E*. Name every segment in this figure.

38. Name every ray with endpoint *E* in the figure for Exercise 37.

1–2 Definitions and Logical Order

In geometry, point, line, and plane are *undefined terms*. These terms form the basis for defining other geometric terms.

A **definition** is a statement that gives clear meaning to a word or phrase. Good definitions use only undefined terms, defined terms, and the common words of ordinary language.

Definitions

> **Collinear points** are points that lie on the same line.
>
> **Noncollinear points** are points that do not lie on the same line.
>
> **Coplanar points** are points that lie in the same plane.
>
> **Noncoplanar points** are points that do not lie in the same plane.

A series of definitions should have a logical order. For example, if

"A perf is a karm with six legs,"

then the word *karm* should have been defined earlier.

The following table lists several terms defined in a logical order. Undefined terms and terms that have been previously defined are underlined.

Definition	Example
Ray *AB* ($\overrightarrow{AB}$) is that part of line *AB* which contains point *A* and extends without end through point *B*. *A* is the **endpoint** of $\overrightarrow{AB}$.	A B C $\overrightarrow{BA}$: Endpoint *B* $\overrightarrow{BC}$: Endpoint *B* $\overrightarrow{CA}$: Endpoint *C*
Noncollinear rays are rays that do not lie on the same line.	*R* *S* *T* Noncollinear rays: $\overrightarrow{RT}$ and $\overrightarrow{ST}$
An **angle** is the figure formed by two noncollinear rays having the same endpoint.	*E* *D* $\angle DEF$, or $\angle E$ Vertex: *E* *F* Sides: $\overrightarrow{ED}$ and $\overrightarrow{EF}$
If *Y* is between *X* and *Z* on $\overleftrightarrow{XZ}$, then $\overrightarrow{YX}$ and $\overrightarrow{YZ}$ are **opposite rays**.	*X* *Y* *Z* Opposite rays: $\overrightarrow{YZ}$ and $\overrightarrow{YX}$

The definition of opposite rays uses *between* as an undefined term. Also using between as an undefined term, you can define *line segment*, or simply, *segment*. Then, following a logical order, you can use segment to define triangle. This is illustrated in the following definitions.

Definitions

> A **line segment,** or **segment,** consists of any two distinct (different) points on a line and all the points between them.
>
> A **triangle** is the figure formed by three segments which join three noncollinear points.

EXAMPLE Write the given terms in the logical order for defining them.

a. Scalene triangle, triangle

b. Isosceles triangle, triangle, base angles of an isosceles triangle

Solutions:

a. Triangle, scalene triangle

b. Triangle, isosceles triangle, base angles of an isosceles triangle

A good definition has several characteristics (see Written Exercises 27–32). One characteristic of a good definition is that it can be written in two ways as shown below. Both statements must have the same meaning.

Collinear points are points that lie on the same line. ◄── **Good definition**

Points that lie on the same line are collinear points. ◄── **Same meaning**

The following statement is not a good definition.

A segment is a set of points. ◄────── **True statement**

A set of points is a segment. ◄────── **False; a ray is also a set of points.**

CLASSROOM EXERCISES

Write the given terms in the logical order for defining them.

1. a. equilateral triangle
   b. triangle

2. a. angle
   b. ray
   c. noncollinear rays

3. a. triangle
   b. scalene triangle
   c. line segment

WRITTEN EXERCISES

A In Exercises 1–6, state which of the two given terms is an undefined term.

1. segment; point

2. line; ray

3. plane; space

4. angle; line

5. line; point

6. point; space

Write the given terms in the logical order for defining them.

7. a. angle
   b. ray

8. a. noncollinear points
   b. triangle

9. a. triangle
   b. segment

10. a. angle
    b. endpoint of a ray
    c. ray

11. a. vertex angle
    b. isosceles triangle
    c. triangle

12. a. triangle
    b. noncollinear points
    c. segment

Write a definition for each term. Write the definition in two ways.

13. coplanar points
14. coplanar lines
15. isosceles triangle
16. collinear rays
17. equilateral triangle
18. vertex of an angle

In Exercises 19–25, tell whether each pair of statements has the same meaning. If they do not, give an example to show why not.

19. a. Lines are geometric figures.   **b.** Geometric figures are lines.

20. a. A ray is formed by points on a line.   **b.** Points on a line form a ray.

21. a. An angle is formed by two rays.   **b.** Two rays form an angle.

22. a. Opposite rays have the same endpoint.
    b. Rays with the same endpoint are opposite rays.

23. a. An acute triangle is a triangle with three acute angles.
    b. A triangle with three acute angles is an acute triangle.

24. a. Noncollinear rays are rays that do not lie on the same line.
    b. Rays that do not lie on the same line are noncollinear rays.

25. a. A triangle is the figure formed by three segments.
    b. A figure formed by three segments is a triangle.

26. Which of the pairs of statements in Exercises 19–25 are definitions? Give a reason for your answer.

In addition to the characteristic noted on page 8, a good definition has several other characteristics.

    1 The term being defined must be named.

    2 The words used must be undefined or previously defined terms.

    3 The definition must identify the set to which the term belongs and include just enough additional information to distinguish it from other members of that set.

Refer to the characteristics of a good definition outlined above to tell why each statement in Exercises 27–32 is *not* a good definition.

27. It is two different rays with a common endpoint.

28. They are points on the same line.

29. Coplanar points are in the same plane.

30. A ray is part of a line.

31. A quadrilateral is a polygon with four sides.

32. A triangle is when you have three angles and three sides.

C

33. Write an alternate definition of opposite rays.

1-3 Postulates and Theorems

In the same way that certain geometric terms are accepted as undefined, so certain statements about geometry are accepted without proof. These statements are called **postulates.**

Postulate 1	Every line contains at least two distinct (different) points.
Postulate 2	Every plane contains at least three distinct, noncollinear points.
Postulate 3	Space contains at least four noncoplanar points.

Postulates 1, 2, and 3 establish the *least number of points* for lines, planes, and space.

Clearly, the number of points in a line, in a plane, and in space is infinite.

Postulate 4	For any two distinct points, there is exactly one line containing them.
Postulate 5	For any three distinct noncollinear points, there is exactly one plane containing them.

Postulates 4 and 5 are often stated as follows.

Two points determine a line. ◄———— **Postulate 4**

Three noncollinear points determine a plane. ◄———— **Postulate 5**

Postulate 6	If any two distinct points lie in a plane, the line containing these points lies in the plane.
Postulate 7	If two distinct planes have one point in common, they have at least two points in common.

The figure below shows two conclusions that result from Postulates 4 and 6.

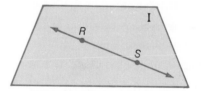

Conclusions:

1. You can draw exactly one line, line RS, through R and S. (Postulate 4)
2. Line RS lies in plane I. (Postulate 6)

EXAMPLE   In this figure, planes I and II have point
A in common. Use the postulates to ex-
plain why the intersection of the planes
is a line.

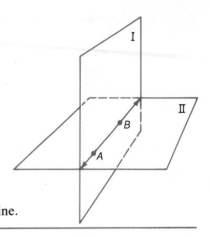

Solution:

There must be a second
common point. Call it B.   ◄─────── **By Postulate 7**

A and B determine $\overleftrightarrow{AB}$.   ◄─────── **By Postulate 4**

$\overleftrightarrow{AB}$ lies in plane I.   ◄─────── **By Postulate 6**

$\overleftrightarrow{AB}$ lies in plane II.   ◄─────── **By Postulate 6**

Since $\overleftrightarrow{AB}$ lies in both planes, their intersection is a line.

The Example is actually a *proof* of a mathematical statement; it is part of
the proof of Theorem 1–1. A **theorem** is a mathematical statement that can
be proved.

Theorem 1–1 | If two distinct planes intersect, then their intersection is a line.

Theorems 1–2 and 1–3 involve simple relationships among lines, planes,
and points.

Theorem 1–2 | If two distinct lines intersect, then their intersection is a point.
Theorem 1–3 | If a line and a plane intersect and the line does not lie in the plane,
then their intersection is a point.

The figures below illustrate the theorems.

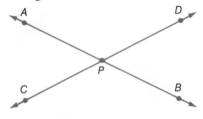

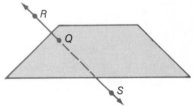

CLASSROOM EXERCISES

In the figure at the right, plane I con-
tains point D and collinear points A,
B, and C. Point E is not in plane I.
Use this information for Exercises 1–5.

1. What postulate tells you there is exactly one plane
containing points E, B, and A?

2. What postulate tells you there is exactly one line containing points D and A?

3. What postulate tells you that if D and C are in plane I, then all points of $\overleftrightarrow{DC}$ are in plane I?

4. What is the intersection of plane I and the plane determined by E, B, and C?

5. What is the intersection of plane I and $\overleftrightarrow{EB}$?

WRITTEN EXERCISES

A   In the figure at the right below, points E, B, and D are collinear. Points A and C are not on $\overleftrightarrow{ED}$.

Use this information in Exercises 1–10 to classify each statement as true, T, or false, F. State the definition(s), postulates, and theorem(s) that give the reason(s) for each answer.

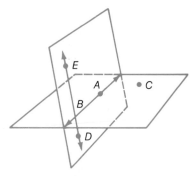

1. $\overleftrightarrow{ED}$ and $\overleftrightarrow{AB}$ intersect in B.

2. Points D, B, and C determine a plane.

3. The plane determined by A, B, and E contains D.

4. Points A and B determine a plane.

5. Only one plane contains points E, B, and D.

6. Only one plane contains $\overleftrightarrow{EB}$ and A.

7. Points A, B, C, and D are coplanar.

8. Points A, B, D, and E are coplanar.

9. The intersection of the planes determined by E, D, and A and by A, B, and C is $\overleftrightarrow{AB}$.

10. The intersection of $\overleftrightarrow{ED}$ and the plane determined by points B, A, and C is $\overleftrightarrow{ED}$.

In Exercises 11–15, choose the answer that best completes each statement.

11. The intersection of two distinct planes is a __?__ . (point, line)

12. A plane does not contain line ST. If $\overleftrightarrow{ST}$ and the plane intersect, their intersection is a __?__ . (point, line)

13. Two distinct lines intersect in at most __?__ . (1 point, 2 points)

14. A plane is determined by three __?__ points. (collinear, noncollinear)

15. A __?__ is accepted without proof. (postulate, theorem)

In this figure, points P, Z, X, and Y are in plane I. Point W is not in plane I. Use this information in Exercises 16–23 to state the definition(s), postulate(s), or theorem(s) that give the reason(s) for each answer.

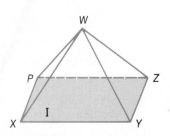

16. What is the intersection of $\overleftrightarrow{XW}$ and $\overleftrightarrow{YW}$?

17. Name three points in plane I.

18. Name the lines determined by the points in your answer to Exercise 17.

19. What is the point of intersection of $\overleftrightarrow{WZ}$ and plane I?

20. What is the point of intersection of plane I and $\overleftrightarrow{WX}$?

B

21. Name four planes, other than plane I, shown in the figure.

22. What is the intersection of plane I and the plane determined by points W, X, and Y?

23. What is the intersection of the plane determined by points W, P, and Z and the plane determined by W, Y, and Z?

24. Show that two intersecting lines determine a plane by giving the reasons for statements **a–c** below. In the figure, lines m and k intersect at A. (You can use letters such as k and m to name a line.)

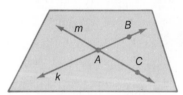

    a. Line k contains at least one point other than A. Call it B.

    b. Line m contains at least one point other than A. Call it C.

    c. Since A, B, and C are not collinear, they determine a plane.

In Exercises 25–32, state the greatest number of planes that can pass through each given set of points.

25. One point

26. Two points

27. One line

28. Three noncollinear points

29. An angle

30. Three collinear points

31. A line and a point not on the line

32. The intersection of two planes

C

33. What is the greatest number of planes determined by four points, no three of which are collinear?

34. What is the greatest number of planes determined by five points, no three of which are collinear?

Puzzle

How can six toothpicks be glued together to form exactly four triangles?

(HINT: The triangles need not be coplanar.)

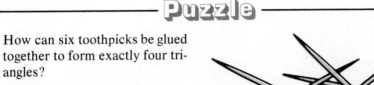

Career Applications

Geometry and Design Engineering

Design engineers work in many fields,—engineering, architecture, industrial design, and so on. Often they find it necessary to draw three-dimensional figures on a two-dimensional surface. Such figures are called **perspective drawings.** The different views in perspective drawings depend upon the choice of a point in the distance, called the **vanishing point.**

EXAMPLE 1 Draw the front view of a plane in perspective.

Solution: ☐1 Draw a horizontal segment, AB. Position a vanishing point, V, such that V is above $\overline{AB}$ and halfway between A and B.

☐2 Using dashed segments, join the endpoints of $\overline{AB}$ to V.

☐3 Choose a point C on $\overrightarrow{VA}$ and a point D on $\overrightarrow{VB}$ such that $\overline{CD}$ is horizontal. Draw $\overline{CD}$. Darken $\overline{CA}$ and $\overline{DB}$.

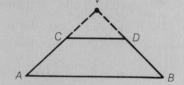

NOTE: Since $\overline{AB}$ is horizontal, $\overline{CD}$ must also be horizontal.

You can follow a similar procedure to draw two intersecting planes in perspective.

EXAMPLE 2 Draw a right view of two intersecting planes.

Solution:

☐1 Draw $\overline{AB}$ and $\overline{CD}$ to represent the front edge of each plane.

Position the vanishing point, V, off to the right.

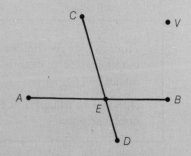

2 Draw dashed segments CV, AV, EV, DV, and BV.

Select a point $\overline{G}$ on $\overline{BV}$ and draw $\overline{FG}$ and $\overline{HI}$ as shown.

NOTE: Since $\overline{AB}$ is horizontal, $\overline{FG}$ must also be horizontal. $\overline{HI}$ must have the same direction as $\overline{CD}$.

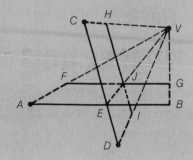

3 Darken $\overline{CH}$, $\overline{AF}$, $\overline{EJ}$, $\overline{DI}$, and $\overline{GB}$. Erase all dashed lines and the vanishing point, V.

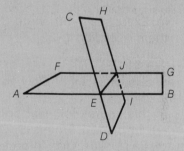

EXERCISES

In Exercises 1–3, first copy the given line segment. Use this segment to draw two views of a plane in perspective.

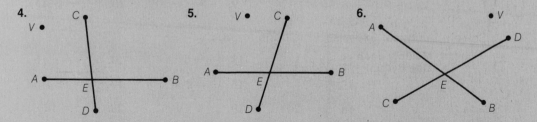

1.

A ● ————— ● B

2.

A
●
 ╲
  ╲
   ● B

3.

A ●
  ╲
   ● B

In Exercises 4–6, copy $\overline{AB}$, $\overline{CD}$, and point V. Use these intersecting segments and the vanishing point to draw two intersecting planes in perspective.

4.
V ●   C ●
A ●————————● B
      E
      ● D

5.
V ●   C ●
A ●————————● B
      E
    ● D

6.
A ●   ● V
   ╲   ● D
    ╲   ╱
     ╲ E ╱
      ╳
C ●   ● B

───── Review ─────

In Exercises 1–6, refer to the figure at
the right. *(Section 1–1)*

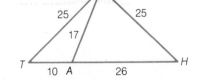

1. Name the legs of $\triangle WHT$.
2. What kind of triangle is $\triangle WHT$?
3. Name the base angles of $\triangle WHT$ in two ways.
4. Name two other triangles in the figure.
5. Name three collinear points.   6. Name three noncollinear points.

In Exercises 7–10, write the given terms in the logical order for defining
them. *(Section 1–2)*

7. angle, triangle, ray
8. segment, triangle
9. opposite rays, endpoint of a ray, ray
10. triangle, segment, equilateral triangle

In this figure, collinear points *A, D, E,* and *B*
are in plane I. Points *C, G,* and *F* are not in
plane I. Use this information in Exercises
11–14, to state the definition(s), postulate(s),
or theorem(s) that give the reason(s) for each
answer. *(Section 1–3)*

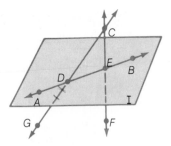

11. What is the intersection of $\overleftrightarrow{EF}$ and $\overrightarrow{DG}$?
12. What is the intersection of plane I and $\overleftrightarrow{GC}$?
13. Name three collinear points.   14. Name five coplanar points.

───── ALGEBRA REVIEW CAPSULE FOR SECTION 1–4 ─────

Evaluate.

Examples: a. $|3 - 9| = |-6| = 6$ **b.** $|5 - (-1)| = |5 + 1| = |6| = 6$

1. $|3 - 9|$ 2. $|6 - 12|$ 3. $|4 - 15|$ 4. $|-3 - 2|$ 5. $|-5 - 8|$
6. $|-1 - 3|$ 7. $|3 - (-9)|$ 8. $|6 - (-14)|$ 9. $|-5 - (-5)|$ 10. $|-7 - (-15)|$

Solve and check. Exercise 11 is done for you.

11. $\frac{3}{4}x = 12$ ⟵ **Multiply each side by $\frac{4}{3}$.**   12. $\frac{1}{2}x = 5$ 13. $\frac{1}{3}x = 3$ 14. $-\frac{1}{4}x = -16$

$\frac{4}{3}(\frac{3}{4}x) = \frac{4}{3}(12)$ 15. $\frac{x}{8} = 2$ 16. $\frac{x}{10} = 2.4$ 17. $\frac{3}{4}x = 15$

$x = 16$ 18. $\frac{3}{5}x = 20$ 19. $\frac{7}{8}x = 19$ 20. $-\frac{1}{4}x = 12$

1–4 Segments

You can find the length of the credit card below by finding the measure of line segment AB.

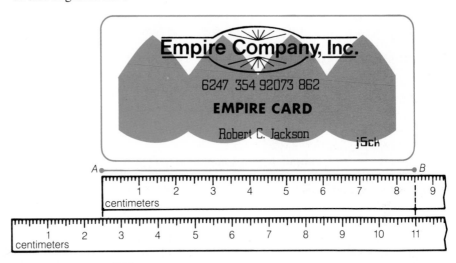

The measure of $\overline{AB}$ (written AB or BA) is the distance between points A and B on the number line. Note that changing the position of the ruler as shown does not change the measure of $\overline{AB}$.

REMEMBER: The symbol, AB, represents the distance between points A and B, or the length of $\overline{AB}$.

Postulate 8

> **The Ruler Postulate**
> **a.** To every distinct pair of points there corresponds exactly one positive number. This number is the distance between the two points.
> **b.** To every real number there corresponds a point on the number line. To every point on the number line there corresponds a real number.

Definition

> A number associated with a point on a number line is the **coordinate** of the point.

Since a distance measure is always positive, you can use *absolute value notation* to find the distance between any two points on the number line.

Definition

> The **distance**, AB, between two points A and B with coordinates a and b respectively can be written as
> $$AB = |a - b| \text{ or } |b - a|.$$

EXAMPLE 1 Use the given number line to find each distance.

a. DG **b.** AG **c.** AC

Solution:

a. $DG = |6 - 1| = |5| = \mathbf{5}$, or $|1 - 6| = |-5| = \mathbf{5}$

b. $AG = |6 - (-2)| = |6 + 2| = |8| = \mathbf{8}$, or $|-2 - 6| = |-8| = \mathbf{8}$

c. $AC = |-\frac{1}{2} - (-2)| = |-\frac{1}{2} + 2| = |1\frac{1}{2}| = \mathbf{1\frac{1}{2}}$, or

$AC = |-2 - (-\frac{1}{2})| = |-2 + \frac{1}{2}| = |-1\frac{1}{2}| = \mathbf{1\frac{1}{2}}$

In Example 1, you found that $DG = 5$ and $AG = 8$. Similarly, you could find $AD = 3$. Thus,

$$AD + DG = AG.$$

This leads to a definition of *betweenness* for points.

Definition

For three distinct points A, B, and C, A is **between** B and C if

☐1 A, B, and C are collinear,

☐2 and $BA + AC = BC$.

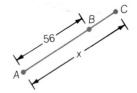

EXAMPLE 2 Three points, A, B, and C, are collinear. Point B lies between A and C. If $AB = \frac{2}{3}AC$ and $AB = 56$, find $\frac{1}{2}AC$.

Solution: Let $x = $ the distance from A to C, or AC.

Since $AB = \frac{2}{3}AC$, ⟵ Replace **AB** with **56** and **AC** with **x**.

$56 = \frac{2}{3}x$ ⟵ Solve for **x**.

$\frac{3}{2}(56) = \frac{\overset{1}{\cancel{3}}}{\underset{1}{\cancel{2}}}(\frac{\overset{1}{\cancel{2}}}{\underset{1}{\cancel{3}}}x)$

$84 = x$ ⟵ Don't forget to find $\frac{1}{2}x$.

$\frac{1}{2}x = \frac{1}{2}(84) = 42$ Thus, $\frac{1}{2}AC = \mathbf{42}$.

There is a point on every segment that divides it into two equal parts. This halfway point is called the *midpoint* of the segment. The midpoint is equally distant, or equidistant, from the endpoints of the segment.

Definition

Point M is the **midpoint** of $\overline{AB}$ if M is between A and B and if $AM = MB$.

Two theorems follow directly from the definition.

Theorem 1–4

Theorem 1–5

A segment has exactly one midpoint.

Midpoint Theorem: If M is the midpoint of $\overline{AB}$, then $AM = \frac{1}{2}AB$.

In each figure below, M is the midpoint of $\overline{AB}$. That is, point M *bisects* $\overline{AB}$. In geometry, to **bisect** means to separate into two equal parts. In the figures, segment RS, line ST, ray ST, and plane I are bisectors of $\overline{AB}$.

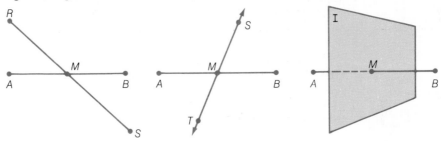

In each figure, $\overline{AM}$ and $\overline{MB}$ have the same measure, or $AM = MB$. Thus, $\overline{AM}$ and $\overline{MB}$ are *congruent*. The symbol for "is congruent to" is $\cong$.

$$\overline{AM} \cong \overline{MB} \longleftarrow \text{Read: "}\overline{\textbf{AM}}\text{ is congruent to }\overline{\textbf{MB}}\text{."}$$

Definition

Congruent segments are segments whose measures are equal.

CLASSROOM EXERCISES

Refer to the number line to complete each statement.

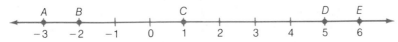

1. The distance from C to D is $|1 - 5|$, or __?__ .
2. The distance from C to __?__ is $|1 - (-2)|$.
3. $|5 - (-2)|$ is the distance from B to __?__ .
4. The length of $\overline{BC}$ is __?__ .
5. The length of $\overline{AD}$ is __?__ .
6. For a point T (not shown), if $AT + TC = 4$, then T is between points __?__ and __?__ .
7. Point __?__ is the midpoint of $\overline{AD}$.
8. If P is the midpoint of $\overline{BD}$, the coordinate of P is __?__ .
9. Point __?__ bisects $\overline{AD}$.   10. Segments AC and __?__ are congruent.
11. AC __?__ CD 12. $\overline{AC}$ __?__ $\overline{CD}$ 13. AB __?__ DE 14. $\overline{AB}$ __?__ $\overline{DE}$

WRITTEN EXERCISES

A In Exercises 1–15, the coordinates of two points on a number line are given. Find the distance between the points.

1. 8; 3
2. 2; 5
3. 7; 0
4. 15; 23
5. −8; 0
6. −3; 10
7. 6; −3
8. −5; 18
9. −11; 9
10. 0; −10
11. −2; −8
12. 0; −9
13. −7; −16
14. 14; 14
15. −12; 12

In Exercises 16–30, use the number line to find each distance.

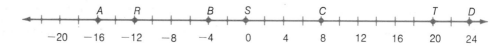

16. *CS*
17. *ST*
18. *CD*
19. *DC*
20. *SB*
21. *BC*
22. *TB*
23. *CR*
24. *AD*
25. *AC*
26. *RC*
27. *TR*
28. *RD*
29. *SA*
30. *AB*

Refer to the figure for Exercises 16–30 to answer Exercises 31–38.

31. Name the point that bisects $\overline{BT}$.
32. Name two segments congruent to $\overline{CT}$.
33. Give the coordinate of the midpoint of $\overline{CD}$.
34. Give the coordinate of the midpoint of $\overline{AB}$.
35. Name one segment congruent to $\overline{AC}$.
36. Name one segment congruent to $\overline{DC}$.
37. Which theorem tells you that $\overline{RC}$ has exactly one midpoint?
38. Which theorem gives the reason for the conclusion that $BC = \frac{1}{2}BT$?

In Exercises 39–41, refer to the number line at the right.

39. Find GH, HJ, and GJ. Does $GH + HJ = GJ$?
40. Find GJ, JK, and GK. Does $GJ + JK = GK$?
41. Show that $|22 - 28| + |28 - 37| = |37 - 22|$. To what three points do these coordinates refer? What betweenness relation exists for the three points?
42. Three points, F, G, and H, lie along a straight line. Point G lies between F and H. If $FG = 13$ and $FG = \frac{1}{3}FH$, find FH.
43. Points N, R, and T lie in a straight line and R lies between N and T. If $RT = \frac{4}{5}NT$, and $RT = 100$, find NT.
44. Three points, A, B, and C, lie on a straight line and B is between A and C. If $AB = 54$ and $AB = \frac{5}{6}(AC)$, find AC.
45. Three points, X, Y, and Z, lie on a straight line and Y lies between X and Z. If $XY = \frac{3}{4}(XZ)$ and $XY = 129$, find $\frac{1}{2}(XZ)$.
46. Three points, R, S, and N, lie on a straight line and S lies between R and N. If $RS = \frac{2}{3}(RN)$ and $RS = 98$, find $\frac{1}{2}(RN)$.

In Exercises 47–54, refer to the number line at the right.

$$V \quad W \quad X \quad\quad Y \quad Z$$
$$-19 \quad -13 \quad -9 \quad\quad -3 \quad\quad 1$$

47. $\overline{VW} \cong$ __?__

48. VW __?__ XY

49. $YZ =$ __?__

50. $\overline{YZ}$ __?__ $\overline{WX}$

51. $VX =$ __?__ $=$ __?__

52. $\overline{VX}$ __?__ $\overline{WY}$ __?__ $\overline{XZ}$

53. Complete each statement in Column A.

Column A	Column B
1. Y is between V and __?__ .	a. $\|-3+9\| + \|1+3\| = \|1+9\|$
2. W is between Y and __?__ .	b. $\|-9+13\| + \|-3+9\| = \|-3+13\|$
3. __?__ is between W and Y.	c. $\|-3+19\| + \|1+3\| = \|1+19\|$
4. Y is between X and __?__ .	d. $\|-13+19\| + \|-3+13\| = \|-3+19\|$

B

54. Match an equation in Column B with each statement in Column A.

In Exercises 55–60, R, S, and T are collinear points with coordinates r, s, and t, respectively.

55. If $RS = 15$, $r > s$, and $r = 13$, find s.

56. If $r < s < t$, which of R, S, and T is between the other two points?

57. If $RS = ST = 19$, $s < r$, and $t = 7$, find s and r.

58. If $TR = RS = 12$ and $s = -14$, find r and t. (HINT: Two answers are possible.)

59. If $r = -12$, $s = 10$, and S is the midpoint of $\overline{RT}$, find t.

60. If $s = 5$, $t = 12$, and T is the midpoint of $\overline{SR}$, find r.

61. Points K, L, and M are collinear and the coordinate of L is greater than the coordinate of K. If $KM = ML = 6$, and the coordinate of M is 3, what are the coordinates of K and L?

62. Point B is the midpoint of $\overline{AC}$, the coordinate of C is 12, and $BC = 8$. Give two possible coordinates for A.

C

In Exercises 63–66, Y is the midpoint of $\overline{XZ}$ and x, y, and z are the coordinates of X, Y, and Z respectively.

63. Find y if $x = \frac{2}{21}$ and $z = \frac{3}{21}$.

64. Find y if $x = \frac{7}{15}$ and $z = \frac{8}{15}$.

65. Find y if $x = \frac{13}{36}$ and $z = \frac{7}{18}$.

66. Find y if $x = \frac{5}{27}$ and $z = \frac{2}{9}$.

67. Explain in your own words why Theorem 1–4 is true.

68. Explain in your own words why Theorem 1–5 is true.

In Exercises 69–71, points A and X are points on the number line with coordinates 3 and x respectively. Find x.

69. $|x - 3| = 7$

70. $|x - 3| = 12$

71. $|x - 3| = 0$

In Exercises 72–74, points B and Y are points on the number line with coordinates -9 and y respectively. Find y.

72. $|y - (-9)| = 5$

73. $|-9 - y| = 8$

74. $|y + 9| \leq 3$

APPLICATIONS

USING SEGMENTS

These exercises apply geometric concepts studied in Section 1–4.

A   The figure below shows yard lines on a football field. On the field, the center point, labeled 50, corresponds to 0 on the number line.

Use this information and the given figure in Exercises 1–4.

1. How many yards is it from the center point on the field to either 10-yard line?

2. How many yards are there between the two 20-yard lines?

3. How many yards is it from the home team's 30-yard line to the visitor's 10-yard line?

4. How many yards is it from the home team's 30-yard line to the visitor's 30-yard line?

B   Three towns, Tilson, Arcade, and Sokay, lie along a highway, although not necessarily in that order. It is 16 kilometers from Tilson to Arcade and 25 kilometers from Arcade to Sokay.

5. Which town is between the other two?

6. There are two possible values for the distance from Tilson to Sokay. What are they?

7. Suppose that the distance from Tilson to Sokay is 9 kilometers. Which town is between the other two?

C

8. Suppose that the distance from Tilson to Arcade is a kilometers, the distance from Tilson to Sokay is b kilometers, and the distance from Arcade to Sokay is $(a + b)$ kilometers. Which town is between the other two?

1-5 Angles

You use a *protractor* to measure an angle. The unit of measure is the *degree*, °. The degree measure of $\angle ABC$ is 1, or ....

$\text{m} \angle ABC = 1$ ⟵ **Read: "The measure of $\angle$ ABC equals 1."**

The measure of an angle is greater than 0 but less than 180.

EXAMPLE 1 Use a protractor to measure each angle.

a. $\angle XYT$ **b.** $\angle XYZ$ **c.** $\angle SYT$ **d.** $\angle TYZ$

Solutions: Place the center of the protractor at the vertex of the angle. Line up the "0" mark on the protractor with one ray of the angle.

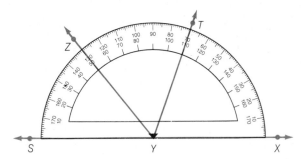

a. $\text{m} \angle XYT = 70$ **b.** $\text{m} \angle XYZ = 130$ **c.** $\text{m} \angle SYT = 110$

d. $\text{m} \angle TYZ = \text{m} \angle XYZ - \text{m} \angle XYT = 130 - 70 = 60$

Example 1 is based on this postulate.

Postulate 9

> ### The Protractor Postulate
>
> **a.** To every angle there corresponds exactly one real number between 0 and 180. This number is the **measure** of the angle.
>
> **b.** Let C be the endpoint of opposite rays CA and CB such that $\overrightarrow{CA}$ is paired with 0 and $\overrightarrow{CB}$ is paired with 180. If P is a point in the plane where P is not on $\overleftrightarrow{AB}$ and n is a real number such that $0 < n < 180$, then there is exactly one ray CE, with E on the same side of $\overleftrightarrow{AB}$ as P, such that $\overrightarrow{CE}$ is paired with n and $\text{m} \angle ACE = n$.

REMEMBER: Angles can be classified by their measures. An angle may be named by using the letter at its vertex as long as there is no confusion.

Angle	Measure	Name	Definition
	55	Acute	An angle whose measure is greater than 0 and less than 90
	90	Right	An angle whose measure is 90
	110	Obtuse	An angle whose measure is greater than 90 and less than 180

EXAMPLE 2 Identify each angle as acute, right, or obtuse. Give the reason for each answer.

a.

b.

c.

d.

Solutions:
a. Acute; m∠A < 90

b. Obtuse; 90 < m∠B < 180

c. Right; m∠C = 90

d. Acute; m∠D < 90

An angle in a plane separates the plane into three sets of points: the angle itself, or the points on the angle, the *interior* of the angle, and the *exterior* of the angle.

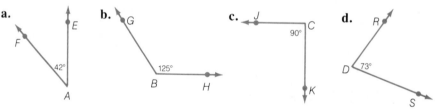

In this figure, points P, K, and T are on ∠P; R is in the **exterior** of the angle; and H is in the **interior** of ∠P. Draw $\overrightarrow{PH}$. Then ray PH is *between* rays PK and PT. This suggests a definition of betweenness for rays.

Definition	For three distinct rays, AX, AY, and AZ, and $\angle XAZ$, $\overrightarrow{AY}$ is **between** $\overrightarrow{AX}$ and $\overrightarrow{AZ}$ if

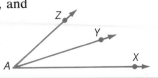

	$\boxed{1}$ $\overrightarrow{AX}$, $\overrightarrow{AY}$, and $\overrightarrow{AZ}$ are coplanar, and
	$\boxed{2}$ $m\angle XAY + m\angle YAZ = m\angle XAZ$.

In the figure for the definition of betweenness for rays, suppose that $m\angle XAY = m\angle YAZ$. Then ray AY bisects $\angle XAZ$.

Definition	Ray AY is the **bisector** of $\angle XAZ$ if $\overrightarrow{AY}$ is between $\overrightarrow{AX}$ and $\overrightarrow{AZ}$ and $m\angle XAY = m\angle YAZ$.

Two theorems follow from this definition.

Theorem 1–6	An angle has exactly one bisector.
Theorem 1–7	**Angle Bisector Theorem**
	If $\overrightarrow{AY}$ is the bisector of $\angle XAZ$, then $m\angle XAY = \frac{1}{2}m\angle XAZ$.

If $\overrightarrow{AY}$ is the bisector of $\angle XAZ$ and $m\angle XAY = 35$, then $m\angle YAZ = 35$. Therefore,

$\angle XAY \cong \angle YAZ$. ← **The angles are congruent.**

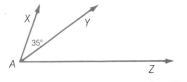

Definition	**Congruent angles** are angles whose measures are equal.

CLASSROOM EXERCISES

In Exercises 1–9, find the measure of each angle.

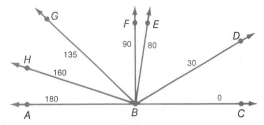

1. $\angle CBD$ 2. $\angle CBE$ 3. $\angle FBC$

4. $\angle ABG$ 5. $\angle HBA$ 6. $\angle EBD$

7. $\angle FBG$ 8. $\angle GBD$ 9. $\angle HBE$

10. Which of the angles in Exercises 1–9 are acute angles?

11. Which of the angles in Exercises 1–9 are right angles?

12. Which of the angles in Exercises 1–9 are obtuse angles?

13. By the definition of betweenness for rays, $m\angle HBG + m\angle GBE = m\angle$ __?__.

14. By the definition of betweenness for rays, $m\angle GBE + m\angle$ __?__ $= m\angle GBD$.

15. Which theorem allows you to conclude that $m\angle HBE = \frac{1}{2}m\angle HBC$?

16. Name a point in the interior of $\angle HBF$.

17. Name the ray which bisects $\angle CBH$.

WRITTEN EXERCISES

In Exercises 1–12, find the measure of each angle.

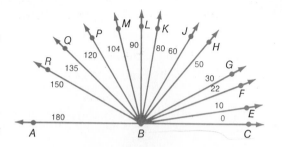

1. ∠CBF   2. ∠CBQ   3. ∠CBR
4. ∠MBA   5. ∠ABH   6. ∠JBA
7. ∠FBH   8. ∠HBL   9. ∠KBQ
10. ∠QBL   11. ∠PBR   12. ∠HBM

In Exercises 13–17, refer to the given figure to supply the missing angle measures.

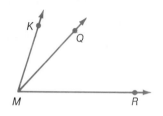

	m∠RMQ	m∠QMK	m∠RMK
13.	18	31	?
14.	37	44	?
15.	24	?	58
16.	?	51	70
17.	43	?	82

In Exercises 18–26, classify each statement as true, *T,* or false, *F.* Give the reason(s) for each answer.

18. Any real number can be the measure of an angle.
19. An angle has exactly one bisector.
20. If $\overrightarrow{BD}$ bisects ∠ABC, then ∠ABD ≅ ∠DBC.
21. The bisector of an acute angle forms two acute angles.
22. The bisector of an obtuse angle forms two obtuse angles.
23. The bisector of a right angle forms two acute angles.
24. If ∠1 ≅ ∠2, then m∠1 = m∠2.
25. If $\overrightarrow{BD}$ is between $\overrightarrow{BA}$ and $\overrightarrow{BC}$, then m∠ABD = m∠CBD.
26. If $\overrightarrow{RQ}$ bisects ∠SRT and $\overrightarrow{RA}$ bisects ∠SRT, then $\overrightarrow{RQ}$ coincides with $\overrightarrow{RA}$.

In Exercises 27–32, refer to the figure at the right to find the angle measure.

27. m∠AOC   28. m∠BOD
29. m∠AOD   30. m∠1 + m∠2 + m∠3
31. m∠AOC − m∠2   32. m∠AOD − m∠3

33. If m∠DAC = 24, m∠DAB = 52, and m∠CAB = 28, which ray is between the other two?

34. If m∠DAC = 24, m∠DAB = 52, and m∠CAB = 76, which ray is between the other two?

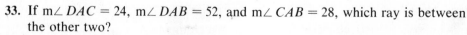

26   *Chapter 1*

In $\triangle HJK$, $\overrightarrow{JP}$ bisects $\angle HJK$. Refer to this figure for Exercises 35–39. Give the reason(s) for each answer.

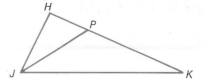

35. If m$\angle HJK = 78$, find m$\angle HJP$.

36. If m$\angle HJP = 27$, find m$\angle KJP$.

37. If m$\angle HJP = 27$, find m$\angle HJK$.   **38.** If m$\angle KJP = 31$, find m$\angle KJH$.

39. Can $\angle KJH$ have any other bisector? Why or why not?

B

40. Make drawings to show how two angles may intersect in 4 points, in 3 points, in 2 points, and in 1 point.

41. Make a drawing to show how two angles may intersect in a ray.

> **Example:** If m$\angle A +$ m$\angle B = 3x + 6$, m$\angle A = x$, and m$\angle B = 4x - 4$, find m$\angle A$ and m$\angle B$.
>
> Solution: $3x + 6 = x + 4x - 4$ ⟵ **Combine like terms.**
>
> $3x + 6 = 5x - 4$ ⟵ **Add** $-5x$ **to each side.**
>
> $-2x + 6 = -4$ ⟵ **Add** -6 **to each side.**
>
> $-2x = -10$ ⟵ **Multiply each side by** $-\frac{1}{2}$.
>
> $x = 5$ Thus, **m$\angle A = 5$ and m$\angle B = 16$.**

42. If m$\angle A +$ m$\angle B = 4x + 7$, m$\angle A = 2x$, and m$\angle B = 3x$, find m$\angle A$ and m$\angle B$.

43. If m$\angle X = a$, m$\angle Y = 2a - 10$, and m$\angle X +$ m$\angle Y = 2a + 10$, find m$\angle Y$.

44. If m$\angle Q = x$, m$\angle P = 6x$, and m$\angle P +$ m$\angle Q = 84$, find m$\angle Q$ and m$\angle P$.

45. If m$\angle D = p$, m$\angle E = 2p - 9$, and m$\angle D +$ m$\angle E = 111$, find m$\angle D$ and m$\angle E$.

46. If m$\angle T +$ m$\angle R = 2y + 12$, m$\angle R = 2y - 12$, and m$\angle T = y$, find m$\angle R$ and m$\angle T$.

47. If m$\angle G +$ m$\angle H = 210$, m$\angle G = 5t$, and m$\angle H = 3t - 30$, find m$\angle G$ and m$\angle H$.

C

48. Make a drawing to show how two angles may intersect in a line segment.

49. If m$\angle SAT = 37$ and m$\angle SAP = 48$, find m$\angle TAP$.

50. If m$\angle BOD = 23$ and m$\angle MOB = 89$, find m$\angle MOD$.

51. In your own words, explain how to prove Theorem 1–6.

52. In your own words, explain how to prove Theorem 1–7.

53. Two different noncollinear rays form one angle; three different rays, no two of which are collinear, form three angles. Continuing in this way, state how many angles are formed by four, five, and six rays.

54. How many angles are formed by r rays? (HINT: See Exercise 53.)

55. In a coordinate system for rays, $\overrightarrow{AR}$, $\overrightarrow{AS}$, and $\overrightarrow{AT}$ have coordinates r, s, and t respectively. Ray AS bisects $\angle TAR$ and m$\angle TAR = 72$. If $s = 104$, find r and t.

56. In a coordinate system, $\overrightarrow{AR}$, $\overrightarrow{AS}$, and $\overrightarrow{AT}$ have coordinates r, s, and t respectively. $\overrightarrow{AS}$ bisects $\angle TAR$ and m$\angle SAT = 27$. If $r = 103$, find s and t.

Solve and check. Exercise 1 is done for you.

1. $2x + x - 30 = 180$ ← **Combine like terms.**   2. $4n + 2n = 180$ 3. $2p + 2p = 180$

   $3x - 30 = 180$ ← **Add 30 to each side.**   4. $5x + 4x = 180$ 5. $4r - 20 = 180$

   $3x = 210$ ← **Multiply each side by $\frac{1}{3}$.**   6. $2t + 30 = 180$ 7. $5f - 35 = 180$

   $x = 70$ 8. $9u + u = 180$ 9. $8m + 8 = 180$

10. $x + x - 20 = 180$ 11. $t + 2t + 15 = 180$ 12. $3z + z - 40 = 180$

13. $4k + 2k + 36 = 180$ 14. $2w + 5w + 5 = 180$ 15. $8w + 4w - 22 = 180$

CALCULATOR APPLICATIONS _____

Checking Equations

A calculator can be used to check the solutions of equations.
The Example shows how to do this.

EXAMPLE Equation: $4m + 5m + 18 = 180$ Solution set: $\{18\}$

SOLUTION Substitute 18, the value to be checked, for the variable, m.

$$4m + 5m + 18 = 180$$
$$4(18) + 5(18) + 18 \overset{?}{=} 180$$

4 $\boxed{\times}$ 18 $\boxed{+}$ 5 $\boxed{\times}$ 18 $\boxed{+}$ 18 $\boxed{=}$ $\boxed{180.}$

EXERCISES

Use a calculator to check your answers to Review Capsule Exercises 1–15.

Puzzle

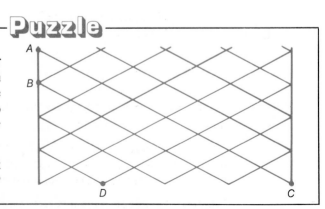

An ant is at point A, the upper left corner of a gate. The ant can walk downward only. Thus, the ant can reach point B in two ways, but there is only one way in which it can reach point C.

In how many ways can the ant walk from point A to point D?

1-6 Important Angle Pairs

Angle pairs that occur often in geometry are given special names.

Name	Definition	Figure
Complementary angles	Two angles whose measures have a sum of 90. Each angle is a **complement** of the other.	20° A B 70°
Supplementary angles	Two angles whose measures have a sum of 180. Each angle is a **supplement** of the other.	P 50° 130° Q
Adjacent angles	Two coplanar angles with the same vertex and a common side but no interior points in common.	A B 1 C 2 D
Linear pair	Adjacent angles such that two of the rays are opposite rays.	R P 1 2 T Q
Vertical angles	The nonadjacent angles formed when two lines intersect.	2 3 1 4

NOTE: Two opposite rays are sometimes said to form a **straight angle.** The measure of a straight angle is 180.

Some of the angle pairs in the table are related. For example, two angles that form a linear pair are *always supplementary.* However, supplementary angles *do not always form a linear pair.*

Example 1 on page 30 points out some of these relationships.

EXAMPLE 1   Complete the table for each pair of angles whose measures are given.

Angles	Complementary?	Supplementary?	Adjacent?	Linear Pair?	Vertical?
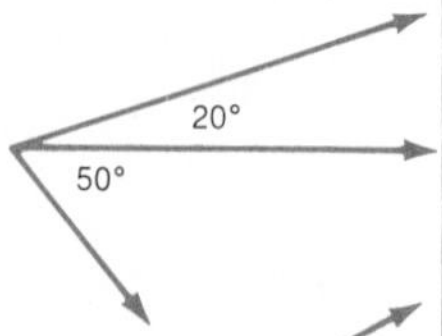 (20°, 50°)	No	No	Yes	No	No
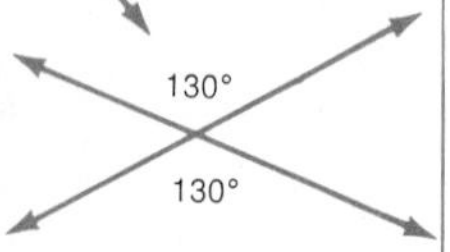 (130°, 130°)	No	No	No	No	Yes
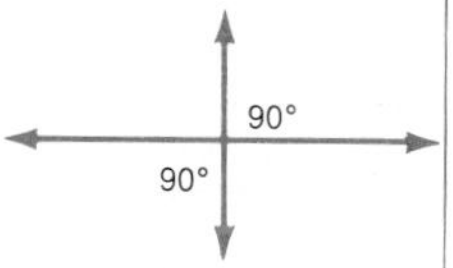 (90°, 90°)	No	Yes	No	No	Yes
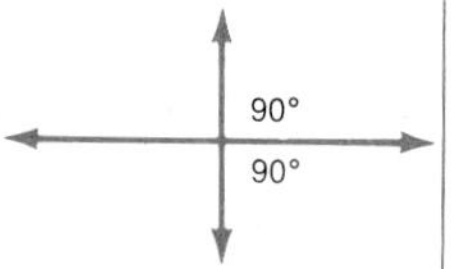 (90°, 90°)	No	Yes	Yes	Yes	No
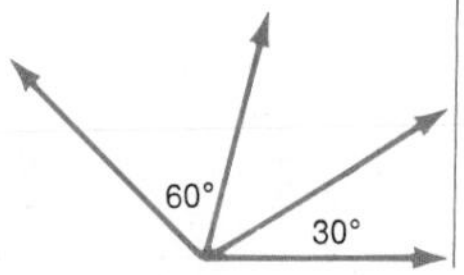 (60°, 30°)	Yes	No	No	No	No

Postulate 10 states the relationship between supplementary angles and a linear pair.

Postulate 10

> **Linear Pair Postulate:**   If two angles form a linear pair, then they are supplementary.

EXAMPLE 2   The measure of an angle is 40 less than its supplement.
   a. Find the measure of the angle and of its supplement.
   b. Find the measure of its complement.

Solution: **a.** Let x = the measure of the supplement.
   Then $x - 40$ = the measure of the angle.

$$x + x - 40 = 180 \longleftarrow \text{ Definition of supplementary angles}$$
$$2x - 40 = 180$$
$$2x = 220$$
$$x = 110 \longleftarrow \text{ Measure of the supplement}$$
$$x - 40 = 70 \longleftarrow \text{ Measure of the angle}$$

   b. Measure of the complement: $90 - 70 = \mathbf{20}$

Sometimes two lines, rays, or segments intersect to form a right angle.

Definition | Two lines (rays, segments) are **perpendicular** if they intersect to form a right angle.

In this figure, $\overleftrightarrow{AB}$ is perpendicular to $\overleftrightarrow{CD}$ at D. The symbol for "is perpendicular to" is "$\perp$."

$\overline{AB} \perp \overline{CD}$ ⟵ **Read:** "$\overline{AB}$ **is perpendicular to** $\overline{CD}$."

In the figure, the symbol "⌐" is used to indicate that the lines are perpendicular.

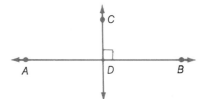

Theorem 1–8 | If two intersecting lines form adjacent angles whose measures are equal, then the lines are perpendicular.

Example 3 shows how you can use definitions and postulates to support an argument.

EXAMPLE 3 In the figure at the right, $\overleftrightarrow{AC}$ and $\overleftrightarrow{DO}$ intersect at O, and $m\angle 1 = m\angle 2$. Explain why $OD \perp \overleftrightarrow{AC}$.

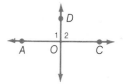

Solution: Since $\angle 1$ and $\angle 2$ are a linear pair, they are adjacent angles by the definition of linear pair.

Since $m\angle 1 = m\angle 2$, they are equal adjacent angles and $\overrightarrow{OD} \perp \overleftrightarrow{AC}$ by Theorem 1–8.

The figures below will help you to understand Theorem 1–9.

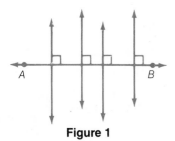

Figure 1

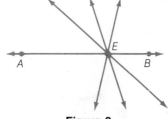

Figure 2

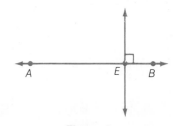

Figure 3

There are many lines perpendicular to a given line.

There are many lines that pass through a given point.

Through a given point on a line, there is exactly one line perpendicular to the given line.

| Through a given point on a line in a plane, there is exactly one line in that plane perpendicular to the given line. |

In the figure at the right, $\overleftrightarrow{CM}$ is perpendicular to $\overline{AB}$ at M, the midpoint of $\overline{AB}$. $\overleftrightarrow{CM}$ is called the *perpendicular bisector* of $\overline{AB}$.

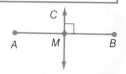

Definition

| In a plane, the **perpendicular bisector** of a segment is the line (segment, ray) that is perpendicular to the segment at its midpoint. |

Just as a line segment has exactly one midpoint, it can have only one perpendicular bisector.

Theorem 1-10

| In a plane, a segment has exactly one perpendicular bisector. |

CLASSROOM EXERCISES

In the figure below, $\overleftrightarrow{AB}$ and $\overleftrightarrow{CD}$ intersect at E, $\overrightarrow{EF} \perp \overleftrightarrow{CD}$, $m\angle AEF = 70$, and $m\angle DEB = 20$. Use this information for Exercises 1-12.

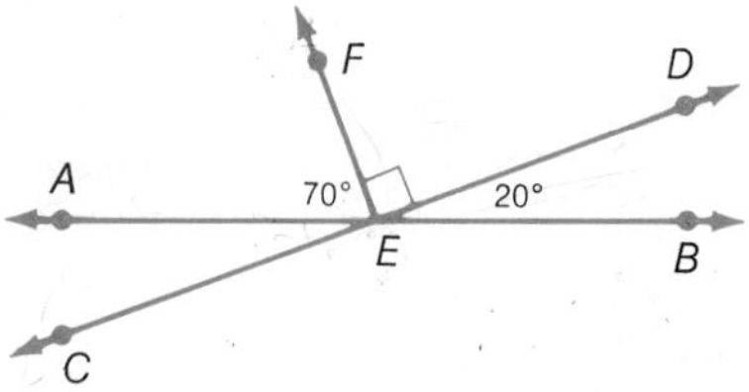

1. Name a pair of vertical angles.
2. Name two right angles.
3. What is the measure of $\angle FEC$?
4. What is the measure of $\angle AED$?
5. What angle forms a linear pair with $\angle AEF$?
6. What right angle is adjacent to $\angle DEB$?
7. What angle is complementary to $\angle DEB$?
8. Name two complementary angles that are also adjacent.
9. If an angle is supplementary to $\angle AEF$, what is its measure?
10. Name a supplement of $\angle AEF$.
11. Is $\overrightarrow{EF}$ the only ray perpendicular to $\overleftrightarrow{CD}$ at E? Give a reason for your answer.
12. If E is the midpoint of $\overline{CD}$, then $\overline{EF}$ determines the perpendicular __?__ of $\overline{CD}$.

WRITTEN EXERCISES

A   Find the measure of the supplement of each angle.

1. 30   2. 50   3. 132   4. 160   5. 115   6. 3

Find the measure of the complement of each angle.

7. 20   8. 30   9. 50   10. 8   11. 42   12. 67

13. ∠A and ∠B are supplementary and m∠A = 125. Which is greater, m∠A or m∠B?

14. ∠A and ∠B are supplementary and m∠A = m∠B. Find m∠A and m∠B.

15. The measure of an angle is 30 more than its complement. Find the measure of the angle and its complement.

16. The measure of an angle is 50 less than its supplement. Find the measure of the angle and of its supplement.

17. The measure of an angle is the same as the measure of its complement. Find the measure of the angle.

18. The measure of an angle is twice that of its supplement. Find the measure of the angle and of its supplement.

19. The measure of an angle is $\frac{2}{3}$ the measure of its supplement. Find the measure of the angle and of its supplement.

20. The measure of an angle is $\frac{3}{4}$ the measure of its complement. Find the measure of the angle and its complement.

21. The measure of an angle is 20 less than the measure of its supplement. Find the measure of the angle, the measure of its supplement, and the measure of its complement.

22. Two angles are complementary. One-half the measure of the larger angle exceeds one-fourth the measure of the smaller by 30. Find the measure of the angle, the measure of its supplement, and the measure of its complement.

23. ∠1 and ∠2 form a linear pair and m∠1 = 2 m∠2. Find the measure of each angle and the measure of the complement of ∠2.

24. ∠D and ∠E form a linear pair and m∠E = 3 m∠D. Find the measure of each angle and the measure of the complement of ∠D.

25. Find the difference between the measure of the supplement and the measure of the complement of an angle with a measure of 60.

26. In the figure at the left below, m∠AEC = 90, m∠BED = 90, and m∠AEB = 65. Find m∠1 and m∠2.

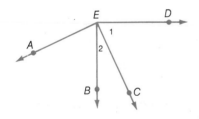 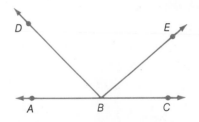

27. In the figure at the right above, point B is between points A and C. Name two pairs of supplementary angles. Which of these are linear pairs?

In figure ABCD, $\overline{AC}$ and $\overline{BD}$ are diagonals.

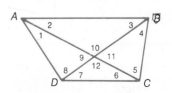

28. Name two pairs of vertical angles.

29. Name four linear pairs.

30. Name eight pairs of adjacent angles.

31. Are the angles of a linear pair also adjacent?

In Exercises 32–41, complete each statement. All statements refer to the figure at the right below in which $\overleftrightarrow{AB} \perp \overleftrightarrow{FD}$ at C.

32. The complement of $\angle 4$ is $\angle$ __?__ .

33. $\angle 1$ and $\angle$ __?__ are complementary.

34. $\angle GCD$ and $\angle$ __?__ are supplementary.

35. An acute angle adjacent to $\angle 4$ is $\angle$ __?__ .

36. Two acute angles adjacent to $\angle 3$ are $\angle$ __?__ and $\angle$ __?__ .

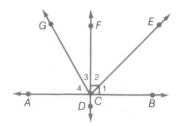

37. $\angle ACE$ and $\angle$ __?__ form a linear pair.

38. $\angle GCB$ and $\angle$ __?__ form a linear pair.

39. If m$\angle 1 = 25$, then m$\angle 2 =$ __?__ .

40. If m$\angle 1 = 45$, then m$\angle ECD =$ __?__ ?

41. If m$\angle 1 = 35$, then m$\angle ACE =$ __?__ .

In Exercises 42–49, classify each statement as true, *T*, or false, *F*. Give the reason(s) for each answer.

42. Two vertical angles may also be complementary.

43. Two vertical angles may also be adjacent.

44. If two congruent angles form a linear pair, then each is a right angle.

45. The complement of an acute angle is an obtuse angle.

46. The supplement of an acute angle is an obtuse angle.

47. Two supplementary angles always form a linear pair.

48. If two supplementary angles are congruent, then each has a measure of 90.

49. If two complementary angles are congruent, then each has a measure of 45.

B   In Exercises 50–53, complete each statement.

50. Angles A and B form a linear pair. If m$\angle A = x$, then m$\angle B =$ __?__ .
    a. $90 - x$ **b.** $90 + x$ **c.** $180 - x$ **d.** $180 + x$

51. Angles C and D are complementary. If m$\angle C = y - 10$, then m$\angle D =$ __?__ .
    a. $80 - y$ **b.** $100 - y$ **c.** $y - 80$ **d.** $y + 100$

52. If the measure of one angle of a linear pair is five times that of the other, then the measure of the larger angle is __?__ .

53. Angle A is supplementary to angle B and angle B is supplementary to angle C. If m$\angle A = x$, then m$\angle C =$ __?__ .

C

54. Show that the difference between the measures of the supplement and the complement of an angle is 90.

55. Show that when the measure of a given angle is added to twice the measure of its complement, the sum equals the measure of its supplement.

56. Show that when the measure of a given angle is added to three times the measure of its complement, the sum equals the sum of the measures of the complement and supplement of the angle.

57. Find half the sum of the measure of a given angle and the measure of its complement.

APPLICATIONS

USING ANGLE PAIRS

These exercises apply geometric concepts studied in Section 1–6.

A   The direction pointers on a weather vane meet to form angles 1, 2, 3, and 4.

1. Name two pairs of vertical angles.
2. Name two angles adjacent to $\angle 3$.
3. Name four linear pairs.
4. On the weather vane, $\angle 1$ and $\angle 4$ form a linear pair and $\angle 1$ and $\angle 2$ are supplementary. Find $m\angle 1$, $m\angle 4$, $m\angle 3$, and $m\angle 2$.

A carpenter builds a brace which forms a linear pair with a floor board as shown. The measure of $\angle 2$ is 20 more than 3 times the measure of $\angle 1$.

5. Find $m\angle 1$ and $m\angle 2$.
6. Find the complement of $\angle 1$.

When a ray of light strikes a smooth surface such as a mirror, the reflected ray leaves the mirror in a direction determined by two rules.

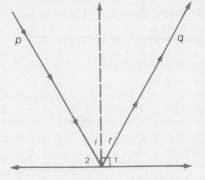

$\boxed{1}$ The ray of light (incident ray), *p*, the reflected ray, *q*, and the line perpendicular to the surface at the point where the light strikes the surface all lie in the same plane.

$\boxed{2}$ The angle of incidence, *i*, equals the angle of reflection, *r*.

Use this information and the given figure in Exercises 7–12.

7. Name two pairs of complementary angles.
8. If $m\angle i = 25$, find the measure of its complement.
9. If $m\angle i = 25$, find $m\angle r$.
10. If $m\angle i = 25$, find the measure of the complement of $\angle r$.
11. If $m\angle i = 30$, find the measure of the complement of $\angle r$.
12. If $m\angle i = 4x$ and $m\angle r = 3x + 8$, find $m\angle i$ and $m\angle r$.

BASIC: ANGLES

Problem: *Given the measures of two angles greater than 0 and less than 180, determine whether they are supplementary.*

Program:
```
10  PRINT "ENTER THE ANGLE MEASURES"
20  INPUT A, B
30  IF A + B = 180 THEN 60
40  PRINT "ANGLES A AND B ARE NOT
    SUPPLEMENTARY."
50  GO TO 70
60  PRINT "ANGLES A AND B ARE SUPPLEMENTARY."
70  PRINT "ANY MORE ANGLES (1 = YES, 0 = NO)";
80  INPUT X
90  IF X = 1 THEN 10
100 END
```

Analysis:

Statement 20: The INPUT statement causes the computer to print a question mark to prompt the user to enter one or more numbers.

Statement 30: The IF . . . THEN statement calls for a decision by the computer based on the value of the sum of the measures of the angles. If A + B does not equal 180, the computer goes to the next statement in the program.

EXERCISES

A   Run the program above for the following values.

1. $A = 40$, $B = 140$ 2. $A = 60$, $B = 120$ 3. $A = 82$, $B = 96$

4. $A = 95$, $B = 85$ 5. $A = 62.3$, $B = 97.6$ 6. $A = 42.5$, $B = 138.5$

B   Write a BASIC program for each problem.

7. Given two angle measures greater than 0 and less than 90, determine whether they are complementary.

8. Given two angle measures greater than 0 and less than 180, determine whether they could be vertical angles.

9. Given two angle measures greater than 0 and less than 180, determine whether they could form a linear pair.

10. Given the measure of an angle greater than 0 and less than 90, compute its complement.

11. Given the measure of an angle greater than 0 and less than 180, compute its supplement.

Review

In Exercises 1–5, the coordinates of two points on a number line are given. Find the distance between the points. *(Section 1–4)*

1. 3; 7   **2.** −2; 8   **3.** −3; −5   **4.** 0; 10   **5.** −8; 11

6. Three points K, L, and M, lie along a straight line. Point M lies between K and L. If $KM = 22$, and $KM = \frac{2}{3}KL$, find KL. *(Section 1–4)*

In Exercises 7–12, refer to the figure at the right to find each measure. *(Section 1–5)*

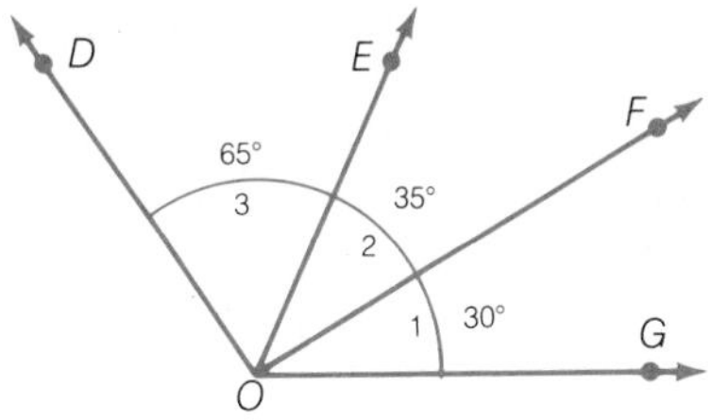

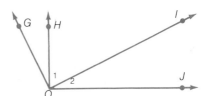

7. m∠ *DOF*   **8.** m∠ *EOG*

9. m∠ *DOG*   **10.** m∠ 1 + m∠ 2

11. m∠ 3 − m∠ 1   **12.** m∠ 2 − m∠ 1

13. Name two acute angles in the figure above.

14. Name one obtuse angle in the figure above.

15. In the figure at the right, m∠ *GOI* = 90, m∠ *HOJ* = 90, and m∠ *GOH* = 25. Find m∠ 1 and m∠ 2. *(Section 1–6)*

16. The measure of an angle is 4 less than the measure of its complement. Find the measure of the angle. *(Section 1–6)*

17. ∠ *B* and ∠ *C* form a linear pair. If m∠ *B* is 30 less than twice m∠ *C*, find m∠ *B* and m∠ *C*. *(Section 1–6)*

Chapter Summary

IMPORTANT TERMS

Absolute value (p. 17)	Degree (p. 23)
Acute angle (p. 24)	Distance between points (p. 17)
Adjacent angles (p. 29)	Endpoints (p. 7)
Angle (p. 7)	Equilateral triangle (p. 3)
Base angles (p. 4)	Exterior of an angle (p. 24)
Base of an isosceles triangle (p. 4)	Interior of an angle (p. 24)
Betweenness of points (p. 18)	Isosceles triangle (p. 3)
Betweenness of rays (p. 25)	Leg of an isosceles triangle (p. 4)
Bisect (p. 19)	Line (p. 2)
Bisector of an angle (p. 25)	Linear pair (p. 29)
Collinear points (p. 7)	Measure of an angle (p. 23)
Complementary angles (p. 29)	Midpoint (p. 18)
Congruent angles (p. 25)	Noncollinear points (p. 7)
Congruent segments (p. 19)	Noncollinear rays (p. 7)
Coordinate (p. 17)	Noncoplanar points (p. 7)
Coplanar points (p. 7)	Obtuse angle (p. 24)

Opposite rays (p. 7)
Perpendicular bisector (p. 32)
Perpendicular lines (p. 31)
Plane (p. 2)
Point (p. 2)
Postulate (p. 10)
Protractor (p. 23)
Ray (p. 2)
Right angle (p. 24)
Scalene triangle (p. 3)

Segment (p. 8)
Space (p. 2)
Straight angle (p. 29)
Supplementary angles (p. 29)
Theorem (p. 11)
Triangle (p. 8)
Vertex angle of an isosceles
   triangle (p. 4)
Vertex of an angle (p. 3)
Vertical angles (p. 29)

IMPORTANT IDEAS

1. Point, line, and plane are undefined terms in geometry.
2. $\overleftrightarrow{AB}$, $\overrightarrow{AB}$, and $\overline{AB}$ represent line AB, ray AB, and segment AB, respectively.
3. There are an infinite number of points on a line, in a plane, and in space.
4. Two points determine a line and three noncollinear points determine a plane.
5. The intersection of two distinct lines is a point, and the intersection of two distinct planes is a line.
6. A segment has exactly one midpoint.
7. An angle has exactly one bisector.
8. If two angles form a linear pair, they are supplementary.
9. If two intersecting lines form equal adjacent angles, the lines are perpendicular.
10. Through any point on a line in a plane, there is exactly one line in that plane perpendicular to the given line.
11. In a plane, a segment has exactly one perpendicular bisector.

—————— Chapter Objectives and Review ——————

Objective: *To distinguish between line, segment, and ray, and to use the symbols for each (Section 1–1)*

Classify each statement as true, *T*, or false, *F*. Refer to the figure.

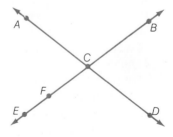

1. $\overrightarrow{CD}$ passes through A.
2. $\overline{EF}$ intersects $\overleftrightarrow{AD}$.
3. $\overrightarrow{EF}$ intersects $\overleftrightarrow{AD}$.
4. $\overleftrightarrow{AD}$ has an endpoint.
5. $\overrightarrow{BE}$ and $\overrightarrow{EB}$ contain the same points.
6. Points D, E, and F are on $\overleftrightarrow{FB}$.
7. $\overline{CB}$ has two endpoints.

Objective: *To classify triangles according to the lengths of their sides (Section 1–1)*

In Exercises 8–11, classify each triangle as *equilateral, isosceles,* or *scalene.*

8.

9.
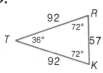

10.
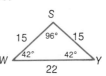

11.

Objective: *To name angles and triangles (Section 1–1)*

In Exercises 12–14, refer to the figure at the right.

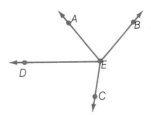

12. Name 5 different angles.

13. Name each angle in Exercise 12 in a different way.

14. Name the common vertex of all these angles.

Objective: *To identify the parts of an isosceles triangle (Section 1–1)*

In Exercises 15–16, refer to the figure at the right.

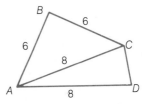

15. Name two isosceles triangles.

16. Name the base, base angles, and vertex angle of each triangle in Exercise 15.

Objective: *To identify undefined and defined terms in geometry (Section 1–2)*

In Exercises 17–24, tell whether each of the following is an undefined or a defined term in geometry.

17. Point

18. Ray

19. Angle

20. Line

21. Plane

22. Triangle

23. Endpoint

24. Space

Objective: *To identify a good definition (Section 1–2)*

In Exercises 25–28, write *G* if the statement has the characteristics necessary for a good definition, and *NG* if it does not.

If you write *NG,* give a reason for your answer.

25. An angle has two sides.

26. It has three equal angles.

27. Collinear points are points that lie on the same line.

28. Points that do not lie in the same plane are noncoplanar points.

Objective: *To use postulates and theorems to justify statements (Section 1–3)*

Write the postulate or theorem that justifies each conclusion.

29. Points *A* and *B* lie in plane I.
    Conclusion: All points on line *AB* lie in plane I.

30. Points *P*, *Q*, and *R* are noncollinear.
    Conclusion: Points *P*, *Q*, and *R* determine a plane.

31. Line *s* and plane I intersect and line *s* is not in plane I.
    Conclusion: Line *s* and plane I have only one point in common.

32. Lines *p* and *q* intersect.
    Conclusion: Lines *p* and *q* have at least one point in common.

Objective: *To use absolute value to determine the distance between pairs of points on the number line (Section 1–4)*

Find the distance between the points with the given coordinates.

33. 7; 16   34. −3; 8   35. −15; −6   36. 0; −3

Objective: *To use the definitions of betweenness of points and midpoint (Section 1–4)*

Complete each statement.

37. Point *T* is between *Q* and __?__ .

38. __?__ is the midpoint of $\overline{PR}$.

39. $PR = 2$ __?__   40. $QR = \frac{1}{2}$ __?__

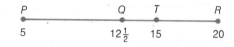

41. Three points *S*, *T*, and *U* are collinear. *T* is between *S* and *U*. $ST = 45$ and $ST = \frac{3}{5}SU$. Find $\frac{1}{2}SU$.

42. Three points *X*, *Y*, and *Z* are collinear. *Z* is between *X* and *Y*; $XZ = 28$ and $XZ = \frac{1}{3}XY$. Find $\frac{1}{2}XY$.

Objective: *To use symbols for "is congruent to" and "has the same measure" (Section 1–4)*

In the figure below at the right, *TR* = 12 and *S* is the midpoint of $\overline{TR}$. Replace each __?__ with ≅ or =.

43. $\overline{TS}$ __?__ $\overline{SR}$ 44. *TS* __?__ *SR*

45. *TS* __?__ 6   46. *SR* __?__ $\frac{1}{2}TR$

Objective: *To use the Protractor Postulate to determine angle measure (Section 1–5)*

Use the figure at the right to find the measure of each angle.

47. ∠*BAE*   48. ∠*DAG*

49. ∠*FAH*   50. ∠*HAC*

51. ∠*BAH*   52. ∠*FAC*

53. ∠*FAB*   54. ∠*DAE*

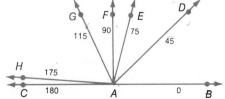

Objective: *To use symbols for angle and measure of an angle (Section 1–5)*

Classify each sentence as true, *T*, or false, *F*.

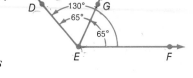

55. $m\angle DEG = 65$

56. $\angle DEG = \angle GEF$

57. $m\angle DEG = m\angle GEF$

58. $\angle DEG \cong \angle GEF$

Objective: *To classify angles according to their measures (Section 1–5)*

Classify each angle as acute, right, or obtuse.

59. $25°$ 60. $99°$ 61. $111°$ 62. $90°$

Objective: *To use the definitions of betweenness for rays and angle bisector to determine angle measures (Section 1–5)*

63. If $m\angle RQP = 69$, $m\angle RQT$ is 31, and $\overrightarrow{QT}$ is between $\overrightarrow{QR}$ and $\overrightarrow{QP}$, find $m\angle TQP$.

64. If $\overrightarrow{QT}$ bisects $\angle PQR$ and $m\angle TQP = 21\frac{1}{2}$, find $m\angle PQR$.

Objective: *To identify supplementary angles, complementary angles, adjacent angles, linear pairs, and vertical angles (Section 1–6)*

Use the figure at the right to classify each pair of angles as supplementary, complementary, adjacent, linear pair, vertical, or none of these.

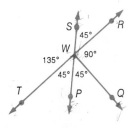

65. $\angle SWR$ and $\angle TWP$

66. $\angle SWT$ and $\angle TWP$

67. $\angle RWQ$ and $\angle QWP$

68. $\angle QWP$ and $\angle PWT$

69. $\angle SWT$ and $\angle QWP$

70. $\angle SWR$ and $\angle QWP$

Complete each statement.

71. If $\angle P$ is a complement of $\angle Q$, then $m\angle P + m\angle Q = \underline{\ ?\ }$.

72. If $\angle P$ and $\angle Q$ form a linear pair, then $m\angle P + m\angle Q = \underline{\ ?\ }$.

73. If $\angle P$ and $\angle Q$ form a linear pair, then $\angle P$ and $\angle Q$ are $\underline{\ ?\ }$ angles.

74. $\angle RST$ and $\angle TSQ$ form a linear pair and $\angle RST \cong \angle TSQ$. Then $TS \underline{\ ?\ } QR$.

75. $\angle RST$ and $\angle TSQ$ form a linear pair. $\angle RST \cong \angle TSQ$, and $\overline{QS} \cong \overline{SR}$. Then $\overleftrightarrow{TS}$ is the $\underline{\ ?\ }$ of $\overline{QR}$.

76. $\angle RST$ and $\angle TSQ$ form a linear pair. If $m\angle RST = x$ and $m\angle TSQ = 2x - 60$, find x.

Objective: *To solve word problems that involve line segments and angle pairs (Pages 22, 35)*

77. In a football game, the home team began a play on the 35-yard line. They lost yardage and finished the play on the 26-yard line. Find the distance the team lost during the play.

78. At the traffic intersection shown at the right, Routes 1 and 3 meet at right angles, Routes 2 and 3 meet at angle a, and Routes 1 and 2 meet at angle b. If $m\angle a = \frac{1}{2}m\angle b$, find $m\angle a$ and $m\angle b$.

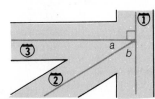

Chapter Test

In Exercises 1–5, use the figure at the right.

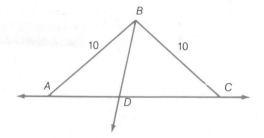

1. Name three collinear points.
2. Name a segment that intersects $\overrightarrow{BD}$.
3. Name three noncollinear points.
4. Name an isosceles triangle.
5. Name the vertex angle of the isosceles triangle.

Write the following terms in a logical order for defining them.

6. base angles; triangle; isosceles triangle
7. angle; endpoint; noncollinear rays

In Exercises 8–10, choose the answer that best completes each statement.

8. Every plane contains at least __?__ distinct noncollinear points.   (three, four)
9. Two points determine a __?__. (line, plane)
10. The intersection of two distinct planes is a __?__.   (ray, line)
11. The coordinate of point A is -17 and the coordinate of point B is 2. Find the distance between A and B.
12. Three points A, B, and C lie on a straight line. B is between A and C. If $AB = 40$ and $AB = \frac{2}{5}AC$, find $\frac{1}{2}AC$.

In $\triangle NPQ$, $\overline{NS}$ bisects $\angle QNP$. Refer to this figure for Exercises 13–15. Give the reason(s) for each answer.

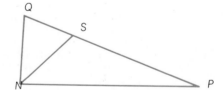

13. If $m\angle QSN = 70$, find $m\angle PSN$.
14. If $m\angle QNP = 86$, find $m\angle QNS$.
15. If $m\angle PNS = 39$, find $m\angle SNQ$.

Use the figure at the right in Exercises 16–19.

16. Name two right angles.
17. Name a linear pair.
18. Name two complementary angles.
19. Find $m\angle CFE$.

20. The measure of an angle is 60 less than its supplement. Find the measure of the angle and of its supplement.

CHAPTER 2 Introduction to Proof

Sections

2-1 Algebraic Properties and Proof

2-2 Conditionals and Deductive Reasoning

2-3 Deductive Reasoning and Proof

2-4 Two–Column Proofs

2-5 Theorems about Perpendicular Lines

2-6 Polygons

Applications: Using Polygons

2-7 Inductive Reasoning

Applications: Using Inductive Reasoning

Features

Consumer Application: Geometric Figures and Driving

Computer Application: Perimeter

Puzzle

Review and Testing

Geometry Review Capsule

Review: Sections 2–1 through 2–4

Review: Sections 2–5 through 2–7

Chapter Summary

Chapter Objectives and Review

Chapter Test

2-1 Algebraic Properties and Proof

The measures of line segments and of angles are real numbers. Thus, the properties of real numbers are also important in geometry.

Equality of real numbers is an **equivalence relation** because it has the following properties for all real numbers a, b, and c.

Properties of Equality		
Reflexive Property	$a = a$	
Symmetric Property	If $a = b$, then $b = a$.	
Transitive Property	If $a = b$ and $b = c$, then $a = c$.	

Example 1 shows that these three properties held for congruence of angles.

EXAMPLE 1 Refer to the figures in the table to determine whether congruence for angles is reflexive, symmetric, and transitive.

Solution:

Property	Figure	True or False?
Reflexive	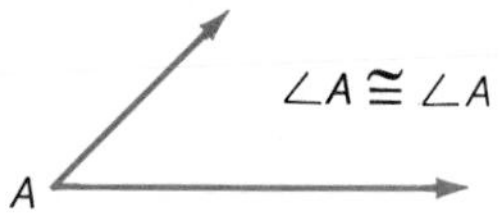 $\angle A \cong \angle A$	True; an angle is congruent to itself.
Symmetric	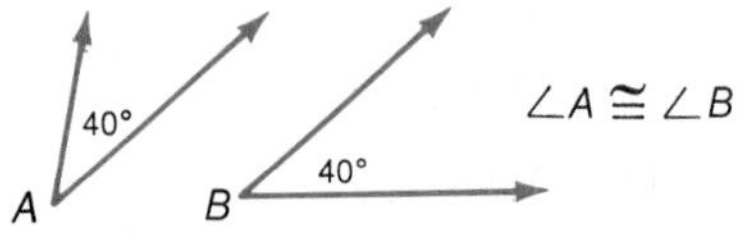 $\angle A \cong \angle B$	True; if $\angle A \cong \angle B$, then $\angle B \cong \angle A$.
Transitive	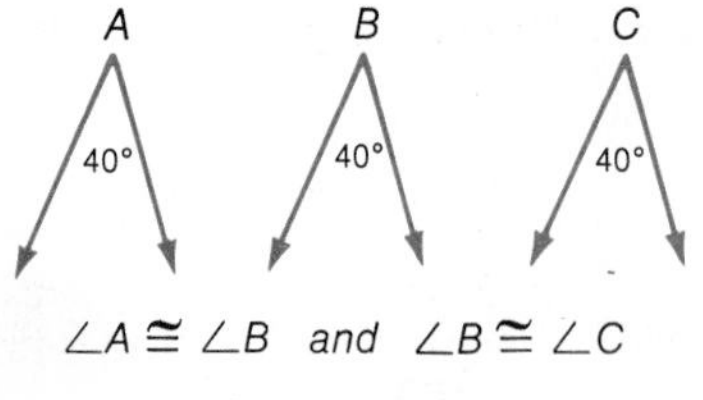 $\angle A \cong \angle B$ and $\angle B \cong \angle C$	True; if $\angle A \cong \angle B$ and $\angle B \cong \angle C$, then $\angle A \cong \angle C$.

Theorem 2-1 states the results of the Example.

don't need to know this

Theorem 2-1

Congruence is an equivalence relation.

Other properties of real numbers that are used often in geometry are listed in the table on page 45.

Property	Example
Addition	
If $a = b$ and $c = d$, then $a + c = b + d$.	If $x - 5 = 9$ and $5 = 5$, then $x - 5 + \mathbf{5} = 9 + \mathbf{5}$.
	If $x + 5 = 9$ and $-5 = -5$, then $x + 5 + \mathbf{(-5)} = 9 + \mathbf{(-5)}$.
Multiplication	
If $a = b$, then $ca = cb$.	If $x = 4$, then $3x = 3(4)$.
	If $6x = 18$, then $\frac{1}{6}(6x) = \frac{1}{6}(18)$.
Substitution	
If $a = b$, then a may be replaced by b.	If $23 = 7 + x$ and $7 + x = y$, then $23 = y$.
Distributive Multiplication over Addition	
$a(b + c) = ab + ac$	$4(6 + z) = 4(6) + 4(z)$
$ba + ca = (b + c)a$	$3x + 2x = (3 + 2)x$, or $5x$

NOTE: The examples in the table are often written in a shorter form.

If $x - 5 = 9$, then $x = 14$.
If $x + 5 = 9$, then $x = 4$. ⟵ **Addition Property**

If $x = 4$, then $3x = 12$.
If $6x = 18$, then $x = 3$. ⟵ **Multiplication Property**

Example 2 shows how several properties are used to solve an equation.

EXAMPLE 2   Solve $2(x - 7) = 6$. State the reason for each step of the solution.

Proof:

Statements	Reasons
1. $2(x - 7) = 6$	1. Given
2. $2x - 14 = 6$	2. Distributive property
3. $2x = 20$	3. Addition property
4. $x = 10$	4. Multiplication property

The statements and reasons in Example 2 prove the following statement.
If $2(x - 7) = 6$, then $x = 10$.

CLASSROOM EXERCISES

Each statement in Exercises 1–5 illustrates a property of congruence for segments or angles. Use the indicated property to complete each statement.

1. *Transitive Property:* If $\overline{AB}$ is congruent to $\overline{CD}$ and $\overline{CD}$ is congruent to $\overline{EF}$, then $\overline{AB}$ is congruent to __?__.

2. *Symmetric Property:* If $\overline{RS} \cong \overline{SK}$, then __?__ $\cong \overline{RS}$.

3. *Reflexive Property:* $\angle A \cong$ __?__.

4. *Transitive Property:* If $\angle T \cong \angle R$ and $\angle R \cong \angle G$, then __?__ $\cong$ __?__.

5. *Transitive Property:* If $\overline{MP} \cong \overline{PQ}$ and __?__ $\cong \overline{QR}$, then $\overline{MP} \cong \overline{QR}$.

State the property illustrated by each of the following.

6. If $x - 8 = 24$, then $x = 32$.

7. If $4(5 + x) = 32$, then $20 + 4x = 32$.

8. If $AB + AB = CD$, then $2(AB) = CD$.

9. If $b = a$ and $a = 3x - 9$, then $b = 3x - 9$.

10. If $2x - 14 = 6$, then $x - 7 = 3$.

11. Supply the missing reasons for the statements of this proof.

Statements	Reasons
1. $5x - 5 = 3x + 2$	1. Given
2. $2x - 5 = 2$	2. __?__
3. $2x = 7$	3. __?__
4. $x = \frac{7}{2}$	4. __?__

12. Write the statement that is proved in Exercise 11.

WRITTEN EXERCISES

A   In Exercises 1–8, name the property of equality illustrated.

1. If $m\angle ABC = m\angle 1$ and $m\angle 1 = m\angle GHK$, then $m\angle ABC = m\angle GHK$.

2. If $RS = DW$, then $DW = RS$.

3. The length of segment AC is equal to itself.

4. $m\angle D = m\angle D$.

5. If $m\angle A = m\angle D$ and $m\angle D = m\angle E$, then $m\angle A = m\angle E$.

6. If $CE = BA$ and $BA = \frac{1}{2}(BD)$, then $CE = \frac{1}{2}(BD)$.

7. If $WR = PQ + 2(ST)$, then $PQ + 2(ST) = WR$.

8. If $m\angle 1 + m\angle 2 = 90$ and $90 = m\angle 3 + m\angle 4$, then $m\angle 1 + m\angle 2 = m\angle 3 + m\angle 4$.

In Exercises 9–20, state the property illustrated.

9. If $AB = BC$, then $AB + OR = BC + OR$.
10. If $AB = BC$, then $AB - OR = BC - OR$.
11. If $5x - 7 = 23$, then $5x = 30$.
12. If $y - 19 = 21$, then $y = 40$.
13. If $2(t + 8) = 1$, then $2t + 16 = 1$.
14. If $7x = 91$, then $x = 13$.
15. If $4(x + 9) = 5(x + 4)$, then $4x + 36 = 5x + 20$.
16. If $49 = 147x$, then $\frac{1}{3} = x$.
17. If $2x + 6 = x - 2$, then $x + 6 = -2$.
18. If $3x + 8 = x + 12$, then $2x = 4$.
19. If $m\angle A = 40$, then $3\ m\angle A = 120$.
20. If $m\angle A = m\angle B$ and $m\angle B = m\angle C$, then $m\angle A = m\angle C$.

In Exercises 21–24, state the missing reasons for each proof.

21.

Statements		Reasons
1. $4x + 20 = -4 - 2x$		1. Given
2. $6x + 20 = -4$		2. ?
3. $6x = -24$		3. ?
4. $x = -4$		4. ?

22.

Statements		Reasons
1. $\frac{2}{3}(12 + 6) - x = 3$		1. Given
2. $8 + 4 - x = 3$		2. ?
3. $-x = -9$		3. ?
4. $x = 9$		4. ?

23.

Statements		Reasons
1. $90 - x = 2x$		1. Given
2. $90 = 3x$		2. ?
3. $30 = x$		3. ?
4. $x = 30$		4. ?

24.

Statements		Reasons
1. $\frac{2}{3}x + x = 25$		1. Given
2. $\frac{5}{3}x = 25$		2. ?
3. $x = 15$		3. ?

In Exercises 25–34, give the reason for each statement.

25. If $WY = RT$, then $\frac{1}{2}(WY) = \frac{1}{2}(RT)$.
26. If $\frac{1}{2}(WY) = \frac{1}{2}(RT)$, and $RS = \frac{1}{2}(RT)$, and $WS = \frac{1}{2}(WY)$, then $RS = WS$.

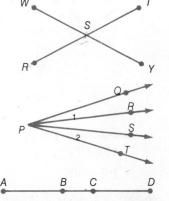

27. If $m\angle 2 = m\angle 1$, then $m\angle QPS = m\angle RPT$.
28. If $m\angle QPS = m\angle RPT$, then $m\angle 2 = m\angle 1$.
29. If $m\angle 2 = m\angle 1$, then $5\ m\angle 2 = 5\ m\angle 1$.

30. $BC = BC$

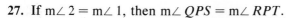

31. If $AB = CD$, then $AB + BC = CD + BC$.

32. If $AB + BC = BC + CD$, and $AC = AB + BC$, and $BD = BC + CD$, then $AC = BD$.

33. If $m\angle 1 + m\angle 2 = 180$ and $m\angle 3 = m\angle 1$, $m\angle 3 + m\angle 2 = 180$.

34. If $m\angle 4 = m\angle 3$ and $m\angle 3 = m\angle 5$ and $m\angle 5 = m\angle 1$, then $m\angle 4 = m\angle 1$.

In Exercises 35–36, state whether each relation is reflexive. Give an example in each case.

35. *Is supplementary to*, for angles   **36.** *Is perpendicular to*, for lines

In Exercises 37–38, state whether each relation is symmetric. Give an example in each case.

37. *Is perpendicular to*, for lines   **38.** *Is complementary to*, for angles

In Exercises 39–40, state whether each relation is transitive. Give an example in each case.

39. *Is supplementary to*, for angles   **40.** *Is perpendicular to*, for lines

A relation that is reflexive, symmetric, and transitive is an **equivalence relation.** Which of these are equivalence relations? Answer *Yes* or *No*.

41. *Is perpendicular to*, for lines   **42.** *Is supplementary to*, for angles

43. *Has the same measure*, for angles   **44.** *Is coplanar with*, for lines

In Exercises 45–47, give the missing reasons in each proof.

45. Congruence of line segments is reflexive.

Statements	Reasons
1. $\overline{PQ}$ is a segment.	1. Given
2. $PQ = PQ$	2. ?
3. $\overline{PQ} \cong \overline{PQ}$	3. ?

46. Congruence of line segments is symmetric.

Statements	Reasons
1. $\overline{PQ} \cong \overline{RS}$	1. Given
2. $PQ = RS$	2. ?
3. $RS = PQ$	3. ?
4. $\overline{RS} \cong \overline{PQ}$	4. ?

47. The transitive property holds for congruence of segments.

Statements	Reasons
1. $\overline{PQ} \cong \overline{RS}$ and $\overline{RS} \cong \overline{TU}$	1. Given
2. $PQ = RS$ and $RS = TU$	2. ?
3. $PQ = TU$	3. ?
4. $\overline{PQ} \cong \overline{TU}$	4. ?

48. Write a single theorem that states what was proved in Exercises 45–47.

2-2 Conditionals and Deductive Reasoning

You have probably noticed that many theorems are written in *if–then* form. A statement in *if–then* form is called a **conditional.** Theorems 2–2 and 2–3 are stated as conditionals.

Theorem 2–2

> If a point is not on a line, then the point and the line determine exactly one plane.

Theorem 2–3

> If two distinct lines intersect, then they determine exactly one plane.

An *if–then* statement can also be written in the general form

$$p \longrightarrow q \longleftarrow \text{Read "If } p \text{, then } q.\text{"}$$

where p and q represent simple statements.

In a conditional statement, the *if–part* (p) is the *hypothesis*. The **hypothesis** (p) tells you the given facts on which to base the proof. It also suggests the figure you are to draw and label. The *then–part* (q) of the conditional is the **conclusion.** It tells you what is to be proved about the figure.

EXAMPLE 1
a. Write the hypothesis (p) and conclusion (q) for Theorem 2–2.
b. Write the *Given* and the *Prove*. Draw and label a figure for the theorem.

Solutions:
a. **Hypothesis** (p): A point is not on a line.
   Conclusion (q): The point and the line determine exactly one plane.

b. **Given:** Line h and point P not on line h
   Prove: Point P and line h determine exactly one plane.

Statements not expressed in if–then form can be written as conditionals.

EXAMPLE 2 Write a conditional for this statement.

Collinear points lie on the same line.

Solution: **Conditional ($p \rightarrow q$):** *If points are collinear, then they lie on the same line.*

If–then statements are used in deductive reasoning. To determine when an if–then statement is true, you can think of the conditional as a *promise*.

Promise: If you have no more than 2 errors, you will get an A.

EVENT 1 You had fewer than 2 errors. You got an A.   ← **The promise is kept.**
          (p is true.)   **(q is true.)**   **p ⟶ q is true.**

EVENT 2 You had more than 2 errors. You didn't get an A. ← **The promise is kept.**
          (p is false.)   **(q is false.)**   **p ⟶ q is true.**

EVENT 3 You had more than 2 errors. You got an A.   ← **The promise is kept.**
          (p is false.)   **(q is true.)**   **p ⟶ q is true.**

EVENT 4 You had fewer than 2 errors. You didn't get an A. ← **The promise is not kept.**
          (p is true.)   **(q is false.)**   **p ⟶ q is false.**

The results of the table can be summarized as follows.

Summary   A conditional is false when the hypothesis is true and the conclusion is false (Event 4). Otherwise, a conditional is true.

CLASSROOM EXERCISES

In Exercises 1–4, write the hypothesis and conclusion for each conditional. Then write the *Given* and *Prove* and draw a figure.

1. If two angles each have a measure of 35, then the angles are congruent.
2. If a triangle is isosceles, then it has two congruent angles.
3. If $\overrightarrow{AB}$ bisects $\angle DAC$, then B is in the interior of $\angle DAC$.
4. The three angles of a triangle are congruent if the three sides are congruent.

WRITTEN EXERCISES

A   Write a conditional for each statement.

1. Coplanar points are points that lie in the same plane.
2. A scalene triangle has no two sides equal.
3. Vertical angles are congruent.
4. An equilateral triangle is a triangle with three equal sides.

B   Indicate when each conditional is false given that the hypothesis (p) is true.

5. If it is raining, then I use my umbrella.
6. If Sharon won the essay contest, then she received an award of $150.
7. If a United States citizen is 18, then that citizen can vote.

C

8. Complete this "truth table" for the conditional $p \longrightarrow q$.

   In the table, T stands for *True* and F stands for *False*.

p	q	$p \longrightarrow q$
T	T	_?_
T	F	_?_
F	T	_?_
F	F	_?_

2-3 Deductive Reasoning and Proof

In writing a proof of a theorem, you use deductive reasoning. In **deductive reasoning,** you *arrive at conclusions from accepted facts.* Each statement in the proof represents a conclusion that follows logically from the hypothesis *(Given),* or from a previous statement or statements in the proof.

EXAMPLE   Supply the reasons in this proof.

Given: S is between R and T.

Prove: $RS = RT - ST$

Proof:

Statements	Reasons
1. S is between R and T.	1. Given
2. $RS + ST = RT$	2. Definition of betweenness for points
3. $RS = RT - ST$	3. Addition property

The pattern of reasoning in the proof can be written as follows.

$p \longrightarrow q$	**True conditional: If S is between R and T, then $RS + ST = RT$.**
$\underline{p}$	**True hypothesis: S is between R and T.**
q	**The conclusion must be true (see Event 1 on page 50).**

Proofs of theorems in geometry are examples of deductive reasoning.

Steps in Deductive Reasoning

1. Begin with an accepted fact or facts (hypothesis).

2. Continue in a step-by-step fashion with statements that are justified by stating the hypothesis, postulates, theorems, or definitions as reasons.

3. Each statement should lead to another statement until you reach the last statement which is the conclusion.

The only statements acceptable as reasons in a proof are the following.

Summary

Reasons Used in Proofs

1. Given information
2. Definitions
3. Postulates

4. Properties from algebra, such as the properties of equality
5. Previously proved theorems

CLASSROOM EXERCISES

In Exercises 1–6, state the conclusion that can be drawn from the given information. More than one conclusion may be possible in some cases. Give the reason for each conclusion.

1.

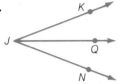

Given: $\vec{JQ}$ bisects $\angle KJN$.

2.

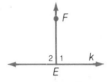

Given: $\vec{EF} \perp k$

3.

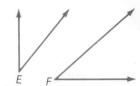

Given: $\angle E$ and $\angle F$ are complementary.

4.

Given: M is the midpoint of PQ.

5.

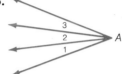

Given: $\angle 1 \cong \angle 2$; $\angle 2 \cong \angle 3$

6.

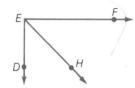

Given: $m\angle DEF = 90$; $m\angle DEH = 45$

WRITTEN EXERCISES

A In Exercises 1–6, write the conclusion that can be drawn from the *Given*. More than one conclusion may be possible in some cases. Give the reason(s) for each conclusion you write.

1.

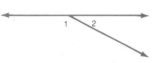

Given: Angles 1 and 2 are supplementary.

2.

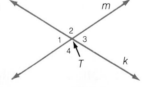

Given: Lines k and m intersect at T.

3.

Given: $PR = MA$

4.

Given: $\angle I \cong \angle R$

5.

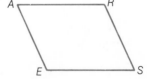

Given: $m\angle A + m\angle R = 180$

6.

Given: Opposite rays OR and OA; adjacent angles ROP and AOP

In Exercises 7–24, supply the missing reasons and statements.

7. Given: $m\angle 1 = m\angle 2$

Prove: $m\angle 1 = \frac{1}{2}m\angle BAT$

Statements	Reasons
1. $m\angle 1 = m\angle 2$	1. ___?___
2. $m\angle 1 = \frac{1}{2}m\angle BAT$	2. ___?___

8. Given: $\angle SQT$; $\overrightarrow{QA}$ lies between $\overrightarrow{QS}$ and $\overrightarrow{QT}$.

Prove: $m\angle SQA = m\angle SQT - m\angle AQT$

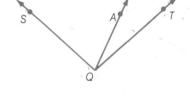

Statements	Reasons
1. $\angle SQT$; $\overrightarrow{QA}$ lies between $\overrightarrow{QS}$ and $\overrightarrow{QT}$.	1. Given
2. $m\angle SQA + m\angle AQT = m\angle SQT$	2. ___?___
3. $m\angle SQA = m\angle SQT - m\angle$ ___?___	3. ___?___

9. Given: $\overrightarrow{OF}$ and $\overrightarrow{OT}$ are opposite rays; $\overrightarrow{OR}$ lies between $\overrightarrow{OT}$ and $\overrightarrow{OF}$.

Prove: $\angle 1$ and $\angle 2$ are supplementary.

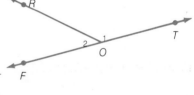

Statements	Reasons
1. $\overrightarrow{OF}$ and $\overrightarrow{OT}$ are opposite rays; $\overrightarrow{OR}$ lies between $\overrightarrow{OF}$ and $\overrightarrow{OT}$.	1. Given
2. $\angle 1$ and $\angle 2$ form a linear pair.	2. ___?___
3. $\angle 1$ and $\angle 2$ are supplementary.	3. ___?___

10. Given: $\overline{TR} \cong \overline{TY}$

Prove: $\triangle TRY$ is isosceles.

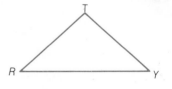

Statements	Reasons
1. $\overline{TR} \cong \overline{TY}$	1. ___?___
2. $TR = TY$	2. ___?___
3. $\triangle TRY$ is isosceles.	3. ___?___

11. Given: $m\angle Q = 20$; $m\angle S = 70$

Prove: Angles Q and S are complementary.

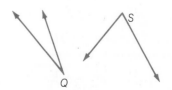

Statements	Reasons
1. $m\angle Q = 20$; $m\angle S = 70$	1. ___?___
2. $m\angle Q + m\angle S = 90$	2. ___?___
3. Angles Q and S are complementary.	3. ___?___

12. Given: $CE = ED$

Prove: $CE = \frac{1}{2}CD$

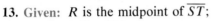

Statements	Reasons
1. $CE = ED$	1. ___?___
2. E is the midpoint of $\overline{CD}$.	2. ___?___
3. $CE = \frac{1}{2}CD$	3. ___?___

13. Given: R is the midpoint of $\overline{ST}$;

$RK = RS$

Prove: $RK = \frac{1}{2}ST$

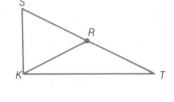

Statements	Reasons
1. R is the midpoint of $\overline{ST}$.	1. ___?___
2. $RS = \frac{1}{2}ST$	2. ___?___
3. $RK = RS$	3. ___?___
4. $RK = \frac{1}{2}ST$	4. ___?___

14. Given: $m\angle 3 = m\angle 1$; $m\angle 3 = m\angle 2$;

Prove: $m\angle 1 = \frac{1}{2}m\angle PEN$

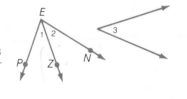

Statements	Reasons
1. $m\angle 3 = m\angle 1$; $m\angle 3 = m\angle 2$	1. ___?___
2. $m\angle 1 = m\angle 2$	2. ___?___
3. $\overrightarrow{EZ}$ is the bisector of $\angle PEN$.	3. ___?___
4. $m\angle 1 = \frac{1}{2}m\angle PEN$	4. ___?___

15. Given: $TA = ED$ Prove: $AM = TM - ED$

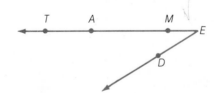

Statements	Reasons
1. $TA + AM = TM$	1. Definition of betweenness of points
2. $AM = TM - TA$	2. ___?___
3. $TA = ED$	3. ___?___
4. $AM = TM - ED$	4. ___?___

16. Given: $\angle 1 \cong \angle 3$

Prove: Angles 2 and 3 are supplementary.

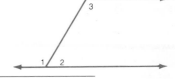

Statements	Reasons
1. $\angle 1$ and $\angle 2$ are a linear pair.	1. Definition of linear pair
2. $m\angle 1 + m\angle 2 = 180$	2. ?
3. $\angle 1 \cong \angle 3$	3. ?
4. $m\angle 1 = m\angle 3$	4. ?
5. $m\angle 3 + m\angle 2 = 180$	5. ?
6. Angles 2 and 3 are supplementary.	6. ?

17. Given: $\angle 1 \cong \angle 2$

Prove: $\overrightarrow{PQ} \perp \overrightarrow{AB}$

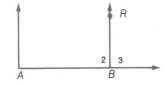

Statements	Reasons
1. $\angle 1 \cong \angle 2$	1. ?
2. $\overleftrightarrow{PQ} \perp \overleftrightarrow{AB}$	2. ?

18. Given: $\angle A \cong \angle 2$; $\angle A \cong \angle 3$

Prove: $\overrightarrow{BR} \perp \overrightarrow{AB}$

Statements	Reasons
1. $\angle A \cong \angle 2$; $\angle A \cong \angle 3$	1. ?
2. $\angle 2 \cong \angle 3$	2. ?
3. $\overrightarrow{BR} \perp \overrightarrow{AB}$	3. ?

B

19. Given: $AB = CD$

Prove: $AC = BD$

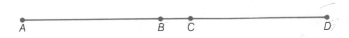

Statements	Reasons
1. ? $AB = CD$	1. Given
2. $AC + CD = AD$; $AB + BD = AD$	2. ?
3. $AC + CD = AB + BD$	3. ?
4. ?	4. ?

20. Given: $m\angle A + m\angle B = 90$; $m\angle B = 3m\angle A$

Prove: $m\angle A = 22\frac{1}{2}$

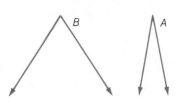

Statements	Reasons
1. $m\angle A + m\angle B = 90$	1. ?
2. $m\angle B = 3m\angle A$	2. ?
3. $m\angle A + 3m\angle A = 90$	3. ?
4. ?	4. ?
5. ?	5. ?

21. Given: $AB = 4CB$

Prove: $CB = \frac{1}{5}AC$

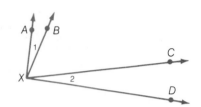

Statements	Reasons
1. $AC - CB = AB$	1. __?__
2. $AB = 4CB$	2. __?__
3. __?__	3. Substitution property
4. __?__	4. __?__
5. __?__	5. __?__

22. Given: $m\angle 1 = m\angle 2$

Prove: $m\angle BXD = m\angle AXC$

Statements	Reasons
1. __?__	1. __?__
2. $m\angle 1 + m\angle BXD = m\angle AXD$; $m\angle AXC + m\angle 2 = m\angle AXD$	2. __?__
3. __?__	3. __?__
4. __?__	4. __?__

C

23. Given: $AC = BD$

Prove: $AB = CD$

Statements	Reasons
1. $AC = BD$	1. __?__
2. $AB + BD = AD$; $AC + CD = AD$	2. __?__
3. __?__	3. __?__
4. __?__	4. __?__

24. Given: Lines p and r intersect at E.

Prove: $m\angle 1 = m\angle 3$

Statements	Reasons
1. Angles 1 and 2 are a linear pair; Angles 3 and 2 are a __?__	1. __?__
2. $m\angle 1 + m\angle 2 = $ __?__ ; $m\angle 3 + m\angle 2 = $ __?__	2. __?__
3. __?__	3. __?__
4. __?__	4. __?__

Complete the proof.

25. Given: $\angle M$ and $\angle V$ are right angles.

Prove: $\angle M \cong \angle V$

2–4 Two-Column Proofs

You can now use what you learned in the previous three sections to write a two-column proof. The steps are summarized below.

Summary

Steps for Writing a Two–Column Proof
[1] Determine the *Given* and the *Prove*. (If a theorem is not in the form of a conditional, it may help to write it as a conditional.)
[2] Draw a figure to represent the *Given* and the *Prove*.
[3] Plan the proof.
[4] Write the statements and reasons.

Theorem 2–4 relates supplementary angles and congruence of angles.

Theorem 2–4

If two angles are supplements of the same angle, then they are congruent.

EXAMPLE 1 Prove Theorem 2–4.

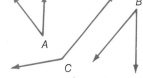

Given: $\angle A$ and $\angle C$ are supplementary.
    $\angle B$ and $\angle C$ are supplementary.

Prove: $\angle A \cong \angle B$

Plan: Show that $m\angle A + m\angle C = 180$ and $m\angle B + m\angle C = 180$. Then, $m\angle A + m\angle C = m\angle B + m\angle C$ and $m\angle A = m\angle B$.

Proof:

Statements	Reasons
1. $\angle A$ and $\angle C$ are supplementary. $\angle B$ and $\angle C$ are supplementary.	1. Given
2. $m\angle A + m\angle C = 180$ $m\angle B + m\angle C = 180$	2. (1). Definition of supplementary angles
3. $m\angle A + m\angle C = m\angle B + m\angle C$	3. (2). Substitution property
4. $m\angle A = m\angle B$	4. (3). Addition property
5. $\therefore \angle A \cong \angle B$ — Read: "therefore."	5. (4). Definition of congruent angles

NOTE: Recall that each statement in a proof (except the *Given*) is a conclusion that is reached by using the statement or statements that preceded it. Thus, the numbers in parentheses in the "Reasons" column, such as (1), (2), (3), and so on, indicate which statements were used to arrive at the given statement.

Statement 3 was used to arrive at Statement 4.

4. (3). Addition property

Theorem 2–5 also concerns supplementary angles.

Theorem 2–5	If two angles are supplements of congruent angles, then they are congruent.

EXAMPLE 2   Prove Theorem 2–5.

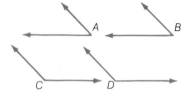

Given: $\angle A \cong \angle B$;
$\angle A$ and $\angle C$ are supplementary;
$\angle B$ and $\angle D$ are supplementary

Prove: $\angle C \cong \angle D$

Plan: Show that $m\angle A + m\angle C = 180$ and that $m\angle B + m\angle D = 180$.
Then $m\angle A + m\angle C = m\angle B + m\angle D$.
Use the *Given* to show that $m\angle A = m\angle B$.
Then, substituting $m\angle A$ for $m\angle B$, show that $m\angle C = m\angle D$ and $\angle C \cong \angle D$.

Proof:

Statements	Reasons
1. $\angle A$ and $\angle C$ are supplementary; $\angle B$ and $\angle D$ are supplementary.	1. Given
2. $m\angle A + m\angle C = 180$; $m\angle B + m\angle D = 180$	2. (1). Definition of supplementary angles
3. $m\angle A + m\angle C = m\angle B + m\angle D$	3. (2). Substitution property
4. $\angle A \cong \angle B$	4. Given
5. $m\angle A = m\angle B$	5. (4). If two angles are congruent, then their measures are equal.
6. $m\angle A + m\angle C = m\angle A + m\angle D$	6. (3), (5). Substitution property
7. $m\angle C = m\angle D$	7. (6). Addition property
8. $\therefore \angle C \cong \angle D$	8. (7). Definition of congruent angles

In a proof, a statement and its reason are called a **step**.

NOTE: In the reason for Step 6 of the proof in Example 2, the numbers (3) and (5) indicate that two statements, Statements 3 and 5, were used to arrive at Statement 6.

Two theorems similar to Theorems 2–4 and 2–5 are given below. You are asked to prove them in the Written Exercises.

Theorem 2–6	If two angles are complements of the same angle, then they are congruent.
Theorem 2–7	If two angles are complements of congruent angles, then they are congruent.

The short form of Theorem 2–8 which is stated below can also be written as a conditional. You are asked to write it as a conditional in the Classroom Exercises.

Theorem 2–8

Vertical Angle Theorem: Vertical angles are congruent.

EXAMPLE 3   Prove Theorem 2–8.

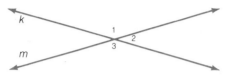

Given: Vertical angles 1 and 3

Prove: $\angle 1 \cong \angle 3$

Plan: Show that $\angle 1$ and $\angle 2$ are a linear pair and that $\angle 2$ and $\angle 3$ are a linear pair.
Then show that $\angle 1$ and $\angle 2$ are supplementary and that $\angle 2$ and $\angle 3$ are supplementary.
Use Theorem 2–6 to show $\angle 1 \cong \angle 3$.

Proof:

Statements	Reasons
1. $\angle 1$ and $\angle 2$ are a linear pair; $\angle 3$ and $\angle 2$ are a linear pair.	1. Definition of linear pair
2. $\angle 1$ and $\angle 2$ are supplementary; $\angle 3$ and $\angle 2$ are supplementary.	2. (1). If two angles form a linear pair, then they are supplementary.
3. $\therefore \angle 1 \cong \angle 3$	3. (2). If two angles are supplements of the same angle, then they are congruent.

When writing proofs, you are allowed to conclude certain things from the figure itself.

Acceptable Conclusions	Reason
$AD + DC = AC$	Definition of betweenness of points
$m\angle 1 + m\angle 2 = m\angle ABC$	Definition of betweenness of rays
$\angle 3$ and $\angle 4$ form a linear pair.	Definition of linear pair
$\angle 4 \cong \angle 5$	Vertical angles are congruent.

Unless you have additional information, you cannot conclude any of the following from the figure.

$$\overline{BA} \cong \overline{BC} \qquad \overline{DA} \cong \overline{DC} \qquad \overline{BD} \perp \overline{AC}$$

$$\angle 1 \cong \angle 2 \qquad \angle A \cong \angle C \qquad \angle 3 \cong \angle 4$$

CLASSROOM EXERCISES

In Exercises 1–4, state the theorem that allows this conclusion.

Conclusion: $\angle 1 \cong \angle 3$

1. Given: $\angle 1$ and $\angle 2$ are complementary;
$\angle 3$ and $\angle 2$ are complementary.

2. Given: Lines t and k intersect at E.

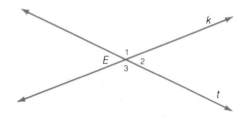

3. Given: $\angle 2 \cong \angle 4$;
$\angle 1$ and $\angle 2$ are supplementary;
$\angle 3$ and $\angle 4$ are supplementary.

4. Given: $\angle 3$ and $\angle 2$ are supplementary;
$\angle 1$ and $\angle 2$ are supplementary.

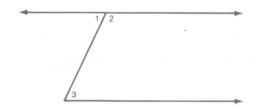

5. Supply the reasons in this proof.

Given: $\angle 1$ and $\angle 2$ are supplementary. **Prove:** $\angle 1 \cong \angle 3$

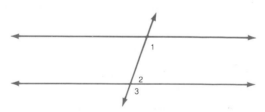

Plan: Show that $\angle 1$ and $\angle 3$ are supplements of $\angle 2$.
Then use Theorem 2–4 to show $\angle 1 \cong \angle 3$.

Statements	Reasons
1. $\angle 3$ and $\angle 2$ are a linear pair.	1. __?__
2. $\angle 3$ and $\angle 2$ are supplementary.	2. (1). __?__
3. $\angle 1$ and $\angle 2$ are supplementary.	3. __?__
4. $\therefore \angle 1 \cong \angle 3$	4. (2), (3). __?__

6. Write Theorem 2–8 as a conditional.

WRITTEN EXERCISES

A

1. Supply the reasons for the proof of Theorem 2–6.

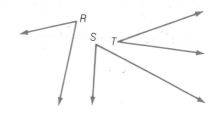

Given: ∠R and ∠T are complementary;
∠S and ∠T are complementary.

Prove: ∠R ≅ ∠S

Statements	Reasons
1. ∠R and ∠T are complementary; ∠S and ∠T are complementary.	1. __?__
2. m∠R + m∠T = 90; m∠S + m∠T = 90	2. (1). __?__
3. m∠R + m∠T = m∠S + m∠T	3. (2). __?__
4. m∠R = m∠S	4. (3). __?__
5. ∠R ≅ ∠S	5. (4). __?__

2. Supply the reasons for the proof of Theorem 2–7.

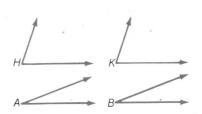

Given: ∠H ≅ ∠K;
∠A and ∠H are complementary;
∠B and ∠K are complementary.

Prove: ∠A ≅ ∠B

Statements	Reasons
1. ∠A and ∠H are complementary; ∠B and ∠K are complementary.	1. __?__
2. m∠A + m∠H = 90; m∠B + m∠K = 90	2. (1). __?__
3. m∠A + m∠H = m∠B + m∠K	3. (2). __?__
4. ∠H ≅ ∠K	4. __?__
5. m∠H = m∠K	5. (4). __?__
6. m∠A + m∠H = m∠B + m∠H	6. (3), (5). __?__
7. m∠A = m∠B	7. (6). __?__
8. ∴ ∠A ≅ ∠B	8. (7). __?__

In Exercises 3–6, supply the missing reasons in each proof.

3. Given: ∠1 and ∠2 are supplementary.   Prove: ∠1 ≅ ∠3

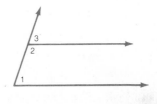

Statements	Reasons
1. ∠1 and ∠2 are supplementary.	1. __?__
2. ∠3 and ∠2 are a linear pair.	2. __?__
3. ∠3 and ∠2 are supplementary.	3. (2). __?__
4. ∠1 ≅ ∠3	4. (1), (3). __?__

4. Given: ∠1 and ∠3 are supplementary.

Prove: ∠1 ≅ ∠2

Statements	Reasons
1. ∠1 and ∠3 are supplementary.	1. __?__
2. ∠2 and ∠3 are a linear pair.	2. __?__
3. ∠2 and ∠3 are supplementary.	3. (2). __?__
4. ∠1 ≅ ∠2	4. (1), (3). __?__

5. Given: ∠3 ≅ ∠2   Prove: ∠3 ≅ ∠1

Statements	Reasons
1. ∠3 ≅ ∠2	1. __?__
2. ∠2 ≅ ∠1	2. __?__
3. ∠3 ≅ ∠1	3. (1), (2). __?__

6. Given: $FC = AE$
Prove: $CE = FA$

Statements	Reasons
1. $FC = AE$	1. __?__
2. $FC + CE = FE$; $FA + AE = FE$	2. __?__
3. $FC + CE = FA + AE$	3. (2). __?__
4. $FC + CE = FA + FC$	4. (1), (3). __?__
5. $CE = FA$	5. (4). __?__

In Exercises 7–10, supply the missing statements and reasons.

7. Given: ∠1 ≅ ∠2   Prove: ∠1 ≅ ∠3

Statements	Reasons
1. __?__	1. Given
2. ∠2 ≅ ∠ __?__	2. __?__
3. __?__	3. (1), (2). __?__

8. Given: ∠1 and ∠2 are complementary.   Prove: $\overrightarrow{XA} \perp \overrightarrow{XC}$

Statements	Reasons
1. ∠1 and ∠2 are complementary.	1. __?__
2. m∠1 + m∠2 = __?__	2. (1). __?__
3. m∠1 + m∠2 = m∠AXC	3. Definition of __?__
4. m∠AXC = __?__	4. (2), (3). __?__
5. ∠AXC is a right angle.	5. (4). __?__
6. __?__	6. (5). __?__

9. Given: ∠ 1 and ∠ 2 are supplementary.

Prove: ∠ 3 and ∠ 4 are supplementary.

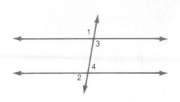

Statements	Reasons
1. __?__	1. Given
2. m∠ __?__ + m∠ __?__ = 180	2. (1). __?__
3. ∠ 1 ≅ ∠ 3; ∠ 2 ≅ ∠ 4	3. __?__
4. m∠ 1 = m∠ 3; m∠ 2 = m∠ 4	4. (3). __?__
5. m∠ 3 + m∠ 4 = 180	5. (2), (4). __?__
6. __?__	6. (5). __?__

10. Given: ∠ 1 ≅ ∠ 4   **Prove:** ∠ 2 ≅ ∠ 3

Statements	Reasons
1. ∠ 1 ≅ ∠ 4	1. __?__
2. __?__	2. Definition of __?__
3. ∠ 1 and ∠ 3 are __?__ ; ∠ 4 and ∠ 2 are __?__ .	3. (2). __?__
4. ∴ ∠ 2 ≅ ∠ 3	4. (1), (3). __?__

B   In Exercises 11–23, write a two-column proof for each exercise. Refer to the figure at the right below for Exercises 11–14.

11. Given: ∠ 1 ≅ ∠ 8

Prove: ∠ 1 ≅ ∠ 5

12. Given: ∠ 1 ≅ ∠ 8

Prove: ∠ 2 ≅ ∠ 7

13. Given: ∠ 2 and ∠ 5 are supplementary.

Prove: ∠ 3 and ∠ 8 are supplementary.

14. Given: ∠ 1 and ∠ 7 are supplementary.

Prove: ∠ 4 and ∠ 6 are supplementary.

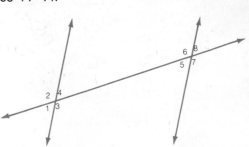

15. Given: ∠ 1 and ∠ 2 are complementary;
   ∠ 3 and ∠ 4 are complementary;
   ∠ 1 ≅ ∠ 4

Prove: ∠ 2 ≅ ∠ 3

16. Given: $AB = CD$

Prove: $BD = AC$

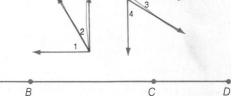

17. Given: In △ABC, ∠ABC is a right angle;
   ∠ 1 ≅ ∠ C; ∠ 2 ≅ ∠ A

Prove: ∠ A and ∠ C are complementary.

18. Given: $\overrightarrow{BA} \perp \overline{BC}$; $\overrightarrow{CD} \perp \overline{BC}$;
$\angle 2 \cong \angle 4$

Prove: $\angle 1 \cong \angle 3$

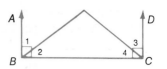

19. Given: $m\angle 1 = 2m\angle B$;
$m\angle B = m\angle D$

Prove: $m\angle 2 = 2m\angle D$

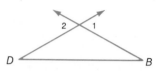

20. Given: $CH = AL$; $HL = CK$

Prove: $\triangle CAK$ is isosceles.

21. Given: $\triangle ABC$ is isosceles with base AC;
$\triangle ABD$ is isosceles with base AD.

Prove: $\triangle BCD$ is isosceles.

NOTE: $\triangle BCD$ is in plane I;
point A is not in plane I.

C

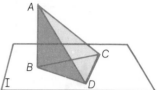

22. Given: $AB = BC$; D is the midpoint of $\overline{AB}$;
$DE = \frac{1}{2}BC$

Prove: $\triangle ADE$ is isosceles.

23. Given: $\angle 1$ and $\angle 4$ are supplementary.

Prove: $\angle 2$ and $\angle 3$ are supplementary.

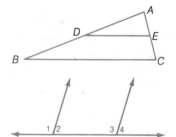

Review

State the property of equality illustrated by each statement. *(Section 2–1)*

1. If $MN = OP$, then $OP = MN$.

2. If $3m\angle 2 = 90$, then $m\angle 2 = 30$.

3. If $AB + BC = AC$ and $BC = EF$, then
$AB + EF = AC$.

4. $RS + RS = 2RS$.

In Exercises 5–6, state the missing reasons. *(Section 2–1)*

5.

Statements	Reasons
1. $4(x - 40) = 2x + 10$	1. Given
2. $4x - 160 = 2x + 10$	2. __?__
3. $2x - 160 = 10$	3. __?__
4. $2x = 170$	4. __?__
5. $x = 85$	5. __?__

6.

Statements	Reasons
1. $\frac{3}{4}x = \frac{1}{2}(x + 60)$	1. Given
2. $\frac{3}{4}x = \frac{1}{2}x + 30$	2. __?__
3. $\frac{1}{4}x = 30$	3. __?__
4. $x = 120$	4. __?__

In Exercises 7–9:

a. Write the hypothesis and conclusion for each conditional.

b. Write the *Given* and *Prove* and draw a figure. *(Section 2–2)*

7. If a triangle is equilateral, the measure of each angle is 60.

8. If three points are noncollinear, then they determine a plane.

9. Two lines are perpendicular if they intersect to form right angles.

Supply the missing reasons for this proof. *(Section 2–3)*

10. **Given:** $\overleftrightarrow{WE} \perp \overline{ST}$

    Prove: $m\angle 1 = 90$

Statements	Reasons
1. $\overleftrightarrow{WE} \perp \overline{ST}$	1. _?_
2. $\angle 1$ is a right angle.	2. _?_
3. $m\angle 1 = 90$	3. _?_

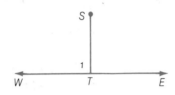

In Exercises 11–12, supply the missing statements and reasons in each proof. *(Section 2–4)*

11. **Given:** $\angle 1$ is a right angle;
    $\angle 2$ is a right angle.

    Prove: $\angle 1 \cong \angle 2$

Statements	Reasons
1. $\angle 1$ is a right angle; $\angle 2$ is a right angle.	1. _?_
2. $m\angle 1 = 90$; $m\angle 2 = 90$	2. (1). _?_
3. $m\angle 1 = m\angle 2$	3. (2). _?_
4. $\angle 1 \cong \angle 2$	4. (3). _?_

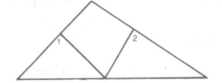

12. **Given:** $\angle 2 \cong \angle 3$

    Prove: $\angle 1$ and $\angle 3$ are supplementary.

Statements	Reasons
1. $\angle 2 \cong \angle 3$	1. Given
2. $m\angle 2 = m\angle 3$	2. (1). If two angles are congruent, then _?_ .
3. $\angle 1$ and $\angle 2$ form a _?_ .	3. _?_
4. $\angle 1$ and $\angle 2$ are _?_ .	4. (3). If two angles form a linear pair, then _?_ .
5. $m\angle 1 + m\angle 2 = 180$	5. (4). _?_
6. $m\angle 1 + m\angle 3 = 180$	6. (2), (5). _?_
7. $\angle 1$ and $\angle 3$ are _?_ .	7. (6). _?_

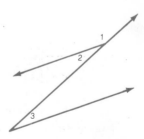

2–5 Theorems About Perpendicular Lines

Theorem 2–9 relates a linear pair with right angles.

Theorem 2–9

> If one angle of a linear pair is a right angle, then the other is also a right angle.

Remember to prepare a plan (or outline) of a proof before you begin to write the statements and reasons. The plan should include the major steps of the proof.

Given: ∠1 and ∠2 are a linear pair;
∠1 is a right angle.

Prove: ∠2 is a right angle.

Plan: Show that m∠1 + m∠2 = 180 and that m∠1 = 90.
Then show m∠2 = 90.

You are asked to complete the proof in the Written Exercises. Theorem 2–9 is used in the proof of Theorem 2–10.

Theorem 2–10

> If two intersecting lines form one right angle, then they form four right angles.

EXAMPLE   Prove Theorem 2–10.

Given: Lines k and m intersect, forming angles 1, 2, 3, and 4; ∠1 is a right angle.

Prove: Angles 2, 3, and 4 are right angles.

Plan: Show that each of the following pairs of angles is a linear pair: ∠1 and ∠2, ∠1 and ∠4, ∠2 and ∠3. Then use Theorem 2–9 to show that angles 2, 3, and 4 are right angles.

Proof:

Statements	Reasons
1. Lines k and m intersect forming angles 1, 2, 3, and 4; ∠1 is a right angle.	1. Given
2. ∠1 and ∠2 are a linear pair; ∠1 and ∠4 are a linear pair.	2. (1). Definition of linear pair
3. ∠2 is a right angle; ∠4 is a right angle.	3. (1), (2). Theorem 2–9
4. ∠2 and ∠3 are a linear pair.	4. (1). Definition of linear pair
5. ∠3 is a right angle.	5. (3), (4). Same as Reason 3

A **corollary** is a theorem that follows directly from another theorem or from accepted statements, such as definitions. Corollaries, like theorems, postulates, and definitions, can be used as reasons in proofs.

Corollary 2–11

Perpendicular lines form four right angles.

Corollary 2–12 follows from the definitions of right angle and congruent angles.

Corollary 2–12

All right angles are congruent.

Theorem 2–13 is useful in proofs when you know that two lines are perpendicular and you wish to show that two or more angles formed by these lines are congruent. The proof is asked for in the Written Exercises.

Theorem 2–13

If two lines are perpendicular, then they form congruent adjacent angles.

Theorem 2–14 can be derived from Theorem 1–8 (see page 31).

Theorem 2–14

If two intersecting lines form congruent adjacent angles, then the lines are perpendicular.

Theorems 2–13 and 2–14 are *converses* of each other. When the "if-" and "then-" parts of a conditional are interchanged, the **converse** is formed.

$$\textbf{Conditional: } p \longrightarrow q \qquad \textbf{Converse: } q \longrightarrow p$$

NOTE: When a conditional is true, its converse is *not necessarily true*.

Conditional $(p \longrightarrow q)$: If two angles are right angles, then they are congruent. (**true**)

Converse: $(p \longrightarrow q)$: If two angles are congruent, then they are right angles (**not necessarily true**).

When both a conditional and its converse are true, they can be written as one statement using the words "if and only if." An *if and only if* statement is called a **biconditional**. The biconditional for Theorems 2–13 and 2–14 can be written in either of the following ways.

$p \longleftrightarrow q$
p if and only if q. Two intersecting lines form congruent adjacent angles *if and only if* the lines are perpendicular.

$q \longleftrightarrow p$
q if and only if p. Two lines are perpendicular *if and only if* they form congruent adjacent angles.

To prove a biconditional, you must prove both the conditional $(p \longrightarrow q)$ and its converse $(q \longrightarrow p)$.

NOTE: Every definition can be expressed as a biconditional.

Definition: Congruent angles are angles whose measures are equal.

Biconditional: Two angles are congruent if and only if their measures are equal.

CLASSROOM EXERCISES

Classify each statement as true, *T*, or false, *F*.

1. If $\overleftrightarrow{PQ} \perp \overleftrightarrow{ST}$ at *R*, then $\angle PRT \cong \angle TRQ$.
2. If $\angle 1$ and $\angle 2$ are a linear pair and m$\angle 1 = 90$, then m$\angle 2 < 90$.
3. If $\overleftrightarrow{PQ} \perp \overleftrightarrow{ST}$ at *R*, then $\angle PRT$ and $\angle SRQ$ are adjacent angles.
4. If m$\angle TER = 90$ and m$\angle TES = 90$, then *R*, *E*, and *S* are noncollinear points.
5. If two angles are congruent and complementary, then each angle is a right angle.

In Exercises 6–7, write two biconditionals for each pair of conditionals.

6. **a.** If a triangle has two congruent sides, then it is isosceles.
   b. If a triangle is isosceles, then it has two congruent sides.
7. **a.** If two angles are complementary, then the sum of their measures is 90.
   b. If the sum of the measures of two angles is 90, then they are complementary.
8. **a.** If an angle is a right angle, then its measure is 90.
   b. If the measure of an angle is 90, then it is a right angle.

WRITTEN EXERCISES

A In Exercises 1–6, state the theorem or corollary that justifies each statement. Use the figure at the right below for Exercises 1–3.

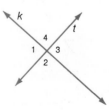

1. If $\angle 1$ is a right angle, then $\angle 2$, $\angle 3$, and $\angle 4$ are right angles.
2. If lines *k* and *t* are perpendicular, then $\angle 1 \cong \angle 2$.
3. If $\angle 2 \cong \angle 3$, then lines *k* and *t* are perpendicular.
4. Angles *A* and *B* are a linear pair and $\angle A$ is a right angle. Therefore $\angle B$ is a right angle.
5. Lines *AB* and *CD* intersect at *E*. If adjacent angles *CEB* and *CEA* are congruent, then $\overleftrightarrow{AB} \perp \overleftrightarrow{CD}$.
6. If $\angle Q$ and $\angle R$ are right angles, then $\angle Q \cong \angle R$.

In Exercises 7–10, write one or more conclusions that follow from the *Given*. Justify your answer with a definition, theorem, or corollary.

7. Given: $\overline{AB} \perp \overline{CD}$
   Conclusion: __?__

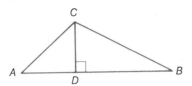

8. Given: $\angle 1 \cong \angle 2$
   Conclusion: __?__

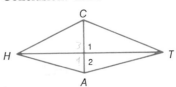

9. Given: $\angle KQH$ is a right angle.
   Conclusion: __?__

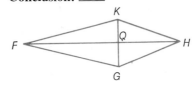

10. Given: $\overline{FH} \perp \overline{KQ}$
   Conclusion: __?__

B   In Exercises 11–15, write the converse of each conditional.

11. If two angles form a linear pair, then they are supplementary.

12. If two angles are supplements of the same angle, then they are congruent.

13. If two angles are complements of congruent angles, then they are congruent.

14. If point E is between points D and F and $DE = EF$, then E is the midpoint of $\overline{DF}$.

15. If two angles are vertical angles, then they are congruent.

16. For Exercises 11–15, classify the converse of each conditional as true, T, or false, F.

17. Prove Theorem 2–9. (HINT: Follow the *Plan* on page 66.)

18. Prove Theorem 2–13.

19. Prove Theorem 2–14.

C   Prove each statement.

20. If two angles are congruent and supplementary, then each is a right angle.

21. If two lines intersect, then four pairs of supplementary angles are formed.

—  —

Copy the figure at the right.

Draw four segments that will pass through each of the ten dots without lifting your pencil from the paper.

The following summaries list ways of proof that you have studied up to this point. These summaries will help you to plan and write proofs of the type indicated in each summary.

Summary

Ways to Prove Two Segments Congruent

1. Prove that their measures are equal.
2. Use the Addition, Multiplication, or Substitution properties of equality to prove that their measures are equal.
3. Prove each is congruent to a third segment.
4. Prove they are formed by a segment that is bisected.

Summary

Ways to Prove Two Angles Congruent

1. Prove that their measures are equal.
2. Use the Addition, Multiplication, or Substitution properties of equality to prove that their measures are equal.
3. Prove each is congruent to a third angle.
4. Prove they are formed by an angle bisector.
5. Prove they are supplements or complements of the same angle.
6. Prove they are supplements or complements of congruent angles.
7. Prove they are vertical angles.
8. Prove they are right angles.
9. Prove they are formed by perpendicular lines.

Summary

Ways to Prove an Angle is a Right Angle

1. Prove its measure is 90.
2. Prove it is one angle of a linear pair and the other angle is a right angle.
3. Prove it is formed by perpendicular lines, segments, or rays.

Summary

Ways to Prove Two Lines Perpendicular

1. Prove that the lines meet to form a right angle.
2. Prove that the lines meet to form equal adjacent angles.

Tell whether or not point *M* is a midpoint. Answer *Yes* or *No*.
(HINT: Draw and label a figure for each exercise.) *(Pages 17–19)*

1. M is between A and B and $AM = MB$.   **2.** B is between A and M and $AB = BM$.

3. M is between A and B and $AB = 2AM$.   **4.** M is between A and B and $AM = \frac{1}{2}MB$.

2-6 Polygons

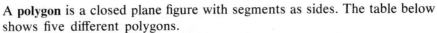

A **polygon** is a closed plane figure with segments as sides. The table below shows five different polygons.

Polygon	Figure	Number of Sides
Triangle		3
Quadrilateral		4
Pentagon		5
Hexagon		6
Octagon		8

A **convex polygon** is a polygon such that no line containing a side of the polygon also contains a point in the interior of the polygon.

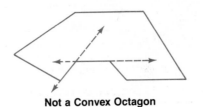

Not a Convex Octagon   **Convex Octagon**

In this book, polygon always means *convex polygon,* such as hexagon *ABCDEF* at the right. Any two sides with a common endpoint, such as $\overline{CD}$ and $\overline{DE}$, are **consecutive**, or **adjacent, sides.** Any two angles with a common side, such as $\angle E$ and $\angle F$, are **consecutive angles.** Segments such as $\overline{AE}$ or $\overline{AD}$ are *diagonals* of the polygon.

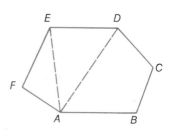

Definition	A **diagonal** of a polygon is a segment, other than a side, joining two vertices.

A **triangle** is a polygon with three sides. A triangle has no diagonals because each of its sides is adjacent to the other two. However, certain other segments relate to triangles.

Segment	Figure	Definition
Median *AD*	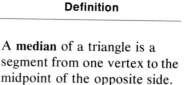	A **median** of a triangle is a segment from one vertex to the midpoint of the opposite side.
Altitude *BP*	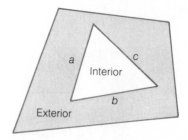	An **altitude of a triangle** is a segment from one vertex perpendicular to the opposite side, or perpendicular to the line containing the opposite side.

The **perimeter** of a polygon is the sum of the lengths of its sides. Thus, for the triangle at the right,

$$P = a + b + c.$$

A triangle separates the plane into three parts: the points interior to the triangle, the points exterior to the triangle, and the points of the triangle.

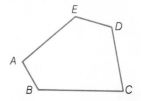

CLASSROOM EXERCISES

Complete each statement. Refer to the figure at the right.

1. Polygon *ABCDE* is a __?__ .

2. $\overline{AB}$ and __?__ are adjacent sides.

3. ∠C and __?__ are consecutive angles.

4. In polygon ABCDE, a diagonal with A as an endpoint is __?__.

5. If $\overline{AD}$ is drawn, polygon ABCD is a __?__.

6. If F is the midpoint of $\overline{AD}$, then $\overline{EF}$ is a __?__ of triangle ADE.

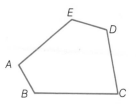

WRITTEN EXERCISES

A Refer to the figure at the right for Exercises 1–6.

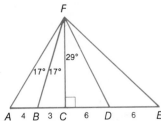

1. What two sides are adjacent to side BC?

2. What sides are adjacent to side $\overline{FG}$? to $\overline{DE}$?

3. Name all the diagonals that have H as one endpoint.

4. Which diagonals have E as one endpoint?

5. Angle A and angle B are consecutive angles. What other pair of consecutive angles includes A? What other pair includes B?

6. What is the name of a polygon ABCDEFGH?

In Exercises 7–14, $\overline{FC} \perp \overline{AE}$. Classify each statement as true, T, or false, F.

7. $\overline{FC}$ is an altitude of △BFD.

8. In △AFC, $\overrightarrow{FB}$ is an angle bisector.

9. In △AFC, $\overline{FB}$ is a median.

10. $\overline{FC}$ is a median of △AFD.

11. $\overline{FC}$ is an altitude of △DEF.

12. In △BFD, $\overrightarrow{FC}$ is an angle bisector.

13. $\overline{FC}$ is an altitude of △ACF.

14. In △CEF, $\overline{FD}$ is a median.

In Exercises 15–17, tell whether $\overline{CD}$ is an altitude or a median of △ABC.

15.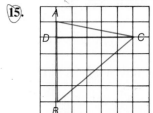

16.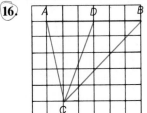

17.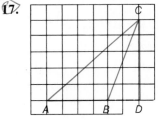

In quadrilateral ABCD, $\overline{AC} \perp \overline{BD}$ at E. Use the given information to identify any altitudes, medians, or angles bisectors for the indicated triangles.

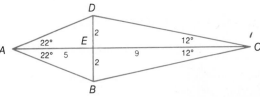

18. △ADB   19. △ADC   20. △DCE   21. △DCB   22. △ABC   23. △ABE

24. What is the perimeter of a triangle if the length of each side is 2.4?

25. The length of each side of a pentagon is 8.6. What is the perimeter of the pentagon?

26. The perimeter of a quadrilateral is 47. If the lengths of three consecutive sides are 8, 10, and 15, what is the length of the fourth side?

27. In $\triangle RTS$ at the right, $ST = TR$, $\overline{RW}$ is a median, $WS = 3\frac{1}{2}$, and $RS = 8$. Find the perimeter of the triangle.

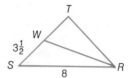

B

28. The perimeter of a pentagon is 37. Two sides of the pentagon are congruent and the lengths of the other sides are 8.5, 3.7, and 9.5. What is the length of each of the congruent sides?

29. The sides of a triangle have lengths of $6y + 2$, $6y + 2$, and $4y - 1$. Express the perimeter in terms of y.

30. The base of an isosceles triangle is 19 and its perimeter is 65. Find the length of each leg.

31. The lengths of the sides of a scalene triangle are consecutive integers. The perimeter of the triangle is 144 centimeters. Find the length of each side.

32. The perimeter of a triangle is 96 millimeters and the lengths of the sides are consecutive even integers. What is the length of each side?

33. The perimeter of a quadrilateral is 176. The lengths of the sides are four consecutive odd integers. What is the length of the longest side of the quadrilateral?

C   In Exercises 34–37, complete the table.

Polygon	Number of Diagonals	Polygon	Number of Diagonals
34. Quadrilateral	?	**35.** Pentagon	?
36. Hexagon	?	**37.** Octagon	?

38. Use your answers to Exercises 34–37 to find an expression for the number of diagonals in a polygon of n sides.

Write a two–column proof for each of Exercises 39–40.

39. Given: $\overleftrightarrow{AB} \perp \overleftrightarrow{XY}$; $\angle 1 \cong \angle 4$
Prove: $\overrightarrow{XY}$ bisects $\angle WXZ$.

40. Given: $\overleftrightarrow{AB} \perp \overleftrightarrow{XY}$; $\overrightarrow{XY}$ bisects $\angle WXZ$;
$\angle 1 \cong \angle 2$
Prove: $\angle 3 \cong \angle 4$

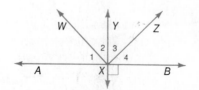

APPLICATIONS

USING POLYGONS

These exercises apply the geometric concepts studied in Section 2–6.

A

1. A rectangular vegetable garden requires 28 meters of cord to rope off its perimeter. The length of the garden is 4 meters more than the width. Find the dimensions (length and width) of the garden.

2. Each side of this octagon is 20 centimeters long. What would be the length of each side of a square having the same perimeter? (HINT: A square has four equal sides.)

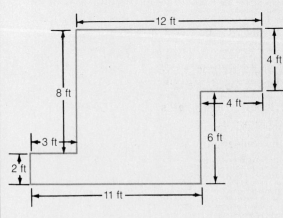

A carpenter is putting strips of molding around the base of the walls of the room with floor plan shown on the left.

3. How many feet of molding are needed?
4. At $1.79 per foot, how much will the molding cost?

B

5. Each of three persons talks to the other two by telephone. How many calls take place?

6. Each of four persons talks to the other three by telephone. How many calls take place?

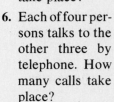

7. Each of five persons talks to the other four by telephone. How many calls were made?

8. Each of six persons talks to the other five by telephone. How many calls were made?

9. Use polygons to represent each of the situations in Exercises 5–8.

2-7 Inductive Reasoning

You have used deductive reasoning in writing proofs of theorems. In deductive reasoning, you arrive at a conclusion that is true for all cases that satisfy the given conditions (hypothesis).

Another kind of reasoning, called **inductive reasoning**, is often used in science and everyday life. Example 1 illustrates inductive reasoning.

EXAMPLE   Determine whether there is a relationship between the length of the median to the hypotenuse and the length of the hypotenuse in a right triangle.

Procedure: 1⃣ Draw four right triangles, each of a different size.

2⃣ In each triangle, draw the median to the hypotenuse. Measure the length of the median and the length of the hypotenuse.

3⃣ Compare the length of the median to the length of the hypotenuse.

Median:	10 mm	9 mm	12.5 mm	15 mm
Hypotenuse:	20 mm	18 mm	25 mm	30 mm

Conclusion: In a right triangle, the length of the median to the hypotenuse is one half its length.

In inductive reasoning, you arrive at a conclusion based on several observations. The greater the number of observations, the greater is the likelihood that the conclusion is correct. The following table lists some important differences between deductive and inductive reasoning.

Deductive Reasoning	Inductive Reasoning
1. Conclusions are based on accepted statements (definitions, properties, postulates, previous theorems, and given information).	1. Conclusions are based on observations.
2. Conclusions *must* be true if the hypotheses are true.	2. Conclusions may be, but are *not necessarily,* true.

REMEMBER: Inductive reasoning is *not* a method of proof. However, inductive reasoning can lead to the formulation of general statements that can be proved deductively.

CLASSROOM EXERCISES

In each exercise, tell whether the reasoning is inductive or deductive.

1. By using the definitions of opposite rays and of a straight angle, Raoul concluded that opposite rays form a straight angle.

2. By measuring 10 pairs of vertical angles, Elena concluded that vertical angles are congruent.

3. By using the definitions of equilateral triangle and of perimeter, Harry concludes that the perimeter of an equilateral with side of length s equals $3s$.

WRITTEN EXERCISES

In these exercises, you will be using inductive reasoning to reach a conclusion. REMEMBER: A conclusion arrived at by inductive reasoning has not been proved. To be sure of a conclusion, you use a deductive proof.

1. Draw a scalene triangle, a right triangle, an isosceles triangle, and an equilateral triangle. Use a protractor to measure each angle of each triangle. Find the sum of the angles of each triangle.

   Conclusion: *The sum of the measures of the angles of a triangle is __?__ .*

   Draw three pentagons like those shown in Figures 1, 2, and 3 below. Extend the sides of each figure as shown. Use these figures in Exercises 2–6.

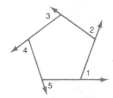
Figure 1

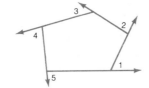
Figure 2

Figure 3

2. Measure each of the numbered angles in Figure 1. Use the results to complete this statement.
   Each of the numbered angles in Figure 1 is __?__ . (acute, right, obtuse).

3. Measure each of the numbered angles in Figure 2. Use the results to complete this statement.
   Each of the numbered angles in Figure 2 is __?__ (acute, right, obtuse).

4. Use the results obtained in Exercises 2 and 3 to complete this statement arrived at by inductive reasoning based on the results of Exercises 2 and 3.

   Conclusion: *When the sides of a pentagon are extended in order, the angles formed are __?__ angles.*

5. Measure each of the numbered angles in Figure 3. What does this tell you about the conclusion in Exercise 4?

6. Use the results of Exercises 2–5 to complete this statement: *Conclusions arrived at by inductive reasoning are* __?__ (*always, sometimes, never*) *true.*

Draw four quadrilaterals each of which has all of its vertices on a circle. Label the vertices as shown in the figure at the right. Measure each angle of each quadrilateral. Use this information in Exercises 7–9.

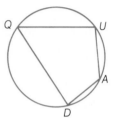

7. In each quadrilateral, m∠ A + m∠ Q = __?__ .

8. In each quadrilateral, m∠ D + m∠ U = __?__ .

9. Complete this statement arrived at by inductive reasoning:

Conclusion: *The sum of the measures of the opposite angles of a quadrilateral each of whose vertices lies on a circle is* __?__ .

Look for the pattern in **A, B, C,** and **D.** Use this pattern to write each product in Exercise 10–13.

A. 25 × 25 = 625   **B.** 75 × 75 = 5625   **C.** 45 × 45 = 2025   **D.** 95 × 95 = 9025

10. 35 × 35   **11.** 55 × 55   **12.** 65 × 65   **13.** 85 × 85

B   When a chord is drawn connecting two points on a circle, the region inside the circle is divided into two subregions. For three points on the circle, there will be four subregions. For four points, there are eight subregions.
Use this information in Exercises 14–17.

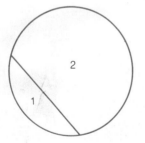
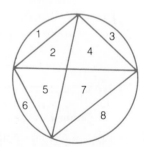

14. Draw a circle and show that for five points on the circle there are 16 subregions.

15. Complete the table. Use inductive reasoning to write the number of regions for *n* = 6.

Number of points	2	3	4	5	6
Number of subregions	?	?	?	?	?

16. Now draw a circle and carefully count the number of regions when chords are drawn for 6 points on the circle.

17. Compare your answers to Exercises 15–16. Complete this statement:

A conclusion arrived at by __?__ reasoning is not a proof.

In Exercises 18–23, use inductive reasoning to determine the pattern in each sequence.

a. Use the pattern to write the next two terms in the sequence.

b. Write a formula that describes the pattern algebraically.

Example: 3, 9, 27, _?_, _?_

Solution: 3^1 3^2 3^3 ... ⟶ Formula: 3^n Next two terms: **81, 243**

18. 5, 25, 125, _?_, _?_   **19.** 1, 4, 9, _?_, _?_   **20.** $1, \frac{1}{2}, \frac{1}{3},$ _?_, _?_

21. 0, 3, 8, _?_, _?_   **22.** 2, 8, 18, _?_, _?_   **23.** 0, 7, 26, _?_, _?_

C

24. Evaluate the expression $x^2 + x + 11$ for $x = 1, 2, 3, 4, 5$.

25. Use inductive reasoning to guess whether the number obtained by evaluating the expression in Exercise 24 for $x = 10$ will be a prime number or a composite number.

26. Test the conclusion arrived at in Exercise 25 by evaluating the expression in Exercise 24 for $x = 10$. Explain the result.

APPLICATIONS

USING INDUCTIVE REASONING

In each exercise, classify the reasoning as inductive or deductive.

1. Mary Eagle tried to sharpen three pencils. The pencil points kept breaking in the sharpener. Mary concluded that the sharpener was out of order.

2. A manufacturer tested two detergents, Brand A and Brand B on 7000 users. More than three-fourths preferred Brand B. The manufacturer concluded that Brand B should be marketed and Brand A should not.

3. The Tip-Top Insurance Company charges a yearly premium of $394.80 for liability insurance if a person has had no driver training. For persons with driver training, the yearly premium is $321.60. David concludes that he can save about $70 per year for insurance if he has driver training.

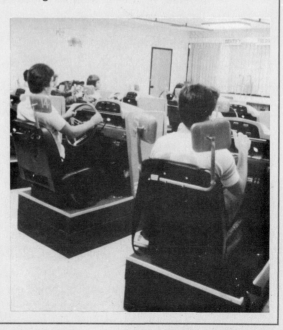

Introduction to Proof   **79**

Review

In Exercises 1–3, state the theorem or corollary that justifies each statement. Refer to the figure at the right. *(Section 2–5)*

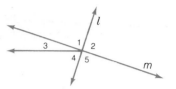

1. If ∠1 is a right angle, then ∠2 is a right angle.

2. If ∠2 and ∠5 are right angles, then ∠2 ≅ ∠5.

3. If lines *l* and *m* are perpendicular, then ∠1 ≅ ∠2.

In Exercises 4–5, write one or more conclusions that follow from the *Given.* Justify your answer with a definition, theorem, or corollary. *(Section 2–5)*

4. Given: ∠ADC is a right angle.

   Conclusion: __?__

5. Given: m∠1 = 90

   Conclusion: __?__

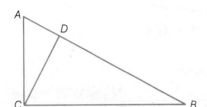

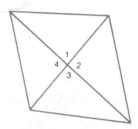

In Exercises 6–9, $\overline{BE} \perp \overline{AC}$. Classify each statement as true, *T*, or false, *F*. Give a reason for each answer. *(Section 2–6)*

6. $\overline{BE}$ is a median of △ABC.

7. $\overline{BE}$ is an altitude of △ABC.

8. $\overline{BD}$ bisects ∠EBC.

9. $\overline{BD}$ is an altitude of △ABC.

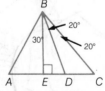

10. The perimeter of a quadrilateral is 49. If the lengths of three consecutive sides are 9, 10, and 14, what is the length of the fourth side? *(Section 2–6)*

In Exercises 11–13, tell whether the reasoning is inductive or deductive. *(Section 2–7)*

11. Jeanne has found robins' eggs four times. Each time the eggs were blue. She concludes that robins' eggs are always blue.

12. By using the definitions of complementary angles, right angles, and adjacent angles, Juan concluded that two complementary adjacent angles form a right angle.

13. By measuring six linear pairs, Louise concluded that when two angles form a linear pair, the sum of their measures is 180.

Geometric Figures and Driving

The alert driver, concerned for personal safety and for the safety of others, must be able to identify certain traffic signs by their shape.

OCTAGON: Indicates a complete stop.

PENTAGON: Indicates a school crossing zone.

TRIANGLE: Indicates slowing or stopping.

DIAMOND (Square standing on a vertex): Indicates danger.

RECTANGLE: Gives important instructions.

EXERCISES

In Exercises 1–9, match each warning or instruction with the correct polygon. Choose a, b, c, or d.

a.   b.

c.   d.

1. LEFT LANE MUST TURN LEFT

2. DO NOT PASS

3. TRUCK CROSSING

4. KEEP RIGHT

5. YIELD

6. STOP

7. EXIT

8. DIP

9. MERGE

BASIC: PERIMETER

Problem: *Given the measures of the sides of a triangle, find the perimeter of the triangle.*

Program:
```
10 PRINT "ENTER THE MEASURES OF THE SIDES."
20 INPUT A, B, C
30 LET P = A + B + C
40 PRINT "THE PERIMETER IS "; P
50 PRINT "ANY MORE TRIANGLES (1 = YES, 0 = NO)";
60 INPUT X
70 IF X = 1 THEN 10
80 END
```

Analysis:

Statements 50 and 60: The semicolon at the end of Statement 50 tells the computer to put the output from the next statement on the same line as the output from Statement 50. This output is the question mark from the INPUT statement.

Statement 70: This is another IF . . . THEN statement that causes the computer to start the program again if the user enters a 1. If the user enters a 0, the program ends.

EXERCISES

A   Run the program above with the following measures.

1. $A = 4$, $B = 9$, $C = 12$
2. $A = 3$, $B = 12$, $C = 13$
3. $A = 26$, $B = 49$, $C = 35$
4. $A = 48$, $B = 29$, $C = 20$
5. $A = 6.2$, $B = 4.9$, $C = 7.8$
6. $A = 3.2$, $B = 5.6$, $C = 8.1$
7. $A = 21.2$, $B = 25.4$, $C = 14.9$
8. $A = 32.1$, $B = 28.7$, $C = 26.9$

B   Write a BASIC program for each problem.

9. Given the measures of the sides of a quadrilateral, compute the perimeter of the quadrilateral.

10. Given the measures of the base and one of the congruent sides of an isosceles triangle, compute its perimeter.

11. Given the measure of one side of an equilateral triangle, compute its perimeter.

12. Given the measure of one of the five congruent sides of a regular pentagon, compute its perimeter.

Chapter Summary

IMPORTANT TERMS

Adjacent sides of a polygon (p. 72)
Altitude of a triangle (p. 72)
Biconditional (p. 67)
Conclusion (p. 49)
Conditional (p. 49)
Consecutive angles of a polygon (p. 72)
Converse (p. 67)
Convex polygon (p. 71)
Corollary (p. 67)
Deductive reasoning (p. 51)
Diagonal (p. 72)
Equivalence relation (p. 44)

Hexagon (p. 71)
Hypothesis (p. 49)
Inductive reasoning (p. 76)
Median (p. 72)
Octagon (p. 71)
Pentagon (p. 71)
Perimeter (p. 72)
Polygon (p. 71)
Quadrilateral (p. 71)
Reflexive property (p. 44)
Symmetric property (p. 44)
Transitive property (p. 44)

IMPORTANT IDEAS

1. The reflexive, symmetric, and transitive properties of equality hold for congruence.

2. Many theorems in geometry are stated as conditionals. The if-part of the conditional is the hypothesis and the then-part is the conclusion of the theorem.

3. **Steps in deductive reasoning**
   1. Begin with an accepted fact or facts.
   2. Continue in a step-by-step fashion with statements justified by the hypothesis, or by postulates, theorems, or definitions.
   3. End with the last statement, which is the conclusion.

4. **Steps for writing a two-column proof**
   1. Determine the *Given* and the *Prove*.
   2. Draw a figure to represent the *Given* and the *Prove*.
   3. Plan the proof.
   4. Write the statements and reasons.

5. **Congruence of angles**
   Two angles are congruent if:
   a. they are supplements or complements of the same angle.
   b. they are supplements or complements of congruent angles.
   c. they are vertical angles.

6. **Right angles**
   If one angle of a linear pair is a right angle, then the other is also a right angle.

   If two intersecting lines form one right angle, then they form four right angles.

   Two lines are perpendicular if and only if they form congruent adjacent angles.

7. Polygons are classified by the number of their sides.

8. Inductive reasoning can lead to the formulation of general statements that can be proved deductively.

Chapter Objectives and Review

Objective: *To use the properties of equality to solve equations (Section 2–1)*

In Exercises 1–5, name the property illustrated by each statement.

1. If $3AB = 78$, then $AB = 26$.
2. If $QR - 9 = 43$, then $QR = 52$.
3. If $a = 7$ and $GH = a + 9$, then $GH = 16$.
4. If $AC = \frac{1}{2}AB$, then $\frac{1}{2}AB = AC$.
5. If $2(AB + BC) = 3(DE + EF)$, then $2AB + 2BC = 3DE + 3EF$.

In Exercises 6–7, state the missing reasons in each proof.

6. Statements	Reasons
1. $4x + 7 = 2x - 11$	1. Given
2. $2x + 7 = -11$	2. ?
3. $2x = -18$	3. ?
4. $x = -9$	4. ?

7. Statements	Reasons
1. $3(x - 2) = 21$	1. Given
2. $3x - 6 = 21$	2. ?
3. $3x = 27$	3. ?
4. $x = 9$	4. ?

Objective: *To write the Given and the Prove for a conditional (Section 2–2)*

In Exercises 8–10:
a. Write the hypothesis and conclusion for each conditional.
b. Write the *Given* and the *Prove* and draw a figure for the conditional.

8. If a triangle is equilateral, then it has three congruent sides.

9. Two angles are congruent if they are complements of the same angle.

10. If the three angles of a triangle are congruent, the three sides are congruent.

Objective: *To draw conclusions from given information (Section 2–3)*

In Exercises 11–13 write the conclusion that can be drawn from the *Given*. More than one conclusion may be possible in some cases. Give the reason(s) for each conclusion you write.

11. **Given:** $AB = BC$

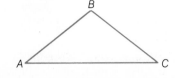

12. **Given:** $m\angle DEG = \frac{1}{2}m\angle DEF$

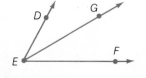

13. **Given:** $\angle 1 \cong \angle 2$

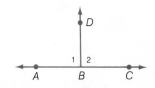

Objective: *To supply reasons for statements in two-column proofs (Section 2–3)*

In Exercises 14–15, supply the missing reasons in each proof.

14. Given: D is the midpoint of $\overline{BC}$;   Prove: $CD = AE$
$AE = \frac{1}{2}BC$

Statements	Reasons
1. D is the midpoint of $\overline{BC}$.	1. ?
2. $CD = \frac{1}{2}BC$ —	2. ?
3. $AE = \frac{1}{2}BC$	3. ?
4. $CD = AE$	4. ?

15. Given: $\angle 1 \cong \angle 2$; $\angle 1$ and $\angle 2$ are a linear pair.

Prove: $t \perp s$

Statements	Reasons
1. $\angle 1 \cong \angle 2$	1. ?
2. $\angle 1$ and $\angle 2$ are a linear pair.	2. ?
3. $\angle 1$ and $\angle 2$ are adjacent angles.	3. ?
4. $t \perp s$	4. ?

Objective: *To write two–column proofs (Section 2–4)*

In Exercises 16–17, supply the missing statements and reasons.

16. Given: $\angle 1 \cong \angle 2$; $\angle 3 \cong \angle 4$ Prove: $\angle 1 \cong \angle 4$

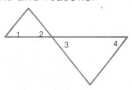

Statements	Reasons
1. $\angle 1 \cong \angle 2$; $\angle 3 \cong \angle 4$	1. ?
2. $\angle 2 \cong \angle 3$	2. ?
3. $\angle 1 \cong \angle 4$	3. (1), (2). ?

17. Given: $\angle 1$ and $\angle 2$ are complementary;
$\angle 3$ and $\angle 4$ are complementary.

Prove: $\angle 1 \cong \angle 4$

Statements	Reasons
1. $\angle 1$ and $\angle 2$ are complementary. $\angle 3$ and $\angle 4$ are complementary.	1. ?
2. $m\angle 1 + m\angle 2 = $? ; $m\angle 3 + $? $= $?	2. (1). ? Def of Complementum
3. $m\angle 1 + m\angle 2 = m\angle 3 + m\angle 4$	3. (2). ? Substitution
4. $\angle 2 \cong \angle 3$	4. ? Vertical angis ue cagruent
5. $m\angle 2 = m\angle 3$	5. (4). ? Def of congrut Ayls
6. $m\angle 1 + m\angle 3 = m\angle 3 + m\angle 4$	6. (3), (5). ? Substith'n
7. ? $m\angle 1 = m\angle 4$	7. (6). Addition prop. of equality
8. $\angle 1 \cong \angle 4$	8. (7). ? Def of congrunt angls

In Exercises 18–19, write a two–column proof for each exercise.

18. Given: $p \perp q$; $\angle 1$ is
complementary to $\angle 3$.

    Prove: $m\angle 2 = m\angle 3$

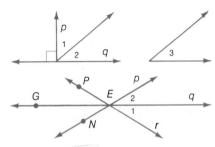

19. Given: Lines p, q, and r
intersect at E;
$\angle 1 \cong \angle 2$

    Prove: $\overrightarrow{EG}$ bisects $\angle PEN$

Objective: *To use theorems about perpendicular lines (Section 2–5)*

In Exercises 20–21, write one or more conclusions that follow from the *Given*.
Justify your answer with a definition, theorem or corollary.

20. ABC is a right triangle with right angle
at C; $\overline{CD} \perp \overline{AB}$.

21. Ray DC is perpendicular to line AB
and $\angle 2 \cong \angle 3$.

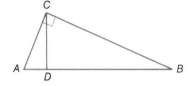

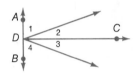

Objective: *To identify polygons and some properties of polygons (Section 2–6)*

22. Polygon $PQRSTV$ is a __?__ .

23. In polygon $PQRSTV$, $\overline{SR}$ and __?__ are consecutive
sides.

24. In polygon $PQRSTV$, $\angle V$ and $\angle$__?__ are consecutive
angles.

25. In polygon $PQRSTV$, $\overline{SP}$ is a __?__ of the polygon.

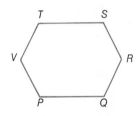

26. If $\overline{DE} \perp \overline{AC}$, then $\overline{DE}$ is an altitude of $\triangle$__?__ .

27. If $\overline{EF} \cong \overline{FC}$, then $\overline{DF}$ is a median of $\triangle$__?__ .

28. If $m\angle 1 = m\angle 2$, then $\overrightarrow{EG}$ is an angle bisector of $\triangle$__?__ .

29. If $\overline{DE}$ is a median of $\triangle DAC$, $EF = 7$ and $AC = 39$,
$FC = $__?__ .

30. If $\overline{DE}$ is an altitude of $\triangle DAF$, and $\overrightarrow{EG}$ bisects
$\angle DEA$, $m\angle 2 = $__?__ .

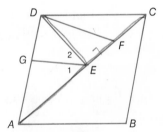

Objective: *To reach a conclusion by inductive reasoning
(Section 2–7)*

31. Draw several different right triangles and in each triangle draw the altitude from the vertex of the right
angle. $\overline{CD}$, in the figure, is one such altitude. Measure
angles A and 1 in each triangle. State your conclusion.

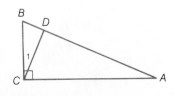

32. What are the next two numbers in this sequence?

$$36, 28, 20, 12, \underline{\ ?\ }, \underline{\ ?\ }$$

Objective: *To solve word problems that involve polygons* (Page 75)

33. The perimeter of the Pentagon in Washington, D.C. is 1400 meters. Each side of the building is the same length. Find the length of each side of the Pentagon.

Chapter Test

1. Supply the reasons for the following proof.

Given: $6x + 23 = 14 - 3x$

Prove: $x = -1$

Statements	Reasons
1. $6x + 23 = 14 - 3x$	1. __?__
2. $9x + 23 = 14$	2. __?__
3. $9x = -9$	3. __?__
4. $x = -1$	4. __?__

In Exercises 2–3, write the *Given* and the *Prove* for each statement.

2. If two distinct lines intersect, then they determine exactly one plane.

3. If two lines are perpendicular, then they form congruent adjacent angles.

In Exercises 4–5, write the conclusion that can be drawn from the *Given*. More than one conclusion may be possible in some cases. Give the reason(s) for each conclusion you write.

4. Given: E is the midpoint of AC.

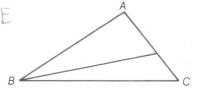

5. Given: Angles ABC and CBD are complementary.

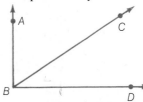

6. Supply the missing reasons in the following proof.

Given: $\angle 2$ and $\angle 3$ are complementary;
$\overline{CD} \perp \overline{AB}$

Prove: $\angle ACB \cong \angle 1$

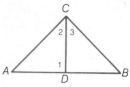

Statements	Reasons
1. $\angle 2$ and $\angle 3$ are complementary.	1. _?_
2. $m\angle 2 + m\angle 3 = 90$	2. (1). _?_
3. $m\angle 2 + m\angle 3 = m\angle ACB$	3. _?_
4. $m\angle ACB = 90$	4. (2), (3). _?_
5. $\overline{CD} \perp \overline{AB}$	5. _?_
6. $m\angle 1 = 90$	6. (5). _?_
7. $m\angle ACB = m\angle 1$	7. (4), (6). _?_
8. $\angle ACB \cong \angle 1$	8. (7). _?_

In Exercises 7–8, write a two-column proof.

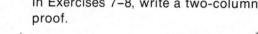

7. Given: $\angle 1 \cong \angle 3$;
$\angle 2 \cong \angle 3$

Prove: $a \perp b$

8. Given: $\angle 1 \cong \angle 2$

Prove: $\angle 3 \cong \angle 4$

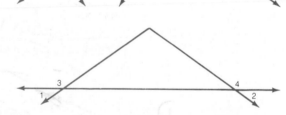

Complete each statement.

9. Polygon $PQRST$ is a _?_ .

10. $\overline{SQ}$ is a _?_ .

11. $\overline{PQ}$ and $\overline{QR}$ are _?_ sides.

12. $\angle T$ and $\angle$ _?_ are consecutive angles.

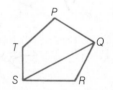

In Exercises 13–15, state whether the reasoning is inductive or deductive.

13. For three months in a row, Miles received his telephone bill on the fifteenth of the month. Miles concludes that he will get his next telephone bill on the fifteenth.

14. Judy concludes that a certain type of flower is always red after having seen five of these flowers. Each of the five flowers was red.

15. From the definition of a right angle and of complementary angles, Susan concludes that the sum of the measures of two complementary angles is the measure of a right angle.

CHAPTER 3 **Congruent Triangles**

Sections   3-1   **Congruence**

3-2   **Congruent Triangles: SAS Postulate**

3-3   **Congruent Triangles: ASA and SSS Postulates**

Applications: Using Triangles

3-4   **Isosceles Triangle Theorems**

3-5   **More Isosceles Triangle Theorems**

Applications: Using Isosceles Triangles

3-6   **Congruence and Overlapping Triangles**

3-7   **Indirect Proof in Geometry**

3-8   **Congruence in Right Triangles**

3-9   **Contrapositives and Biconditionals**

Features   **Consumer Application: Logical Reasoning and Advertising Puzzles**

Review and Testing   **Geometry Review Capsules**

Review: Sections 3–1 through 3–3

Review: Sections 3–4 through 3–6

Review: Sections 3–7 through 3–9

Chapter Summary

Chapter Objectives and Review

Chapter Test

Cumulative Review: Chapters 1–3

Preparing for College Entrance Tests

3-1 Congruence

Triangles that have the same size and shape are congruent. In triangles ABC and DEF,

$$\angle A \cong \angle D \qquad \overline{AB} \cong \overline{DE}$$

$$\angle B \cong \angle E \qquad \overline{BC} \cong \overline{EF}$$

$$\angle C \cong \angle F \qquad \overline{CA} \cong \overline{FD}$$

Each angle of $\triangle ABC$ *corresponds* to a particular angle of $\triangle DEF$, and each side of $\triangle ABC$ *corresponds* to a particular side of $\triangle DEF$.

$$ABC \leftrightarrow DEF \quad \longleftarrow \quad \textbf{Read: "ABC corresponds to DEF."}$$

Definition

> A correspondence between two triangles is a **congruence** if the corresponding angles and the corresponding sides are congruent.

In triangles ABC and DEF, the corresponding angles are congruent and the corresponding sides are congruent. Thus,

$$\triangle ABC \cong \triangle DEF \quad \longleftarrow \quad \textbf{Read "}\triangle \textbf{ABC is congruent to } \triangle \textbf{DEF."}$$

EXAMPLE 1 Given that $\triangle THE \cong \triangle QNR$, name the corresponding congruent parts.

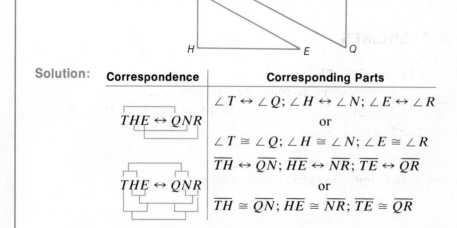

Solution:

Correspondence	Corresponding Parts
$THE \leftrightarrow QNR$	$\angle T \leftrightarrow \angle Q$; $\angle H \leftrightarrow \angle N$; $\angle E \leftrightarrow \angle R$ or $\angle T \cong \angle Q$; $\angle H \cong \angle N$; $\angle E \cong \angle R$
$THE \leftrightarrow QNR$	$\overline{TH} \leftrightarrow \overline{QN}$; $\overline{HE} \leftrightarrow \overline{NR}$; $\overline{TE} \leftrightarrow \overline{QR}$ or $\overline{TH} \cong \overline{QN}$; $\overline{HE} \cong \overline{NR}$; $\overline{TE} \cong \overline{QR}$

In Example 1, $THE \leftrightarrow QNR$ is a congruence, but $THE \leftrightarrow QRN$ is not a congruence. That is, the correspondence $THE \leftrightarrow QNR$ is *not* the same as $THE \leftrightarrow QRN$.

EXAMPLE 2   Given that $\triangle RST \cong \triangle XYZ$, which of these correspondences is a congruence?

    a. $RST \leftrightarrow XYZ$
    b. $TSR \leftrightarrow ZXY$
    c. $STR \leftrightarrow YZX$
    d. $SRT \leftrightarrow YZX$

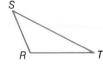 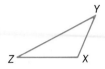

Solution: Since $\triangle RST \cong \triangle XYZ$, $\angle R \leftrightarrow \angle X$, $\angle S \leftrightarrow \angle Y$, and $\angle T \leftrightarrow \angle Z$.

    a. $RST \leftrightarrow XYZ$ **Yes**   **b.** $TSR \leftrightarrow ZXY$ **No**

    c. $STR \leftrightarrow YZX$ **Yes**   **d.** $SRT \leftrightarrow YZX$ **No**

Recall that a definition can be written as two conditionals.

If the corresponding parts of two triangles are congruent, then the triangles are congruent.

If two triangles are congruent, then their corresponding parts are congruent.

The second form is often abbreviated as

CPCTC. ◄——— **Corresponding parts of congruent triangles are congruent.**

A geometric figure is congruent to itself by the reflexive property of congruence. In a proof, you may refer to this property as *Identity*.

CLASSROOM EXERCISES

Complete each statement.

1. $\triangle ABC \cong \triangle DEF$. The corresponding congruent parts are __?__.
2. $\triangle RST \cong \triangle XYZ$. $\overline{ST} \leftrightarrow$ __?__   3. $\triangle QPV \cong \triangle GHJ$. $\angle V \leftrightarrow$ __?__
4. $\triangle FCZ \cong \triangle RPT$. $\overline{ZF} \cong$ __?__   5. $\triangle GFH \cong \triangle JKP$. $\angle F \cong \angle$ __?__

In the triangle at the right, $ACB \leftrightarrow ACD$ is a congruence. Name the correspondences below that are *not* congruences.

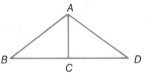

6. $BAC \leftrightarrow DAC$ 7. $CBA \leftrightarrow CAD$ 8. $DCA \leftrightarrow BAC$

$\triangle RST \cong \triangle HGK$. Complete each correspondence correctly.

9. RT __?__ $\leftrightarrow HK$ __?__   10. $STR \leftrightarrow$ __?__ K __?__
11. __?__ __?__ $R \leftrightarrow$ __?__ GH 12. $TRS \leftrightarrow$ __?__ __?__ __?__

WRITTEN EXERCISES

A   In the figure below, △ ACB ≅ △ DFE. Refer to these triangles in Exercises 1–8 to complete each statement.

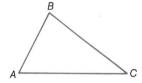 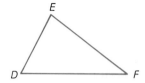

1. The correspondence A _?_ _?_ ↔ _?_ FE is a congruence.

2. The correspondence BA _?_ ↔ _?_ _?_ _?_ is a congruence.

3. ∠A ≅ ∠ _?_   4. ∠C ≅ ∠ _?_   5. ∠B ≅ ∠ _?_

6. $\overline{AC}$ ≅ _?_   7. $\overline{CB}$ ≅ _?_   8. $\overline{BA}$ ≅ _?_

9. If the correspondence GHR ↔ JKP is a congruence, name three pairs of congruent angles and three pairs of congruent sides in the triangles at the right.

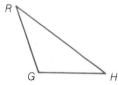 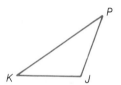

Given that △AHR ≅ △MBK, determine which correspondences in Exercises 10–17 are congruences.

10. ARH ↔ MKB   11. ARH ↔ MBK

12. RHA ↔ MBK   13. RHA ↔ KBM

14. HAR ↔ BKM   15. RAH ↔ KMB

16. HAR ↔ BMK   17. AHR ↔ MBK

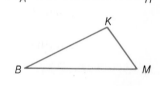

Given that △TXY ≅ △SXZ, complete the correspondences so that they are congruences.

18. YXT ↔ _?_ X _?_   19. YTX ↔ _?_ _?_ X

20. XTY ↔ _?_ _?_ _?_   21. TXY ↔ _?_ _?_ _?_

22. XYT ↔ _?_ Z _?_   23. TYX ↔ _?_ _?_ _?_

In Exercises 24–26, refer to the figure for Exercises 18–23.

24. What angle in △XZS corresponds to ∠Y in △XYT?

25. Which side of △XZS corresponds to $\overline{YT}$ in △XYT?

26. Which side of △XZS corresponds to $\overline{YX}$ in △XYT?

27. Is a line segment congruent to itself? Why?

28. Is an angle congruent to itself? Why?   29. Is a triangle congruent to itself? Why?

In Exercises 30–32, use the given figure and information to name three pairs of congruent angles and three pairs of congruent sides.

30. △EHG ≅ △KFG

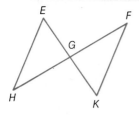

31. △ABC ≅ △CDA

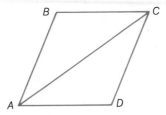

32. △ABC ≅ △BAD; △ACE ≅ △BDE

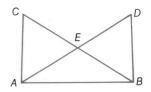

33. Name the triangles in the figure at the left below that appear to be congruent. Name the three pairs of corresponding sides.

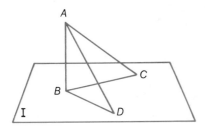

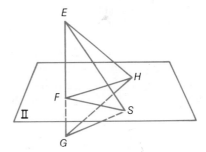

34. Use the figure at the right above to name two pairs of triangles that appear to be congruent.

Use the figure at the right above and Exercise 34 to complete each statement.

35. ∠FES ≅ ∠ __?__

36. ∠EHF ≅ ∠ __?__

37. $\overline{FS}$ ≅ __?__

38. $\overline{GS}$ ≅ __?__

39. $\overline{FE}$ ≅ __?__

40. ∠GSF ≅ ∠ __?__

_____ **GEOMETRY REVIEW CAPSULE FOR SECTION 3-2** _____

Refer to the figure at the right. Write true, *T*, or false, *F*, for each statement. Give the reason for each answer. *(Pages 2–4, 7, 11)*

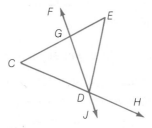

1. $\overrightarrow{CH}$ is a line.

2. $\overline{CE}$ is a line segment.

3. *C* is the vertex of ∠ECD.

4. If *CD* = *DE*, then △CDE is scalene.

5. $\overleftrightarrow{FJ}$ has two endpoints.

6. *C*, *G*, and *E* are collinear points.

7. Points *C* and *D* determine a plane.

8. $\overrightarrow{CH}$ and $\overrightarrow{GJ}$ intersect at point *D*.

3-2 Congruent Triangles: SAS Postulate

To show that two triangles are congruent, it is not necessary to know that all six corresponding parts are congruent. Look at the table below and on the following page to determine the *least* number of congruent corresponding parts needed.

Number of Congruent Parts	Figures	Triangles Congruent?
One Part		
One side	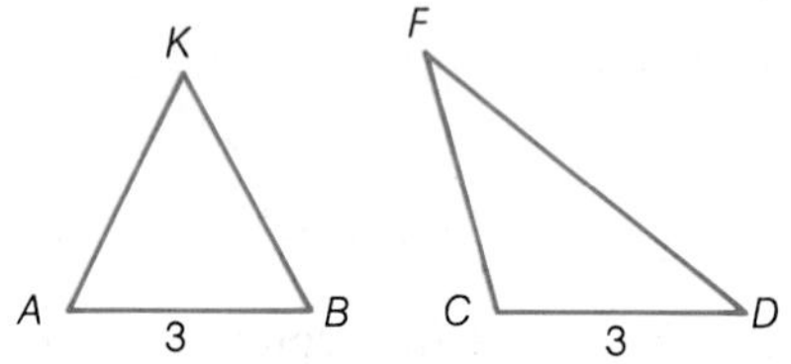	No
One angle	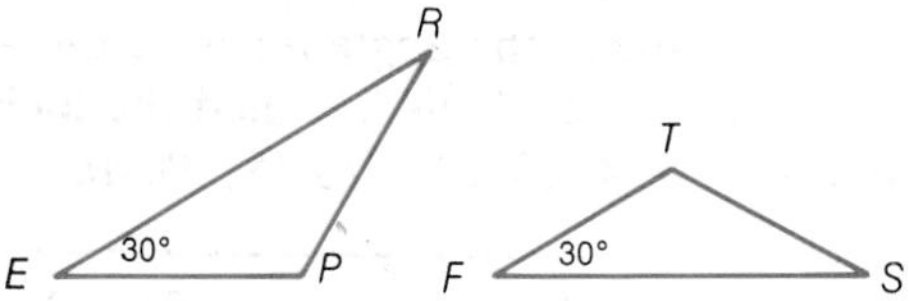	No
Two Parts		
Two sides	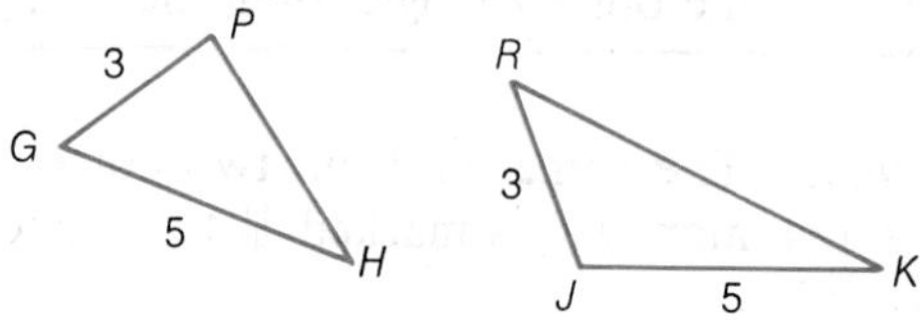	No
Two angles	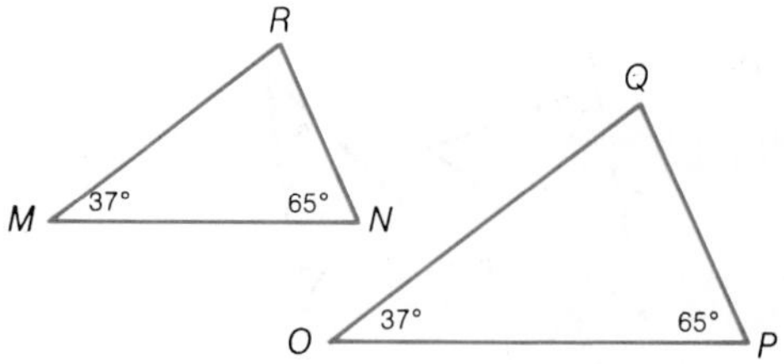	No
One side, one angle	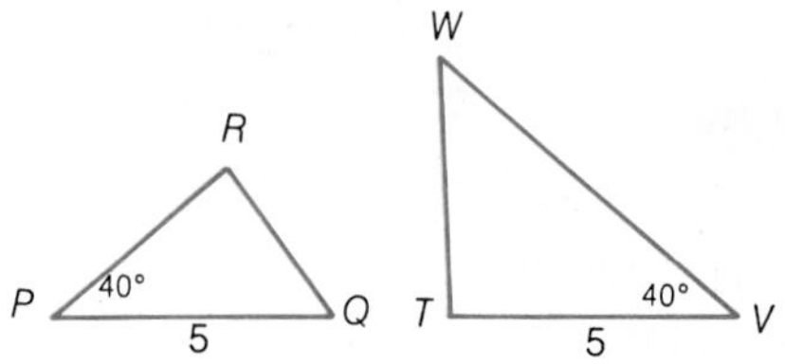	No

Number of Congruent Parts	Figures	Triangles Congruent?
Three Parts		
Two sides, one angle		**No**
Two sides, included angle		**Yes**

The table shows that you need at least three corresponding congruent parts to conclude that two triangles are congruent. Also, in the case of two sides and one angle, the angle *must* be the angle formed by the two correspond-congruent sides. This is called the **included angle.** The congruence is stated in the *Side-Angle-Side (SAS) Postulate.*

Postulate 11

> **SAS Postulate**
>
> If two triangles have two sides and the included angle of one triangle congruent respectively to two sides and the included angle of the other triangle, then the triangles are congruent.

NOTE: The same mark on two corresponding parts indicates congruence. A common side is marked ||| to remind you that it is congruent by identity.

EXAMPLE 1 Name the pairs of triangles that are congruent by the SAS Postulate.

a.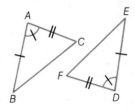

b.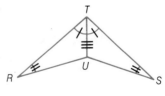

c.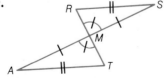

d.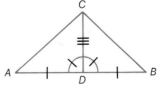

Solutions: In **a**, $\triangle ABC \cong \triangle DEF$; in **d**, $\triangle ADC \cong \triangle BDC$.

Unless otherwise indicated, you may assume the following from the appearance of the figure. You will need to make these assumptions in writing proofs.

Summary

Assumptions From a Figure
1 Lines, segments, rays, and angles
2 Collinearity of points on a line
3 Betweenness with respect to points on a line
4 Betweenness with respect to coplanar rays with the same vertex
5 Intersection of lines, rays, or segments
6 Adjacent angles and linear pairs

EXAMPLE 2 Tell which statements can be assumed from the appearance of the figure at the left below.

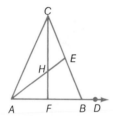

a. $\overrightarrow{AD}$ is a ray.

b. A, H, and E are collinear points.

c. $\overline{CF} \perp \overline{AB}$.

d. $\overline{CF}$ bisects $\angle ACB$.

e. Angles CAE and EAF are adjacent angles.

f. $\overline{CF}$ and $\overline{AE}$ intersect at H.

Solutions: Statements **a, b, e,** and **f** can be assumed from the appearance of the figure (see the Summary above).

Statements **c** and **d** cannot.

CLASSROOM EXERCISES

In Exercises 1–6, name the pairs of triangles that are congruent by the SAS Postulate.

1.
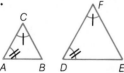

2.
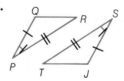

3.
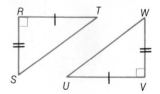

4.
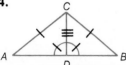

5.
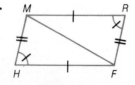

6.
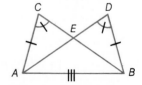

In Exercises 7–14, write *Yes* if the statement can be assumed from the appearance of the figure. Otherwise, write *No*.

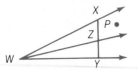

7. $\overrightarrow{WX}$, $\overrightarrow{WZ}$, and $\overrightarrow{WY}$ are rays.

8. W, Z, and P are collinear.

9. $\overline{XZ}$ and $\overline{WZ}$ are segments.

10. $\overrightarrow{WZ}$ and $\overline{XY}$ intersect at Z.

11. $m\angle WYX = 90$

12. $\overrightarrow{WZ}$ bisects $\angle XWY$.

13. $\overrightarrow{WY}$ determines a line.

14. Z is the midpoint of $\overline{XY}$.

WRITTEN EXERCISES

A   The SAS relationship can occur in three ways in a triangle. These ways are shown for △ABC below.

In Exercises 1–3, make similar drawings to show how the SAS relationship could occur in each triangle.

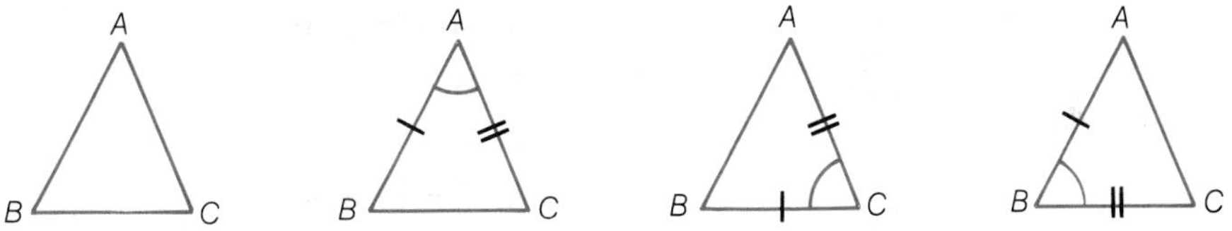

1.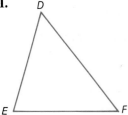

2.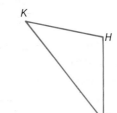

3.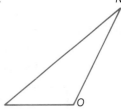

In Exercises 4–9, name the pairs of triangles that are congruent by the SAS Postulate.

4.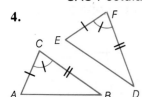

5.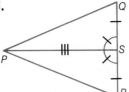

6.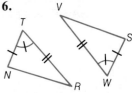

7.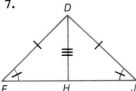

8.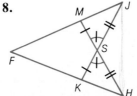

9.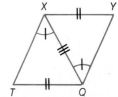

In Exercises 10–12, tell why the triangles are *not* congruent by the SAS Postulate.

10.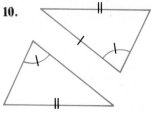

11.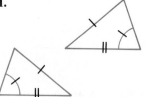

12.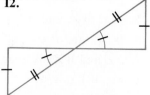

In Exercises 13–14, tell whether the triangles are congruent by SAS.

13.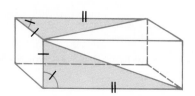

14.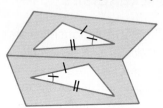

In Exercises 15–16, supply the missing statements and reasons.

15. Given: $\overline{BC} \cong \overline{EC}$; $\angle 1 \cong \angle 2$;
C is the midpoint of $\overline{AD}$.

Prove: $\triangle ABC \cong \triangle DEC$

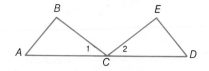

Statements	Reasons
1. $\overline{BC} \cong \overline{EC}$; $\angle 1 \cong \angle 2$	1. ___?___
2. C is the midpoint of $\overline{AD}$.	2. ___?___
3. $\overline{AC} \cong \overline{CD}$	3. (2). ___?___
4. $\triangle ABC \cong \triangle DEC$	4. (1), (3). ___?___

16. Given: $\overline{AB}$ and $\overline{CD}$ bisect each other at E.

Prove: $\angle D \cong \angle C$

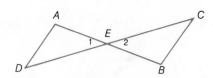

Statements	Reasons
1. $\angle 1 \cong \angle 2$	1. ___?___
2. $\overline{AB}$ bisects $\overline{CD}$; $\overline{CD}$ bisects $\overline{AB}$.	2. ___?___
3. $\overline{AE} \cong \overline{EB}$; $\overline{CE} \cong \overline{ED}$	3. (2). ___?___
4. $\triangle AED \cong \triangle$ ___?___	4. (1), (3). SAS Postulate
5. $\angle$ ___?___ $\cong \angle$ ___?___	5. (4). Corresponding parts of congruent triangles are congruent.

In Exercises 17–18, complete each proof by supplying the necessary statements and reasons. It may be necessary to add additional steps.

17. Given: $\overline{AB} \cong \overline{CD}$; $\angle ABD \cong \angle CDB$ Prove: $\overline{AD} \cong \overline{CB}$

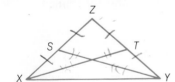

Statements	Reasons
1. $\overline{AB} \cong \overline{CD}$; $\angle ABD \cong \angle CDB$	1. ?
2. $\overline{BD} \cong \overline{BD}$	2. ?

18. Given: $\overline{AR} \cong \overline{MS}$; C bisects $\overline{RS}$; $\angle S$ and $\angle 2$ are supplementary.

Prove: $\angle A \cong \angle M$

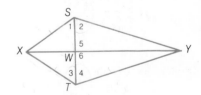

Statements	Reasons
1. $\overline{AR} \cong \overline{MS}$	1. ?
2. C bisects $\overline{RS}$.	2. ?
3. $\overline{RC} \cong \overline{SC}$	3. (2). ?
4. $\angle 1$ and $\angle 2$ form a linear pair.	4. ?
5. $\angle 1$ and $\angle 2$ are supplementary.	5. ?

19. Use the *Given* and figure of Exercise 15, but change the *Prove* to: $\overline{BA} \cong \overline{ED}$. Write the complete proof.

20. Use the *Given* and figure of Exercise 16, but change the *Prove* to: $\angle A \cong \angle B$. Write the complete proof.

21. Given: $\triangle XYZ$ is isosceles with base $\overline{XY}$;
S is the midpoint of $\overline{XZ}$;
T is the midpoint of $\overline{YZ}$.

Prove: $\angle YSZ \cong \angle XTZ$

22. Given: $\overline{XS} \cong \overline{XT}$; $\overline{YS} \cong \overline{YT}$;
$\angle 1 \cong \angle 3$; $\angle 2 \cong \angle 4$

Prove: $\angle 5 \cong \triangle 6$

GEOMETRY REVIEW CAPSULE FOR SECTION 3-3

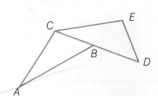

In the figure at the right, $\triangle ABC \cong \triangle CDE$.
Complete each statement. *(Pages 90–91)*

1. The correspondence $CBA \leftrightarrow$? is a congruence.
2. The correspondence ? $\leftrightarrow ECD$ is a congruence.
3. $\angle A \cong$?   4. $\overline{DE} \cong$?   5. $\angle D \cong$?
6. ? $\cong \overline{AB}$ 7. ? $\cong \angle DCE$ 8. $\overline{CE} \cong$?

3-3 Congruent Triangles: ASA and SSS Postulates

Other combinations of congruent angles and sides can be used to prove triangles congruent.

Number of Congruent Parts	Figures	Triangles Congruent?
Three Parts		
Two angles, included side	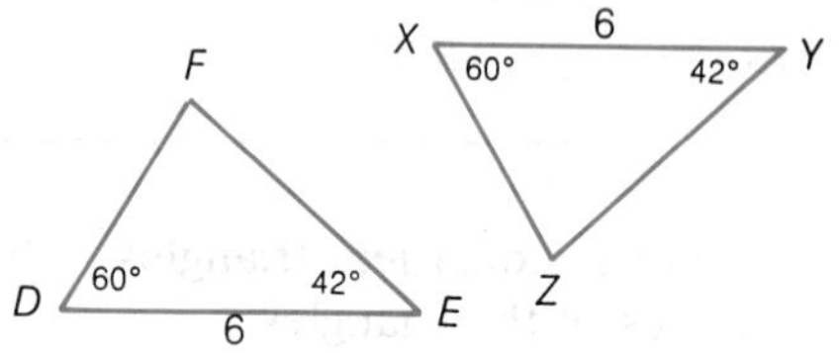	**Yes**
Three sides	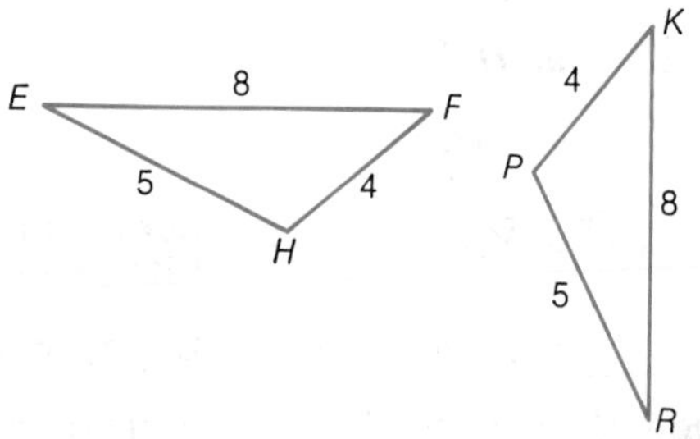	**Yes**

The first example in the table leads to the *Angle-Side-Angle (ASA) Postulate*. Note that the congruent sides must be those **included** by the corresponding congruent angles.

Postulate 12

ASA Postulate

If two triangles have two angles and the included side of one triangle congruent respectively to two angles and the included side of the other triangle, then the triangles are congruent.

The second pair of triangles in the table suggests the *Side-Side-Side (SSS) Postulate*.

Postulate 13

SSS Postulate

If two triangles have three sides of one triangle congruent respectively to the three sides of the other triangle, then the triangles are congruent.

EXAMPLE 1 For each pair of triangles, state whether they are congruent by ASA, congruent by SSS, or not congruent.

a. 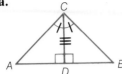   b. 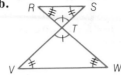   c.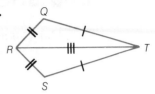

Solutions: a. Congruent by ASA ◀—— **Side *DC* is included between congruent angles.**

b. Not congruent

c. Congruent by SSS

You can use congruent triangles to find the unknown measures of the sides and angles of the triangles.

EXAMPLE 2 **Given:** $\triangle QHT \cong \triangle PYT$

Find: a. HT

b. $m\angle Y$

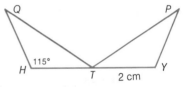

Solutions: a. $\overline{HT} \cong \overline{YT}$ ◀——— **Corresponding parts of congruent triangles are congruent (CPCTC).**

$HT = 2$ cm ◀——— **Corresponding parts have equal measures**

b. $\angle Y \cong \angle H$ ◀——— **Corresponding congruent angles**

$m\angle Y = 115$ ◀——— **Corresponding parts have equal measures.**

The following statements will serve as acceptable definitions when used in proofs. Select the word "equal" or "congruent" from the two given forms.

Definitions

> The **midpoint of a segment** forms two equal (congruent) segments.
>
> The **bisector of a segment** forms two equal (congruent) segments.
>
> The **bisector of an angle** forms two equal (congruent) angles.
>
> An **isosceles triangle** has two equal (congruent) sides.
>
> An **equilateral triangle** has three equal (congruent) sides.
>
> An **equiangular triangle** has three equal (congruent) angles.

The summary on page 102 lists four ways to prove triangles congruent.

Summary

Ways of Proving Triangles Congruent
1 By the definition of congruent triangles
2 By the SAS Postulate
3 By the ASA Postulate
4 By the SSS Postulate

Using congruent triangles provides another way of proving segments and angles congruent.

Summary

To prove segments or angles congruent:
1 Prove two triangles congruent.
2 Use CPCTC.

CLASSROOM EXERCISES

1. Given: △ABC ≅ △DBE
   Find: AB, BE, ED

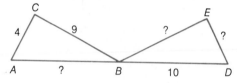

2. Given: △FJH ≅ △HGF
   Find: m∠HFG, m∠FHG

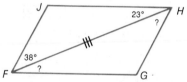

In Exercises 3–5, the corresponding congruent parts of a pair of triangles are marked. State whether each pair is congruent by SAS, by SSS, or by ASA.

3.

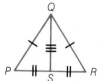

4.

5.

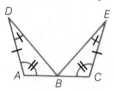

WRITTEN EXERCISES

A The ASA relationship can occur in three ways. These are shown for △ABC below. In Exercises 1–3, make similar drawings to show how the ASA relationship could occur in each triangle.

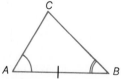

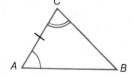

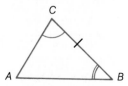

1.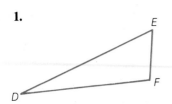

2.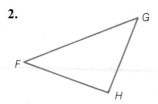

3.

In Exercises 4–21, replace the ? with the required angle or side so that the indicated relationship is correct.

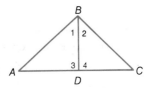

4. SAS for △ABD: $\overline{BD}$; ∠3; __?__

5. ASA for △ABD: ∠A; __?__; ∠1

6. ASA for △BDC: ∠2; $\overline{BC}$; __?__

7. SSS for △ABD: $\overline{AB}$; $\overline{BD}$; __?__

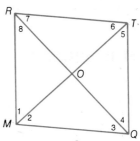

8. SAS for △MTR: $\overline{RT}$; __?__; $\overline{MT}$

9. SAS for △MTQ: __?__; ∠5; __?__

10. ASA for △MTQ: __?__; $\overline{MT}$; __?__

11. SAS for △TOR: $\overline{TR}$; __?__; $\overline{RO}$

12. ASA for △MOQ: ∠3; $\overline{MQ}$; __?__

13. SSS for △MOR: $\overline{RO}$; __?__; $\overline{MR}$

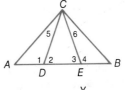

14. ASA for △CEB: __?__; $\overline{CE}$; __?__

15. SAS for △CDB: __?__; ∠2; __?__

16. SAS for △ACD: __?__; ∠5; __?__

17. SSS for △ACE: $\overline{CA}$; __?__; $\overline{AE}$

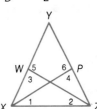

18. SAS for △XYP: __?__; ∠Y; __?__

19. ASA for △XZW: __?__; $\overline{XZ}$; __?__

20. ASA for △XZY: __?__; $\overline{XZ}$; __?__

21. SSS for △WXZ: __?__; $\overline{WZ}$; $\overline{ZX}$

In Exercises 22–27, state whether each pair of triangles is congruent by the SAS, ASA, or SSS Postulates. If none of these applies, write *None.*

22.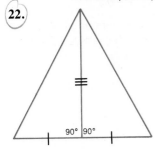

23.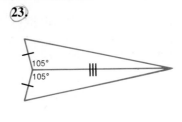

24.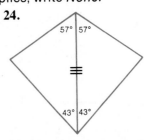

25.

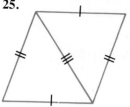

26.

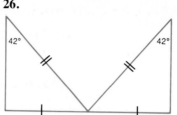

27.

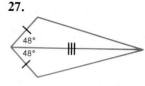

Exercises 28–32 will help you learn to state conclusions from the given conditions, and not from the appearance of the figure. Use △ *BAC* for these exercises.

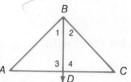

28. In △ *BAC*, $\overrightarrow{BD}$ bisects ∠ *ABC*. Choose the only correct conclusion.

   a. $\overline{BA} \cong \overline{BC}$ **b.** ∠ 1 ≅ ∠ 2   **c.** ∠ 3 ≅ ∠ 4   **d.** ∠ *A* ≅ ∠ *C*

29. In △ *BAC*, $\overline{BD} \perp \overline{AC}$. Choose the only correct conclusion.

   a. $\overline{BA} \cong \overline{BC}$ **b.** ∠ 1 ≅ ∠ 2   **c.** ∠ 3 ≅ ∠ 4   **d.** ∠ *A* ≅ ∠ *C*

30. In △ *BAC*, $\overrightarrow{BD}$ bisects $\overline{AC}$. Choose the only correct conclusion.

   a. $\overline{BA} \cong \overline{BC}$ **b.** ∠ 3 ≅ ∠ 4   **c.** ∠ *A* ≅ ∠ *C*   **d.** $\overline{AD} \cong \overline{DC}$

31. If the only thing you know about △ *BAC* is that $\overline{BD} \perp \overline{AC}$, can you draw the figure so that $\overline{AB}$ is not congruent to $\overline{CB}$? If so, draw it. If not, state why not.

32. If the only thing you know about △ *BAC* is that $\overline{BD}$ bisects $\overline{AC}$, can you draw the figure so that $\overline{AB}$ is not congruent to $\overline{CB}$? If so, draw it. If not, state why not.

B   Write a two-column proof for each exercise. Plan each proof, either mentally or in writing. Refer to △ *ABC* for Exercises 33–36.

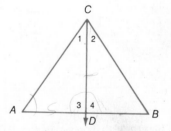

33. Given: ∠ 1 ≅ ∠ 2; ∠ 3 ≅ ∠ 4
    Prove: △ *ADC* ≅ △ *BDC*

34. Given: $\overline{AC} \cong \overline{BC}$; ∠ 1 ≅ ∠ 2
    Prove: △ *CDA* ≅ △ *CDB*

35. Given: ∠ *A* ≅ ∠ *B*; $\overline{AD} \cong \overline{BD}$, ∠ 3 ≅ ∠ 4
    Prove: ∠ 1 ≅ ∠ 2

36. Given: $\overrightarrow{CD}$ bisects ∠ *ACB*; ∠ 3 ≅ ∠ 4
    Prove: ∠ *A* ≅ ∠ *B*

Use the figure at the right below for Exercises 37–39.

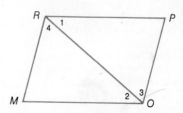

37. Given: ∠ 1 ≅ ∠ 2; ∠ 3 ≅ ∠ 4
    Prove: $\overline{PR} \cong \overline{MO}$

38. Given: $\overline{MO} \cong \overline{PR}$; $\overline{RM} \cong \overline{OP}$
    Prove: ∠ 1 ≅ ∠ 2

39. Given: $\overline{RM} \cong \overline{OP}$; ∠ 3 ≅ ∠ 4
    Prove: ∠ 1 ≅ ∠ 2

Write a two-column proof for each exercise. Plan each proof.

40. **Given:** $\angle 1$ and $\angle B$ are supplementary; $\overline{BC} \cong \overline{EG}$; $\overline{DB} \cong \overline{HE}$

Prove: $\angle D \cong \angle H$

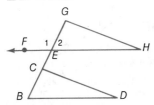

42. **Given:** $\angle YWX \cong \angle ZWX$; $\angle YXW \cong \angle ZXW$

Prove: $\triangle WXY \cong \triangle WXZ$; $\overline{WY} \cong \overline{WZ}$

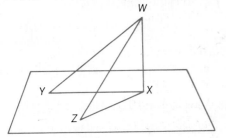

41. **Given:** $\angle 1 \cong \angle J$; $\angle 2$ is a right angle; $\angle M \cong \angle K$; $\overline{MO} \cong \overline{KJ}$

Prove: $\angle Q \cong \angle 3$

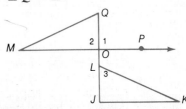

43. **Given:** $\overline{AB} \cong \overline{CD}$; $\angle ABC \cong \angle CDB$; $\overline{BC} \cong \overline{DB}$

Prove: $\triangle CBA \cong \triangle BDC$

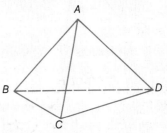

C

44. **Given:** $\overline{GN} \perp \overline{NA}$; $\overline{TA} \perp \overline{NA}$; $\angle 1 \cong \angle 2$

Prove: $\angle G \cong \angle T$

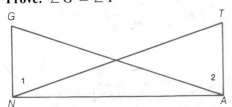

45. **Given:** $\angle 1 \cong \angle 2$; $\angle 3 \cong \angle 4$; $\overline{AG} \cong \overline{HC}$

Prove: $\overline{DC} \cong \overline{BA}$

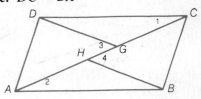

46. **Given:** P is the midpoint of $\overline{YQ}$, $\overline{WS}$, and $\overline{TR}$.

Prove: $\triangle SRQ \cong \triangle WTY$

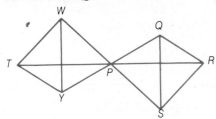

47. **Given:** $\overline{AF} \cong \overline{FH} \cong \overline{HT}$; $\overline{MF} \cong \overline{FB} \cong \overline{BR}$; $AF = FB$

Prove: $\triangle ABT \cong \triangle MHR$

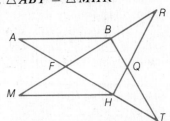

APPLICATIONS

USING TRIANGLES

These exercises apply geometric concepts studied in Sections 3–1 through 3–3.

A

1. Triangles *ZAV* and *TSR* are the triangles formed by the two legs of a stepladder and the floor as shown. Prove that $\triangle ZAV \cong \triangle TSR$.

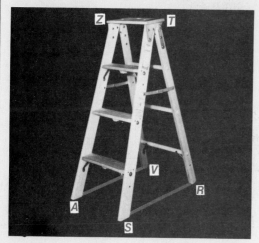

2. To make a triangular brace for a gate, Pilar cuts two strips of wood of length *k* to form sides *AB* and *CD*. Then she cuts a strip of length *s* to form brace *AC* as shown. Prove that the triangles thus formed are congruent.

3. Two cottages are located at points *B* and *C* on either side of a lake. Distances *PB*, *PC*, *PA*, and *PD* were measured and *AD* was calculated as 1.3 kilometers. Find *BC*, the distance between the cottages.

4. Prove that your answer to Exercise 3 is correct.

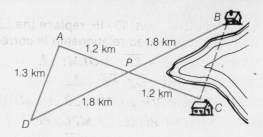

B

5. A ship at sea loses power and is stranded at *S*. The ship is in line as shown with stations at *B* and *C* and point *P* is equally distant from *B* and *C*. The measurements shown are calculated from data obtained by radio and radar. How far is the ship from station *C*?

6. Prove that your answer to Exercise 5 is correct.

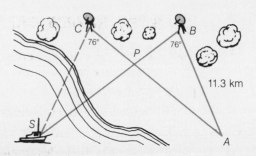

Review

In Exercises 1–5, refer to the figure below in which $\triangle PQR \cong \triangle JKR$. Complete each statement. *(Section 3–1)*

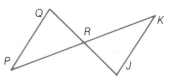

1. The correspondence $RPQ \leftrightarrow$ __?__ is a congruence.
2. The correspondence __?__ $\leftrightarrow KRJ$ is a congruence.
3. $\overline{PR} \cong$ __?__   4. $\angle K \cong$ __?__   5. __?__ $\cong \overline{JK}$

Tell whether each pair of triangles is congruent by the SAS Postulate. *(Section 3–2)*

6. 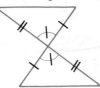   7. 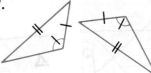   8.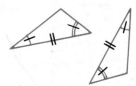

9. Complete the following proof. *(Section 3–2)*

Given: $\overline{BP} \cong \overline{MR}$; $\angle 1 \cong \angle 2$ Prove: $\overline{BR} \cong \overline{PM}$

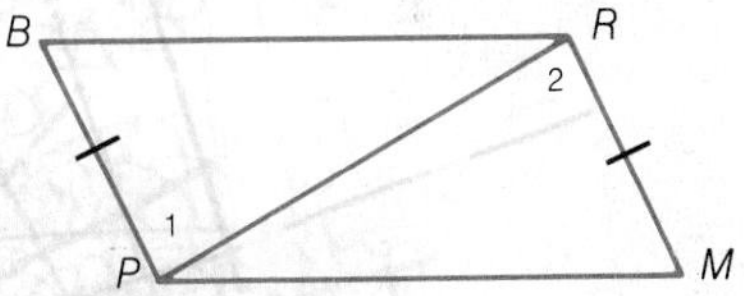

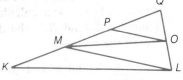

Statements	Reasons
1. $\overline{BP} \cong \overline{MR}$; $\angle 1 \cong \angle 2$	1. __?__
2. __?__	2. Identity
3. $\triangle PRB \cong \triangle RPM$	3. (1), (2). __?__
4. __?__	4. (3). __?__

In Exercises 10–15, replace the __?__ with the required angle or side so that the indicated relationship is correct. *(Section 3–3)*

10. SAS for $\triangle MLO$: $\overline{LM}$; $\angle OLM$; __?__
11. SSS for $\triangle KLQ$: $\overline{LQ}$; $\overline{KL}$; __?__
12. ASA for $\triangle MOQ$: $\angle QMO$; __?__; $\angle MOQ$
13. SAS for $\triangle MOP$: __?__; $\angle MPO$; $\overline{PO}$
14. ASA for $\triangle MLQ$: $\angle QLM$; $\overline{ML}$; __?__
15. SSS for $\triangle KLM$: $\overline{LM}$; __?__; $\overline{KL}$

GEOMETRY REVIEW CAPSULE FOR SECTION 3–4

Match each statement in Exercises 1–5 with a term in the box at the right. *(Pages 2–4)*

1. A triangle with two equal sides
2. The angle opposite the base of an isosceles triangle
3. A triangle whose sides are of different length
4. The two equal sides of an isosceles triangle
5. A triangle whose sides are of equal length

> scalene
> vertex
> legs
> isosceles
> equilateral
> base

3-4 Isosceles Triangle Theorems

Recall that an isosceles triangle has two congruent sides called the *legs* of the triangle. The angle formed by the legs is the *vertex angle*. The side opposite the vertex angle is the *base* of the triangle.

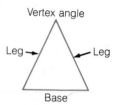

Theorem 3-1 states another property of isosceles triangles.

Theorem 3-1

> ### Isosceles Triangle Theorem
> If two sides of a triangle are congruent, then the angles opposite these sides are congruent.

To prove Theorem 3-1, you draw the bisector of the vertex angle.

EXAMPLE

Prove Theorem 3-1.

Given: $\triangle ABC$ with $\overline{AC} \cong \overline{BC}$

Prove: $\angle A \cong \angle B$

Plan: ☐1 Draw $\overrightarrow{CD}$ bisecting $\angle C$.

☐2 Prove $\triangle ACD \cong \triangle BCD$. Then $\angle A \cong \angle B$ by CPCTC.

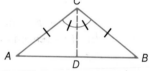

Proof:

Statements	Reasons
1. Draw a ray bisecting $\angle ACB$ and meeting $\overline{AB}$ at D.	1. An angle has exactly one bisector.
2. $m\angle ACD = m\angle BCD$	2. (1). Definition of angle bisector
3. $\angle ACD \cong \angle BCD$	3. (2). Angles that have the same measure are congruent.
4. $\overline{AC} \cong \overline{BC}$	4. Given
5. $\overline{CD} \cong \overline{CD}$	5. Identity
6. $\therefore \triangle ACD \cong \triangle BCD$	6. (3), (4), (5). SAS Postulate
7. $\therefore \angle A \cong \angle B$	7. (6). CPCTC

Since an equilateral triangle has three congruent sides, the Isosceles Triangle Theorem is extended to equilateral triangles in Corollary 3-2. The proof of this corollary is asked for in the Written Exercises.

Corollary 3-2

> ### Equilateral Triangle Corollary
> If three sides of a triangle are congruent, then the three angles are also congruent.

A triangle with three equal angles is **equiangular.**

The converse of Theorem 3–1 is also a theorem. Recall that the converse of a conditional is formed by interchanging the hypothesis (if–part) and the conclusion (then–part).

Theorem 3–3

> ### Converse of Isosceles Triangle Theorem
> If two angles of a triangle are congruent, then the sides opposite these angles are congruent.

The converse of Corollary 3–2 is also a corollary.

Corollary 3–4

> ### Converse of Equilateral Triangle Corollary
> If the three angles of a triangle are congruent, then the three sides are congruent.

The proofs of Theorem 3–3 and Corollary 3–4 are asked for in the Written Exercises.

REMEMBER: Theorems 3–1 and 3–3 and Corollaries 3–2 and 3–4 can be used as reasons in proofs.

CLASSROOM EXERCISES

In Exercises 1–3, name the theorem or corollary stated in each exercise.

1. An equilateral triangle is equiangular.
2. The base angles of an isosceles triangle are congruent.
3. An equiangular triangle is equilateral.
4. Write Theorems 3–1 and 3–3 as a biconditional.
5. Write Corollaries 3–2 and 3–4 as a biconditional.

In Exercises 6–8, use the information indicated in each figure to state whatever conclusions you can about the unmarked sides and angles in the figure. Give the reason(s) for each conclusion.

6.
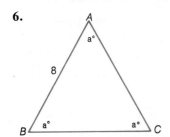

7.
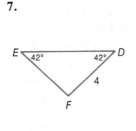

8.
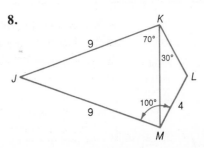

WRITTEN EXERCISES

A

1. In the figure at the right, $\overline{CA} \cong \overline{CB}$. Explain how to prove that $\angle 3 \cong \angle 4$.

2. In the figure at the right, $\angle 3 \cong \angle 4$. Explain how to prove that $\triangle ABC$ is isosceles.

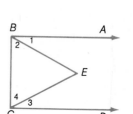

In Exercises 3–5, refer to $\triangle BEC$.

3. If $\angle 2 \cong \angle 4$, explain why $\triangle BEC$ is isosceles.

In Exercises 4–7, complete each proof by supplying the missing statements and reasons.

4. **Given:** $\overline{BE} \cong \overline{CE}$; $\angle ABC \cong \angle DCB$

   Prove: $\angle 1 \cong \angle 3$

Statements	Reasons
1. $\angle ABC \cong \angle DCB$	1. ?
2. $m\angle ABC = m\angle DCB$	2. (1). ?
3. $m\angle 1 + m\angle 2 = m\angle ABC$; $m\angle 3 + m\angle 4 = m\angle DCB$	3. ?
4. $m\angle 1 + m\angle 2 = m\angle 3 + m\angle 4$	4. (2), (3). ?
5. $\overline{BE} \cong \overline{CE}$	5. ?
6. $\angle 2 \cong \angle 4$	6. (5). ?
7. $m\angle 2 = $?	7. (6). ?
8. $m\angle 1 = m\angle 3$	8. ?
9. $\angle 1 \cong \angle 3$	9. ?

5. **Given:** $\overline{BE} \cong \overline{CE}$, $\overrightarrow{BA} \perp \overline{BC}$; $\overrightarrow{CD} \perp \overline{BC}$ **Prove:** $\angle 1 \cong \angle 3$

Statements	Reasons
1. $\overrightarrow{BA} \perp \overline{BC}$; $\overrightarrow{CD} \perp \overline{BC}$	1. ?
2. Angles ABC and DCB are right angles.	2. (1). ?
3. $m\angle ABC = 90$; $m\angle DCB = 90$	3. (2). ?
4. $m\angle 1 + m\angle 2 = m\angle ABC$; $m\angle 3 + m\angle 4 = m\angle DCB$	4. ?
5. $m\angle 1 + m\angle 2 = 90$; $m\angle 3 + m\angle 4 = 90$	5. (3), (4). ?
6. Angles 1 and 2 are ? ; Angles 3 and 4 are ? .	6. (5). ?
7. $\overline{BE} \cong \overline{CE}$	7. ?
8. ?	8. (7). ?
9. $\angle 1 \cong \angle 3$	9. (6), (8). ?

Refer to the figure at the right below for Exercises 6–11.

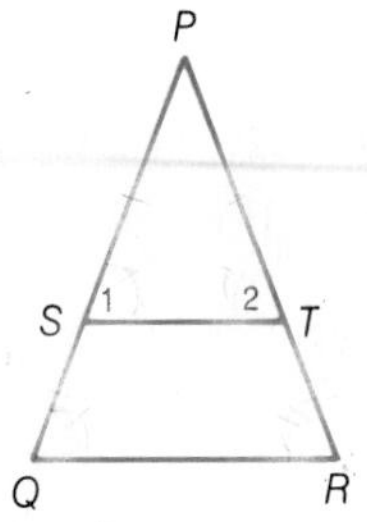

6. Given: $\overline{PQ} \cong \overline{PR}; \overline{SQ} \cong \overline{TR}$

Prove: $\angle 1 \cong \angle 2$

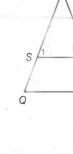

Statements	Reasons
1. _?_	1. Given
2. $PQ = PR; SQ = TR$	2. (1). _?_
3. $PS + SQ = PQ; PT + TR = PR$	3. _?_
4. $PS + SQ = PT + TR$	4. (2), (3). _?_
5. $PS = PT$	5. (2), (4). _?_
6. _?_	6. (5). _?_
7. _?_	7. (6). _?_

7. Given: $\angle Q \cong \angle R; \angle 1 \cong \angle 2$

Prove: $\overline{SQ} \cong \overline{TR}$

Statements	Reasons
1. $\angle Q \cong \angle R; \angle 1 \cong \angle 2$	1. _?_
2. $\overline{PR} \cong \overline{PQ}; \overline{PT} \cong \overline{PS}$	2. (1). _?_
3. _?_	3. (2). _?_
4. $PS + SQ = PQ; PT + TR = PR$	4. _?_
5. $PS + SQ = PT + TR$	5. (3), (4). _?_
6. $SQ = TR$	6. (3), (5). _?_
7. _?_	7. (6). _?_

B

8. Given: $\overline{PS} \cong \overline{PT}; \overline{SQ} \cong \overline{TR}$

Prove: $\angle Q \cong \angle R$

Plan: Show that $PQ = PR$ by proving that $PS + SQ = PT + TR$. Then prove $\angle Q \cong \angle R$.

9. Given: $\angle 1 \cong \angle 2; \overline{SQ} \cong \overline{TR}$

Prove: $\angle Q \cong \angle R$

Plan: Show that $PS = PT$ and that $PQ = PR$ (see Exercise 8). Then prove $\angle Q \cong \angle R$.

10. Given: $\overline{PS} \cong \overline{PT}; \angle Q \cong \angle 1; \angle R \cong \angle 2$

Prove: $\triangle RQP$ is isosceles.

Plan: First, prove $\angle 1 \cong \angle 2$. Then prove $\angle Q \cong \angle R$ and $\overline{PQ} \cong \overline{PR}$.

11. Given: $\overline{PS} \cong \overline{SQ}; \overline{PT} \cong \overline{TR}; \overline{PQ} \cong \overline{PR}$

Prove: $\angle 1 \cong \angle 2$

Plan: Prove $\overline{PS} \cong \overline{PT}$ by proving $PQ - SQ = PR - TR$. Then prove $\angle 1 \cong \angle 2$.

12. Prove Corollary 3–2.

Given: $\overline{AC} \cong \overline{BC} \cong \overline{AB}$

Prove: $\angle A \cong \angle B \cong \angle C$

Plan: Prove $\angle A \cong \angle B$ and $\angle A \cong \angle C$. Then $\angle A \cong \angle B \cong \angle C$.

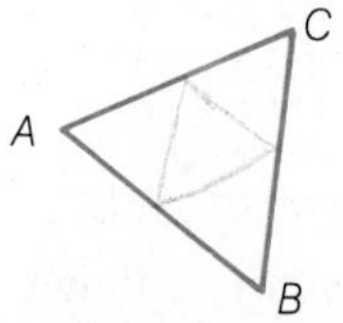

13. Prove Corollary 3–4. (Use the figure for Exercise 12. Assume that Theorem 3–3 has already been proved.)

Given: $\angle A \cong \angle B \cong \angle C$

Prove: $\overline{AC} \cong \overline{BC} \cong \overline{AB}$

Plan: First prove $\overline{AC} \cong \overline{BC}$. Then prove $\overline{AB} \cong \overline{BC}$. Then $\overline{AC} \cong \overline{BC} \cong \overline{AB}$.

14. **Given:** $\triangle ABC$ is isosceles with base BC; D, E, and F are the midpoints of $\overline{AB}$, $\overline{AC}$, and $\overline{BC}$ respectively. ("Respectively" means that the items are taken in order; that is, D is the midpoint of $\overline{AB}$, E the midpoint of $\overline{AC}$, and F the midpoint of $\overline{BC}$.)

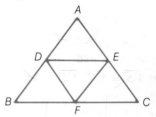

Prove: $\triangle DEF$ is isosceles.

Plan: ☐1 Prove $\overline{AB} \cong \overline{AC}$ and $\angle B \cong \angle C$. Also prove $BD = \frac{1}{2}AB$, $CE = \frac{1}{2}AC$, and $BD = CE$. Thus, $\overline{BD} \cong \overline{CE}$.

☐2 Prove $\triangle DBF \cong \triangle ECF$ by the SAS Postulate and $\overline{FD} \cong \overline{FE}$ by CPCTC.

☐3 Prove $\triangle DEF$ is isosceles by definition.

Refer to the figure at the right for Exercises 15–18.

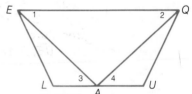

15. **Given:** $\angle 1 \cong \angle 2$; $\angle 3 \cong \angle 4$; A is the midpoint of $\overline{LU}$.

Prove: $\overline{EL} \cong \overline{QU}$

Plan: Given that $\angle 1 \cong \angle 2$, prove $\overline{EA} \cong \overline{QA}$. Then prove $\triangle EAL \cong \triangle QAU$ by the SAS Postulate. Finally, prove $\overline{EL} \cong \overline{QU}$.

16. In Exercise 15, why is it incorrect to conclude that $\overline{EL} \cong \overline{QU}$ by Theorem 3–3, given that $\angle 3 \cong \angle 4$?

17. **Given:** $\angle L \cong \angle U$; $\angle 3 \cong \angle 4$; A is the midpoint of $\overline{LU}$.

Prove: $\angle 1 \cong \angle 2$

Plan: Prove $\triangle AEL \cong \triangle AQU$ by the ASA Postulate. Then prove $\overline{AE} \cong \overline{AQ}$ and $\angle 1 \cong \angle 2$.

18. Refer to the figure for Exercise 15. Suppose that it is given that $\overline{AE}$ and $\overline{AQ}$ are congruent. Why would it be incorrect to conclude that $\angle L \cong \angle U$ by the Isosceles Triangle Theorem?

Use the theorems and corollaries of this lesson to draw any conclusions you can from Exercises 19–22. Give the reason(s) for each conclusion.

19. No two angles of $\triangle ABC$ are congruent. 20. No two sides of $\triangle XYZ$ are congruent.

21. A triangle is not equiangular. 22. A triangle is not equilateral.

In the figure at the right $\triangle VQW$ is in plane I and $\triangle TQW \cong \triangle TQV$. Use this information for Exercises 23–26.

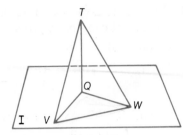

23. Prove that $\triangle QVW$ is isosceles.
24. Prove that $\angle QVW \cong \angle QWV$.
25. Prove that $\triangle TVW$ is isosceles.
26. Prove that $\angle TVW \cong \angle TWV$.

C   Refer to the figure at the right for Exercises 27–28.

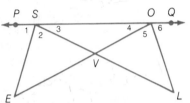

27. **Given:** $\overline{VS} \cong \overline{VO}$; $\overline{VE} \cong \overline{VL}$
    Prove: $\angle 1 \cong \angle 6$
28. **Given:** $\angle 1 \cong \angle 6$; $\angle 2 \cong \angle 5$
    Prove: $\angle E \cong \angle L$

29. Prove Theorem 3–3. Follow the plan.
    Given: $\angle A \cong \angle B$ **Prove:** $\overline{CA} \cong \overline{CB}$

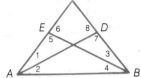

    Plan: Let $\overrightarrow{AD}$ and $\overrightarrow{BE}$ bisect $\angle A$ and $\angle B$ respectively. Prove $\angle 2 \cong \angle 4$, and $\triangle ABD \cong \triangle ABE$ by the ASA Postulate. Then prove $\angle 5 \cong \angle 7$ by CPCTC and $\angle 6 \cong \angle 8$ by Theorem 2–5. Following a procedure similar to that for proving $\angle 2 \cong \angle 4$, prove $\angle 1 \cong \angle 3$. Then prove $\overline{AD} \cong \overline{BE}$, $\triangle ADC \cong \triangle BEC$, and $\overline{CA} \cong \overline{CB}$.

—————— **GEOMETRY REVIEW CAPSULE FOR SECTION 3–5** ——————

In Exercises 1–4, refer to the figure at the right. Write *Yes* or *No* to indicate whether $\overrightarrow{BF}$ bisects $\angle CBD$. *(Pages 24–25)*

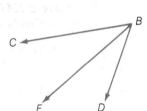

1. $\angle FBD \cong \angle CBF$
2. $m\angle CBF > m\angle FBD$ **3.** $m\angle FBD = m\angle CBF$
4. There is another ray, $\overrightarrow{BG}$, which bisects $\angle CBD$.

In Exercises 5–10, refer to the figure at the right. Answer *Yes* or *No*. *(Pages 17–19, 66–67)*

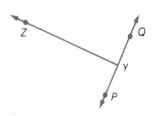

5. If $\angle PYZ$ is a right angle, then $\angle QYZ$ is a right angle.
6. If $\overline{YQ} \cong \overline{PY}$, then Y is the midpoint of $\overline{PQ}$.
7. If $\overrightarrow{PV}$ meets $\overleftrightarrow{PQ}$ at right angles, then $\overrightarrow{PV}$ is also perpendicular to $\overleftrightarrow{PQ}$.
8. If $m\angle PYZ + m\angle QYZ = 180$, then $\overrightarrow{YZ}$ must be perpendicular to $\overleftrightarrow{PQ}$.
9. If $PY = 2PQ$, then Y is the midpoint of $\overline{PQ}$.
10. If Y is the midpoint of $\overline{PQ}$, then $\overline{YZ}$ is the median of $\triangle PQZ$.

3-5 More Isosceles Triangle Theorems

By definition, the bisector of an angle is a ray. However, for convenience, you may refer to any segment that lies on the bisector of an angle as the *bisector of the angle*.

Two congruent triangles are formed by the bisector of the vertex angle of an isosceles triangle and by the median to the base of an isosceles triangle.

Figure	Given	Plan of Proof
	Triangle ABC; $\overline{AC} \cong \overline{BC}$; $\overline{CD}$ bisects $\angle C$.	Use the SAS Postulate to prove $\triangle ACD \cong \triangle BCD$.
	Triangle ABC; $\overline{AC} \cong \overline{BC}$; $\overline{CD}$ is the median to $\overline{AB}$.	Use the definition of median and the SSS Postulate to prove $\triangle ACD \cong \triangle BCD$.

For both triangles above, you can also prove that the angles at D are right angles, and that $\overline{CD} \perp \overline{AB}$. Thus, $\overline{CD}$ is the **perpendicular bisector of $\overline{AB}$**.

Theorem 3-5

> The bisector of the vertex angle of an isosceles triangle is the perpendicular bisector of the base.

Theorem 3-6

> The median from the vertex angle of an isosceles triangle is perpendicular to the base and bisects the vertex angle.

The proofs of these theorems are asked for in the Written Exercises.

In the figure at the right, point P is *equidistant* from points A and B because $PA = PB = 3$ centimeters. Similarly, point Q is equidistant from points A and B because $QA = QB = 2$ centimeters.

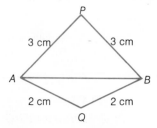

Definition	A point P is **equidistant** from two other points A and B if $PA = PB$.

This definition applies to points in space as well as to points in one plane. In the figure at the right, points P, Q, and R are equidistant from A and B if $PA = PB$, $QA = QB$, and $RA = RB$.

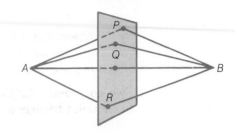

Theorem 3–7	If a point lies on the perpendicular bisector of a segment, then the point is equidistant from the endpoints of the segment.

EXAMPLE   Prove Theorem 3–7.

Given: $\overleftrightarrow{CD}$ is the perpendicular bisector of $\overline{AB}$.

Prove: C is equidistant from A and B.

Plan: Prove $\triangle ACE \cong \triangle BCE$ by the SAS Postulate. Then prove $AC = BC$.

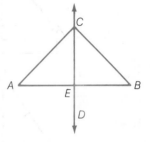

Proof:

Statements	Reasons
1. $\overleftrightarrow{CD}$ bisects $\overline{AB}$.	1. Given
2. $\overline{AE} \cong \overline{BE}$	2. (1). Definition of segment bisector
3. $\overleftrightarrow{CD} \perp \overline{AB}$	3. Given
4. $\angle CEA \cong \angle CEB$	4. (3). Perpendicular lines form congruent adjacent angles.
5. $\overline{CE} \cong \overline{CE}$	5. Identity
6. $\triangle ACE \cong \triangle BCE$	6. (2), (4), (5). SAS Postulate
7. $\overline{AC} \cong \overline{BC}$	7. (6). CPCTC
8. $AC = BC$	8. (7). Definition of congruent segments
9. Point C is equidistant from A and B.	9. (8). Definition of equidistant

The converse of Theorem 3–7 is stated on page 116. The proof of Theorem 3–8 is asked for in the Written Exercises.

Theorem 3-8

> If a point is equidistant from the endpoints of a segment, then the point lies on the perpendicular bisector of the segment.

REMEMBER: To prove that $\overleftrightarrow{PQ}$ is the perpendicular bisector of $\overline{XY}$, prove that

1. $\overleftrightarrow{PQ} \perp \overline{XY}$ and
2. $\overleftrightarrow{PQ}$ bisects $\overline{XY}$.

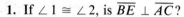

Corollary 3-9 is convenient to use when proving that a line is a perpendicular bisector.

Corollary 3-9

> If two points are each equidistant from the endpoints of a segment, they determine its perpendicular bisector.

CLASSROOM EXERCISES

Refer to $\triangle ABC$ for Exercises 1–4.

1. If $\angle 1 \cong \angle 2$, is $\overline{BE} \perp \overline{AC}$?
2. If $\overline{AB} \cong \overline{BC}$ and $\angle 1 \cong \angle 2$, is $\overline{BE} \perp \overline{AC}$?
3. If $\overline{AB} \cong \overline{BC}$ and $\angle 1 \cong \angle 2$, is $\overline{AE} \cong \overline{EC}$?
4. If $\overline{AB} \cong \overline{BC}$ and $\angle 1 \cong \angle 2$, is $\overline{BE}$ the perpendicular bisector of $\overline{AC}$?

In Exercises 5–9, refer to $\triangle ADC$ in the figure above.

5. If $\overline{DE}$ is the median to $\overline{AC}$, is $\overline{DE} \perp \overline{AC}$?
6. If $\overline{DE}$ is the median to $\overline{AC}$, is $\angle 3 \cong \angle 4$?
7. If $\overline{AD} \cong \overline{CD}$ and $\overline{DE}$ is the median to $\overline{AC}$, is $\overline{DE} \perp \overline{AC}$?
8. If $\overline{AD} \cong \overline{CD}$ and $\overline{DE}$ is the median to $\overline{AC}$, is $\angle 3 \cong \angle 4$?
9. If $\overline{AC} \cong \overline{CD}$, is point D equidistant from points A and C?
10. E is a point on $\overline{AC}$ and E is on the perpendicular bisector of $\overline{AC}$. Is $\overline{AE} \cong \overline{CE}$?
11. Point D is equidistant from points A and C and point B is equidistant from points A and C. Is $\overleftrightarrow{DB}$ the perpendicular bisector of $\overline{AC}$?
12. $\overline{AB} \cong \overline{BC}$ and $\overline{AD} \cong \overline{DC}$. Is $\overleftrightarrow{AC}$ the perpendicular bisector of $\overline{DB}$?

WRITTEN EXERCISES

A

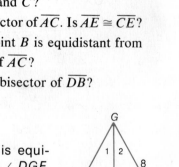

In the figure at the right, triangle DFG is equilateral, $GF = 8$, $m\angle F = 60$, and $\overline{GE}$ bisects $\angle DGF$.

Use this information for Exercises 1–2.

1. Find DG, DF, DE, and EF.
2. Find $m\angle D$, $m\angle 1$, $m\angle 2$, $m\angle 3$, $m\angle 4$.

3. In the figure at the right, $\overline{HQ} \cong \overline{HJ}$, $\overline{QK} \cong \overline{JK}$, m∠ 2 = 72, m∠ 3 = 24, and $QJ = 18$.
Find m∠ 1, m∠ 4, m∠ HQK, m∠ HJK, QM, and MJ.

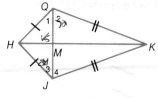

In the figure at the right, $\overline{PQ} \cong \overline{QR} \cong \overline{RS} \cong \overline{SP}$.

Use this information for Exercises 4–5.

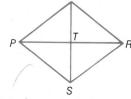

4. Name four right triangles.

5. Name four isosceles triangles.

In Exercises 6–7, refer to △ABC to explain why each statement is true.

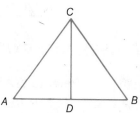

6. In an isosceles triangle, the perpendicular bisector of the base bisects the vertex angle.

7. If the perpendicular bisector of one side of a triangle passes through the opposite vertex, the triangle is isosceles.

8. Complete the proof.

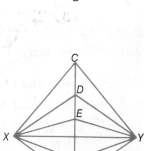

Given: Isosceles triangles XCY, XDY, XEY, XFY, and XGY with base $\overline{XY}$.

Prove: Points C, D, E, F, and G are collinear.

Statements	Reasons
1. ___?___	1. Given
2. $\overline{CX} \cong \overline{CY}$; $\overline{DX} \cong \overline{DY}$; $\overline{EX} \cong \overline{EY}$; $\overline{FX} \cong \overline{FY}$; $\overline{GX} \cong \overline{GY}$	2. (1). ___?___
3. Points C, D, E, F, and G lie on the perpendicular bisector of $\overline{XY}$.	3. (2). ___?___
4. ___?___	4. (3). ___?___

9. Prove Theorem 3–5.

Given: Triangle ABC; $\overline{AC} \cong \overline{BC}$; $\overline{CD}$ bisects $\angle ACB$.

Prove: $\overline{CD}$ is the perpendicular bisector of $\overline{AB}$.
(HINT: Use the Plan of Proof on page 114.)

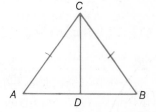

10. Prove Theorem 3–6.

Given: Triangle ABC; $\overline{AC} \cong \overline{BC}$; $\overline{CD}$ is the median to $\overline{AB}$.

Prove: $\overline{CD} \perp \overline{AB}$; $\overline{CD}$ bisects $\angle ACB$.
(HINT: Use the Plan of Proof on page 114.)

11. Complete the proof.

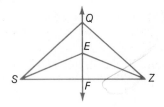

> **Given:** Triangles *SQZ* and *SEZ* with base $\overline{SZ}$ are isosceles.
>
> **Prove:** $\overleftrightarrow{QE}$ is the perpendicular bisector of $\overline{SZ}$.

Statements	Reasons
1. __?__	1. Given
2. __?__	2. (1). Definition of isosceles triangle
3. *Q* and *E* determine the perpendicular bisector of $\overline{SZ}$.	3. (2). __?__

12. Write Theorems 3–7 and 3–8 as a biconditional.

13. Complete the proof for Theorem 3–8.

> **Given:** *Q* is equidistant from *X* and *Y*.
>
> **Prove:** *Q* is on the perpendicular bisector of $\overline{XY}$.

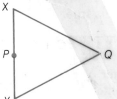

Figure 1

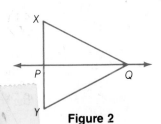

Figure 2

Statements	Reasons
1. __?__	1. Given
2. $QX = QY$	2. (1). Definition of __?__
3. $\overline{QX} \cong \overline{QY}$	3. (2). Definition of __?__
4. Let *P* be the midpoint of $\overline{XY}$. (See Figure 1.)	4. A segment has exactly one midpoint.
5. Draw $\overleftrightarrow{PQ}$. (See Figure 2.)	5. Two points determine a line.
6. $\overline{PX} \cong \overline{PY}$	6. (4). Definition of midpoint
7. __?__	7. Identity
8. $\triangle XQP \cong \triangle YQP$	8. (3), (6), (7). __?__
9. $\angle XPQ \cong \angle$ __?__	9. (8). __?__
10. $\overleftrightarrow{PQ} \perp \overline{XY}$	10. (9). If two lines form congruent adjacent angles, then they are __?__
11. $\overleftrightarrow{PQ}$ is the perpendicular bisector of $\overline{XY}$.	11. (6), (10). Definition of __?__

14. Prove Corollary 3–9. Refer to the figure for Exercise 11.

> **Given:** $QS = QZ$; $ES = EZ$
>
> **Prove:** *Q* and *E* determine the perpendicular bisector of $\overline{SZ}$.
>
> **Plan:** Use Theorem 3–8 to show that points *Q* and *E* lie on the perpendicular bisector of $\overline{SZ}$.

15. Give the location of all the points that are equidistant from two given points.

Use the figure at the right and the following information for Exercises 16–18.

Given: $\overline{AC}$ lies in plane I; $\overline{BD}$ intersects plane I at A.

$\overline{AC}$ is the perpendicular bisector of $\overline{BD}$.

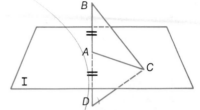

16. **Prove:** $\triangle BAC \cong \triangle DAC$ 17. **Prove:** $\angle B \cong \angle D$ 18. **Prove:** $\triangle BCD$ is isosceles.

In Exercises 19–26, write a two-column proof for each conditional.

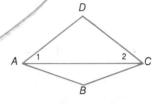

19. In the figure at the right, if $\overline{DA} \cong \overline{DC}$ and $\overline{BA} \cong \overline{BC}$, then $\angle DAB \cong \angle DCB$.

20. In the figure at the right, if $\overline{BA} \cong \overline{BC}$ and $\angle DAB \cong \angle DCB$, then $\angle 1 \cong \angle 2$.

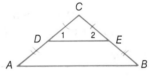

21. In the figure at the right, if $\angle ADE \cong \angle BED$, then $\overline{DC} \cong \overline{EC}$.

22. In the figure at the right, if D is the midpoint of $\overline{AC}$, E is the midpoint of $\overline{BC}$, and $\angle 1 \cong \angle 2$, then $\triangle ABC$ is isosceles.

23. In the figures below, if $\overline{AB} \cong \overline{DE}$, $\overline{BC} \cong \overline{EF}$, $\overline{AC} \cong \overline{DF}$, and $\angle 1 \cong \angle 2$, then $\overline{CG} \cong \overline{FH}$.

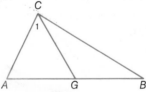
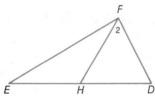

24. In the figure for Exercise 23, if $\overline{AB} \cong \overline{DE}$, $\overline{BC} \cong \overline{EF}$, $\overline{AC} \cong \overline{DF}$, and G and H are the midpoints of $\overline{AB}$ and $\overline{DE}$ respectively, then $\overline{CG} \cong \overline{FH}$.

25. In the figure at the right, if $\overline{MS} \cong \overline{RS}$ and $\overline{MT} \cong \overline{RT}$, then $\overline{MO} \cong \overline{RO}$.

26. In the figure at the right, if $\overline{MS} \cong \overline{RS}$ and $\overline{MO} \cong \overline{RO}$, then $\overline{MT} \cong \overline{RT}$.

27. Explain how to locate all the points in space that are equidistant from three given noncollinear points.

28. Prove this biconditional: The bisector of one angle of a triangle is perpendicular to the opposite side if and only if it bisects the opposite side and the triangle is isosceles.

APPLICATIONS

USING ISOSCELES TRIANGLES

These exercises apply geometric concepts studied in Sections 3–4 through 3–5.

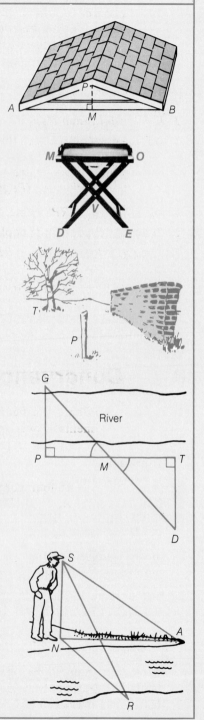

A

1. In building a gable roof, a carpenter joins rafters *PA* and *PB* such that the end of the ridgepole *P* is directly above *M*, the midpoint of tie beam *AB*. Show that the triangle formed by the rafters and the tie beam (△*APB*) is isosceles.

2. The legs of the serving table in the figure are bolted together at their midpoint, *V*. Given that *ME* = *OD*, prove that triangles *MOV* and *EDV* are congruent isosceles triangles.

3. Three municipal maintenance workers are trying to locate the intersection of two underground cables. The cables meet at a point which is 5 meters from a wall and equidistant from a tree at point *T* and a post at point *P*. Explain how to solve the repair workers' problem.

4. Claire wishes to know the distance across a river. First, she marks point *P*, which is directly in line with a gasoline station at *G* on the opposite side of the river such that $\overline{GP} \perp \overline{PT}$. Next she marks *M*, the midpoint of $\overline{PT}$. Then, from point *T*, she walks in a path perpendicular to $\overline{PT}$ until *D*, the point of intersection of $\overrightarrow{GM}$ and $\overrightarrow{TD}$, is determined. Which segment in the figure will have the same length as $\overline{TD}$?

5. In Exercise 4, what postulate can be used to prove △*PMG* ≅ △*TMD*? Explain your answer.

6. Tom has another way of determining the width of the river. First, he pulls the visor of his cap down over his eyes until his line of vision views a spot, *R*, on the opposite shore. Without changing the position of his hat, he turns and sights along the visor to a point, *A*, on the shore. Which segment in the figure will have the same length as $\overline{NR}$?

7. In Exercise 6, what postulate can be used to prove △*SNR* ≅ △*SNA*? Explain your answer.

In Exercises 1–8, use definitions, postulates, and theorems to give a reason for each statement. Refer to the figure at the right for Exercises 1–4. *(Pages 17–19)*

1. $HJ + JK + KL = HL$
2. If $HJ = 5$ and $JK = 8$, then $HK = 13$.
3. If $HJ = KL$, then $HJ + JK = KL + JK$.
4. If P is a point on $\overline{HL}$ such that $HP = PL$, then P is the midpoint of $\overline{HL}$.

Refer to the figure at the right for Exercises 5–8. *(Pages 23–25)*

5. $m\angle QPR + m\angle RPS + m\angle SPT = m\angle QPT$
6. Points Q, P, and T are coplanar points.
7. If $m\angle QPR = 22$ and $m\angle RPS = 42$, then $m\angle QPS = 64$.
8. If $m\angle QPR = m\angle SPT$, then $m\angle QPR + m\angle RPS = m\angle SPT + m\angle RPS$.

3-6 Congruence and Overlapping Triangles

Geometric figures often overlap. The figures may share overlapping segments or overlapping angles. Theorem 3–10 concerns overlapping segments.

Theorem 3–10

Common Segment Theorem

If four collinear points, in order, are A, B, C, D (Figure 1), or A, C, B, D (Figure 2), and $\overline{AB} \cong \overline{CD}$, then $\overline{AC} \cong \overline{BD}$.

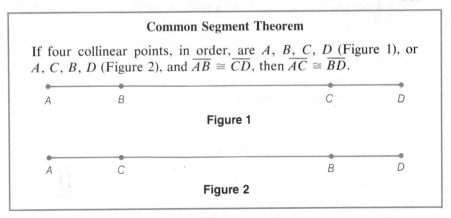

You can use the Addition Property to prove Theorem 3–10. (See Exercise 9 on page 47.) The theorem is useful in proving triangles congruent when the triangles share an overlapping side.

EXAMPLE 1 **Given:** $\overline{ST} \cong \overline{RT}$; $\overline{SA} \cong \overline{RB}$
Prove: $\overline{TB} \cong \overline{TA}$
Plan: Prove $\triangle TSA \cong \triangle TRB$.
Then prove $\overline{TA} \cong \overline{TB}$.

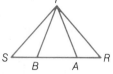

Proof:

Statements	Reasons
1. $\overline{ST} \cong \overline{RT}$	1. Given
2. $\angle S \cong \angle R$	2. (2). Isosceles Triangle Theorem
3. $\overline{SA} \cong \overline{RB}$	3. Given
4. $\overline{SB} \cong \overline{RA}$	4. (3). Common Segment Theorem
5. $\triangle TSA \cong \triangle TRB$	5. (1), (2), (4). SAS Postulate
6. $\overline{TA} \cong \overline{TB}$	6. (5). CPCTC

The Common Angle Theorem concerns overlapping angles.

Theorem 3–11

Common Angle Theorem

If four coplanar rays are, in order, $\overrightarrow{XA}$, $\overrightarrow{XB}$, $\overrightarrow{XC}$, $\overrightarrow{XD}$ (Figure 3), or $\overrightarrow{XA}$, $\overrightarrow{XC}$, $\overrightarrow{XB}$, $\overrightarrow{XD}$ (Figure 4), and $\angle AXB \cong \angle CXD$, then $\angle AXC \cong \angle BXD$.

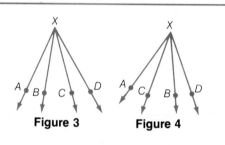

Figure 3   **Figure 4**

Theorem 3–11 is useful when two triangles share an overlapping angle.

EXAMPLE 2 **Given:** $\angle GKR \cong \angle JKH$; $\overline{GK} \cong \overline{JK}$
Prove: $\triangle GKH \cong \triangle JKR$
Plan: ☐1 Prove $\angle 1 \cong \angle 3$ and $\angle G \cong \angle J$.
☐2 Prove $\triangle GKH \cong \triangle JKR$ by ASA.

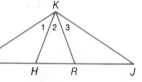

Proof:

Statements	Reasons
1. $\angle GKR \cong \angle JKH$	1. Given
2. $\angle 1 \cong \angle 3$	2. (1). Common Angle Theorem
3. $\overline{GK} \cong \overline{JK}$	3. Given
4. $\angle G \cong \angle J$	4. (3). Isosceles Triangle Theorem
5. $\triangle GKH \cong \triangle JKR$	5. (2), (3), (4). ASA Postulate

Sometimes you need to draw additional segments in order to begin, or to continue, a proof. In such cases, be careful not to impose impossible conditions.

EXAMPLE 3 State whether you can draw each line segment. Explain.

   a. Draw $\overline{FG}$, the median from F to $\overline{DE}$.

   b. Draw $\overline{FG}$, the bisector of $\angle F$, where G is a point on $\overline{DE}$.

   c. Draw $\overline{FG}$, the bisector of $\angle F$ where G is the midpoint of $\overline{DE}$.

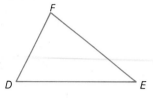

Solutions:

   a. Yes. Every line segment has one midpoint, and two points (F and G) determine a line.

   b. Yes. Every angle has a bisector. It will intersect the opposite side of the triangle at some point.

   c. No. Every angle has a bisector, but it will not always intersect the opposite side of the triangle at its midpoint.

CLASSROOM EXERCISES

For every pair of congruent triangles, state the corresponding congruent parts.

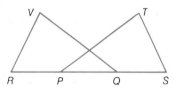

Given: $\triangle RQV \cong \triangle SPT$

1. $\overline{RQ} \cong$ ___?___

2. $\angle R \cong \angle$ ___?___

3. $\overline{VR} \cong$ ___?___

4. $\angle VQR \cong \angle$ ___?___

Given: $\triangle CDB \cong \triangle CEA$

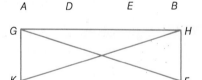

5. $\angle ACE \cong \angle$ ___?___

6. $\overline{CD} \cong$ ___?___

7. $\angle CEA \cong \angle$ ___?___

8. $\overline{BD} \cong$ ___?___

Given: $\triangle GHF \cong \triangle HGK$

9. $\overline{GH} \cong$ ___?___

10. $\angle KGH \cong \angle$ ___?___

11. $\angle K \cong \angle$ ___?___

12. $\angle HGF \cong \angle$ ___?___

WRITTEN EXERCISES

A

1. In figure $HQGF$ below, name three pairs of triangles that appear to be congruent. Do the same for $\triangle KRM$.

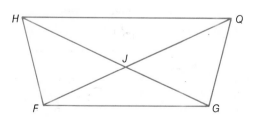

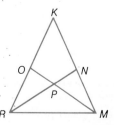

In Exercises 2–5, refer to quadrilateral *HQGF* and triangle *KMR* at the bottom of page 123 to list the corresponding parts needed to complete each congruence correspondence.

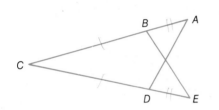

SAS	ASA	SSS

2. $\triangle FGQ$: __?__; $\angle QFG$; $\overline{FG}$ $\angle GQF$; $\overline{QF}$; __?__ $\overline{FG}$; $\overline{GQ}$; __?__
   $\triangle GFH$: $\overline{HG}$; __?__; $\overline{GF}$ $\angle FGH$; __?__; $\angle GHF$ $\overline{GF}$; __?__; $\overline{HG}$

3. $\triangle KNR$: $\overline{RK}$; __?__; $\overline{KN}$ $\angle KRN$; $\overline{RN}$; __?__ $\overline{RK}$; $\overline{KN}$; __?__
   $\triangle KOM$: $\overline{MK}$; __?__; $\overline{KO}$ __?__; $\overline{MO}$; __?__   __?__; $\overline{KO}$; $\overline{OM}$

4. $\triangle HJF$: __?__; $\angle HFJ$; __?__   __?__; $\overline{HJ}$; __?__ $\overline{HJ}$; __?__; __?__
   $\triangle QJG$: __?__; $\angle QGJ$; __?__   __?__; $\overline{QJ}$; __?__ $\overline{QJ}$; __?__; __?__

5. $\triangle RMN$: __?__; $\angle MNR$; __?__   __?__; $\overline{NR}$; __?__   __?__; $\overline{RM}$; __?__
   $\triangle MRO$: __?__; $\angle ROM$; __?__   __?__; $\overline{OM}$; __?__   __?__; $\overline{MR}$; __?__

B   The figure at the left below includes overlapping triangles. In the figure at the right, the triangles have been separated for you. Use these figures for Exercises 6–7.

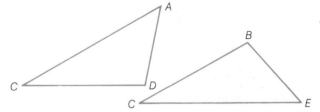

6. If $\overline{BC} \cong \overline{DC}$ and $\overline{AB} \cong \overline{ED}$, what triangle appears to be congruent to $\triangle ACD$?

7. **Given:** $\overline{BC} \cong \overline{DC}$; $\overline{AB} \cong \overline{ED}$ **Prove:** $\triangle ACD \cong \triangle ECB$

In Exercises 8–11, state whether it is always possible to draw each line or segment. Give the reason(s) for each answer.

Given: Segment *RS* and *Q*, a point not on $\overline{RS}$.

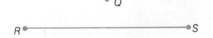

8. Let *M* be the midpoint of $\overline{RS}$. Draw $\overline{QM}$.

9. Let *M* be the midpoint of $\overline{RS}$. Draw line *QM* perpendicular to $\overline{RS}$ at *M*.

10. Let *M* be the midpoint of $\overline{RS}$. Through *M*, draw a line that is perpendicular to $\overline{RS}$ and that contains point *Q*.

11. From *Q*, draw a line perpendicular to $\overleftrightarrow{RS}$.

Refer to the figure at the right for Exercises 12–13.

12. **Given:** $\overline{XW} \cong \overline{YU}$; $\angle ZXY \cong \angle ZYX$

   Prove: $\overline{XU} \cong \overline{YW}$
   Plan: Prove $\triangle XWY \cong \triangle YUX$.
       Then prove $\overline{XU} \cong \overline{YW}$ by CPCTC.

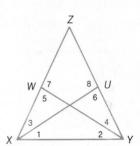

13. **Given:** $\overline{XZ} \cong \overline{YZ}$; $\overline{XW} \cong \overline{YU}$

   Prove: $\angle 7 \cong \angle 8$ (HINT: Draw $\triangle XUZ$ and $\triangle YWZ$ separately, as shown.)

   Plan: Since $\angle Z \cong \angle Z$, prove $\triangle XUZ \cong \triangle YWZ$ by the SAS Postulate. Then prove $\angle 7 \cong \angle 8$.

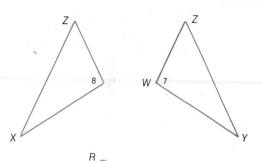

14. **Given:** $\overline{TR} \cong \overline{TW}$; $\overline{VR} \cong \overline{VW}$

   Prove: $\angle W \cong \angle R$

   Plan: Draw diagonal TV. Prove $\triangle TRV \cong \triangle TWV$.

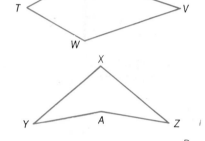

15. **Given:** $\overline{XY} \cong \overline{XZ}$; $\overline{AY} \cong \overline{AZ}$

   Prove: $\angle Y \cong \angle Z$

   Plan: Draw diagonal XA. Prove $\triangle XAY \cong \triangle XAZ$.

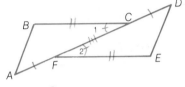

16. **Given:** $\overline{AF} \cong \overline{DC}$; $\angle 1 \cong \angle 2$; $\overline{CB} \cong \overline{FE}$

   Prove: $\angle A \cong \angle D$

17. **Given:** $\overline{PA} \cong \overline{ST}$; $\angle 1 \cong \angle 2$; $\overline{TQ} \cong \overline{AR}$

   Prove: $\angle Q \cong \angle R$

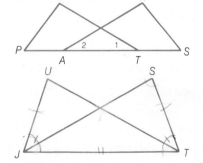

Refer to the figure at the right for Exercises 18–19.

18. **Given:** $\overline{UJ} \cong \overline{ST}$; $\angle TJU \cong \angle JTS$

   Prove: $\angle U \cong \angle S$

19. **Given:** $\angle UJT \cong \angle STJ$; $\angle SJT \cong \angle UTJ$

   Prove: $\overline{UJ} \cong \overline{ST}$

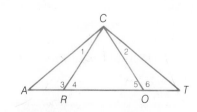

Refer to $\triangle ATC$ for Exercises 20–22.

20. **Given:** $\overline{CA} \cong \overline{CT}$; $\angle 1 \cong \angle 2$

   Prove: $\angle 4 \cong \angle 5$

21. **Given:** $\angle A \cong \angle T$; $\overline{AO} \cong \overline{TR}$

   Prove: $\angle 4 \cong \angle 5$

22. **Given:** $\angle 4 \cong \angle 5$; $\overline{AR} \cong \overline{TO}$ **Prove:** $\overline{CA} \cong \overline{CT}$

Use the figure at the right for
Exercise 23.

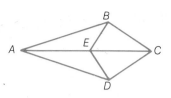

23. **Given:** $\overline{AB} \cong \overline{AD}$; $\angle BAE \cong \angle DAE$

    Prove: $\angle EBC \cong \angle EDC$

C   In Exercises 24–25, prove each conditional.

24. Corresponding angle bisectors of congruent triangles are congruent.

25. Corresponding medians of congruent triangles are congruent.

26. **Given:** $\overline{BD} \cong \overline{CA}$; $\overline{BA} \cong \overline{CD}$
    Prove: $\overline{AE} \cong \overline{DE}$

27. **Given:** $\overline{CA} \cong \overline{CE}$; $\overline{CF}$ bisects $\angle ACE$.
    Prove: $\angle 1 \cong \angle 2$

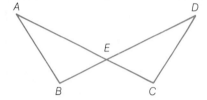

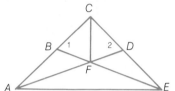

___ **Review** ___

1. Complete the Plan of Proof. *(Section 3–4)*

    Given: $\angle DCE \cong \angle CDE \cong \angle DEC$;
            $\angle CDB \cong \angle CBD$

    Prove: $\overline{BC} \cong \overline{DE}$

    Plan: a. $\overline{DE} \cong \overline{CE} \cong \overline{DC}$ because __?__.
                b. $\overline{BC} \cong \overline{DC}$ because __?__.
            c. $\therefore \overline{BC} \cong \overline{DE}$ because __?__.

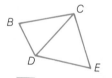

In Exercises 2–7, refer to $\triangle PQR$. Answer true,
T, or false, *F*, for each statement. Give the
reason for each answer. *(Section 3–5)*

2. $\angle PMR \cong \angle QMR$

3. $m\angle QMR + m\angle PMR = 180$

4. $PM > MQ$

5. $\angle PRM + \angle MRQ = \angle PRQ$

6. $m\angle PRM \neq m\angle MRQ$

7. $m\angle RPQ = m\angle PQR$

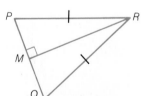

Refer to the figure at the right for Exercises
8–15. Write *Yes* or *No*, and give the reason(s)
for each answer. *(Section 3–6)*

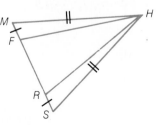

8. $\angle M \cong \angle S$

9. $\triangle MFH \cong \triangle RSH$

10. $MR \neq FS$

11. $\angle MHF \cong \angle RHS$

12. $\angle MHR \cong \angle FHS$

13. $FH < HR$

14. $MF + FH = RS + RH$

15. $2RS + FR = MS$

3-7 Indirect Proof in Geometry

Mathematical statements are either true or false.

All right angles are congruent. ⟵ **True**

A triangle can have more than one obtuse angle. ⟵ **False**

No mathematical statement is *both* true and false at the same time. Such a statement would be a **contradiction.**

$5 < 7$ and $5 \not< 7$ ⟵ **Contradiction**

The **negation** of a statement says the opposite of the original statement. The negation is false if the original statement is true; it is true if the original statement is false.

Statement	True or False?	Negation	True or False?
All right angles are congruent.	T	Not all right angles are congruent.	F
A 45°-angle is not an acute angle.	F	A 45°-angle is an acute angle.	T

In an **indirect proof,** you begin by writing the negation of the conclusion.

Conclusion: q Negation: $\sim q$ ⟵ **Read; "not q."**

EXAMPLE 1 Write the first step in an indirect proof of each conditional.

a. If $\angle 1 \cong \angle 2$, then $m\angle 1 = m\angle 2$.

b. If $m\angle 1 + m\angle 2 \neq 90$, then $\angle 1$ and $\angle 2$ are not complementary.

Solutions: a. Assume $m\angle 1 \neq m\angle 2$.   b. Assume $\angle 1$ and $\angle 2$ are complementary.

After assuming the negation of the conclusion in an indirect proof, you reason from this until you reach a contradiction of a known fact.

Fact: p **Contradiction:** p and $\sim p$

EXAMPLE 2 Write an indirect proof for the following.

Given: $\angle A$ is not congruent to $\angle B$.

Prove: $\angle A$ and $\angle B$ are not both right angles.

Solution: ⬛1 Assume $\angle A$ and $\angle B$ are right $\angle s$. ⟵ **Assume the negation of the statement to be proved.**

⬛2 $\therefore \angle A \cong \angle B$ ⟵ **All right angles are congruent.**

But $\angle A$ is not congruent to $\angle B$. ⟵ **Given. Statements 2 and 3 contradict each other.**

⬛3 Therefore, $\angle A$ and $\angle B$ are not both right angles. ⟵ **The assumption leads to a contradiction, so it must be false and the original statement must be true.**

This summary outlines the steps in writing an indirect proof.

Summary

> **Steps in Writing an Indirect Proof**
> ① Assume the negation of what you want to prove.
> ② Reason directly until you reach a contradiction.
> ③ State that the assumption in Step 1 must have been false, so the original conclusion must be true.

An indirect proof is usually written in paragraph form.

EXAMPLE 3   Prove by the indirect method:

If $\angle A$ is not congruent to $\angle B$, then $\overline{BC}$ is not congruent to $\overline{AC}$.

Given: $\angle A$ is not congruent to $\angle B$.

Prove: $\overline{BC}$ is not congruent to $\overline{AC}$.

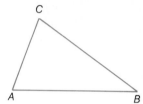

Proof: Assume that $\overline{BC} \cong \overline{AC}$.

Then $\triangle ABC$ is isosceles and $\angle A \cong \angle B$ by the Isosceles Triangle Theorem.

But, by hypothesis, $\angle A$ is not congruent to $\angle B$.

Thus, $\angle A \cong \angle B$ and $\angle A \not\cong \angle B$ is a contradiction.

Therefore, the assumption that $\overline{BC} \cong \overline{AC}$ is false, and $\overline{BC}$ is not congruent to $\overline{AC}$.

CLASSROOM EXERCISES

In Exercises 1–6, write the negation of each statement.

1. $\angle 1 \cong \angle 2$ **2.** $\overline{AB} \perp \overline{CD}$ **3.** $m\angle C \neq m\angle D$

4. Angles 3 and 4 are not complementary.

5. Angles A and B are supplementary.

6. Segments AB and CD are not congruent.

In Exercises 7–10, choose the two given statements that contradict each other.

7. a. $\angle T$ is a right $\angle$.   **b.** $\angle T$ is an acute $\angle$.   **c.** $\angle T$ is not a right $\angle$.

8. a. $AB = 5$ cm   **b.** $AB = 9$ cm   **c.** $AB \neq 9$ cm

9. a. $\overline{XY}$ does not bisect $\angle R$.   **b.** $\overline{XY}$ bisects $\angle R$.   **c.** $\overline{XY} \perp \overline{YZ}$

10. a. $\triangle ABC$ is not scalene.   **b.** $\triangle ABC$ is isosceles.   **c.** $\triangle ABC$ is scalene.

WRITTEN EXERCISES

A   In Exercises 1–2, complete the indirect proof for each conditional. The symbol "≇" means "is not congruent to."

1. If $\angle A \not\cong \angle B$, then $\angle A$ and $\angle B$ are not vertical angles.

   Given: __?__   Prove: __?__

   Proof: a. Assume that $\angle A$ and $\angle B$ are __?__ angles.
        b. Then $\angle A$ __?__ $\angle B$.
        c. But, by hypothesis, $\angle A$ __?__ $\angle B$.
        d. Thus, $\angle A \not\cong \angle B$ and $\angle A \cong \angle B$ is a __?__ .
        e. Therefore, the assumption that angles A and B are vertical angles is false, and __?__ .

2. If $m\angle 1 \neq m\angle 2$, then line k is not perpendicular to line m.

   Given: __?__   Prove: __?__

   Proof: a. Assume that __?__ .
        b. Then $\angle 1 \cong \angle 2$ because __?__ .
        c. If $\angle 1 \cong \angle 2$, then $m\angle$ __?__ $= m\angle$ __?__ because __?__ .
        d. But, by hypothesis, $m\angle 1$ __?__ $m\angle 2$.
        e. Thus, __?__ and __?__ is a contradiction.
        f. Therefore, __?__ .

   Write an indirect proof for each conditional.

3. If $m\angle T = 48$ and $m\angle B = 32$, then angles T and B are not complementary.

4. If $m\angle R = 105$ and $m\angle S = 85$, then angles R and S are not supplementary.

   In Exercises 5–25, use the indirect method of proof.

5. **Given:** $\angle 1 \not\cong \angle 2$

   Prove: $\angle 1 \not\cong \angle 3$

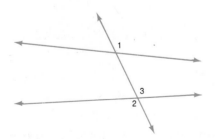

6. **Given:** $\angle 1 \not\cong \angle 3$

   Prove: $\angle 1$ and $\angle 2$ are not supplementary.

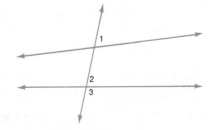

7. Given: $\angle 1 \not\equiv \angle 3$

Prove: $\angle 2 \not\equiv \angle 4$

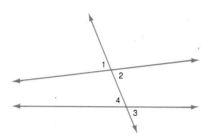

8. Given: $\angle 5$ and $\angle 7$ are not supplementary.

Prove: $\angle 6$ and $\angle 8$ are not supplementary.

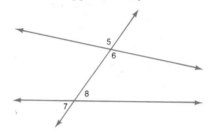

9. Given: $\overline{MT}$ bisects $\angle HMS$; $\overline{MT}$ is not a median.

Prove: $\overline{MS} \not\equiv \overline{MH}$

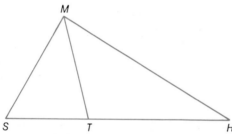

10. Given: $\overline{RN} \cong \overline{RA}$; $\angle 1 \not\equiv \angle 2$

Prove: $\overline{RK}$ is not a median.

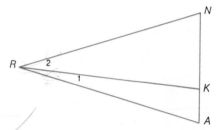

11. Given: $\overline{ZG}$ is a median; $\angle 1 \not\equiv \angle 2$

Prove: $\overline{ZQ} \not\equiv \overline{ZP}$

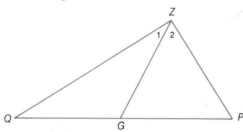

12. Given: $\angle 1 \not\equiv \angle 2$

Prove: $m\angle 1 \neq 90$

13. Given: $\overline{CT} \not\equiv \overline{BK}$

Prove: $\overline{BC}$ and $\overline{KT}$ do not bisect each other.

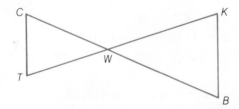

14. Given: $\triangle MRT$ is scalene; $\overline{RS}$ bisects $\angle R$.

Prove: $\overline{RS}$ is not perpendicular to $\overline{MT}$.

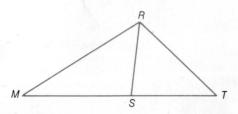

15. Given: $\overline{RS}$ bisects $\angle MRT$; $\overline{RS}$ is not perpendicular to $\overline{MT}$.

Prove: $\overline{RM} \not\cong \overline{RT}$ (Refer to the figure for Exercise 14.)

B

16. Given: $\overline{BK} \perp \overline{KH}$; $\overline{RH} \perp \overline{KH}$;
$\angle B \not\cong \angle R$

Prove: $\overline{RH} \not\cong \overline{BK}$

17. Given: $\overline{RX} \cong \overline{RH}$; $\overline{RS} \not\cong \overline{RM}$

Prove: $\angle X \not\cong \angle H$

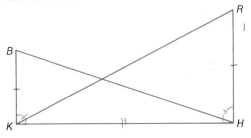
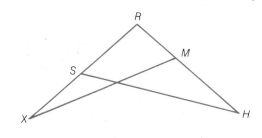

In Exercises 18–19, refer to the figure at the right below.

18. Given: $\overline{CR} \not\cong \overline{CS}$

Prove: $\triangle VRS \not\cong \triangle TSR$

19. Given: $\angle CRS \not\cong \angle CSR$

Prove: $\triangle VRC \not\cong \triangle TSC$

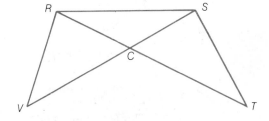

In Exercises 20–21, refer to the figure at the right below.

20. Given: $\overline{TA} \cong \overline{TB}$;
$m\angle 1 \not= m\angle 2$

Prove: $AX \not= BW$

21. Given: $\overline{TW} \not\cong \overline{TX}$;
$\overline{TA} \cong \overline{TB}$

Prove: $BX \not= AW$

C

22. Prove: In acute scalene triangle ABC, the altitude BD to the base AC does not bisect angle B.

23. Prove: In scalene triangle ABC, the median BD is not perpendicular to $\overline{AC}$.

24. Prove: If two distinct lines intersect, then their intersection is only one point.

25. Prove: If a line and a plane intersect and the plane does not contain the line, then their intersection is only one point.

Complete the following proof.
(Pages 44–45)

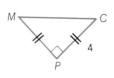

1. **Given:** Isosceles right triangles
   FGH and CPM; $FG = 4$; $CP = 4$

   Prove: $\triangle FGH \cong \triangle CPM$

Statements	Reasons
1. $FG = 4$; $CP = 4$	1. __?__
2. __?__	2. (1). Line segments of equal measure are congruent.
3. $\overline{FG} \cong \overline{HG}$; __?__	3. Definition of isosceles triangle
4. $\overline{HG} \cong \overline{MP}$	4. (2), (3). __?__
5. $m\angle G = 90$; $m\angle P = 90$	5. __?__
6. __?__	6. (5). Angles of equal measure are congruent.
7. $\triangle FGH \cong \triangle CPM$	7. (2), (4), (6). __?__

3-8 Congruence in Right Triangles

In a right triangle, the side opposite the right angle is the **hypotenuse**. The other two sides are **legs** of the triangle. The **acute angles** are the angles opposite the legs.

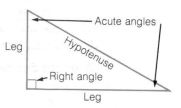

The *Hypotenuse–Acute Angle (HA) Postulate* can be used to prove right triangles congruent.

Postulate 14

> **HA Postulate**
>
> If two right triangles have the hypotenuse and an acute angle of one triangle congruent respectively to the hypotenuse and an acute angle of the other, then the triangles are congruent.

The *Hypotenuse–Leg (HL) Theorem* provides another way to prove right triangles congruent. A proof of this theorem is asked for in the Written Exercises.

Theorem 3-12

> **HL Theorem**
>
> If two right triangles have the hypotenuse and one leg of one triangle congruent respectively to the hypotenuse and one leg of the other, then the triangles are congruent.

EXAMPLE   State whether each pair of triangles is congruent. Give a reason for each answer.

a.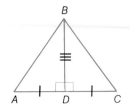

b.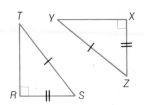

c.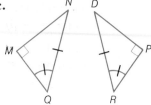

Solutions: **a. Yes,** by the SAS Postulate.   or ∠∠

b. Yes, by the HL Theorem.

c. Yes, by the HA Postulate.

Corollary 3–13 follows directly from Theorem 3–12. You are asked to prove this corollary in the Written Exercises.

Corollary 3–13   In an isosceles triangle, the altitude to the base bisects the base and bisects the vertex angle.

know this →

The distance from a point to a line is the length of the segment perpendicular to the line from the point. Theorem 3–14 says that there is only one such line.

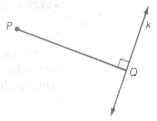

Thus, the distance from P to line k is PQ where $\overline{PQ} \perp k$.

Theorem 3–14   Through a point not on a line, there is exactly one line perpendicular to the given line.

NOTE: In Theorem 3–14, the words "exactly one" mean *one and only one.* A proof that there *is* one line perpendicular to the given line is called an **existence proof.** A proof that there is *only one* line perpendicular to a given line is called a **uniqueness proof.** (Proofs of uniqueness often employ the indirect method.)

In the figure at the right, point C is 1.1 units from each side of $\angle X$. Point C is said to be **equidistant** from the sides of the angle. That is, $CD = CE$.

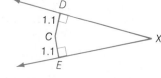

Theorem 3–15   If a point is on the bisector of an angle, it is equidistant from the sides of the angle.

The converse of Theorem 3–15 is also a theorem.

**Theorem
3–16**

> If a point in the interior of an angle is equidistant from the sides of
> the angle, then it is on the bisector of the angle.

Theorem 3–15 and 3–16 can be stated as a biconditional. You are asked to
write the biconditional and to prove each theorem in the Written Exercises.

CLASSROOM EXERCISES

In Exercises 1–3, state whether each pair of triangles is congruent. Give a
reason for each answer.

1. 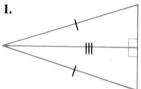   **2.** 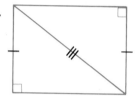   **3.**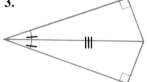

4. Write Theorems 3–15 and 3–16 as a biconditional.

WRITTEN EXERCISES

A

In Exercises 1–3, supply the missing statements and reasons in each proof.

1. Given: Angles P and R are right angles;
    $\angle 1 \cong \angle 2$

Prove: $\overline{PS} \cong \overline{RQ}$

Statements	Reasons
1. Angles P and R are right angles.	1. __?__
2. $\triangle PQS$ and $\triangle RSQ$ are right triangles.	2. (1). __?__
3. $\angle 1 \cong \angle 2$	3. __?__
4. $\overline{SQ} \cong \overline{SQ}$	4. __?__
5. $\triangle PQS \cong \triangle RSQ$	5. (2), (3), (4). __?__
6. __?__	6. (5). __?__

2. Given: $\overline{OF} \perp \overline{OR}$; $\overline{EG} \perp \overline{ER}$;
    $\overline{OE}$ bisects $\overline{FG}$

Prove: $\overline{RO} \cong \overline{RE}$

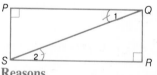

Statements	Reasons
1. $\overline{OF} \perp \overline{OR}$; $\overline{EG} \perp \overline{ER}$	1. ___?___
2. Angles O and E are right angles.	2. (1). ___?___
3. $\triangle FRO$ and $\triangle GRE$ are right triangles.	3. (2). ___?___
4. ___?___	4. Given
5. $\overline{RF} \cong \overline{RG}$	5. (4). ___?___
6. $\angle FRO \cong \angle GRE$	6. ___?___
7. $\triangle FRO \cong \triangle GRE$	7. (3), (5), (6). ___?___
8. ___?___	8. (7). ___?___

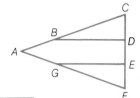

3. **Given:** $\overline{BD} \perp \overline{DC}$; $\overline{GE} \perp \overline{EF}$;
$\overline{CB} \cong \overline{FG}$; $\overline{CE} \cong \overline{FD}$

Prove: $\triangle ACF$ is isosceles.

Statements	Reasons
1. $\overline{BD} \perp \overline{DC}$; $\overline{GE} \perp \overline{EF}$	1. ___?___
2. Angles CDB and FEG are ___?___.	2. (1). ___?___
3. $\triangle CDB$ and $\triangle FEG$ are ___?___.	3. (2). ___?___
4. $\overline{CE} \cong \overline{FD}$	4. ___?___
5. $\overline{CD} \cong \overline{FE}$	5. (4). ___?___
6. $\overline{CB} \cong \overline{FG}$	6. ___?___
7. $\triangle CDB \cong \triangle$ ___?___	7. (3), (5), (6). ___?___
8. $\angle C \cong \angle$ ___?___	8. (7). ___?___
9. $\overline{CA} \cong$ ___?___	9. (8). ___?___
10. ___?___	10. (9). ___?___

B

4. Prove Corollary 3–13.

5. Prove Theorem 3–15.
   Given: $\overrightarrow{BD}$ bisects $\angle ABC$;
   G is any point on $\overrightarrow{BD}$.
   Prove: $GF = GE$
   Plan: Prove $\triangle BGF \cong \triangle BGE$.
   Then $\overline{GF} \cong \overline{GE}$ and $GF = GE$.

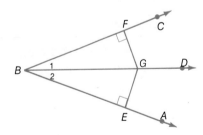

6. Prove Theorem 3–16.
   Given: $QR = QS$; $\overline{QR} \perp \overrightarrow{TR}$ and $\overline{QS} \perp \overrightarrow{TS}$.
   Prove: $\overrightarrow{TQ}$ bisects $\angle RTS$.
   Plan: Use T and Q to determine $\overrightarrow{TQ}$.
   Prove $\triangle TRQ \cong \triangle TSQ$.
   Then prove $\angle 1 \cong \angle 2$.

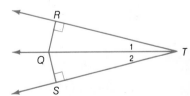

7. Given: Isosceles $\triangle ABC$ with base BC;
$\overline{AD}$ is an altitude.

Prove: $\angle 1 \cong \angle 2$

8. Given: In $\triangle ABC$, $\overline{AB} \perp \overline{BC}$.

Prove: $\triangle ABC$ is a right triangle. (HINT: Draw a figure.)

9. Given: Polygon $RSTUV$;
$\angle S$ and $\angle V$ are right angles;
$\overline{ST} \cong \overline{VU}$; $\angle RTU \cong \angle RUT$

Prove: $\overline{VR} \cong \overline{SR}$

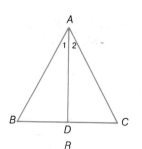

Refer to $\triangle ABC$ for Exercises 10–11.

10. Given: Isosceles $\triangle ABC$; $\overline{AB} \cong \overline{CB}$;
$\overline{BD}$ is the altitude to $\overline{AC}$;
E is any point between B and D.

Prove: $\triangle EAD \cong \triangle ECD$

11. Given: Same as in Exercise 10

Prove: $\triangle BAE \cong \triangle BCE$

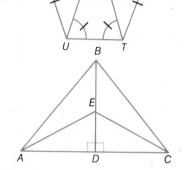

Refer to this figure for Exercises 12–13.

12. Given: Triangle AYB is in plane I;
X is a point not in plane I;
$\overline{XY} \perp \overline{AY}$; $\overline{XY} \perp \overline{BY}$; $\overline{XA} \cong \overline{XB}$

Prove: $\triangle AYB$ is isosceles.

13. Given: Triangle AYB is in plane I;
X is a point not in plane I;
$\overline{XY} \perp \overline{AY}$; $\overline{XY} \perp \overline{BY}$; $\angle XAB \cong \angle XBA$

Prove: $\angle YAB \cong \angle YBA$

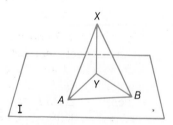

14. Given: $\overline{AB} \cong \overline{CD}$; $\overline{BE} \cong \overline{DF}$;
$\overline{AE} \perp \overline{BD}$; $\overline{CF} \perp \overline{BD}$

Prove: $\angle 1 \cong \angle 2$

15. Given: $\overline{PA} \cong \overline{PD}$; $\overline{AT} \cong \overline{DO}$;
$\overline{UP} \perp \overline{AD}$ at M.

Prove: $\triangle PUT \cong \triangle PUO$

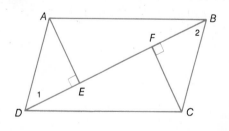

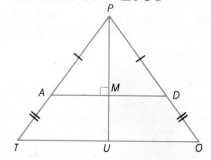

16. Given: In $\triangle AKS$, $\overline{KQ} \perp \overline{AS}$; $\overline{SP} \perp \overline{AK}$; $KQ \cong SP$

Prove that there are three pairs of congruent triangles.

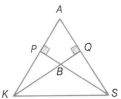

17. Given: $\angle D$ and $\angle E$ are right angles; $\angle 1 \cong \angle 2$

Prove: $\overline{DQ} \cong \overline{EQ}$

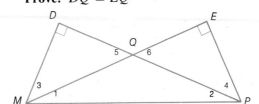

18. In the figure for Exercise 16, $\triangle AKS$ is isosceles with base KS. $\overline{SP}$ and $\overline{KQ}$ are altitudes from S and K respectively. Prove that $\angle BKS \cong \angle BSK$.

C

19. Given: $\overline{AB} \perp \overline{BE}$; $\overline{CB} \perp \overline{BD}$; $\overline{BD} \cong \overline{BE}$; $\overline{AD} \cong \overline{CE}$

Prove: $\overline{BA} \cong \overline{BC}$

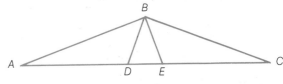

20. Prove the Hypotenuse–Leg Theorem.

Given: Triangles RST and XYZ in which $\overline{RS} \cong \overline{XY}$; $\overline{RT} \cong \overline{XZ}$; $\angle T$ and $\angle Z$ are right angles.

Prove: $\triangle RST \cong \triangle XYZ$

Plan: On the ray opposite $\overrightarrow{ZY}$, choose point A such that $\overline{ZA} \cong \overline{TS}$. Draw $\overline{AX}$. Angles 1 and 2 are a linear pair, so $\angle 1$ is a right angle and $\angle 1 \cong \angle T$. Therefore $\triangle RST \cong \triangle XAZ$. Since $\overline{RS} \cong \overline{XA}$, then $\overline{XA} \cong \overline{XY}$. In $\triangle XAY$, $\angle A \cong \angle Y$. Since $\angle S \cong \angle A$, $\angle S \cong \angle Y$. In right triangles RST and XYZ, $\overline{RS} \cong \overline{XY}$ and $\angle S \cong \angle Y$. Now prove the triangles congruent.

Puzzle

Study the five blocks shown at the left below. Each block is covered with paper showing six figures arranged the same way. The paper cover is shown at the right. What figures should appear in squares 1, 2, and 3?

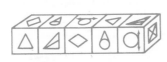

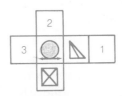

—— SUMMARY: Aids in Proof ——

The following summaries list ways of proof you have studied up to this point. These summaries will help you to plan and write proofs of the type indicated in each summary.

Summary

Ways of Proving Triangles Congruent

1. Prove them congruent by the definition of congruent triangles.
2. Prove them congruent by the SAS, ASA, or SSS Postulates.
3. If they are right triangles, prove them congruent by the HA Postulate or the HL Theorem.

Summary

Ways of Proving Segments Congruent

1. Prove they are corresponding sides of congruent triangles.
2. Prove they are opposite congruent angles in a triangle.
3. Prove they are formed at the base of an isosceles triangle by the bisector of the vertex angle.
4. Prove they are formed at the base of an isosceles triangle by the altitude from the vertex of the vertex angle.
5. Prove that they satisfy the conditions of the Common Segment Theorem.
6. Prove that they join the endpoints of a segment to any point on the perpendicular bisector of the segment.
7. Prove they are perpendicular to the sides of an angle from the same point on the angle bisector.
8. Prove they are formed by the median to a side of the triangle.

Summary

Ways of Proving Angles Congruent

1. Prove they are corresponding angles in congruent triangles.
2. Prove they are opposite congruent sides in congruent triangles.
3. Prove they are formed at the vertex angle of an isosceles triangle by the median or altitude to the base.
4. Prove that they satisfy the conditions of the Common Angle Theorem.
5. Prove they are formed at the vertex of an angle by the ray from the vertex to a point in the interior of the angle that is equidistant from the sides of the angle.

Ways of Proving Lines or Segments Perpendicular

1. Prove that one is the base of an isosceles triangle and the other is the bisector of the vertex angle.

2. Prove that one is the base of an isosceles triangle and the other is the median from the vertex angle.

3. Prove that one is a segment and the other is determined by two points, each equidistant from the endpoints of the segment.

4. Prove that the lines or segments are formed by an altitude of a triangle.

Puzzle

Each figure below can be formed from two pieces of a rectangle measuring 4 units by 6 units. Draw three such rectangles. Then cut each into two pieces that fit together to form one of the three figures. A piece may be flipped over.

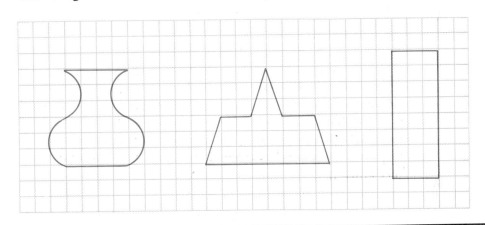

GEOMETRY REVIEW CAPSULE FOR SECTION 3–9

Write each pair of statements as a conditional. State the hypothesis and the conclusion of each conditional. *(Pages 49–50)*

1. Two angles form a linear pair; two angles are supplementary

2. An angle has a measure of 125; an angle is obtuse

3. An angle is acute; an angle has a measure less than 90

4. Two legs of a triangle measure 4 centimeters; the triangle is isosceles

5. Segment AB measures 7 units; segment AM measures 3 units and segment MB measures 4 units

3-9 Contrapositives and Biconditionals

Recall from Section 2-3 that the converse of a conditional (if-then) statement is formed by interchanging the hypothesis (if-part) and conclusion (then-part) of the conditional.

REMEMBER: If a conditional is true, its converse is not necessarily true.

Conditional ($p \longrightarrow q$)	Converse ($q \longrightarrow p$)
If two angles are complementary, then they are acute angles. (True)	If two angles are acute angles, then they are complementary. (Not necessarily true)

When both parts of a conditional are negated, the **inverse** is formed.

$$\text{Conditional: } p \longrightarrow q \qquad \text{Inverse: } \sim p \longrightarrow \sim q$$

REMEMBER: If a conditional is true, its inverse is not necessarily true.

When the "if" and "then" parts of the inverse are interchanged, the **contrapositive** of the original conditional is formed.

$$\text{Conditional: } p \longrightarrow q \qquad \text{Contrapositive: } \sim q \longrightarrow \sim p$$

REMEMBER: If a conditional is true, its contrapositive is true. If a conditional is false, its contrapositive is false.

Inverse ($\sim p \longrightarrow \sim \mathbf{q}$)	Contrapositive ($\sim q \longrightarrow \sim p$)
If two angles are not complementary, then they are not acute angles. (Not necessarily true)	If two angles are not acute angles, then they are not complementary. (True)

EXAMPLE 1 Write the converse, inverse and contrapositive of the given conditional. Tell whether each statement is true or false.

If two angles are right angles, then they are congruent.

Conditional: If two angles are right angles, then they are congruent.	True, it is a theorem.
Converse: If two angles are congruent, then they are right angles.	False. Two angles each with a measure of 70 are congruent. They are not right angles.
Inverse: If two angles are not right angles, then they are not congruent.	False. Two angles each with a measure of 40 are not right angles, but they are congruent.
Contrapositive: If two angles are not congruent, then they are not right angles.	True.

In Example 1, the converse and inverse of the original conditional were shown to be false by giving an example for which the hypothesis was true and the conclusion was false. Such an example is called a **counterexample.**

It takes only one counterexample to disprove a statement.

EXAMPLE 2 Prove or disprove: *Complementary angles are right angles.*

Solution: Give a counterexample to disprove the statement.

Counterexample: Angles with measures of 30 and 60 are complementary. Neither is a right angle.

Recall that when a conditional and its converse are both true, the two statements can be written as a biconditional (if and only if form). All definitions can be written as "if and only if" statements.

CLASSROOM EXERCISES

1. Write the converse, inverse, and contrapositive of this conditional.

   If two segments are congruent, then they have equal measures.

2. Write the biconditional for the definition in Exercise 1.

3. Write the converse, inverse, and contrapositive of this conditional. Tell whether each statement is true or false.

   If a triangle is equilateral, it is equiangular.

4. Can the conditional and its converse in Exercise 3 be written as a biconditional? If so, write the biconditional.

5. **a.** Write the definition of a right angle as a conditional.

   b. Write the converse of the conditional.

   c. Express the definition as a biconditional.

WRITTEN EXERCISES

A In Exercises 1–5, write the converse, inverse, and contrapositive of each conditional.

1. If two angles are supplements of the same angle, then they are congruent.

2. If two intersecting lines form congruent adjacent angles, then the lines are perpendicular.

3. If two lines are perpendicular, then they form four right angles.

4. If two angles of a triangle are congruent, then the sides opposite these angles are congruent.

5. If a point is on the bisector of an angle, then it is equidistant from the sides of the angle.

6. Which of the given conditionals in Exercises 1–5 are true?

7. Which of the converses of the given conditionals in Exercises 1–5 are true? If a converse is false, give a counterexample to show it is false.

8. Which of the inverses of the given conditionals in Exercises 1–5 are true? If an inverse is false, give a counterexample to show it is false.

9. Which of the contrapositives in Exercises 1–5 are true?

10. Write a biconditional for each conditional and its converse identified as true in Exercise 7.

Give a counterexample to disprove each statement.

11. The acute angles in a right triangle have equal measures.

12. Supplementary angles are right angles.

13. All vertical angles are right angles.

14. All supplementary angles form a linear pair.

B   Refer to statements **A, B, C,** and **D** in Exercises 15–22.

   A. If a kap is a dren, then a lep is a frim.

   B. If a lep is not a frim, then a kap is not a dren.

   C. If a lep is a frim, then a kap is a dren.

   D. If a kap is not a dren, then a lep is not a frim.

   Identify each statement.

15. Converse of B   16. Converse of A   17. Inverse of C

18. Inverse of D   19. Contrapositive of D   20. Contrapositive of A

21. Write a biconditional for A and C.

22. If statement B is true, which statement other than B is also true?

In Exercises 23–26, write two conditional statements for each biconditional.

23. $c = d$ if and only if $c - d = 0$.   24. $c \neq d$ if and only if $c - d \neq 0$.

25. An angle is an obtuse angle if and only if its measure is greater than 90 and less than 180.

26. A point is not on the bisector of an angle if and only if it is not equidistant from the sides of the angle.

C   Complete each statement. Use the words *converse, inverse,* or *contrapositive.*

27. The converse of the inverse of a conditional is the __?__.

28. The contrapositive of the converse of a conditional is the __?__.

29. The inverse of the converse of a conditional is the __?__.

Complete the "truth table" for each exercise. Recall that a conditional is false when the hypothesis is true and the conclusion is false.

30. Conditional:

p	q	$p \longrightarrow q$
T	T	?
T	F	?
F	T	?
F	F	?

31. Converse:

p	q	$q \longrightarrow p$
T	T	?
T	F	?
F	T	?
F	F	?

32. Inverse:

p	$\sim p$	q	$\sim q$	$\sim p \longrightarrow \sim q$
T	F	T	?	?
T	F	F	?	?
F	T	T	?	?
F	T	F	?	?

33. Contrapositive:

p	$\sim p$	q	$\sim q$	$\sim q \longrightarrow \sim p$
T	?	T	?	?
T	?	F	?	?
F	?	T	?	?
F	?	F	?	?

Review

1. Complete the following indirect proof. *(Section 3–7)*
   If $\angle F \not\cong \angle H$, then $FG \neq HG$.
   Given: __?__   **Prove:** __?__
   Proof: a. Assume that FG __?__ HG.
       b. Then $\overline{FG}$ __?__ $\overline{HG}$.
       c. If $\overline{FG}$ __?__ $\overline{HG}$, then $\angle F \cong \angle H$ because __?__ .
       d. But, by hypothesis, $\angle F$ __?__ $\angle H$.
       e. Therefore, the assumption that $FG = HG$ is false, and __?__ .

Write *Yes* or *No* to indicate whether each pair of triangles is congruent. Give the reason for each answer. *(Section 3–8)*

2.
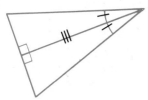

3.

4.
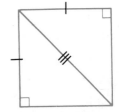

In Exercises 5–6, refer to the following conditional. *(Section 3–9)*
If triangles are congruent, then their corresponding parts are congruent.

5. Write the converse, inverse, and contrapositive.
6. Can the conditional and its converse be expressed as a biconditional? Explain your answer.

Consumer Applications
Logical Reasoning and Advertising

The mathematical logic presented in Chapters 2 and 3 can be applied in many everyday consumer situations, particularly to consumer advertising in newspapers and magazines.

PROBLEM: The advertisement below appeared in the February 9 issue of the Glendale Daily News.

QUALITY SUITS
Bring in this ad before
February 9!
We'll give you 20% off!

Mike Porter had decided to buy a new suit. When he saw the ad on February 10, he wondered whether he could still get the 20% discount.

Analysis: First, Mike wrote the "promise" in the ad as a conditional. Then he analyzed the promise by considering the converse, inverse, and contrapositive of the conditional.

Conditional: If you bring in this ad before February 9 (p), you will receive 20% off on your purchase (q). ($p \longrightarrow q$: Mike assumed that the conditional was true.)

Converse: If you receive 20% off on your purchase, then you brought in the ad before February 9. ($q \longrightarrow p$: Not necessarily true)

Inverse: If you don't bring in the ad before February 9, then you won't receive 20% off. ($\sim p \longrightarrow \sim q$: Not necessarily true)

Contrapositive: If you don't get 20% off, then you didn't bring in the ad before February 9 ($\sim q \longrightarrow \sim p$: True when the original conditional is true)

Conclusion: Mike concluded that his situation was similar to that described in the inverse. Since the inverse is not necessarily true, he took the ad to the store to see whether he would receive the discount. Mike bought a suit at 20% off!

8. Complete the proof by supplying the missing statements and reasons.

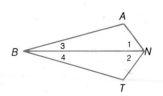

Given: $\overline{AN} \cong \overline{TN}$; $\angle 1 \cong \angle 2$

Prove: $\angle 3 \cong \angle 4$

Statements	Reasons
1. $\overline{AN} \cong \overline{TN}$; $\angle 1 \cong \angle 2$	1. __?__
2. __?__	2. Identity
3. $\triangle ANB \cong \triangle TNB$	3. (1), (2). __?__
4. __?__	4. (3). __?__

Objective: *To use the ASA and SSS Postulates to determine whether two triangles are congruent (Section 3–3)*

In Exercises 9–12, tell whether each pair of triangles can be proved congruent by SAS, ASA, or SSS.
If two ways are possible, state both.

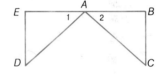

9. Given: $\angle 1 \cong \angle 2$; $\overline{DA} \cong \overline{CA}$; $\angle D \cong \angle C$
Prove: $\triangle EAD \cong \triangle BAC$

10. Given: A is the midpoint of $\overline{EB}$;
$\overline{DE} \cong \overline{CB}$; $\overline{DA} \cong \overline{CA}$
Prove: $\triangle EAD \cong \triangle BAC$

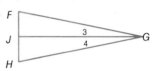

11. Given: $\overline{GJ}$ bisects $\angle FGH$;
$\overline{FG} \cong \overline{HG}$; $\angle F \cong \angle H$
Prove: $\triangle GJF \cong \triangle GJH$

12. Given: $\angle GJF \cong \angle GJH$;
J is the midpoint of $\overline{FH}$.
Prove: $\triangle GJF \cong \triangle GJH$

Objective: *To apply the Isosceles Triangle Theorem and its converse (Section 3–4)*

Use the figures below to prove the statements in Exercises 13–15.

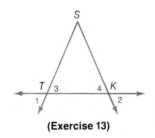

(Exercise 13)

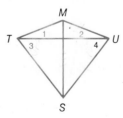

(Exercise 14)

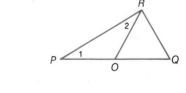

(Exercise 15)

13. If $\angle 1 \cong \angle 2$, then $\triangle TKS$ is isosceles.

14. If $\angle 1 \cong \angle 2$ and $\angle 3 \cong \angle 4$, then $\triangle STM \cong \triangle SUM$.

15. If O is the midpoint of $\overline{PQ}$ and $\overline{OQ} \cong \overline{OR}$, then $\angle 1 \cong \angle 2$.

Objective: *To apply other theorems associated with an isosceles triangle (Section 3–5)*

In Exercises 16–17:

a. Complete the conclusion.

b. Name the theorem that gives the reason for the conclusion.

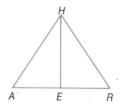

16. **Given:** $\triangle HAR$ is isosceles with vertex angle AHR;
    $\overline{HE}$ bisects $\angle AHR$.

    Conclusion: __?__ $\perp$ __?__ and __?__ bisects __?__ .

17. **Given:** $\triangle HAR$ is isosceles with $\overline{HA} \cong \overline{HR}$;
    $\overline{HE}$ is a median.

    Conclusion: __?__ $\perp$ __?__ and __?__ bisects __?__ .

Objective: *To identify the perpendicular bisector of a segment (Section 3–5)*

Determine whether each statement is true, *T*, or false, *F*.

Write the reason for each answer.

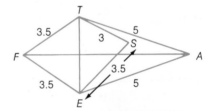

18. Point A is equidistant from T and E.

19. Point S is equidistant from T and E.

20. Point E is equidistant from F and A.

21. $\overline{FA}$ is the perpendicular bisector of $\overline{TE}$.

22. $\overline{TE}$ is the perpendicular bisector of $\overline{FA}$.

Objective: *To identify corresponding congruent parts of overlapping triangles (Section 3–6)*

Refer to the figure at the right below for Exercises 23–26.

Determine whether each statement is true, *T*, or false, *F*.

Write the reason for each answer.

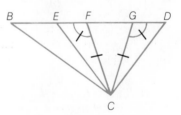

23. If $\overline{EF} \cong \overline{DG}$, then $\triangle ECF \cong \triangle DCG$.

24. If $\overline{EF} \cong \overline{GD}$, then $EG = FD$.

25. If $m\angle ECF = m\angle DCG$, then $\angle ECG \neq \angle DCF$.

26. If $\overline{BE} \cong \overline{FG}$ and $\overline{EF} \cong \overline{GD}$, then F is the mid-point of $\overline{BD}$.

Objective: *To use the indirect method of proof (Section 3–7)*

Write the negation of each statement.

27. $\triangle RTS$ is an isosceles triangle.

28. $m\angle 1 + m\angle 2 \neq m\angle A$

Prove by the indirect method.

29. Given: $\overline{BC} \not\equiv \overline{BA}$; $\overline{BD} \perp \overline{CA}$

   Prove: $\overline{DC} \not\equiv \overline{DA}$

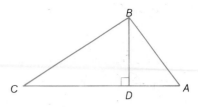

Objective: *To use the HA Postulate and the HL Theorem to prove two right triangles are congruent (Section 3–8)*

Write *Yes* or *No* to indicate whether each pair of triangles is congruent. Give the reason for each answer.

30.

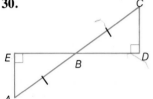

31.

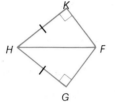

32.

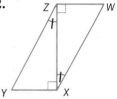

Objective: *To write the converse, inverse, and contrapositive of a conditional statement, and to express a conditional as a biconditional (Section 3–9)*

In Exercises 33–36, refer to the following conditional.

   If the three angles of a triangle are congruent, then the three sides are congruent.

33. Write the converse of the conditional. Is it true?

34. Write the inverse of the conditional. Is it true?

35. Write the contrapositive of the conditional. Is it true?

36. Write the conditional as a biconditional, if possible.

Objective: *To solve word problems that involve congruent triangles (Page 106)*

37. A telephone pole is supported by two guy wires, as shown at the right. Each wire is anchored 2 meters from the base of the telephone pole. Prove that the two wires are the same length.

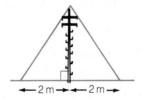

Objective: *To solve word problems that involve isosceles triangles and perpendicular lines (Page 120)*

38. A certain searchlight mounted on a helicopter can pivot 10° left or right from its mounted position. Show that the entire area lighted by the searchlight on a hovering helicopter is an isosceles triangle.

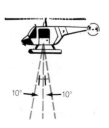

Chapter Test

In the figure at the right, △DRT ≅ △SNT. Complete each statement.

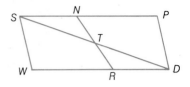

1. RTD ↔ N ___?___ ___?___
2. $\overline{NS}$ ↔ ___?___
3. $\overline{TR}$ ≅ ___?___
4. ∠TDR ≅ ___?___
5. ___?___ ≅ ∠DTR
6. $\overline{ST}$ ≅ ___?___

Determine whether each statement is true, *T*, or false, *F*. Write the reason for each answer.

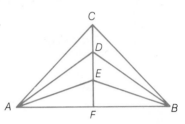

7. If ∠DAF ≅ ∠DBF, then $\overline{AD}$ ≅ $\overline{BD}$.
8. If $AE = EB$, then E is on the perpendicular bisector of $\overline{AB}$.
9. If $AE = EB$ and $AF = FB$, then ∠AEF ≅ ∠BEF.
10. If $\overline{CD}$ ≅ $\overline{EF}$, then $CE = DF$.
11. If m∠CBD ≠ m∠EBF, then ∠CBE ≅ ∠DBF.

In Exercises 12–14, use the given information to tell whether each pair of triangles can be proved congruent. Give the reason for each answer.

12. Given: m∠PSR = 90;
    m∠QRS = 90;
    $\overline{PR}$ ≅ $\overline{QS}$

13. Given: $\overline{AB}$ ≅ $\overline{CD}$;
    $\overline{CF}$ ≅ $\overline{BE}$;
    ∠ACF ≅ ∠DBE

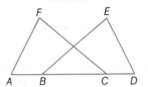

14. Given: $\overline{BE}$ ≅ $\overline{CE}$;
    ∠3 ≅ ∠4

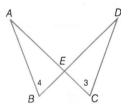

15. Complete the proof.

Given: ∠1 ≅ ∠2; $\overline{AE}$ ≅ $\overline{BC}$;
       ∠E and ∠C are right angles.

Prove: $\overline{ED}$ ≅ $\overline{CD}$

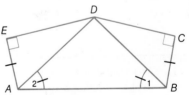

Statements	Reasons
1. ∠1 ≅ ∠2	1. ___?___
2. In △ABD, ___?___ .	2. (1). Theorem 3–3
3. $\overline{AE}$ ≅ $\overline{BC}$, and ∠E and ∠C are right angles.	3. ___?___
4. ___?___ are right triangles.	4. (3). Definition of right triangle
5. △ADE ≅ △BDC	5. (2), (3), (4). ___?___
6. ___?___	6. (5). ___?___

Cumulative Review: Chapters 1–3

In Exercises 1–11 and 14–23,
choose the best answer.
Choose a, b, c, or d.

1. Name the angle formed by the intersection of two noncollinear rays AB and AC.

    a. $\angle ABC$ b. $\angle CBA$ c. $\angle CAB$ d. $\angle ACB$

2. Triangle RST is isosceles with $RS = ST$. Name the base angles.

    a. $\angle R$; $\angle T$ b. $\angle R$; $\angle S$ c. $\angle S$; $\angle T$ d. $\angle S$ only

3. Points A, E, and B are collinear. Point E is on line LM. Name the point of intersection of line AB and line LM.

    a. A b. B c. E d. L

4. Which represents the logical order for defining the given terms?

    a. triangle, segment, equilateral triangle

    b. segment, triangle, equilateral triangle

    c. equilateral triangle, segment, triangle

    d. triangle, equilateral triangle, segment

5. Points A, B, and C lie on a straight line. B is between A and C. If $AB = 24$ and $AB = \frac{2}{3}AC$, find $\frac{1}{4}AC$.

    a. 36   b. 9   c. 12   d. 4

6. Point R bisects $\overline{PQ}$. Which conclusion is correct?

    a. $RP = PQ$ b. $QR = QP$ c. $PR = QP$ d. $PR = RQ$

7. D is the midpoint of $\overline{AC}$ in $\triangle ABC$. Which word best describes $\overline{BD}$?

    a. altitude   b. angle bisector   c. base   d. median

8. Line ER bisects segment LM at S. Which conclusion can be drawn?

    a. $ES = SR$ b. $LS = SM$ c. $ES = SM$ d. $ER = LM$

9. The measure of an angle is 40 less than the measure of its supplement. Find the measure of the angle and of its supplement.

    a. 25; 65   b. 50; 90   c. 70; 110   d. 40; 140

10. Line AB is perpendicular to line CE at E. Which conclusion can be drawn?

    a. $AE = EB$ b. $AB = CE$

    c. $m\angle AEC = 90$ d. $m\angle AEC = 90$ and $AE = EB$

11. Angles AEF and AED form a linear pair. If $m\angle AEF = x$, what is $m\angle AED$?

    a. $x + 180$ b. $90 + x$ c. $90 - x$ d. $180 - x$

12. Name the property that gives the reason for this statement.

    If points A, B, C, and D are collinear, B lies between A and C, C lies between B and D, and $AB = CD$, then $AC = BD$.

13. Name the property that gives the reason for this statement.

If points A, B, C, and D are collinear, C lies between A and B, B lies between C and D, and $AB = CD$, then $AC = BD$.

14. In triangle ABC, D is the midpoint of AB and $CD = AD$. Which conclusion can be drawn?

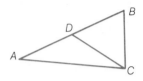

   a. $BC = AC$ **b.** $AB = AC$

   c. $DC = DB$ **d.** $m\angle ADC = m\angle CDB$

15. In triangle FHG, GP bisects angle FGH. Which conclusion can be drawn?

   a. $m\angle F = m\angle H$

   b. $m\angle H = m\angle FGH$

   c. $m\angle FGP = m\angle PGH$

   d. $m\angle FPG = m\angle GPH$

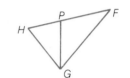

In the figure at the right $\triangle ABE \cong \triangle DCE$. Refer to this figure in Exercises 16–20.

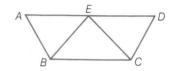

16. If $\triangle AEB \cong \triangle DCE$, which of the following correspondences is a congruence?

   a. $\triangle ABE \cong \triangle DEC$ **b.** $\triangle BEA \cong \triangle CED$

   c. $\triangle EBA \cong \triangle EDC$ **d.** $\triangle EAB \cong \triangle ECD$

17. Which side of $\triangle DCE$ corresponds to $\overline{AE}$ in $\triangle ABE$?

   a. $\overline{DC}$ **b.** $\overline{ED}$ **c.** $\overline{CE}$ **d.** $\overline{CD}$

18. What angle in $\triangle EDC$ corresponds to $\angle ABE$ in $\triangle EAB$?

   a. $\angle EDC$ **b.** $\angle CED$ **c.** $\angle CDE$ **d.** $\angle ECD$

19. Which side in $\triangle ECD$ corresponds to $\overline{AB}$ in $\triangle EBA$?

   a. $\overline{CE}$ **b.** $\overline{ED}$ **c.** $\overline{EC}$ **d.** $\overline{DC}$

20. What angle in $\triangle AEB$ corresponds to $\angle CDE$ in $\triangle DEC$?

   a. $\angle BAE$ **b.** $\angle EBA$ **c.** $\angle BEA$ **d.** $\angle ABE$

In Exercises 21–23, choose the postulate or theorem named below that can be used to prove $\triangle RST \cong \triangle WXY$.

   a. ASA Postulate   **b.** SSS Postulate

   c. SAS Postulate   **d.** HL Theorem

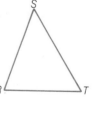

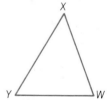

21. $\angle R \cong \angle W$; $\angle S \cong \angle X$; $\overline{RS} \cong \overline{XW}$

22. $m\angle S = m\angle X = 90$; $\overline{RT} \cong \overline{YW}$; $\overline{ST} \cong \overline{XY}$

23. $\overline{RT} \cong \overline{WY}$; $\angle T \cong \angle Y$; $\overline{ST} \cong \overline{XY}$

Preparing for College Entrance Tests

Writing an equation to represent the problem is a useful technique in solving problems of the following type on College Entrance tests.

EXAMPLE   In the figure at the right, m∠AEC = 70, m∠BED = 80, and m∠AED = 110. Find m∠BEC.

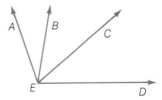

   a. 10   **b.** 20   **c.** 30

   d. 40   **e.** 50

Solution: Let $x = m∠BEC$. ⟵——— **Represent the unknowns.**

Then m∠AEB = 70 − x and m∠AED = 80 − x.

$70 − x + x + 80 − x = 110$ ⟵——— **Write an equation for the problem.**

$150 − x = 110$

$x = 40$ **Answer: d**

Choose the best answer. Choose *a, b, c, d,* or *e.*

1. In the figure at the right, *PQ* is a line.
   Find m∠*QRF*.

   a. 22.5   **b.** 30   **c.** 45

   d. 60   **e.** 180

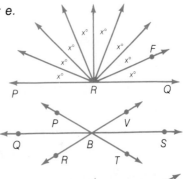

2. If m∠*RBQ* = m∠*TBS* = 30, find m∠*PBV*.

   a. 90   **b.** 120   **c.** 135

   d. 150   **e.** 165

3. Which statement best expresses the relationship between *x, y,* and *z*?

   a. $x + y > y + z$ **b.** $x + z < y + z$

   c. $x − y − 2z = 0$ **d.** $x + 2z = y$

   e. $x + z = y + z$

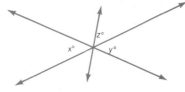

4. In this figure $k \perp t$. Find $x + y$.

   a. 45   **b.** 90   **c.** 120

   d. 180   **e.** 360

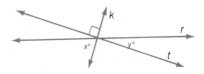

5. Refer to this figure at the right to find $x + y$ in terms of *a.*

   a. $\dfrac{a}{2} - 180$ **b.** $90 - \dfrac{a}{2}$ **c.** $180 - \dfrac{a}{2}$

   d. $a - 180$ **e.** $180 - a$

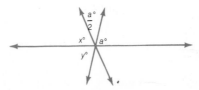

Preparing for College Entrance Tests

This two-step procedure will help you to solve problems of the following type on College Entrance tests.

1 Determine which of **I, II,** and **III** are correct. (More than one can be correct.)

2 Check which of the given choices, **a, b, c, d,** or **e** identifies the correct answers exactly.

EXAMPLE: If $\triangle ABC \cong \triangle DEF$ and $\triangle DEF \cong \triangle GHJ$, which of these is (are) true?

I. $\triangle ABC \cong \triangle GHJ$ **II.** Triangles GHJ and DEF are equilateral.   **III.** $\overline{AC} \cong \overline{GJ}$

a. I only   **b.** I and II only   **c.** I and III only   **d.** II only   **e.** III only

Solution: **1** Statement I: True by the transitive property of congruence.

Statement II: Not necessarily true. (Congruent triangles need not be equilateral.)

Statement III: True by CPCTC

2 Choice **c** identifies "I and III only" as correct.   **Answer: c**

Choose the best answer. Choose *a, b, c, d,* or *e.*

1. If $\triangle KLM \cong \triangle PQR$, which of the following is (are) true?

   I. $\overline{KL} \cong \overline{PQ}, \angle M \cong \angle R, \overline{LM} \cong \overline{QR}$ **II.** $\overline{KM} \cong \overline{RR}, \angle M \cong \angle R, \overline{LM} \cong \overline{QR}$

   III. $\overline{KL} \cong \overline{PQ}$, m$\angle L =$ m$\angle Q = 90$, $\overline{KM} \cong \overline{PR}$

   a. I only   **b.** II only   **c.** I and II only   **d.** II and III only   **e.** III only

2. Which statement gives enough information to prove $\triangle ABC \cong \triangle XYZ$?

   I. $\overline{AB} \cong \overline{XY}, \overline{BC} \cong \overline{XZ}, \angle B \cong \angle X$ **II.** $\overline{AB} \cong \overline{XY}, \overline{AC} \cong \overline{XZ}$

   III. $\angle X \cong \angle A$

   a. I only   **b.** II only   **c.** II and III only   **d.** I and III only   **e.** III only

3. In the figure at the right, $\overline{AB} \cong \overline{AE}$ and $\overline{BC} \cong \overline{DE}$. Which of the following is (are) true?

   I. $\angle B \cong \angle E$ **II.** $\angle ACD \cong \angle ADC$

   III. $\triangle ABC \cong \triangle AED$

   a. I, II, and III   **b.** II and III only   **c.** I and III only   **d.** I and II only   **e.** II only

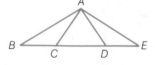

4. In the figure at the right, $\overline{ED} \cong \overline{GF}$, $\overline{DH} \cong \overline{FJ}$, and $\overline{GH} \cong \overline{EJ}$. Which of the following is (are) true?

   I. $\angle EDJ \cong \angle GFH$ **II.** m$\angle GDE =$ m$\angle EFG = 90$

   III. DF bisects $\angle D$ and $\angle F$.

   a. II only   **b.** III only   **c.** I and II only   **d.** II and III only   **e.** I only

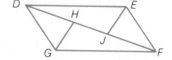

CHAPTER **4** **Parallel Lines**

Sections   4-1   **Interior and Exterior Angles**

4-2   **Parallel Lines and Angles**

4-3   **More Angle Relationships**

4-4   **Corresponding Angles and Parallel Lines**

Applications: Using Parallel Lines

4-5   **Triangle-Sum Theorem**

4-6   **Triangle-Sum Corollaries**

4-7   **Angles of a Polygon**

4-8   **Exterior Angles of a Polygon**

Applications: Using Angles in Polygons

Features   **Career Application: Geometry and Optometry**

Computer Application: Angles in Triangles and Polygons

Calculator Application: Evaluating Formulas

Puzzle

Review
and
Testing   **Algebra Review Capsules**

Geometry Review Capsules

Review: Sections 4–1 through 4–4

Review: Sections 4–5 through 4–8

Chapter Summary

Chapter Objectives and Review

Chapter Test

4–1 Interior and Exterior Angles

In $\triangle ABC$, $\angle 1$ is an **exterior angle of the triangle** because it forms a linear pair with an angle of the triangle. To form an exterior angle of a triangle, extend *one side* of the triangle.

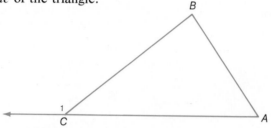

Angles A and B are the **remote interior angles** of $\angle 1$. They are the angles of the triangle *not adjacent* to $\angle 1$.

EXAMPLE 1 **a.** Name the exterior angles shown for $\triangle DEF$.

b. Name the remote interior angles for each exterior angle.

Solutions:

Exterior Angle	Remote Interior Angles
$\angle 1$	$\angle DEF$ and $\angle DFE$
$\angle 2$	$\angle EDF$ and $\angle DFE$
$\angle 3$	$\angle FDE$ and $\angle DEF$

Recall the following symbols from your study of algebra.

$<$ means "*is less than.*" $>$ means "*is greater than.*"

EXAMPLE 2   Use $\triangle GHK$ to compare the measure of each exterior angle shown with the measure of its remote interior angles.

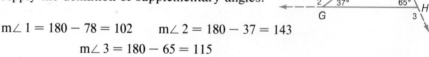

Solution: Apply the definition of supplementary angles.

$$m\angle 1 = 180 - 78 = 102 \qquad m\angle 2 = 180 - 37 = 143$$
$$m\angle 3 = 180 - 65 = 115$$

Exterior Angle	Remote Interior Angles	Comparison
$m\angle 1 = 102$	$m\angle G = 37$ $m\angle H = 65$	$m\angle 1 > m\angle G$ $m\angle 1 > m\angle H$
$m\angle 2 = 143$	$m\angle K = 78$ $m\angle H = 65$	$m\angle 2 > m\angle K$ $m\angle 2 > m\angle H$
$m\angle 3 = 115$	$m\angle G = 37$ $m\angle K = 78$	$m\angle 3 > m\angle G$ $m\angle 3 > m\angle K$

Theorem 4–1 relates the measure of an exterior angle of a triangle and its corresponding remote interior angles.

Theorem 4–1

> **Exterior Angle Inequality Theorem**
>
> The measure of an exterior angle of a triangle is greater than the measure of either of its remote interior angles.

You are asked to prove this theorem in the Written Exercises. To prove this theorem, you apply the definition of $<$ (or $>$).

Definition

> For real numbers a and b, $a < b$ (or $b > a$) if and only if there is a positive real number c such that $a + c = b$.

Thus, from the definition, $AB < AC$ if and only if $AB + BC = AC$.

This table summarizes other properties of inequalities useful in geometry. In the table, a, b, and c represent real numbers.

Property of Inequalities	Example
Comparison Either $a < b$, $a = b$, or $a > b$.	Either $8 < 9$, $8 = 9$, or $8 > 9$.
Transitive If $a < b$ and $b < c$, then $a < c$.	If $EF < GH$ and $GH < JK$, then $EF < JK$.
Addition If $a < b$, then $a + c < b + c$.	If $m\angle 1 < m\angle 2$, then $m\angle 1 + m\angle A < m\angle 2 + m\angle A$.
Multiplication If $a < b$ and $c > 0$, then $ac < bc$. If $a < b$ and $c < 0$, then $ac > bc$.	If $RS < XY$, then $3RS < 3XY$. If $RS < XY$, then $-3RS > -3XY$.

REMEMBER: $a < b$ has the same meaning as $b > a$.

EXAMPLE 3   Refer to the figure at the right to show that $m\angle 1 < m\angle ABC$.

Solution: By the definition of betweenness of rays,

$m\angle 1 + m\angle 2 = m\angle ABC$.

$m\angle 2 > 0$ ⟵ **Definition of angle measure**

$m\angle 1 < m\angle ABC$ ⟵ **Definition of inequality**

Interior and exterior angles can also be defined in terms of lines. A **transversal** is a line that intersects (or cuts) each of two other lines in different points. In the figure below, transversal t intersects lines y and s to form **interior** and **exterior angles.**

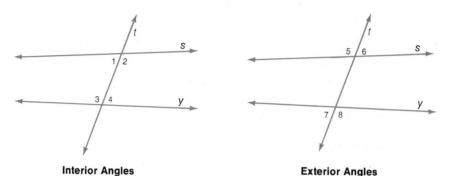

Interior Angles   **Exterior Angles**

Alternate angles are nonadjacent angles on opposite sides of a transversal.

Alternate Interior Angles	Alternate Exterior Angles
$\angle 1$ and $\angle 4$	$\angle 6$ and $\angle 7$
$\angle 2$ and $\angle 3$	$\angle 5$ and $\angle 8$

EXAMPLE 4 Refer to the figure at the right to name each of the following.

  a. Interior angles

  b. Exterior angles

  c. Alternate interior angles

  d. Alternate exterior angles

Solutions: **a.** Interior: $\angle 11$, $\angle 12$, $\angle 13$, $\angle 14$ **b.** Exterior: $\angle 9$, $\angle 10$, $\angle 15$, $\angle 16$

  c. Alternate interior: $\angle 11$ and $\angle 13$, $\angle 12$ and $\angle 14$

  d. Alternate exterior: $\angle 9$ and $\angle 15$, $\angle 10$ and $\angle 16$

CLASSROOM EXERCISES

Refer to $\triangle ABC$ to complete each statement in Exercises 1–4.

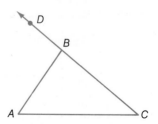

1. Angle __?__ is an exterior angle of $\triangle ABC$.

2. Angle __?__ and angle __?__ are the remote interior angles of $\angle ABD$.

3. $m\angle ABD$ __?__ $m\angle A$ ($>$, $<$, or $=$)

4. $m\angle ABD$ __?__ $m\angle C$ ($>$, $<$, or $=$)

In Exercises 5–10, state the property of inequalities that gives the reason for each conclusion.

5. For segments AB and AC, either $AB < AC$, $AB = AC$, or $AB > AC$.
6. If $XY < XZ$, then $XY + KM < XZ + KM$.
7. If $XY < XZ$, then $XY - KM < XZ - KM$.
8. If $EF + GH = EH$ and $GH > 0$, then $EF < EH$.
9. If $4AB < 2CD$, then $2AB < CD$.
10. If $m\angle T > m\angle P$ and $m\angle P > m\angle Q$, then $m\angle T > m\angle Q$.

Refer to the figure at the right for Exercises 11–15.
Match the pairs of angles with the correct name in **a–e**.

11. $\angle 6$ and $\angle 4$, $\angle 5$ and $\angle 3$

    a. Interior angles

12. $\angle 7$ and $\angle 1$, $\angle 8$ and $\angle 2$

    b. Interior angles on the same side of the transversal

13. $\angle 5$ and $\angle 4$, $\angle 6$ and $\angle 3$

    c. Alternate interior angles

14. $\angle 7$ and $\angle 8$, $\angle 1$ and $\angle 2$

    d. Exterior angles

15. $\angle 5$ and $\angle 6$, $\angle 3$ and $\angle 4$

    e. Alternate exterior angles

WRITTEN EXERCISES

A   In Exercises 1–4, complete each statement. More than one answer may be possible in some cases.

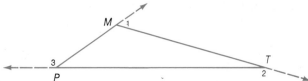

1. $m\angle 3 > m\angle \underline{\ ?\ }$
2. $m\angle MPT < m\angle \underline{\ ?\ }$
3. $m\angle 2 \underline{\ ?\ } m\angle PMT$
4. $m\angle MTP \underline{\ ?\ } m\angle 1$

In the figure at the right, H is a point on $\overline{GF}$. Use the figure to complete each statement in Exercises 5–12.

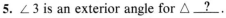

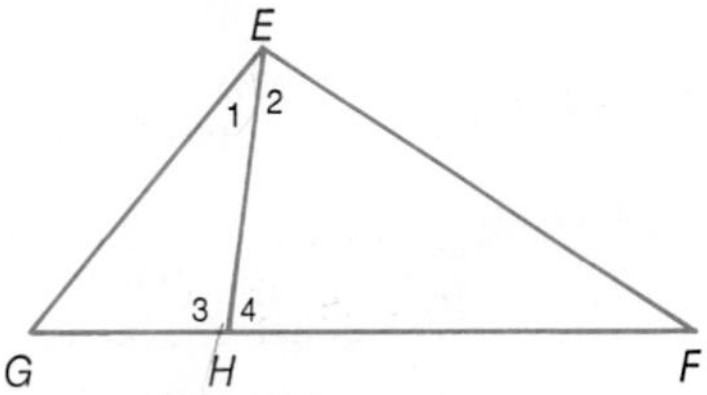

5. $\angle 3$ is an exterior angle for $\triangle \underline{\ ?\ }$.
6. $\angle 4$ is an exterior angle for $\triangle \underline{\ ?\ }$.
7. $\angle \underline{\ ?\ }$ and $\angle \underline{\ ?\ }$ are remote interior angles for $\angle 3$.
8. $\angle \underline{\ ?\ }$ and $\angle \underline{\ ?\ }$ are remote interior angles for $\angle 4$.
9. $m\angle 3 \underline{\ ?\ } m\angle F$ (>, <, or =)
10. $m\angle 1 \underline{\ ?\ } m\angle 4$ (>, <, or =)
11. $m\angle G \underline{\ ?\ } m\angle 4$ (>, <, or =)
12. $m\angle 2 \underline{\ ?\ } m\angle 3$ (>, <, or =)

In Exercises 13–15, complete each statement.

13.

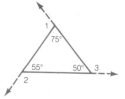

$m\angle 1 = \underline{\ ?\ }$
$m\angle 2 = \underline{\ ?\ }$
$m\angle 3 = \underline{\ ?\ }$

14.

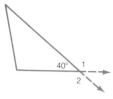

$m\angle 1 = \underline{\ ?\ }$
$m\angle 2 = \underline{\ ?\ }$
$m\angle 1 \underline{\ ?\ } m\angle 2 \ (> \text{or} =)$

15.

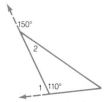

$m\angle 1 = \underline{\ ?\ }$
$m\angle 2 = \underline{\ ?\ }$
$m\angle 1 \underline{\ ?\ } m\angle 2 \ (> \text{or} <)$

16. Supply the missing reasons in this proof of Theorem 4–1.

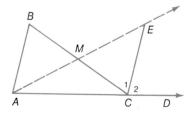

Given: $\angle BCD$ is an exterior angle of $\triangle ABC$.

Prove: $m\angle BCD > m\angle B$

Statements	Reasons
1. Select M, the midpoint of $\overline{BC}$.	1. A segment has exactly one midpoint.
2. A and M determine $\overrightarrow{AM}$.	2. Two points determine a ray.
3. Select E such that $EM = AM$.	3. The Ruler Postulate
4. $\overline{EM} \cong \overline{AM}$	4. (3). $\underline{\ ?\ }$
5. Draw $\overline{CE}$.	5. Two points determine a segment.
6. $\overline{MC} \cong \overline{MB}$	6. (1). $\underline{\ ?\ }$
7. $\angle CME \cong \angle BMA$	7. $\underline{\ ?\ }$
8. $\triangle CME \cong \triangle BMA$	8. (4), (6), (7). $\underline{\ ?\ }$
9. $\angle 1 \cong \angle B$	9. (8). $\underline{\ ?\ }$
10. $m\angle 1 = m\angle B$	10. (9). $\underline{\ ?\ }$
11. $m\angle 1 + m\angle 2 = m\angle BCD$	11. $\underline{\ ?\ }$
12. $m\angle 2 > 0$	12. Definition of angle measure
13. $m\angle BCD > m\angle 1$	13. (11), (12). $\underline{\ ?\ }$
14. $m\angle BCD > m\angle B$	14. (10), (13). $\underline{\ ?\ }$

For each given pair of lines and transversal, name the interior angles, exterior angles, alternate interior angles, and alternate exterior angles.

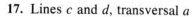

17. Lines c and d, transversal a

18. Lines c and d, transversal b

19. Lines a and b, transversal c

20. Lines a and b, transversal d

B Refer to the figure at the right to complete each statement in Exercises 21–25.

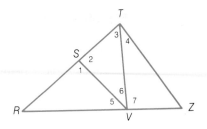

21. $m\angle 1 > m\angle$ ___?___ and $m\angle$ ___?___ .

22. $m\angle 2 > m\angle$ ___?___ and $m\angle$ ___?___ .

23. $m\angle SVZ > m\angle$ ___?___ and $m\angle$ ___?___ .

24. $m\angle 7 > m\angle$ ___?___ and $m\angle$ ___?___ .

25. $m\angle TVR > m\angle$ ___?___ and $m\angle$ ___?___ .

26. Use the *Given* and the figure in Exercise 16 to prove $m\angle BCD > m\angle A$.

    Plan: Begin by extending $\overrightarrow{BC}$ to a point P. Select Q as the midpoint of $\overline{AC}$. Draw $\overline{BQ}$ and extend it to R such that $BQ = RQ$. Prove $\triangle QCR \cong \triangle QAB$. Then continue the proof in a manner similar to steps 9–14 in the proof of Exercise 16.

27. Given: $\triangle ABC$;
            D lies between A and C on $\overrightarrow{CA}$.

    Prove: $m\angle 1 > m\angle 3$

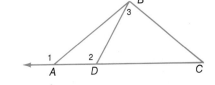

In Exercises 28–30, *a, b, c,* and *d* represent real numbers.

28. Prove: If $a < b$ and $c < d$, then $a + c < b + d$.

29. Prove: If $a = b$ and $c < d$, then $a + c < b + d$.

30. Prove: If $a = b$ and $c < d$, then $a - c > b - d$.

C

31. Given: $AB < CD$

    Prove: $BD > AC$

The proof should apply to either figure above. (HINT: Use the property proved in Exercise 30.)

32. Q is any point in the interior of $\triangle RST$. Prove that $m\angle R < m\angle TQS$.

33. Prove: If a triangle has one obtuse angle, then the other two angles are acute.

_____ **GEOMETRY REVIEW CAPSULE FOR SECTION 4-2** _____

Classify each statement as true, *T*, or false, *F*. When a statement is false, tell why it is false. *(Pages 127–128)*

1. A mathematical statement can be both true and false at the same time.

2. The negation of a statement is its converse.

3. The statement "$\angle A \cong \angle B$ and $\angle A \ncong \angle B$" is a contradiction.

4. The first step in an indirect proof is to assume the contrapositive of what you want to prove.

4-2 Parallel Lines and Angles

Parallel lines are lines in the same plane that do not intersect. Lines *r* and *s* below are parallel.

r ∥ *s* ◄──── Read: "Line *r* is parallel to line *s*."

Lines that do *not intersect* and are *not parallel* are **skew lines.** If the airplanes at the right maintain their same respective altitudes, the flight paths of the planes will represent skew lines.

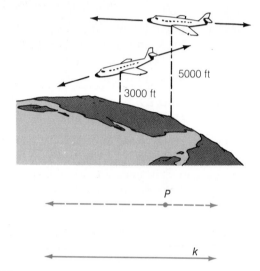

5000 ft

3000 ft

Suppose that a point and a line, such as point *P* and line *k*, are given. Postulate 15 states that there is exactly one line through *P* parallel to line *k*.

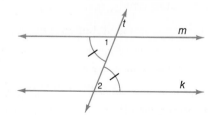

P

k

Postulate 15

> Through a point not on a given line, there is exactly one line parallel to the given line.

Theorem 4–2 and its converse, Theorem 4–3, relate parallel lines cut by a transversal and the alternate interior angles formed. The indirect method of proof is used to prove both theorems.

Theorem 4–2

> If two lines are cut by a transversal so that alternate interior angles are congruent, then the lines are parallel.

Recall that an indirect proof is usually written in paragraph form.

EXAMPLE 1   Prove Theorem 4–2.

Given: Lines *k* and *m* cut by transversal *t*;
∠1 ≅ ∠2

Prove: *k* ∥ *m*

t

m

1

2

k

Proof: Assume *k* is *not* parallel to *m* (see the figure below).

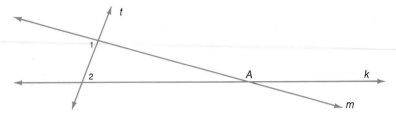

If *k* and *m* are not parallel, then they intersect in some point *A*.

∠ 1 is an exterior angle of the triangle formed by lines *k*, *m*, and *t*.

Then m∠ 1 > m∠ 2 by the Exterior Angle Inequality Theorem.

Thus, m∠ 1 = m∠ 2 and m∠ 1 ≠ m∠ 2. This is a contradiction.

The assumption that *k* is not parallel to *m* must be false. ∴ *k* ∥ *m*.

Theorem 4–3 is the converse of Theorem 4–2. Thus, these two theorems can be written as a biconditional.

Theorem 4–3

> If two parallel lines are cut by a transversal, then alternate interior angles are congruent.

EXAMPLE 2   Prove Theorem 4–3.

Given: Line *t* is a transversal.
    k ∥ *m*

Prove: ∠ 1 ≅ ∠ 2

Proof: Assume ∠ 1 ≇ ∠ 2 (see the figure below).

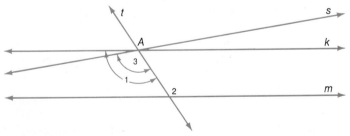

By Postulate 9 there is an angle, ∠ 3, formed by line *t* and a line *s* through a point *A* such that ∠ 3 ≅ ∠ 2.

Thus, *s* ∥ *m* by Theorem 4–2.

Two lines, *s* and *k*, are parallel to *m* and pass through point *A*. This contradicts Postulate 15.

The assumption that ∠ 1 is not congruent to ∠ 2 must be false. ∴ ∠ 1 ≅ ∠ 2.

REMEMBER: Segments of parallel lines are parallel. Also, lines and rays determined by parallel segments are parallel.

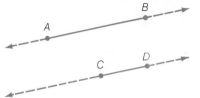

If $\overline{AB} \parallel \overline{CD}$, then $\overleftrightarrow{AB} \parallel \overleftrightarrow{CD}$.
If $\overleftrightarrow{AB} \parallel \overleftrightarrow{CD}$, then $\overline{AB} \parallel \overline{CD}$.

CLASSROOM EXERCISES

In each figure below, $\angle 1 \cong \angle 2$. Name the parallel lines or segments.

1.
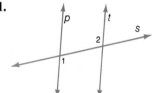

2.
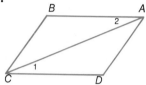

3.
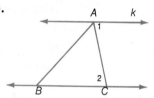

In each figure below, line a is parallel to line b. Name only the pairs of congruent alternate interior angles that are numbered.

4.
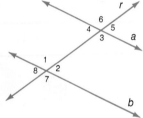

5.
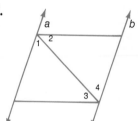

6.
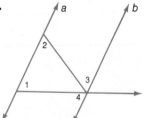

7. Write Theorems 4–2 and 4–3 as a biconditional in two ways.

WRITTEN EXERCISES

A   In Exercises 1–4, complete each conclusion.

1. Given: $\angle 4 \cong \angle 6$
    Conclusion: __?__ $\parallel$ __?__

2. **Given:** $\angle 5 \cong \angle 9$
    Conclusion: __?__ $\parallel$ __?__

3. Given: $\angle 13 \cong \angle 11$
    Conclusion: __?__ $\parallel$ __?__

4. **Given:** $\angle 4 \cong \angle 16$
    Conclusion: __?__ $\parallel$ __?__

In Exercises 5–6, refer to the figure for Exercises 1–4.

5. If $p \parallel q$, name 4 pairs of congruent alternate interior angles.

6. If $r \parallel s$, name 4 pairs of congruent alternate interior angles.

In Exercises 7–12, use the given information and figure to complete each conclusion.

7. **Given:** $\angle 1 \cong \angle SYT$

   Conclusion: __?__ $\parallel$ __?__

8. **Given:** $\angle T \cong \angle TYS$

   Conclusion: __?__ $\parallel$ __?__

9. **Given:** $\overline{MN} \parallel \overline{PO}$

   Conclusion: $\angle$ __?__ $\cong \angle$ __?__

10. **Given:** $\overline{MP} \parallel \overline{NO}$

    Conclusion: $\angle$ __?__ $\cong \angle$ __?__

11. **Given:** $\angle 1 \cong \angle W$

    Conclusion: __?__

12. **Given:** $\angle 2 \cong \angle X$

    Conclusion: __?__

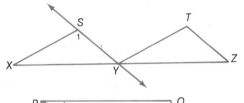

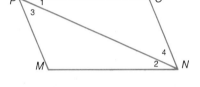

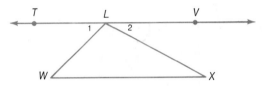

Refer to the figure at the right below for Exercises 13–14.

13. **Given:** $\overleftrightarrow{AB} \parallel \overleftrightarrow{CD}$; $m\angle 3 = 100$

    Find: $m\angle 5$; $m\angle 6$; $m\angle 7$

14. **Given:** $\overleftrightarrow{AB} \parallel \overleftrightarrow{CD}$; $m\angle 6 = 38$

    Find: $m\angle 4$; $m\angle 2$

B Refer to the figure at the right below for Exercises 15–16.

15. **Given:** $\overline{XY} \cong \overline{ZW}$; $\overline{TZ} \cong \overline{SY}$; $\angle 1 \cong \angle 2$

    Prove: $\overline{XT} \parallel \overline{WS}$

16. **Given:** $\overline{XT} \cong \overline{WS}$; $\overline{XY} \cong \overline{ZW}$; $\overline{TZ} \cong \overline{SY}$

    Prove: $\overline{TZ} \parallel \overline{SY}$

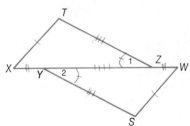

Prove each statement.

17. If two lines are cut by a transversal so that alternate exterior angles are congruent, then the lines are parallel.

Prove each statement.

18. If two parallel lines are cut by a transversal, then the alternate exterior angles are congruent.

19. If both pairs of opposite sides of a quadrilateral are congruent, then they are also parallel.

20. In the figure at the left below, $\overrightarrow{FK}$ bisects $\angle GFH$, $\overrightarrow{HJ}$ bisects $\angle PHF$, and $\angle 1 \cong \angle 2$. Prove: $\overrightarrow{FG} \parallel \overrightarrow{HP}$.

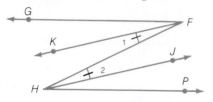
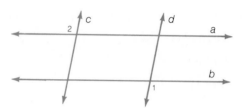

21. In the figure at the right above, $a \parallel b$ and $c \parallel d$. Prove: $\angle 1 \cong \angle 2$.

Ⓒ

22. Given: $\overrightarrow{TR} \parallel \overline{XY}$;
$\overrightarrow{TR}$ bisects $\angle YTS$.
Prove: $\triangle XYT$ is isosceles.

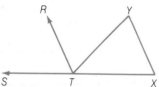

23. Given: C is the midpoint of $\overline{AE}$;
$\overline{AB} \parallel \overline{CD}$; $\overline{ED} \parallel \overline{CB}$.
Prove: $\overline{ED} \cong \overline{CB}$.

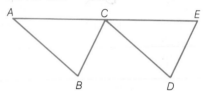

24. Given: $\overleftrightarrow{MT} \parallel \overleftrightarrow{NR}$; $\angle 5 \cong \angle 6$
Prove: $\overrightarrow{NR}$ bisects $\angle TNP$.

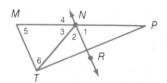

GEOMETRY REVIEW CAPSULE FOR SECTION 4-3

State one conclusion that can be drawn from each *Given*. Give the reason(s) for each answer. *(Pages 29–32, 66–67, 156–158)*

1. Given: $\angle 1$ and $\angle 2$ form a linear pair.

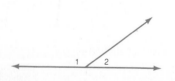

2. Given: Line $l \perp$ line m

3. Given: $m\angle B = 60$;
$m\angle BCD = 110$

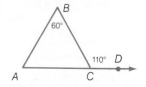

Career Applications
Geometry and Optometry

Optometrists treat persons with vision problems. Besides prescribing lenses, some optometrists adjust and fit contact lenses.

There are two basic kinds of lenses. Light bends on passing through either kind.

Convex (converging) Lens   **Concave (diverging) Lens**

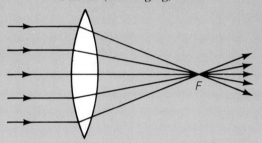 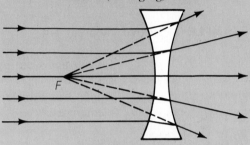

A **convex lens** is thicker at the middle than at the edges. Parallel light rays passing through the lens bend inward (*converge*) to meet at F, the focal point.

A **concave lens** is thicker at the edges than at the middle. Parallel light rays passing through the lens bend outward (*diverge*).

The **focal distance** of a lens is the distance between the focal point and the center of the lens. The reciprocal of the focal length is called the **power** of the lens. A lens having **one diopter**, D, of power will bring parallel rays of light to focus at a distance of one meter.

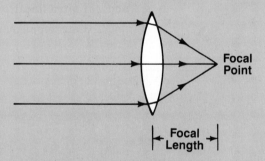

EXAMPLE   Find the focal length in centimeters of a 4.00 D convex lens.

Solution: $D = \dfrac{1}{f}$ ⟵——— **D = 4.00**

$4.00 = \dfrac{1}{f}$ and $f = \dfrac{1}{4} = 0.25$ Thus, $f =$ **0.25 meter**, or **25 centimeters.**

EXERCISES

Find f, the focal length. Express answers to the nearest centimeter.

1. $D = 0.50$ **2.** $D = 4.50$ **3.** $D = 1.50$ **4.** $D = 0.1$

5. Find the focal length in centimeters of a 2.5 D lens.

6. Find the focal length to the nearest centimeter of a 4.25 lens.

4-3 More Angle Relationships

You can use supplementary interior angles on the same side of a transversal to prove that two lines are parallel.

Theorem 4-4	If two lines are cut by a transversal so that interior angles on the same side of the transversal are supplementary, then the lines are parallel.

EXAMPLE 1   Prove Theorem 4-4.

Given: Lines r and s cut by transversal t.

Angle 1 and angle 2 are supplementary.

Prove: $r \parallel s$

Proof:

Statements	Reasons
1. $\angle 1$ and $\angle 2$ are supplementary.	1. Given
2. $\angle 1$ and $\angle 3$ are a linear pair.	2. Definition of linear pair
3. $\angle 1$ and $\angle 3$ are supplementary.	3. (2). If two angles form a linear pair, then they are supplementary.
4. $\angle 2 \cong \angle 3$	4. (1), (3). If two angles are supplements of the same angle, then they are congruent.
5. $r \parallel s$	5. (4). If two lines are cut by a transversal so that alternate interior angles are congruent, then the lines are parallel.

If you know that two lines are parallel, you can prove that interior angles on the same side of the transversal are supplementary.

Theorem 4-5	If two parallel lines are cut by a transversal, then interior angles on the same side of the transversal are supplementary.

You are asked to prove Theorem 4-5 in the Written Exercises. Theorems 4-4 and 4-5 are converses of each other. Thus, they can be written as a biconditional.

Several theorems relate to parallel and perpendicular lines in a plane.

Theorem 4–6 | In a plane, if two lines are both perpendicular to a third line, then the lines are parallel.

EXAMPLE 2 Prove Theorem 4–6.

Given: $m \perp t$; $k \perp t$

Prove: $m \parallel k$

Proof:

Statements	Reasons
1. $m \perp t$; $k \perp t$	1. Given
2. Angles 1 and 2 are right angles.	2. (1). Perpendicular lines form four right angles.
3. $\angle 1 \cong \angle 2$	3. (2). All right angles are congruent.
4. Angles 1 and 2 are alternate interior angles.	4. (1). Definition of alternate interior angles
5. $k \parallel m$	5. (4). If two lines are cut by a transversal so that alternate interior angles are congruent, then the lines are parallel.

Example 3 also deals with parallel and perpendicular lines.

EXAMPLE 3 In the figure at the right, $n \parallel p$ and $n \perp q$. Explain why $q \perp p$.

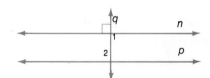

Solution:

$\angle 1 \cong \angle 2$	← If two parallel lines are cut by a transversal, then alternate interior angles are congruent.
$m\angle 1 = m\angle 2$	← Congruent angles have equal measures.
$m\angle 1 = 90$	← Perpendicular lines form four right angles.
$m\angle 2 = 90$	← Substitution property
$q \perp p$	← Definition of perpendicular lines

The relationship in Example 3 can be expressed as a theorem. You are asked to prove this theorem in the Written Exercises.

Theorem 4–7 | In a plane, if a line is perpendicular to one of two parallel lines, then it is perpendicular to the other line also.

CLASSROOM EXERCISES

In Exercises 1–4, line $s \parallel$ line t.

1. If $m\angle 2 = 63$, find $m\angle 3$.
2. If $m\angle 4 = 87$, find $m\angle 6$.
3. If $m\angle 6 = 3m\angle 7$, find $m\angle 6$ and $m\angle 7$.
4. If $m\angle 6 = x$, find $m\angle 7$ in terms of x.

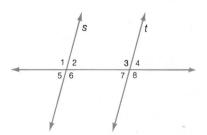

In Exercises 5–6, state the theorem that justifies each conclusion.

5. **Given:** $\overline{AB} \perp \overline{BD}; \overline{DE} \perp \overline{BD}$

   Conclusion: $\overline{AB} \parallel \overline{DE}$

6. **Given:** $\overline{AB} \parallel \overline{DE}; \overline{BD} \perp \overline{AB}$

   Conclusion: $\overline{BD} \perp \overline{DE}$

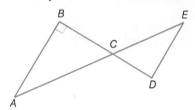

7. Write Theorems 4–4 and 4–5 as a biconditional.

WRITTEN EXERCISES

A   In Exercises 1–9, use the given information to complete the conclusion. Name the definition or theorem that justifies each conclusion.

1. **Given:** $m\angle 3 = 125; m\angle 6 = 55$

   Conclusion: __?__ $\parallel$ __?__

2. **Given:** $s \parallel y; m\angle 4 = 70$

   Conclusion: $m\angle 5 =$ __?__

3. **Given:** $\angle DCB$ and $\angle B$ are supplementary.

   Conclusion: __?__ $\parallel$ __?__

4. **Given:** $\angle ECA$ and $\angle A$ are supplementary.

   Conclusion: __?__ $\parallel$ __?__

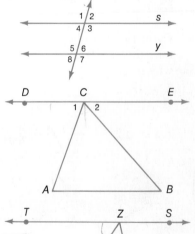

5. **Given:** $\overleftrightarrow{TS} \parallel \overleftrightarrow{XY}$

   Conclusions: a. $\angle XYZ$ and $\angle$ __?__ are alternate interior angles.

   b. $\angle$ __?__ and $\angle XYZ$ are interior angles on the same side of the transversal.

   c. $\angle$ __?__ and $\angle TZX$ are supplementary.

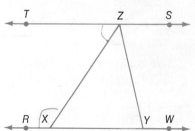

6. Given: $\overleftrightarrow{DE} \parallel \overline{AB}$

   Conclusion: __?__ and ∠ __?__ are congruent alternate interior angles.

   (NOTE: Two answers are possible.)

7. Given: $\overleftrightarrow{DE} \parallel \overline{AB}$

   Conclusion: ∠A and ∠ __?__ are supplementary angles on the same side of the transversal.

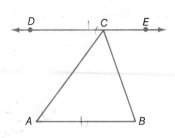

8. Given: $\overline{EF} \parallel \overline{HG}$; $\overline{EG} \perp \overline{HG}$

   Conclusion: $\overline{EG}$ __?__ $\overline{EF}$

9. Given: $\overline{EF} \perp \overline{EG}$; $\overline{HG} \perp \overline{EG}$

   Conclusion: $\overline{EF}$ __?__ $\overline{HG}$

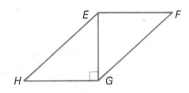

In Exercises 10–11, refer to the given figure and the given information to complete each conclusion.

10. Given: ∠G and ∠GMK are supplementary;
    m∠1 = 58; m∠2 = 48

    Conclusions: m∠KMH = __?__
    m∠H = __?__

11. Given: ∠G and ∠GMK are supplementary;
    m∠1 = 58; m∠2 = 48

    Conclusions: m∠KMG = __?__
    m∠G = __?__

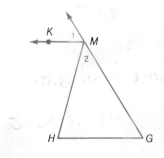

B

12. Supply the missing reasons in this proof.

    Given: ∠A and ∠B are supplementary.

    Prove: ∠C and ∠2 are supplementary.

Statements	Reasons
1. ∠A and ∠B are supplementary.	1. Given
2. $\overrightarrow{AD} \parallel \overline{BC}$	2. (1). __?__
3. ∠C ≅ ∠1	3. (2). __?__
4. ∠1 and ∠2 are a linear pair.	4. __?__
5. m∠1 + m∠2 = 180	5. (4). __?__
6. m∠C = m∠1	6. (3). __?__
7. m∠C + m∠2 = 180	7. (5), (6). __?__
8. ∠C and ∠2 are supplementary.	8. (7). __?__

13. Complete the proof of Theorem 4–5.

Given: $r \parallel s$

Prove: $\angle 1$ and $\angle 3$ are supplementary.

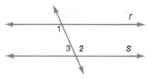

Statements	Reasons
1. $r \parallel s$	1. ____?____
2. $\angle 1 \cong \angle 2$	2. (1). __?__
3. $\angle 2$ and $\angle 3$ form a linear pair.	3. ____?____
4. $m\angle 2 + m\angle 3 = 180$	4. (3). __?__
5. $m\angle 1 = m\angle 2$	5. (2). __?__
6. $m\angle 1 + m\angle 3 = 180$	6. (4), (5). __?__
7. $\angle 1$ and $\angle 3$ are supplementary.	7. (6). __?__

In Exercises 14–15, refer to $\triangle ABC$ at the right.

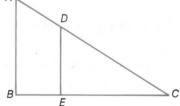

14. Given: $\overline{DE} \perp \overline{BC}$; $m\angle B = 90$

Prove: $\overline{AB} \parallel \overline{DE}$

15. Given: $\angle B$ is a right angle; $\overline{AB} \parallel \overline{DE}$.

Prove: $\triangle DEC$ is a right triangle.

16. In the figure at the right, $m\angle 1 = 3x + 16$, $m\angle 2 = 2x - 11$ and $k \parallel n$. Find x.

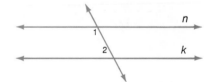

17. Prove Theorem 4–7.
(HINT: See Example 3.)

C   In Exercises 18–20, write a proof for each statement.

18. If two parallel lines are cut by a transversal, then the bisectors of two alternate interior angles are parallel.

19. Given that two lines are cut by a transversal, two alternate exterior angles are not congruent if and only if the two lines are not parallel.

20. If the bisector of an exterior angle at one vertex of a triangle is parallel to the side opposite the vertex, the triangle is isosceles.

21. Given: $\angle THP$ and $\angle HPT$ are complementary;
$\overrightarrow{HT}$ bisects $\angle JHP$;
$\overrightarrow{PT}$ bisects $\angle HPR$.

Prove: $\overrightarrow{HJ} \parallel \overrightarrow{PR}$

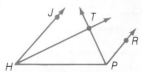

In Exercises 1–6, describe each pair of angles as alternate interior, alternate exterior, or interior angles on the same side of a transversal. *(Pages 156–158)*

1. $\angle 1$ and $\angle 4$
2. $\angle 3$ and $\angle 8$
3. $\angle 6$ and $\angle 7$
4. $\angle 4$ and $\angle 9$
5. $\angle 1$ and $\angle 8$
6. $\angle 2$ and $\angle 5$

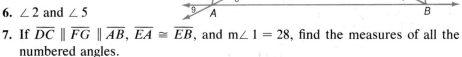

7. If $\overline{DC} \parallel \overline{FG} \parallel \overline{AB}$, $\overline{EA} \cong \overline{EB}$, and m$\angle 1 = 28$, find the measures of all the numbered angles.

4–4   Corresponding Angles and Parallel Lines

In each figure below, $\angle 1$ and $\angle 2$ are *corresponding angles*.

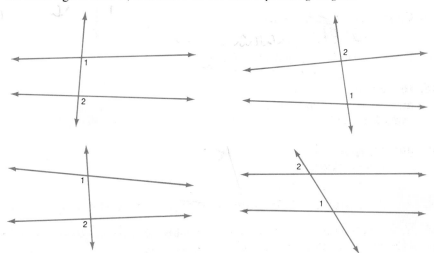

Corresponding angles are two angles in "corresponding" positions relative to the two lines and the transversal.

EXAMPLE 1   Use the given figure to name the corresponding angle for each angle in the table.

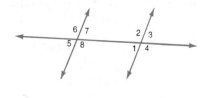

Solution:

Angle	$\angle 1$	$\angle 2$	$\angle 7$	$\angle 8$
Corresponding angle	$\angle 5$	$\angle 6$	$\angle 3$	$\angle 4$

Corresponding angles can be used to show that lines are parallel.

| Theorem 4–8 | If two lines are cut by a transversal so that corresponding angles are congruent, then the lines are parallel. |

EXAMPLE 2 Prove Theorem 4–8.

Given: Lines r and s cut by transversal t; $\angle 1 \cong \angle 2$.

Prove: $r \parallel s$

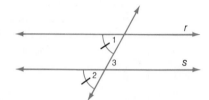

Proof:

Statements	Reasons
1. Lines r and s cut by transversal t; $\angle 1 \cong \angle 2$.	1. Given
2. $\angle 2 \cong \angle 3$	2. (1). Vertical angles are congruent.
3. $\angle 1 \cong \angle 3$	3. (1), (2). Transitive Property of Congruence
4. $r \parallel s$	4. (3). If two lines are cut by a transversal so that alternate interior angles are congruent, then the lines are parallel.

The converse of Theorem 4–8 is also a theorem. Thus, Theorems 4–8 and 4–9 can be written as a biconditional.

| Theorem 4–9 | If two parallel lines are cut by a transversal, then corresponding angles are congruent. |

You are asked to prove Theorem 4–9 in the Written Exercises.

Parallel lines can be used to determine a plane.

| Theorem 4–10 | Two parallel lines determine exactly one plane. |

Theorem 4–11 can be proved for coplanar lines and for three or more lines that are not all coplanar.

| Theorem 4–11 | Two distinct lines parallel to the same line are parallel to each other. |

EXAMPLE 3 Write the *Given* and the *Prove*, draw and label a figure, and write a *Plan of Proof* for Theorem 4–11. Assume that the lines are coplanar.

Solution:

Given: $a \parallel c; b \parallel c$

Prove: $a \parallel b$

Plan: If lines a, b, and c are co-planar, draw transversal t. Prove that $\angle 1 \cong \angle 2$. Then use Theorem 4–8.

CLASSROOM EXERCISES

In Exercises 1–4, refer to the figure at the right to complete the table.

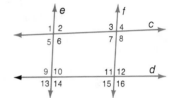

Lines	Transversal	Alternate Interior Angles	Corresponding Angles
1. c, d	e	?	?
2. c, d	f	?	?
3. e, f	c	?	?
4. e, f	d	?	?

5. Write Theorems 4–8 and 4–9 as a biconditional.

WRITTEN EXERCISES

A

1. Name five pairs of corresponding angles in Figure 1.

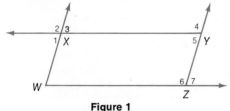

Figure 1

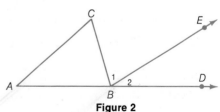

Figure 2

Use Figure 2 to answer Exercises 2–3.

2. For $\overline{AC}$, $\overrightarrow{BE}$ and transversal $\overrightarrow{AD}$, name the corresponding angles.

3. For $\overline{AC}$, $\overrightarrow{BE}$ and transversal $\overline{CB}$, name the alternate interior angles.

In Exercises 4–12, use the given information to complete the conclusion. Name the theorem or postulate that gives the reason for each answer.

Use Figure 1 (see page 175) for Exercises 4–5 and Figure 2 (see page 175) for Exercises 6–8.

4. Given: $\angle W \cong \angle 3$

Conclusion: __?__ || __?__

5. Given: $\angle 1 \cong \angle 5$

Conclusion: __?__ || __?__

6. Given: $\angle A \cong \angle 2$

Conclusion: __?__ || __?__

7. Given: $\angle 1 \cong \angle C$

Conclusion: __?__ || __?__

8. Given: $\overleftrightarrow{AC} \parallel \overleftrightarrow{BE}$; transversal $\overleftrightarrow{AD}$

Conclusion: $\angle$ __?__ $\cong \angle$ __?__

9. Given: $\overline{VP} \parallel \overline{RM}$

Conclusions: $\angle VPM \cong \angle$ __?__

$\angle 5 \cong \angle$ __?__

$\angle 1 \cong \angle$ __?__

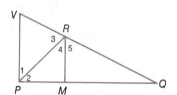

10. Given: $\overline{FD} \parallel \overline{AC}$; $\overline{EF} \parallel \overline{CB}$; m$\angle BDF = 110$; m$\angle A = 40$

Conclusions: m$\angle C =$ __?__

m$\angle AEF =$ __?__

m$\angle 7 =$ __?__

m$\angle 8 =$ __?__

m$\angle B =$ __?__

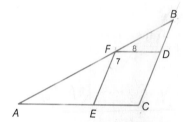

11. Given: $\overline{AB} \parallel \overline{XY}$; $\overline{CD} \parallel \overline{XY}$

Conclusion: __?__ || __?__

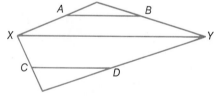

12. Given: $\overline{LM} \parallel \overline{KJ}$; $\overline{LM} \parallel \overline{GH}$

Conclusion: __?__ || __?__

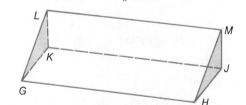

B

13. Complete the proof.

Given: $\overline{ZU} \parallel \overline{WX}$; $\angle 1 \cong \angle 2$ Prove: $\overline{ZW} \cong \overline{ZX}$

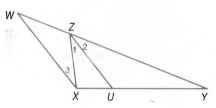

Statements	Reasons
1. $\angle 1 \cong \angle 2$; $\overline{ZU} \parallel \overline{WX}$	1. Given
2. $\angle 1 \cong \angle 3$	2. (1). __?__
3. __?__	3. (1), (2). __?__
4. $\angle 2 \cong \angle W$	4. __?__
5. $\angle 3 \cong \angle W$	5. __?__
6. __?__	6. __?__

14. Complete the proof. Refer to the figure for Exercise 13.

Given: $\overline{ZU}$ bisects $\angle XZY$; $\angle 1 \cong \angle W$
Prove: $\overline{ZU} \parallel \overline{WX}$

Statements	Reasons
1. $\overline{ZU}$ bisects $\angle XZY$.	1. __?__
2. $\angle$ __?__ $\cong \angle$ __?__	2. (1). __?__
3. $\angle 1 \cong \angle$ __?__	3. Given
4. $\angle 2 \cong \angle$ __?__	4. (2), (3). __?__
5. __?__	5. (4). __?__

In Exercises 15–16, line $r \parallel$ line s. Find x.

15.

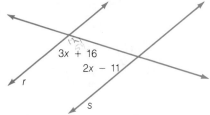

$3x + 16$
$2x - 11$

16.

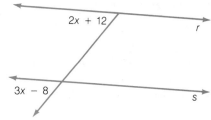

$2x + 12$
$3x - 8$

17. Given: Angle E and angle B
are supplementary;
$m\angle B = m\angle x$

Prove: $\overrightarrow{EF} \parallel \overrightarrow{BC}$

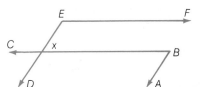

18. Use the given information and the
given figure to prove Theorem 4–9.

Given: $k \parallel q$

Prove: $\angle 1 \cong \angle 2$

Plan: Vertical angles 1 and 3 are
congruent. Alternate interior
angles 2 and 3 are congruent
by Theorem 4–3, so $\angle 1 \cong \angle 2$
by transitivity of congruence.

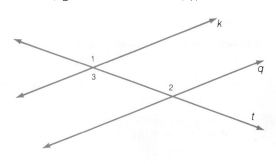

19. Prove Theorem 4–11 for three coplanar lines. (HINT: Follow the plan for
Example 3 on page 175.)

20. In $\triangle ABC$ at the right, $\angle A \cong \angle 1$.
Prove that $\angle B \cong \angle 2$.

(HINT: First use Theorem 4–8. Then
use Theorem 4–9.)

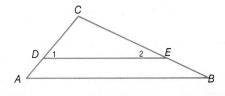

21. In the figure at the left below, $\overline{FD} \parallel \overline{AC}$ and $\overline{EF} \parallel \overline{CB}$. Prove that $\angle C \cong \angle EFD$ and that $\angle CEF \cong \angle FDC$.

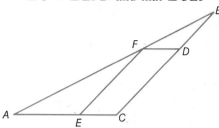
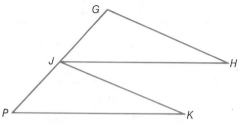

22. In the figure at the right above, J is the midpoint of $\overline{GP}$, $\overline{GH} \parallel \overline{JK}$ and $\overline{PK} \parallel \overline{JH}$. Prove that $\overline{JH} \cong \overline{PK}$.

In the figures at the right, $\overleftrightarrow{BD} \parallel \overrightarrow{EG}$, $\overrightarrow{AC} \parallel \overrightarrow{EF}$, and all points are coplanar.

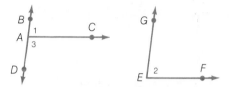

23. Prove that $\angle 1 \cong \angle 2$.

24. Prove that $m\angle 2 + m\angle 3 = 180$.

In the figures at the right, $\overleftrightarrow{BD} \perp \overrightarrow{EG}$, $\overrightarrow{AC} \perp \overrightarrow{EF}$, $\overleftrightarrow{BD} \parallel \overrightarrow{EF}$, and all points are coplanar.

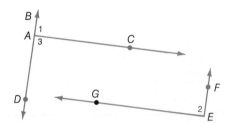

25. Prove that $\angle 1 \cong \angle 2$.

26. Prove that $m\angle 2 + m\angle 3 = 180$.

27. Prove: If two sides of a quadrilateral are parallel and congruent, then the diagonals of the quadrilateral bisect each other.

28. Prove: A triangle is isosceles if the bisector of one exterior angle is parallel to the opposite side of the triangle.

29. Prove: Two lines cut by a transversal are not parallel if and only if the corresponding angles are not congruent.

30. In quadrilateral $ABCD$, $\overline{AB} \parallel \overline{DC}$, E is a point on $\overline{CD}$, and F is a point on $\overline{AB}$. $\overline{EA}$ bisects $\angle DEF$ and $\overline{EB}$ bisects $\angle CEF$. Prove that $\overline{EF}$ is a median of $\triangle ABE$.

31. In the figure at the right, $\overleftrightarrow{AX} \parallel \overleftrightarrow{CY}$. Prove $m\angle B = m\angle XAB + m\angle YCB$.

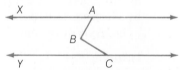

32. Prove Theorem 4–10.

Plan: By definition, parallel lines are coplanar. You must prove that they lie in *exactly* one plane. In the figure, line k is parallel to line m. Line m contains at least two points, A and B. Then line k and point A determine exactly one plane.

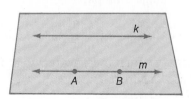

APPLICATIONS

USING PARALLEL LINES

These exercises apply geometric concepts studied in Sections 4–1 through 4–4.

A

1. In this parking lot, line segments l, m, n, p, q, and r each make a 60°-angle with the center curb, c. Explain why $l \parallel m \parallel n \parallel p \parallel q \parallel r$.

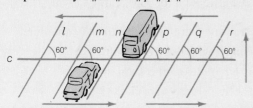

2. In the portions of the stairway shown below, $\overline{CD} \parallel \overline{AB}$ and $\overline{EF} \parallel \overline{AB}$. Explain why $\overline{CD} \parallel \overline{EF}$.

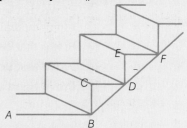

3. Explain why planes A and B are flying in parallel flight paths.

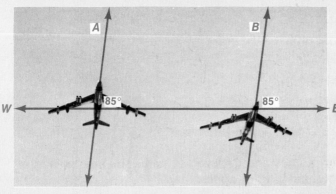

4. If the submarine continues on the same course at a depth of 30 meters below sea level, explain why the travel paths of the ship and the submarine are not parallel.

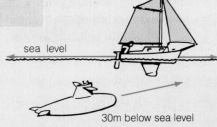

B

5. A real-estate developer decides to form parcels of land by constructing boundary lines parallel to the highway bordering side AC. If m$\angle ACD = 115$, find m$\angle CEF$ and m$\angle EGH$.

6. In the figure for Exercise 5, if $\overline{CA} \perp \overline{AB}$ and $\overline{DB} \perp \overline{AB}$, how are $\overline{CA}$ and $\overline{DB}$ related?

7. In the figure for Exercise 5, if $\overline{CA} \perp \overline{AB}$, $\overline{DB} \perp \overline{AB}$, and m$\angle ACD = 115$, find m$\angle BDC$.

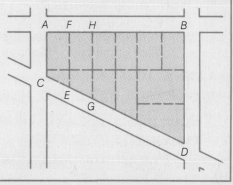

SUMMARY: Aids in Proof

The following summary lists ways of proving lines parallel that you have studied up to this point. The summary will help you to plan and write proofs related to parallel lines.

Summary

Ways of Proving Lines Parallel

1. Prove that alternate interior angles are congruent.
2. Prove that interior angles on the same side of the transversal are supplementary.
3. Prove that two lines are both perpendicular to the same line.
4. Prove that corresponding angles are congruent.
5. Prove that two lines are parallel to the same line.

Review

Use the figure at the right for Exercises 1–3. *(Section 4–1)*

1. ∠ _?_ is an exterior angle of △ *BCD*.

2. ∠2 is an exterior angle of △ _?_ .

3. m∠ 2 > m∠ _?_ and m∠ _?_ .

For each given pair of lines and transversal, name the interior angles, exterior angles, alternate interior angles, and alternate exterior angles. *(Section 4–1)*

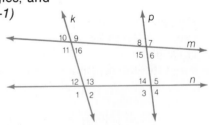

4. Lines *k* and *p*, transversal *m*

5. Lines *k* and *p*, transversal *n*

6. Lines *m* and *n*, transversal *k*

7. Lines *m* and *n*, transversal *p*

In Exercises 8–10, use the given information and figure to complete each conclusion. *(Section 4–2)*

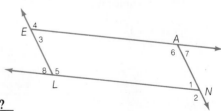

8. **Given:** ∠2 ≅ ∠5
   Conclusion: _?_ ‖ _?_

9. **Given:** m∠3 = m∠8
   Conclusion: _?_ ‖ _?_

10. **Given:** ∠1 ≅ ∠7   **Conclusion:** _?_ ‖ _?_

In Exercises 11–14, use the given information to complete the conclusion. State the definition or theorem that justifies each conclusion. *(Section 4–3)*

11. Given: $m\angle 4 = 110$; $m\angle 5 = 70$

  Conclusion: ___?___ ∥ ___?___

12. Given: $p \parallel q$; $m\angle 3 = 69$

  Conclusion: $m\angle 6 =$ ___?___

13. Given: $\overline{OP} \parallel \overline{MN}$; $\overline{ON} \perp \overline{OP}$

  Conclusion: $\overline{ON}$ ___?___ $\overline{MN}$

14. Given: $\overline{ON} \perp \overline{OP}$; $m\angle N = 90$

  Conclusion: $\overline{MN}$ ___?___ $\overline{OP}$

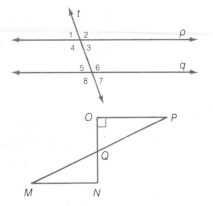

15. In the figure below, $m\angle 1 = 3x - 10$, $m\angle 2 = 4x + 50$, and $a \parallel b$. Find x. *(Section 4–3)*

16. Name 7 pairs of corresponding angles in the figure below. *(Section 4–4)*

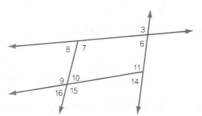

17. Complete the following proof. *(Section 4–4)*

  Given: $a \parallel b$; $c \parallel d$ **Prove:** $\angle 1 \cong \angle 2$

Statements	Reasons
1. $a \parallel b$	1. ___?___
2. $\angle 1 \cong \angle 3$	2. (1). ___?___
3. $c \parallel d$	3. ___?___
4. $\angle 2 \cong \angle$ ___?___	4. (3). ___?___
5. ___?___	5. (2), (4). ___?___

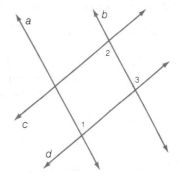

———— **ALGEBRA REVIEW CAPSULE FOR SECTION 4–5** ————

Solve and check each equation. *(Page 28)*

1. $x + x + 2x + 20 = 180$

2. $x + x + 4x - 30 = 180$

3. $x + 5x + 3x + 30 = 180$

4. $2x - 20 + x + 3x - 10 = 180$

5. $x + x + 5x + 40 = 180$

6. $6x + 3x - 50 + x = 180$

7. $2x - 12 + x + 10 + 3x - 40 = 180$

8. $x - 17 + 2x + 23 + 5x - 10 = 180$

9. $3x + 5x + 4x + 60 = 180$

10. $5x + 10 + 2x - 40 + 3x = 180$

4-5 Triangle–Sum Theorem

You have often used the Triangle–Sum Theorem when finding the measures of the angles of a triangle. Now you can prove the theorem.

Theorem 4–12	**Triangle–Sum Theorem** The sum of the measures of the angles of a triangle is 180.

EXAMPLE 1 Prove the Triangle–Sum Theorem.

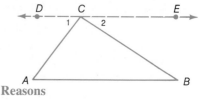

Given: Triangle ABC

Prove: $m\angle A + m\angle B + m\angle ACB = 180$

Proof:

Statements	Reasons
1. Through point C, draw $\overleftrightarrow{DE}$ parallel to $\overline{AB}$.	1. Postulate 15, page 162
2. $\angle 1$ and $\angle ACE$ are a linear pair.	2. Definition of a linear pair
3. $m\angle 1 + m\angle ACE = 180$	3. (2). If two angles form a linear pair, then they are supplementary.
4. $m\angle 2 + m\angle ACB = m\angle ACE$	4. Definition of betweenness of rays
5. $m\angle 1 + m\angle 2 + m\angle ACB = 180$	5. (3), (4). Substitution property
6. $\angle A \cong \angle 1, \angle B \cong \angle 2$	6. (1). If parallel lines are cut by a transversal, alternate interior angles are congruent.
7. $m\angle A = m\angle 1, m\angle B = m\angle 2$	7. (6). Congruent angles have equal measures.
8. $m\angle A + m\angle B + m\angle ACB = 180$	8. (5), (7). Substitution property

You can use the Triangle–Sum Theorem to find the measures of angles in a triangle.

EXAMPLE 2 Find the measure of angle A.

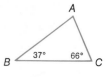

Solution:
$$37 + 66 + m\angle A = 180 \longleftarrow \text{ Triangle–Sum Theorem}$$
$$103 + m\angle A = 180 \longleftarrow \text{ Solve for } m\angle A.$$
$$m\angle A = 180 - 103$$
$$m\angle A = 77$$

The Triangle-Sum Theorem can also be used when the measures of the angles of a triangle are expressed in terms of a variable, such as x.

EXAMPLE 3 Find the measure of each angle of $\triangle RST$.

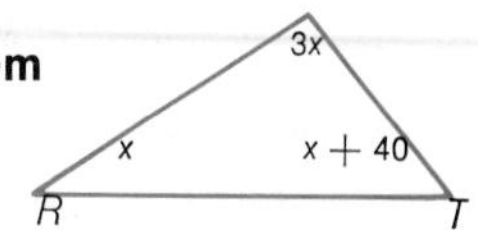

Solution:
$$x + 3x + x + 40 = 180 \longleftarrow \text{Triangle-Sum Theorem}$$
$$5x + 40 = 180 \longleftarrow \text{Solve for } x.$$
$$5x = 140$$
$$x = 28 \longleftarrow \text{Don't forget to find 3x and x + 40.}$$
$$3x = 84$$
$$x + 40 = 68$$

Check: $28 + 84 + 68 \overset{?}{=} 180$ Yes ✓

Corollary 4–13 follows from the Triangle-Sum Theorem.

Corollary 4–13	If two angles of one triangle are congruent to two angles of another triangle, then the third angles are congruent.

Another corollary of the Triangle-Sum Theorem concerns the number of right angles or obtuse angles in a triangle. You are asked to prove both corollaries in the Written Exercises.

Corollary 4–14	A triangle can have no more than one right angle or one obtuse angle.

CLASSROOM EXERCISES

In Exercises 1–6, find m∠ C.

1. In $\triangle ABC$, m∠ $A = 60$, m∠ $B = 70$.

2. In $\triangle ABC$, m∠ $A = 120$, m∠ $B = 34$.

3. $\triangle ABC$ is equilateral.

4. In $\triangle ABC$, m∠ $B = 90$, m∠ $A = 25$.

5. In $\triangle ABC$, m∠ $A = x$, m∠ $B = 2x$, m∠ $C = 3x$.

6. In $\triangle ABC$, $\overline{AB} \cong \overline{AC}$, m∠ $A = 50$.

In Exercises 7 and 8, name the corollary that justifies the conclusion that ∠ 1 ≅ ∠ 2.

7.

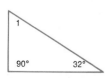

8.

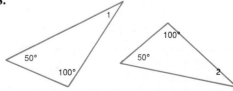

WRITTEN EXERCISES

A   In Exercises 1–7, use the given information and the given figure to complete the conclusion(s).

1. **Given:** $AC = BC$; m$\angle A = 50$
   Conclusion: m$\angle C = $ __?__

2. **Given:** $AC = BC$; m$\angle C = 40$
   Conclusions: m$\angle A = $ __?__
                 m$\angle B = $ __?__

3. **Given:** $AB = BC$; m$\angle A = 60$
   Conclusions: m$\angle C = $ __?__
                 m$\angle B = $ __?__

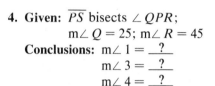

4. **Given:** $\overline{PS}$ bisects $\angle QPR$;
          m$\angle Q = 25$; m$\angle R = 45$
   Conclusions: m$\angle 1 = $ __?__
                 m$\angle 3 = $ __?__
                 m$\angle 4 = $ __?__

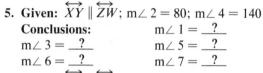

5. **Given:** $\overleftrightarrow{XY} \parallel \overleftrightarrow{ZW}$; m$\angle 2 = 80$; m$\angle 4 = 140$
   Conclusions: m$\angle 1 = $ __?__
   m$\angle 3 = $ __?__   m$\angle 5 = $ __?__
   m$\angle 6 = $ __?__   m$\angle 7 = $ __?__

6. **Given:** $\overleftrightarrow{XY} \parallel \overleftrightarrow{ZW}$; m$\angle 2 = 70$; m$\angle 5 = 30$
   Conclusions: m$\angle 1 = $ __?__
   m$\angle 3 = $ __?__   m$\angle 4 = $ __?__
   m$\angle 6 = $ __?__   m$\angle 7 = $ __?__

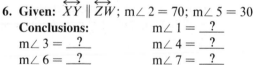

7. **Given:** $\angle ABC$ is a right angle;
          $\overline{BD} \perp \overline{AC}$; m$\angle 1 = 30$
   Conclusions: m$\angle 2 = $ __?__
                 m$\angle 3 = $ __?__
                 m$\angle 4 = $ __?__
                 m$\angle A = $ __?__   m$\angle C = $ __?__

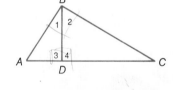

In Exercises 8–10, find m$\angle C$.

8.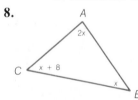

9.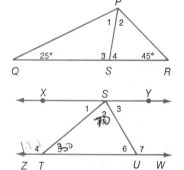

10.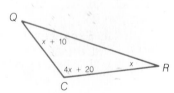

11. Find the measure of each angle of $\triangle ABC$ if m$\angle A = x$, m$\angle B = 3x + 12$, and m$\angle C = 2x + 40$.

12. Find the measure of each angle of $\triangle ABC$ if m$\angle A = 3x$, m$\angle B = 5x - 70$, and m$\angle C = 4x + 10$.

13. The measure of one acute angle of a right triangle is three times the measure of the other. Find the measure of each acute angle.

14. In a triangle, the measure of $\angle B$ is 35 more than the measure of $\angle A$. The measure of $\angle C$ is 5 less than the measure of $\angle A$. Find the measure of each angle of the triangle.

15. The measure of the vertex angle of an isosceles triangle is three times the measure of each base angle. Find the measure of each angle.

16. Each of the equal base angles of an isosceles triangle is 7 less than 4 times the vertex angle. Find the measure of each angle of the triangle.

17. Use Theorem 4–12 to find the sum of the measures of the angles of any quadrilateral. (HINT: Draw a diagonal.)

18. Complete this proof of Corollary 4–13.

Given: $\triangle ABC$ and $\triangle XYZ$;
$\angle A \cong \angle X$; $\angle C \cong \angle Z$

Prove: $\angle B \cong \angle Y$

Plan: By the Triangle–Sum Theorem, $m\angle A + m\angle B + m\angle C = 180$ and $m\angle X + m\angle Y + m\angle Z = 180$. Solve the first equation for $m\angle B$ and solve the second equation for $m\angle Y$. Then apply the Substitution property.

19. In triangles ABC and AED, $\angle 1 \cong \angle 2$. Prove that $\angle B \cong \angle E$. (HINT: $\angle A$ is an angle of both triangles. Use this fact and Corollary 4–13.)

20. Triangles FEJ and GHJ have right angles at E and H. Prove that the corresponding angles of the triangles are congruent.

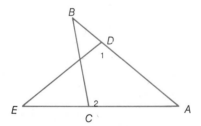

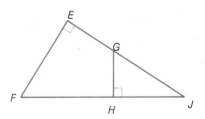

21. In $\triangle JKR$, $\overline{JP}$ is the altitude from J, and $\overline{KQ}$ is the altitude from K.

Prove that the corresponding angles of triangles RPJ and RQK are congruent.

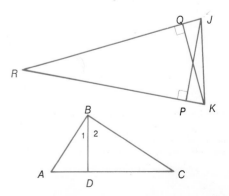

In $\triangle ABC$, $\angle ABC$ is a right angle, and $\overline{BD} \perp \overline{AC}$.

22. Prove that $\angle 1 \cong \angle C$.

23. Prove that $\angle 2 \cong \angle A$.

Use the figures below to explain how to write other proofs of the Triangle–Sum Theorem.

24. In △ABC, side AB is extended through D, and $\overrightarrow{BE} \parallel \overline{AC}$.

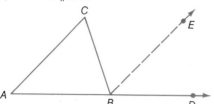

25. In △ABC, D is any point on $\overline{AB}$. $\overline{DE} \parallel \overline{BC}$ and $\overline{DF} \parallel \overline{AC}$.

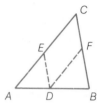

26. $\overline{PQ}$ is the base of isosceles triangle PQR, S is a point on $\overline{RQ}$, and $\overline{PS}$ bisects angle RPQ. If m∠R = 52, find m∠PSQ.

Ⓒ

27. Prove Corollary 4–14. (HINT: Assume the triangle has more than one right angle. Show that this is not possible. Follow a similar procedure to show that a triangle cannot have more than one obtuse angle.)

28. In △ABC below, find x, the measure of the acute angle that is determined by the bisectors of the exterior angles at B and at C.

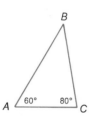
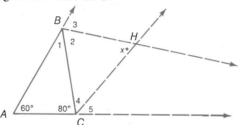

29. In the figure for Exercise 28, let m∠A = y. Express x in terms of y.

30. In Exercise 29, prove that ∠BHC must be acute.

31. In equilateral triangle ABC, E is on $\overline{BC}$ and point D is in the exterior of △ABC. △BDE is also equilateral. Prove that $\overline{AE} \cong \overline{CD}$.

32. **Given:** $\overline{GH} \perp \overline{HK}$; $\overline{GJ} \perp \overline{JH}$; $\overline{GK}$ bisects ∠JGH.

    Prove: $\overline{HK} \cong \overline{HL}$

Puzzle

In triangle XQW, $\overrightarrow{WT}$ bisects angle W. Side XQ is extended to R, and angle b is a right angle.

Find m∠a in terms of m∠x and m∠q.

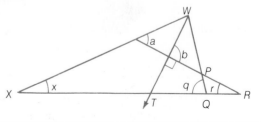

Refer to △ABC in Exercises 1–4.
(Pages 156–158)

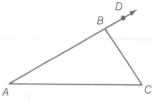

1. ∠DBC is called an __?__ angle of △ABC.
2. Which is greater: m∠DBC or m∠A?
3. Which is greater: m∠C or m∠DBC?
4. m∠DBC + m∠ABC = __?__. Therefore, they are __?__.

Tell whether each pair of triangles can be proved congruent by *SAS*, *ASA*, or *SSS*. If two ways are possible, write both. *(Pages 94–96, 100–102)*

5.
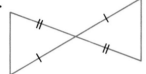

6.

7.
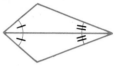

4-6 Triangle–Sum Corollaries

Since a right triangle is a triangle with one right angle and the measure of a right angle is 90, you can use the Triangle–Sum Theorem to show that the acute angles of a right triangle are complementary.

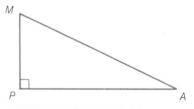

Corollary 4–15

The acute angles of a right triangle are complementary.

Corollary 4–16 also follows from the Triangle–Sum Theorem. You are asked to prove Corollaries 4–15 and 4–16 in the Written Exercises.

Corollary 4–16

The measure of each angle of an equilateral triangle is 60.

Corollary 4–17 gives you another way to prove triangles congruent.

Corollary 4–17

SAA **Corollary**
If two triangles have a side and two angles of one congruent respectively to a side and two angles of the other, then the triangles are congruent.

Corollary 4–18 uses the Triangle–Sum Theorem to relate an exterior angle of a triangle to its remote interior angles.

Corollary 4–18	**Exterior Angle–Sum Corollary for Triangles**
	The measure of one exterior angle of a triangle equals the sum of the measures of its remote interior angles.

EXAMPLE   Prove Corollary 4–18.

Given: $\triangle ABC$; $\angle 1$ is an exterior angle.

Prove: $m\angle 1 = m\angle A + m\angle B$

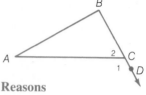

Proof:

Statements	Reasons
1. $\angle 1$ is an exterior angle of $\triangle ABC$.	1. Given
2. $\angle 1$ and $\angle 2$ form a linear pair.	2. (1). Definition of linear pair
3. $\angle 1$ and $\angle 2$ are supplementary.	3. (2). If two angles form a linear pair, then they are supplementary.
4. $m\angle 1 + m\angle 2 = 180$	4. (3). Definition of supplementary angles
5. $m\angle 1 = 180 - m\angle 2$	5. (4). Addition property of equations
6. $m\angle A + m\angle B + m\angle 2 = 180$	6. Triangle–Sum Theorem
7. $m\angle A + m\angle B = 180 - m\angle 2$	7. (6). Addition property of equations
8. $m\angle A + m\angle B = m\angle 1$	8. (5), (7). Substitution property

CLASSROOM EXERCISES

Write the letter of the response that completes each statement.

1. The acute angles of a right triangle are
   a. supplementary.   **b.** complementary.   **c.** a linear pair.

2. The measure of an exterior angle of an equilateral triangle is
   a. 60.   **b.** 90.   **c.** 120.

3. The measure of an exterior angle of one of the acute angles of a right triangle is always
   a. 90.   **b.** greater than 90.   **c.** less than 90.

4. If two right triangles have the hypotenuse and an acute angle of one congruent respectively to the hypotenuse and an acute angle of the other, then the triangles

  a. are always congruent.

  b. are sometimes congruent.

  c. are never congruent.

5. If triangles *ABC* and *DEF* are equilateral triangles, then

  a. their corresponding sides are congruent.

  b. their corresponding angles are congruent.

  c. triangles *ABC* and *DEF* are congruent.

For right triangle *BCA*, state the postulate, theorem, or corollary that justifies each statement. Let $x = m\angle B$, let $y = m\angle BAC$, and let $z = m\angle BAD$.

6. $x + y = 90$

7. $x + 90 = z$

8. $x + y + 90 = 180$

9. $y + z = 180$

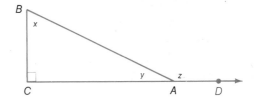

WRITTEN EXERCISES

A Name the pairs of complementary angles in the indicated right triangles.

1. $\triangle ACD$; $\triangle ABE$

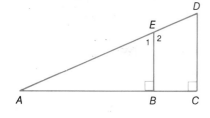

2. $\triangle FGJ$; $\triangle JGH$; $\triangle FJH$

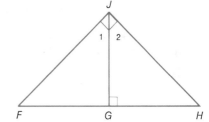

Use the information given to find the measures of the numbered angles.

3. $\overline{YZ} \parallel \overline{WX}$

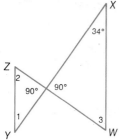

4. $\overline{BC} \parallel \overline{DE}$; $\overline{FD} \perp \overline{DE}$

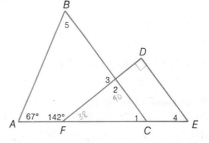

Triangles *ABC* and *DEF* are equilateral. Classify each of the following statements as *sometimes true*, *always true*, or *never true*.

5. $\angle A \cong \angle B$ **6.** $\angle C \cong \angle F$ **7.** $\triangle ABC \cong \triangle DEF$

Copy and complete this table. Refer to $\triangle PQR$.

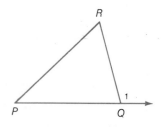

	$m\angle P$	$m\angle R$	$m\angle P + m\angle R$	$m\angle 1$
8.	70	75	?	?
9.	73	82	?	?
10.	Unknown	Unknown	112	?
11.	63	?	?	138
12.	?	87	161	?
13.	x	?	?	159
14.	Unknown	Unknown	?	143

15. Find the measure of each angle in an isosceles triangle if the measure of the exterior angle at the vertex is 124.

16. Point *O* is the center of the circle at the right, $\overline{OB} \cong \overline{OA}$, $\overline{BC}$ contains *O*, and $m\angle B = 35$. Find $m\angle COA$.

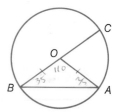

17. In circle *O*, $\overline{OB} \cong \overline{OA}$, $\overline{BC}$ contains *O*, and $m\angle COA = 100$. Find $m\angle B$.

In Exercises 18–22, the measures of the angles of $\triangle ABC$ are given in terms of *x*. Find the measure of each angle in each triangle. Give the names of those triangles that have special names.

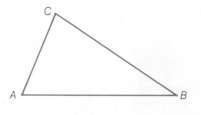

	$m\angle A$	$m\angle B$	$m\angle C$
18.	$3x$	$4x - 20$	$6x - 60$
19.	$4x - 18$	$8x - 6$	$5x$
20.	$5x$	$2x + 9$	$4x - 27$
21.	$4x + 8$	$5x - 2$	$3x - 6$
22.	$3x - 14$	$\frac{1}{2}x$	$2x + 18$

23. The measure of one exterior angle at the base of an isosceles triangle is 130. Find the measure of each angle of the triangle.

24. The measures of two exterior angles of a triangle are 80 and 130. Find the measure of each angle of the triangle and the measure of the exterior angle of the third angle.

25. Two of the angles of an equilateral triangle are bisected and the bisectors meet to form an obtuse angle. What is the measure of this obtuse angle?

26. In the figure at the right, $\overline{MS} \cong \overline{PR}$ and $\angle M \cong \angle P$. Prove that $\overline{SQ} \cong \overline{RQ}$. (HINT: Find another pair of congruent angles. Then prove $\triangle RQP \cong \triangle SQM$ by the SAA Corollary.)

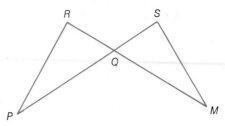

27. Prove Corollary 4–15. (HINT: Use the Triangle–Sum Theorem to prove that the sum of the measures of the acute angles of the triangle is 90.)

28. Prove Corollary 4–16.

29. Prove Corollary 4–17. (**Plan:** Use the Triangle–Sum Theorem to prove the third angle of one triangle congruent to the third angle of the second triangle. Then prove the triangles congruent by the ASA Postulate.

30. In the figure at the left below, $\triangle ABC$ is isosceles with base AB. $\overline{BX}$ bisects $\angle ABC$ and m$\angle C = 30$. Find m$\angle 1$ and m$\angle 2$.

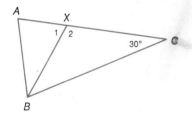

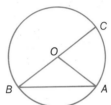

Use the circle at the right above for Exercises 31–32.
In the circle, $\overline{OA} \cong \overline{OB}$.

31. If m$\angle B = a$, find m$\angle COA$.

32. If m$\angle COA = a$, find m$\angle B$.

In Exercises 33–36, refer to $\triangle SPA$.

Given: $\triangle SNP$ is isosceles with base $\overline{NP}$.
$\triangle NAP$ is isosceles with base $\overline{PA}$.

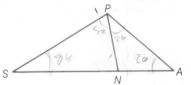

33. If m$\angle S = 20$, find m$\angle A$.

34. If m$\angle A = 26$, find m$\angle S$.

35. If m$\angle A = a$, express m$\angle S$ in terms of a.

36. Prove: m$\angle SPA = 3$m$\angle A$.

37. Refer to the figure at the right to express m$\angle 1$ in terms of m$\angle 2$, m$\angle 3$, and m$\angle 4$.

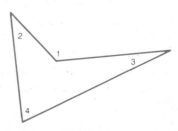

38. In the figure below, $\triangle ABC$ is isosceles with base $\overline{AB}$. $\overline{AD}$ bisects $\angle BAC$ and $\overline{BD}$ bisects $\angle ABC$. Express m$\angle D$ in terms of a, the measure of the exterior angle at A.

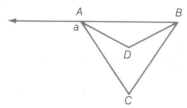

39. In the figure below, $\overline{XR}$ bisects $\angle YXS$, $\overline{YR}$ bisects $\angle XYS$, and m$\angle S = a$. Express the measure of $\angle XRY$ in terms of a.

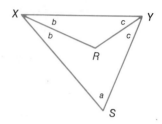

40. Find the measure of each angle of a triangle whose exterior angles have the measures $x + 39$, $2x + 27$, and $3x - 6$.

41. In the figure at the left below, $\overline{PH}$ bisects $\angle KPQ$ and $\overline{KH}$ bisects $\angle MKQ$. Express m$\angle Q$ in terms of m$\angle H$.

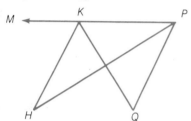

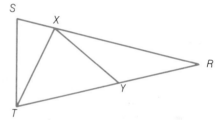

42. In the figure at the right above, triangles STR, XST, YTX, and RXY are isosceles with bases $\overline{ST}$, $\overline{XS}$, $\overline{YT}$, $\overline{RX}$, respectively. Find m$\angle S$.

43. $\triangle WVX$ is isosceles with base $\overline{WX}$. Y is on $\overline{VX}$ and Z is on $\overrightarrow{VW}$ such that W is between Z and V. $\overline{ZY}$ intersects $\overline{WX}$ in U and $ZW = UW$. Express m$\angle VYU$ in terms of m$\angle Z$.

ALGEBRA REVIEW CAPSULE FOR SECTION 4-7 ____

Evaluate each expression for the given value of the variable.
Exercise 1 is done for you.

1. $3(n + 70)$; $n = 24$
$3(24 + 70) = 3(94)$
$\qquad = 282$

2. $5a + 3(a - 6)$; $a = 2$

3. $2b - 60 + 3b$; $b = 25$

4. $\dfrac{16c - 32}{c}$; $c = 4$

5. $\dfrac{4(g + 6) + g}{g}$; $g = 8$

6. $14h - 2(h - 7)$; $h = 6$

7. $180 - (n - 7)$; $n = 34$

8. $\dfrac{3(d + 60)}{d}$; $d = 20$

9. $\dfrac{6(f - 16)}{f + 4}$; $f = 12$

10. $\dfrac{21(p + 6)}{p - 2}$; $p = 4$

4–7 Angles of a Polygon

To find the sum of the measures of the angles of polygons of four or more sides, first draw all possible diagonals from one vertex of the polygon. Then use the Triangle–Sum Theorem.

Polygon	Number of Sides	Number of Triangles	Sum of the Angle Measures
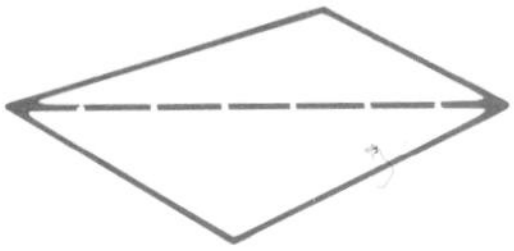	4	2	$2 \times 180 = 360$
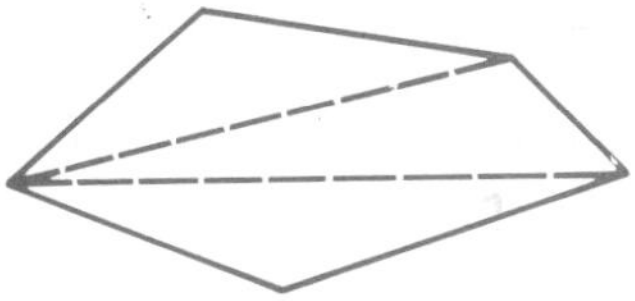	5	3	$3 \times 180 = 540$
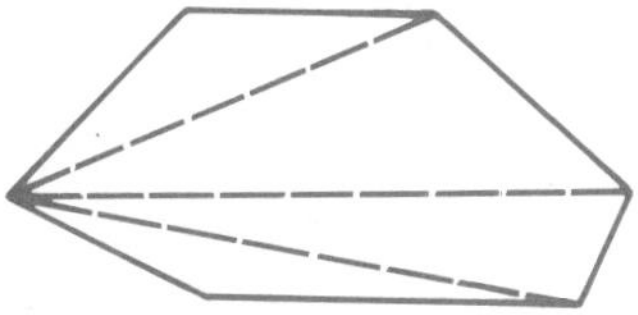	6	4	$4 \times 180 = 720$
⋮	⋮	⋮	⋮
	n	$(n-2)$	$(n-2)180$

The pattern in the table can be expressed as the Angle–Sum Theorem for Polygons.

Theorem 4–19

> ### Angle-Sum Theorem for Polygons
> The formula for the sum, S, of the measures of the angles of a polygon of n sides is
> $$S = (n-2)180.$$

EXAMPLE 1 Find the sum of the measures of the angles of a polygon of 30 sides.

Solution: Apply the Angle–Sum Theorem for Polygons.

$S = (n-2)180$ ⟵——— **Replace *n* with 30.**

$S = (30-2)180$

$S = 28 \cdot 180 = \mathbf{5040}$

If you know that all the angles of a polygon are congruent, then you can use Corollary 4–20 to find the measure of each angle.

Corollary 4–20

> If a polygon has n sides and if all of its angles are congruent, then the formula for the measure, a, of one of its angles is
>
> $$a = \frac{(n-2)180}{n}.$$

EXAMPLE 2 The sides of pentagon $ABCDE$ form five congruent angles. Find the measure of each angle.

Solution: Since the angles are congruent, apply Corollary 4–20.

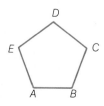

$a = \dfrac{(n-2)\,180}{n}$ ◄——— **Replace n with 5.**

$a = \dfrac{(5-2)\,180}{5}$

$a = \dfrac{3(180)}{5} = 108$ ◄——— **Measure of each angle**

EXAMPLE 3 The measure of each angle of a polygon is 165. Find the number of sides of the polygon.

Solution: Since the angles are congruent, apply Corollary 4–20.

$a = \dfrac{(n-2)\,180}{n}$ ◄——— **Replace a with 165.**

$165 = \dfrac{(n-2)\,180}{n}$ ◄——— **Multiply each side by n.**

$165n = (n-2)\,180$ ◄——— **Solve for n.**

$165n = 180n - 360$

$-15n = -360$

$n = 24$ ◄——— **Number of sides**

If a polygon has all of its angles congruent, it is **equiangular.** If it has all of its sides congruent, it is **equilateral.** If a polygon is both equiangular and equilateral, it is a **regular polygon.**

	Equiangular	Equilateral	Regular
Polygons	9 / 7 / 7 / 9	5, 5, 125°, 55°, 55°, 5, 5, 125°	5 / 5 / 5 / 5

CLASSROOM EXERCISES

In Exercises 1–5, classify each sentence as true, *T*, or false, *F*.
Give the reason for each answer.

1. An isosceles triangle is a regular polygon.

2. An equilateral triangle is a regular polygon.

3. The sum of the measures of the interior angles of a polygon with 9 sides is 1260.

4. The measure of an interior angle of a regular polygon of 18 sides is 140.

5. If the measure of an interior angle of a regular polygon is 174, then the polygon has 60 sides.

WRITTEN EXERCISES

A   In Exercises 1–5, find the sum of the measures of the interior angles of a polygon with the given number of sides.

1. 4   2. 8 *even 24*   3. 10   4. 5   5. 12

6. Would your answers to Exercise 1–5 change if the polygons were regular polygons? Explain.

7. Find the measure of one angle of a regular pentagon.

8. Find the measure of one angle of a regular hexagon.

In Exercises 9–13, find the measure of one angle of a regular polygon having the given number of sides.

9. 8   10. 10   11. 15   12. 9   13. 14

In Exercises 14–18, find the number of sides of a regular polygon if each angle has the following measure.

14. 156   15. 162   16. 168   17. 172   18. 140

In Exercises 19–23, the sum of the measures of the interior angles of a polygon is given. Find the number of sides for each polygon.

19. 900   20. 1980   21. 1260   22. 2700   23. 4860

24. If the sum of the measures of nine of the angles of a polygon having 10 sides is 1290, what is the measure of the tenth angle?

B

25. Show that the sum of the measures of the angles of a polygon cannot be 1350.

26. Show that the sum of the measures of the angles of a polygon cannot be 1700.

27. Show that one angle of a regular polygon cannot have a measure of 152.

28. Show that one angle of a regular polygon cannot have a measure of 148.

In Exercises 29–32, the measure of one angle of an equiangular polygon is given. Find the number of sides of the polygon.

29. $157\frac{1}{2}$ **30.** $174\frac{3}{8}$ **31.** $165\frac{3}{5}$ **32.** $172\frac{4}{5}$

C

33. If the ratio of the measures of the angles of a pentagon is 4:5:6:7:8, find the measure of each angle.

34. Find the measure of each angle of a pentagon if the ratio of the measures of the angles is 4:6:8:10:12.

CALCULATOR APPLICATIONS

Evaluating Formulas

A calculator will help you to evaluate formulas associated with the angles of a polygon.

EXAMPLE 1 Find the sum of the measures of the angles of a polygon of 7 sides.

SOLUTION Use $S = (n - 2)180$ to find S when $n = 7$.

7 $\boxed{-}$ 2 $\boxed{=}$ $\boxed{\times}$ 180 $\boxed{=}$ $\boxed{900.}$

EXAMPLE 2 A seven-sided polygon has seven congruent angles. Find the measure of each angle.

SOLUTION Use $a = \dfrac{(n - 2)180}{n}$ to find a when $n = 7$.

7 $\boxed{-}$ 2 $\boxed{=}$ $\boxed{\times}$ 180 $\boxed{\div}$ 7 $\boxed{=}$ $\boxed{128.57143}$

EXERCISES

Use a calculator to check your answers to Written Exercises 1–5 and 9–13.

_____ GEOMETRY REVIEW CAPSULE FOR SECTION 4-8 _____

Copy and complete this table. Refer to $\triangle RST$. *(Pages 156–158, 182–183)*

	$m\angle R$	$m\angle T$	$m\angle R + m\angle T$	$m\angle 1$
1.	68	73	?	?
2.	49	102	?	?
3.	Unknown	Unknown	121	?
4.	72	?	?	150
5.	?	59	123	?

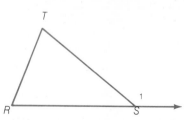

4-8 Exterior Angles of a Polygon

The **exterior angles** of a polygon are formed by extending each side in succession. The interior and exterior angle at each vertex of the polygon form a linear pair.

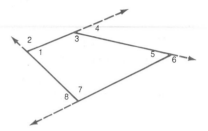

REMEMBER: A polygon has as many sides as vertices.

The table below shows that the sum of the exterior angles of a polygon, one at each vertex, does not depend on the number of sides. The sum is always 360.

Polygon	Sum of Linear Pairs	−	Sum of Interior Angles	=	Sum of Exterior Angles
Quadrilateral	$4 \cdot 180$	−	$(4-2)180$	=	$720 - 360$, or 360
Pentagon	$5 \cdot 180$	−	$(5-2)180$	=	$900 - 540$, or 360
Hexagon	$6 \cdot 180$	−	$(6-2)180$	=	$1080 - 720$, or 360
⋮	⋮		⋮		⋮
n sides	$n \cdot 180$	−	$(n-2)180$	=	$180n - 180n + 360$, or 360

Corollary 4–21

> **Exterior Angle–Sum Corollary for Polygons**
>
> The sum E of the measures of the exterior angles of a polygon made by extending each of its sides in succession is 360.

EXAMPLE 1 Find the measure of one exterior angle of a regular polygon of twelve sides.

Solution: Let e = the measure of one exterior angle.

$12e = 360$ ◄——— **There are 12 congruent angles.**

$e = 30$ ◄——— **Measure of each exterior angle**

The measure of an exterior angle of an equiangular polygon can be written as a formula.

Corollary 4–22

> If a polygon of n sides is equiangular, then the measure e of one of its exterior angles is
>
> $$e = \frac{360}{n}.$$

The formula, $e = \dfrac{360}{n}$, can be used to find the number of sides in an equiangular polygon if you know the measure of an interior angle.

EXAMPLE 2 Each interior angle of a regular polygon has a measure of 162 (a portion is shown below). Find the number of sides.

Solution: Let e = the measure of one exterior angle.

$162 + e = 180$ ←——— **There is a linear pair at each vertex.**

$e = 18$

By Corollary 4–22, $e = \dfrac{360}{n}$. ←——— **Replace e with 18.**

$18 = \dfrac{360}{n}$

$18n = 360$

$n = 20$ ←——— **Number of sides**

CLASSROOM EXERCISES

In Exercises 1–5, find each of the following.

1. The sum of the measures of an interior angle and the adjacent exterior angle of a polygon
2. The sum of the measures of the exterior angles of a polygon of seven sides
3. The sum of the measures of the exterior angles of a hexagon
4. The measure of one exterior angle of a regular pentagon
5. The measure of one exterior angle of a regular polygon of nine sides

WRITTEN EXERCISES

A

1. The measure of each interior angle of a regular polygon is 160. Find the measure of each exterior angle and the number of sides.

   In Exercises 2–7, find the sum of the measures of the exterior angles of a polygon with the given number of sides.

2. 3   **3.** 10   **4.** 16   **5.** 8   **6.** 29   **7.** n

   In Exercises 8–13, find the measure of each exterior angle of a regular polygon with the given number of sides.

8. 12   **9.** 24   **10.** 8   **11.** 10   **12.** 18   **13.** 15

   In Exercises 14–19, find the number of sides of a regular polygon if each exterior angle has the given measure

14. 30   **15.** $22\frac{1}{2}$ **16.** $13\frac{1}{3}$ **17.** 8   **18.** $14\frac{2}{5}$ **19.** $32\frac{8}{11}$

20. The sum of the measures of the interior angles of a regular polygon is ten times as great as the sum of the measures of its exterior angles. Find the number of sides.

21. In pentagon *ABCDE*, diagonals *BE* and *BD* are congruent, and triangles *ABE* and *CBD* are isosceles right triangles with m∠ *EAB* = m∠ *DCB* = 90. The measure of ∠ *ABC* is 15 more than the measure of ∠ *CDE*. Find m∠ *ABC*.

22. The sum of the measures of the interior angles of a regular polygon is 60 more than 30 times that of one of the exterior angles. Find the number of sides.

23. Can the measure of one exterior angle of a regular polygon be 14?

C

24. In a regular polygon, each interior angle is four times the measure of its exterior angle. How many sides does the polygon have?

25. If the ratio of the measures of the exterior angles of a triangle is 2:3:4, what is the ratio of the measures of the respective interior angles?

Review

In Exercises 1–3, find m∠ C. *(Section 4–5)*

1.
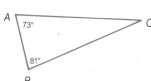

2.
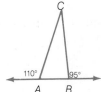

3.
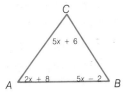

In Exercises 4–5, find the measure of each numbered angle. *(Section 4–6)*

4. $\overline{AB} \parallel \overline{CD}$

5. $\overline{FC} \parallel \overline{ED}$
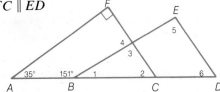

6. Find the sum of the measures of the angles of a polygon of 24 sides. *(Section 4–7)*

7. The measure of each angle of a polygon is 140. Find the number of sides of the polygon. *(Section 4–7)*

In Exercises 8–13, find the measure of each exterior angle of a regular polygon with the given number of sides. *(Section 4–8)*

8. 6   9. 14   10. 28   11. 20   12. 9   13. 16

APPLICATIONS

USING ANGLES IN POLYGONS

These Exercises apply geometric concepts studied in Sections 4–5 through 4–8.

A

1. Find m∠A, the angle this freight ramp makes with the ground.

2. Find the measures of the other two angles of the triangle formed by the coat hanger.

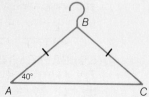

Each end of the gable roof below forms a triangle as shown.

3. Name the triangles formed by each side of the gable roof.

4. Are the triangles coplanar? Explain your answer.

5. Prove that the triangles are congruent.

6. If m∠BCF + m∠EFC = 180, what conclusion can be reached about $\overline{BC}$ and $\overline{EF}$?

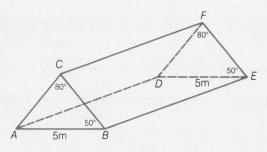

7. A farmer's market has the shape of a 12-sided polygon. Find the sum of the measures of the interior angles.

8. In Exercise 7, suppose that all the interior angles of the polygon are congruent. What is the measure of each interior angle?

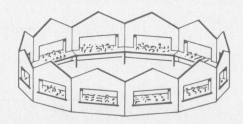

B

9. The distance of a ship from an object on land can be found by following this procedure. A crew member on the ship at point *T* measures the angle at *T* between the object on shore and the direction in which the ship is moving. When the ship reaches point *R* where m∠SRP = 2 m∠T, then *RS = RT*. (The distance *RT* is obtained from computer data.) Prove that *RS = RT*.

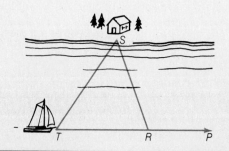

BASIC: ANGLES IN TRIANGLES AND POLYGONS

Problem: *Given the measure of the vertex angle of an isosceles triangle, compute the measure of each base angle.*

Program:
```
10 REM V = THE MEASURE OF THE VERTEX ANGLE
20 PRINT "ENTER THE MEASURE OF THE VERTEX ANGLE."
30 INPUT V
40 LET B = (180 - V)/2
50 PRINT "THE MEASURE OF EACH ANGLE IS ";B
60 PRINT "ANY MORE ANGLES (1 = YES, 0 = NO)";
70 INPUT X
80 IF X = 1 THEN 20
90 END
```

Analysis:

Statement 10: Statement 10 is a REM statement. REM stands for remark. This statement is not an instruction to the computer. It is inserted in the program to make the program easier for the user to understand. REM statements can be inserted anywhere in a program.

Statement 40: Statement 40 gives the formula for the base angle and stores the value it computes in memory location B.

EXERCISES

A   Run the program above for the following values.

1. 40   **2.** 70   **3.** 120   **4.** 32.5   **5.** 15.8   **6.** 92.3

B   Write a BASIC program for each problem.

7. Given the measure of a base angle of an isosceles triangle, compute the vertex angle.

8. Given the measure of two angles of a triangle, compute the third angle.

9. Given the measure of one acute angle in a right triangle, compute the other acute angle.

10. Given the number of sides of a polygon, compute the sum of the measures of its interior angles.

11. Given the sum of the measures of the interior angles of a polygon, compute the number of its sides.

12. Given the number of sides of a regular polygon, compute the measure of one of its interior angles.

Chapter Summary

IMPORTANT TERMS

Alternate angles (p. 158)

Alternate exterior angles (p. 158)

Alternate interior angles (p. 158)

Corresponding angles (p. 173)

Equiangular polygon (p. 194)

Equilateral polygon (p. 194)

Exterior angle
  of a polygon (p. 197)
  of a triangle (p. 156)

Interior angle (p. 158)

Parallel lines (p. 162)

Regular polygon (p. 194)

Remote interior angles (p. 156)

Skew lines (p. 162)

Transversal (p. 158)

IMPORTANT IDEAS

1. The measure of an exterior angle of a triangle is greater than either of its remote interior angles. It is equal to the sum of their measures.

2. Two distinct lines are parallel, are skew, or they intersect.

3. Through a point not on a given line, there is exactly one line parallel to the given line.

4. When two parallel lines are cut by a transversal:
   a. Alternate interior angles are congruent.
   b. Alternate exterior angles are congruent.
   c. Corresponding angles are congruent.
   d. Interior angles on the same side of the transversal are supplementary.
   e. If the transversal is perpendicular to one of the lines, it is perpendicular to the other also.

5. **Ways of proving lines parallel:**
   a. Prove alternate interior angles are congruent.
   b. Prove interior angles on the same side of the transversal are supplementary.
   c. Prove two lines are perpendicular to the same line.
   d. Prove corresponding angles are congruent.
   e. Prove two lines are parallel to the same line.

6. **Angles in polygons**
   a. The sum of the measures of the interior angles of a triangle is 180.
   b. The sum of the measures of the interior angles of a polygon with n sides is $(n - 2)180$.
   c. The sum of the measures of the exterior angles of a polygon made by extending each of its sides in succession is 360.

Chapter Objectives and Review

Objective: *To apply the Exterior Angle Inequality Theorem (Section 4–1)*

Refer to △ABC to complete each sentence.

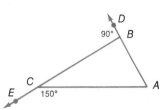

1. The two exterior angles shown in the figure are ∠DBC and ∠ ? .

2. For exterior angle DBC, the remote interior angles are ∠ ? and ∠ ? .

3. m∠ ? and m∠ ? are each less than 150.

4. m∠ ? and m∠ ? are each less than 90.

Objectives: *To identify the angles formed when two lines are cut by a transversal (Sections 4–1 and 4–4)*

In Exercises 5–9, refer to the figure to name the following.

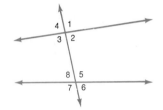

5. The interior angles

6. The exterior angles

7. Two pairs of alternate interior angles

8. Two pairs of alternate exterior angles

9. Four pairs of corresponding angles

Objective: *To recognize the angle relationships that occur when two parallel lines are cut by a transversal (Sections 4–2, 4–3, 4–4)*

10. In the figure at the left below, $\overline{XW} \parallel \overline{YZ}$. Name one pair of congruent angles.

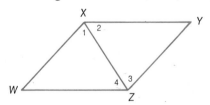

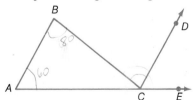

11. In the figure at the right above, $\overrightarrow{AB} \parallel \overrightarrow{CD}$, m∠A = 60, and m∠B = 80. Find m∠BCD.

12. In the figure at the right, $\overleftrightarrow{AB} \parallel \overleftrightarrow{CD}$; m∠4 = 73.

Find m∠5, m∠8, m∠6.

Give the reason for each answer.

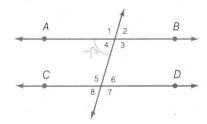

Objective: *To recognize the conditions under which lines may be proved parallel (Sections 4–2, 4–3, and 4–4)*

Use the figure at the right and the given information to state which segments are parallel.

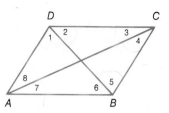

13. $\angle 1 \cong \angle 5$

14. $\angle 2 \cong \angle 6$

15. $\angle 7 \cong \angle 3$

16. $\angle 8 \cong \angle 4$

Complete each statement.

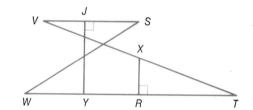

17. If $\overline{VS} \parallel \overline{WT}$ and $\overline{JY} \perp \overline{VS}$, then $\overline{JY}$ __?__ $\overline{WT}$.

18. If $\overline{RX} \perp \overline{WT}$ and $\overline{JY} \perp \overline{WT}$, then $\overline{RX}$ __?__ $\overline{JY}$.

19. Given: $\overline{EF} \perp \overline{EG}$; $\overline{HG} \perp \overline{EG}$

   Prove: $\overline{EF} \parallel \overline{HG}$

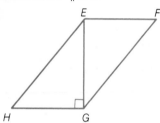

20. Given: $\overline{AD} \cong \overline{AE}$; $\angle ADE \cong \angle C$

   Prove: $\overline{DE} \parallel \overline{BC}$

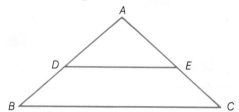

Objective: *To use the Triangle–Sum Theorem (Section 4–5)*

In the figures below, similar markings indicate congruent segments. Find the measures of the numbered angles.

21.

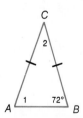

22.

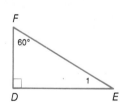

23.

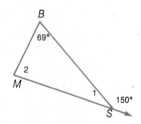

24. The measure of the vertex angle of an isosceles triangle is 82. Find the measure of each base angle.

25. In $\triangle ABC$, $m\angle A = 3x$, $m\angle B = 4x$, and $m\angle C = 3x - 20$. Find $m\angle A$, $m\angle B$, and $m\angle C$.

Objective: *To use the corollaries of the Triangle–Sum Theorem (Section 4–5 and 4–6)*

Classify each statement as true, *T*, or false, *F*.

26. A right triangle can have an exterior angle with a measure of 150.

27. A right triangle can have acute angles with measures of 12 and 78.

28. An exterior angle at the base of an isosceles triangle can have a measure of 50.

29. For triangles *ABC* and *DEF*, $\angle A \cong \angle D$, $\angle B \cong \angle E$, and m$\angle C = 39$. Then m$\angle F = 39$.

30. It is possible for each angle of a triangle to have a measure of 70.

31. In equilateral triangle *ABC*, if the bisectors of $\angle A$ and $\angle B$ meet at *D*, then m$\angle ADB = 60$.

Objective: *To use the Angle–Sum Theorem for Polygons (Section 4–7)*

32. Find the sum of the measures of the interior angles of a hexagon.

33. Find the measure of each interior angle of a regular polygon of 20 sides.

Objective: *To use the Exterior Angle–Sum Corollary for Polygons (Section 4–8)*

34. The sum of the measures of the exterior angles of any polygon is __?__ .

35. The measure of an exterior angle of a regular decagon (10 sides) is __?__ .

36. If the measure of each exterior angle of a regular polygon is 20, then the polygon has __?__ sides.

Objective: *To solve word problems that involve parallel lines (Page 179)*

37. The posts supporting the banister as shown in the figure below make a 55°–angle with the railing. Explain why the posts are parallel.

Objective: *To solve word problems that involve angles in polygons (Page 200)*

38. The angle at the top of the A-frame house below has a measure of 65. Both sides of the roof have the same length. Find the measure of the angles that each side makes with the ground.

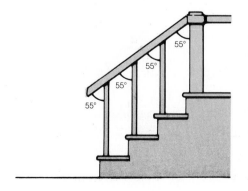

Chapter Test

In Exercises 1–3, state which segments and rays are parallel.

1.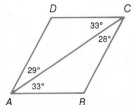

2.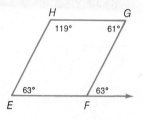

3.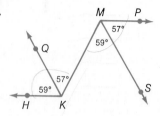

In Exercises 4–6, find m∠ 1 and m∠ 2.

4. Given: $\overrightarrow{RS} \parallel \overline{PQ}$

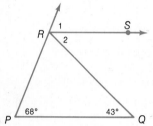

5. Given: $\overleftrightarrow{YN} \parallel \overline{MA}$

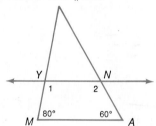

6. Given: $\overline{AC} \parallel \overline{ED}$; $\overline{BD} \cong \overline{CD}$

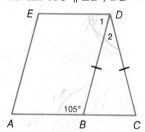

In the figure, $\overrightarrow{BA} \parallel \overrightarrow{CD}$ and $\overline{BE} \perp \overline{CD}$.

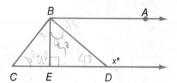

7. Find m∠ ABC + m∠ C.

8. Name complementary angles in △ BEC.

9. If m∠ EBD = 50, find x.

10. Given: Quadrilateral ABCD;
$\overline{CD} \perp \overline{BC}$; $\overline{BA} \perp \overline{BC}$

Prove: ∠ EDA ≅ ∠ A

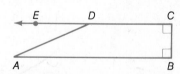

11. In an isosceles triangle, the vertex angle has a measure of 58. Find the measure of each base angle.

12. In △ ABC, m∠ A = 2x, m∠ B = 2x + 15, and m∠ C = 3x − 10. Find the measure of each angle.

13. Find the sum of the measures of the interior angles of a hexagon.

14. Find the measure of each interior angle of a regular pentagon.

15. Each exterior angle of a regular polygon has a measure of 15. Find the number of sides of the polygon.

CHAPTER **5** **Using Parallel Lines**

Sections

5-1 **Parallelograms and their Properties**

5-2 **Proving that a Quadrilateral is a Parallelogram**

5-3 **Rectangles, Rhombuses, and Squares**

5-4 **Midpoints and Parallel Lines**

5-5 **Parallel Lines and Congruent Segments**

Applications: Using Quadrilaterals

5-6 **Inequalities in Triangles**

5-7 **More Inequalities in Triangles**

5-8 **Dihedral Angles**

Applications: Using Inequalities and Dihedral Angles

Features

Career Application: Geometry and Chemistry

Computer Application: Triangles

Puzzles

Review and Testing

Algebra Review Capsules

Geometry Review Capsules

Review: Sections 5–1 through 5–5

Review: Sections 5–6 through 5–8

Chapter Summary

Chapter Objectives and Review

Chapter Test

5-1 Parallelograms and Their Properties

Recall that a quadrilateral is a polygon having four sides. The following table lists some quadrilaterals having special names and properties.

NOTE: In quadrilateral $ABCD$, $\overline{AB}$ and $\overline{DC}$ are **opposite sides**, and $\angle A$ and $\angle C$ are **opposite angles**.

Quadrilateral	Figure	Definition
Trapezoid		A quadrilateral with exactly one pair of parallel sides. The parallel sides are the **bases** of the trapezoid. In an **isosceles trapezoid**, the nonparallel sides are congruent.
Parallelogram		A quadrilateral with both pairs of opposite sides parallel.
Rectangle		A parallelogram with four right angles.
Rhombus		A parallelogram with all four sides congruent.
Square		A rectangle with all four sides congruent.

REMEMBER:
[1] The trapezoid is the only quadrilateral in the table that is not a parallelogram.

[2] Since rectangles, rhombuses, and squares are parallelograms, any theorems or corollaries that pertain to parallelograms also pertain to rectangles, rhombuses, and squares.

Theorem 5-1 | A diagonal of a parallelogram forms two congruent triangles.

EXAMPLE 1 Prove Theorem 5-1.

Given: *ABCD* is a parallelogram
with diagonal *BD*.

Prove: △*ABD* ≅ △*CDB*

Proof:

Statements	Reasons
1. *ABCD* is a parallelogram.	1. Given
2. $\overline{AB} \parallel \overline{CD}$; $\overline{AD} \parallel \overline{CB}$	2. (1). The opposite sides of a parallelogram are parallel.
3. ∠1 ≅ ∠2; ∠3 ≅ ∠4	3. (2). If parallel lines are cut by a transversal, alternate interior angles are congruent.
4. $\overline{BD} \cong \overline{DB}$	4. Identity
5. ∴ △*ABD* ≅ △*CDB*	5. (3), (4). ASA Postulate

Corollaries 5-2 and 5-3 follow from Theorem 5-1. You are asked to prove them in the Written Exercises.

Corollary 5-2 | The opposite sides of a parallelogram are congruent.
Corollary 5-3 | The opposite angles of a parallelogram are congruent.

You can use these corollaries and Theorem 5-1 to find the unknown lengths of sides and the measures of unknown angles of parallelograms.
NOTE: Parallelogram *ABCD* can be written as ▱*ABCD*.

EXAMPLE 2 *DEFG* is a parallelogram.

a. If m∠*F* = 105, find m∠*D*, m∠*E*, and m∠*G*.

b. If *DG* = 50*t* − 1 and *FE* = 9*t* + 19.5, find *DG* and *FE*.

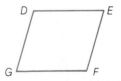

Solutions:

a. Since m∠*F* = 105, **m∠*D* = 105.** ←————— **By Corollary 5-3**

Since m∠*F* = 105, **m∠*G* = 75,** ←—— **Interior ∠s on the same side of**
and, by Corollary 5-3, **m∠*E* = 75.** **a transversal are supplementary.**

b. By Corollary 5-2, *DG* = *FE*. ←—— **Replace *DG* with (50*t* − 1) and *FE* with 9*t* + 19.5.**

50*t* − 1 = 9*t* + 19.5 ←————— **Solve for *t*.**

41*t* = 20.5

t = 0.5 ←————— **Don't forget to find (50*t* − 1).**

50*t* − 1 = 50(0.5) − 1 = 24   Thus, *DG* = *FE* = **24**

You can use properties of parallelograms to show that parallel lines are always the same distance apart.

Corollary 5–4

> Two parallel lines are equidistant at all points.

The proof of this Corollary is asked for in the Written Exercises.

Drawing both diagonals of a parallelogram forms four pairs of congruent triangles. You can use corresponding parts of one of these pairs to prove Theorem 5–5.

Theorem 5–5

> The diagonals of a parallelogram bisect each other.

Theorem 5–6 states another important property of parallelograms. You are asked to prove Theorems 5–5 and 5–6 in the Written Exercises.

NOTE: In quadrilateral $ABCD$, $\overline{AB}$ and $\overline{BC}$ are **consecutive sides,** and $\angle A$ and $\angle B$ are **consecutive angles.**

Theorem 5–6

> Any two consecutive angles of a parallelogram are supplementary.

The properties of a parallelogram are summarized below.

REMEMBER: All the properties of a parallelogram are also properties of any rectangle, rhombus, or square.

Summary

> **Properties of a Parallelogram**
> 1. The opposite sides are parallel.
> 2. The opposite sides are congruent.
> 3. The opposite angles are congruent.
> 4. Two consecutive angles are supplementary.
> 5. Either diagonal forms two congruent triangles.
> 6. The diagonals bisect each other.

CLASSROOM EXERCISES

In Exercises 1–12, refer to ▱$ABCD$.

1. $\overline{DA} \parallel$ __?__
2. $\overline{DC} \cong$ __?__
3. $\angle ADC \cong$ __?__
4. $\triangle ABC \cong \triangle$ __?__
5. $\overline{QC} \cong$ __?__
6. $\triangle ADQ \cong \triangle$ __?__
7. m$\angle 1 =$ __?__
8. m$\angle DAB =$ __?__
9. $DB = 2($ __?__ $)$
10. $AQ = \frac{1}{2}($ __?__ $)$
11. m$\angle DAB +$ m$\angle ABC =$ __?__
12. $\angle ABC$ and $\angle$ __?__ are supplementary.

In Exercises 13–18, refer to ▱*QRST*.

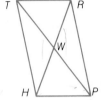

13. Name the congruent segments.

14. Name the alternate interior angles.

15. Name the supplementary angles.

16. Name the congruent angles.

17. If $m\angle 1 = 110$ and $m\angle Q = 45$, find the measure of each of the other angles.

18. If $m\angle 3 = 75$ and $m\angle 1 = 50$, find the measure of each of the other angles.

In Exercises 19–22, refer to ▱*RTHP*. Tell whether each pair of triangles is congruent, *C*, or not congruent, *NC*. When a pair of triangles is congruent, state a theorem or corollary that can be used to prove them congruent.

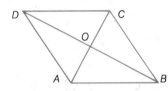

19. $\triangle HPW$ and $\triangle RTW$

20. $\triangle TPH$ and $\triangle PTR$

21. $\triangle RWP$ and $\triangle WHP$

22. $\triangle HWT$ and $\triangle RWP$

WRITTEN EXERCISES

A The statements in Exercises 1–8 refer to ▱*ABCD*. Classify each statement as true, *T*, or false, *F*. State the definition, theorem, or corollary that gives the reason for each answer.

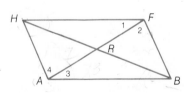

1. $\overline{AB} \cong \overline{CD}$

2. $AO = OC = DO = OB$

3. If $m\angle ABC = 86$, then $m\angle ADC$ cannot equal 84.

4. $\angle DAB$ and $\angle DCB$ are both supplementary to $\angle ABC$.

5. If $AD = 6$, then $BC = 6$.

6. If $AO = 3$, then $CO = 3$.

7. $\triangle ABC \cong \triangle ABD$

8. $\triangle ABD \cong \triangle CDB$

Refer to ▱*BFHA* for Exercises 9–22.

9. If $m\angle F = 72$, $m\angle A = \underline{\ ?\ }$

10. If $m\angle F = 72$, $m\angle B = \underline{\ ?\ }$

11. If $m\angle ABF = 3m\angle HAB$, find $m\angle ABF$ and $m\angle HAB$.

12. If $m\angle 4 = 42$ and $m\angle 3 = 38$, find $m\angle HAB$.

13. If $m\angle AHF = 129$, find $m\angle ABF$, $m\angle HFB$, and $m\angle BAH$.

14. If $RF = 11$, find AF.   15. If $HB = 16$, find HR.

16. If $HF = 2y - 9$ and $AB = y + 2$, find HF.

17. If $BR = 5x + 30$ and $HR = 7x$, find BR.

18. If $FR = 2x + 7$ and $AF = 10x - 4$, find AF.

19. If $AH = 9t - 2$ and $BF = 6t + 10$, find AH.

20. If $m\angle 1 = 2r - 7$ and $m\angle 3 = r + 13$, find $m\angle 1$.

21. If $m\angle 3 = t + 21$, $m\angle 4 = 3t - 18$, and $m\angle HFB = 79$, find $m\angle 2$.

22. If $m\angle BFH = 7q + 20$ and $m\angle ABF = 8q - 20$, find $m\angle FHA$.

23. Complete the proof of Corollary 5–2.

Given: ▱*ABCD* with diagonal *BD*

Prove: $\overline{AD} \cong \overline{CB}$; $\overline{AB} \cong \overline{CD}$

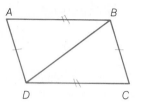

Statements	Reasons
1. ▱*ABCD* with diagonal *BD*	1. ?
2. △*ABD* ≅ △*CDB*	2. (1). ?
3. $\overline{AD} \cong \overline{CB}$; $\overline{AB} \cong \overline{CD}$	3. (2). ?

B

24. Prove Corollary 5–3. (HINT: Follow the method of Exercise 23.)

25. Prove Corollary 5–4.

Given: $k \parallel m$;
$\overline{RY} \perp m$;
$\overline{SZ} \perp m$

Prove: $RY = SZ$

Plan: Since it is given that $\overline{RY}$ and $\overline{SZ}$ are both perpendicular to m, show that $\overline{RY} \parallel \overline{SZ}$. Then, since it is also given that $k \parallel m$, $RYZS$ is a parallelogram and $RY = SZ$.

26. Prove Theorem 5–5.

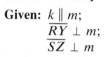

Given: Parallelogram *EFGH*

Prove: $\overline{EG}$ bisects $\overline{FH}$;
$\overline{FH}$ bisects $\overline{EG}$.

Plan: Since $\overline{GH} \parallel \overline{EF}$, $\angle 1 \cong \angle 2$, $\angle 3 \cong \angle 4$, and △*GHJ* ≅ △*EFJ* by the ASA Postulate. Then $\overline{EJ} \cong \overline{GJ}$ and $\overline{FJ} \cong \overline{HJ}$ by CPCTC. ∴ $\overline{EG}$ bisects $\overline{FH}$ and $\overline{FH}$ bisects $\overline{EG}$.

27. In ▱*ABCD* at the left below, $\overline{AE}$ and $\overline{CF}$ are each perpendicular to $\overline{BD}$. Prove that $\overline{AE}$ and $\overline{CF}$ are congruent and parallel.

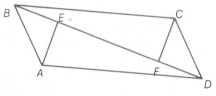
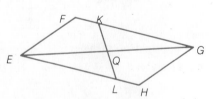

28. In ▱*EFGH* at the right above, Q is the midpoint of $\overline{EG}$, and $\overline{KL}$ is any segment passing through Q. Prove that $\overline{QL} \cong \overline{QK}$.

C

29. Prove Theorem 5–6.

30. Prove that the bisectors of the exterior angles of two opposite angles of a parallelogram are parallel.

31. The diagonals of parallelogram *PQRS* intersect at M, $SM = 2a$, $QM = b + 3$, $PM = 2a - 6$, and $RM = 16 - a - b$. Find the length of each diagonal.

5-2 Proving That a Quadrilateral is a Parallelogram

Examine this table to determine how much it is necessary to know about the sides of a quadrilateral before you can conclude that it is a parallelogram.

Given	Figure	Is it a ▱?	Reason(s)
Exactly one pair of parallel sides		No	It is a trapezoid.
Two pairs of parallel sides		Yes	Definition of parallelogram
Two pairs of congruent sides		Not necessarily	The quadrilateral can have two pairs of congruent sides, but the opposite sides need not be congruent. Such a quadrilateral is often called a **kite**.
Both pairs of opposite sides congruent.		Yes	Draw diagonal AC. $\triangle ABC \cong \triangle CDA$ by SSS, and $\angle 1 \cong \angle 2$. $\therefore \overline{DC} \parallel \overline{AB}$. Also $\angle 3 \cong \angle 4$, so $\overline{DA} \parallel \overline{BC}$. $\therefore ABCD$ is a parallelogram.
One pair of sides both congruent and parallel.		Yes	Draw diagonal KE. $\triangle FEK \cong \triangle DKE$ by SAS. So $\angle 4 \cong \angle 3$ and $\overline{KD} \parallel \overline{EF}$. $\therefore KFED$ is a parallelogram.

The information in the table suggests Theorems 5-7 and 5-8. You are asked to prove these theorems in the Written Exercises.

Theorem 5-7	If both pairs of opposite sides of a quadrilateral are congruent, then the quadrilateral is a parallelogram.
Theorem 5-8	If two sides of a quadrilateral are parallel and congruent, then the quadrilateral is a parallelogram.

You can also conclude that a quadrilateral is a parallelogram if you are given, or can prove, that the diagonals of a quadrilateral bisect each other.

Theorem 5–9
| If the diagonals of a quadrilateral bisect each other, the quadrilateral is a parallelogram. |

The proof of Theorem 5–9 is given in the Example.

EXAMPLE   Prove Theorem 5–9.

Given: Quadrilateral $ABCD$; $\overline{AE} \cong \overline{CE}$; $\overline{BE} \cong \overline{DE}$

Prove: $ABCD$ is a $\square$.

Proof:

Statements	Reasons
1. Quadrilateral $ABCD$; $\overline{AE} \cong \overline{CE}$; $\overline{BE} \cong \overline{DE}$	1. Given
2. $\angle AEB \cong \angle CED$ and $\angle AED \cong \angle CEB$	2. Vertical angles are congruent.
3. $\triangle AEB \cong \triangle CED$ and $\triangle AED \cong \triangle CEB$	3. (1). (2). SAS Postulate
4. $\angle ABE \cong \angle CDE$ and $\angle DAE \cong \angle BCE$	4. (3). CPCTC
5. $\overline{AB} \parallel \overline{DC}$ and $\overline{AD} \parallel \overline{BC}$	5. (4). If congruent alternate interior angles are formed, the lines are parallel.
6. $ABCD$ is a parallelogram.	6. (5). If the opposite sides of a quadrilateral are parallel, it is a parallelogram.

Here is a summary of ways to prove that a quadrilateral is a parallelogram.

Summary
Aids in
Proof

| **Ways of Proving That a Quadrilateral is a Parallelogram** |
| 1 Show that opposite sides are parallel. |
| 2 Show that opposite sides are congruent. |
| 3 Show that two sides are parallel and congruent. |
| 4 Show that the diagonals bisect each other. |
| 5 Show that opposite angles are congruent. (See Written Exercise 32). |
| 6 Show that pairs of consecutive angles are supplementary. (See Written Exercise 31). |

CLASSROOM EXERCISES

Determine whether each quadrilateral is a parallelogram, *P*, or not a parallelogram, *NP*. Give the reason(s) for each answer.

1.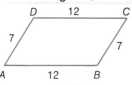

2.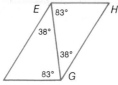

3.

4.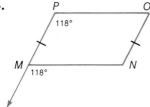

5.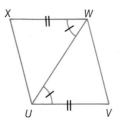

6.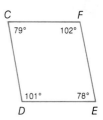

In Exercises 7–13, state the definition, theorem, or corollary that gives the reason for each statement.

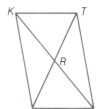

7. If $\overline{PR} \cong \overline{TR}$ and $\overline{VR} \cong \overline{KR}$, then *PKTV* is a parallelogram.

8. If $\overline{KP} \parallel \overline{VT}$ and $\overline{KP} \cong \overline{VT}$, then *PKTV* is a parallelogram.

9. If $\overline{PV} \cong \overline{TK}$ and $\overline{PV} \parallel \overline{TK}$, then *PKTV* is a parallelogram.

10. If $\overline{KT} \cong \overline{VP}$ and $\overline{KP} \cong \overline{VT}$, then *PKTV* is a parallelogram.

11. If $\overline{KP} \parallel \overline{TV}$ and $\overline{VP} \parallel \overline{KT}$, then *PKTV* is a parallelogram.

12. If $\angle VPT \cong \angle KTP$ and $\angle KPT \cong \angle VTP$, then *PKTV* is a parallelogram.

13. If *R* is the midpoint of $\overline{PT}$ and $\overline{KV}$, then *PKTV* is a parallelogram.

WRITTEN EXERCISES

In Exercises 1–3, classify each statement as true, *T*, or false, *F*. Give the reason(s) for each answer.

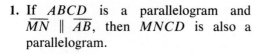

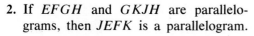

1. If *ABCD* is a parallelogram and $\overline{MN} \parallel \overline{AB}$, then *MNCD* is also a parallelogram.

2. If *EFGH* and *GKJH* are parallelograms, then *JEFK* is a parallelogram.

3. In the Figure for Exercise 2, if $\overline{HG}$ is not coplanar with $\overline{EF}$ and $\overline{JK}$, and if *EFGH* and *GHJK* are parallelograms, then *JEFK* is not a parallelogram.

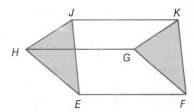

Refer to quadrilateral *WXYZ* for Exercises 4–16. Use the given information to tell whether *WXYZ* is a parallelogram, *P*, or not a parallelogram, *NP*. Give the reason(s) for each answer.

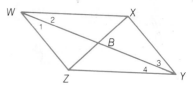

4. $\overline{WX} \cong \overline{XY}$; $\overline{WZ} \cong \overline{YZ}$

5. $\overline{WX} \cong \overline{YZ}$; $\angle 1 \cong \angle 2$

6. $\overline{WX} \cong \overline{YZ}$; $\overline{WZ} \cong \overline{YX}$

7. $\overline{BW} \cong \overline{BY}$; $\overline{BX} \cong \overline{BZ}$

8. $\overline{WX} \cong \overline{YZ}$; $\angle 2 \cong \angle 4$

9. $\angle 1 \cong \angle 3$; $\angle 2 \cong \angle 4$

10. $WZ = 5$; $YX = 5$; $\overline{WZ} \parallel \overline{YX}$

11. $\overline{WX} \parallel \overline{YZ}$; $\overline{WZ} \parallel \overline{YX}$

12. $\triangle ZBY \cong \triangle XBW$

13. $\triangle XBY \cong \triangle ZBW$

14. $m\angle WZY = 135$ and $m\angle XYZ = 135$

15. *B* is the midpoint of $\overline{ZX}$ and $\overline{WY}$.

16. $WB = 4.5$; $YB = 4.5$; $ZB = 2.5$; $XB = 2.5$

In Exercises 17–19, complete the proof.

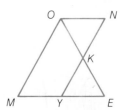

17. **Given:** *K* is the midpoint of $\overline{OE}$ and $\overline{NY}$; *Y* is the midpoint of $\overline{ME}$.

Prove: *MONY* is a parallelogram.

Statements	Reasons
1. *K* is the midpoint of $\overline{OE}$ and $\overline{NY}$; *Y* is the midpoint of $\overline{ME}$.	1. __?__
2. $\overline{KO} \cong \overline{KE}$ and $\overline{KN} \cong \overline{KY}$	2. (1). __?__
3. $\angle NKO \cong \angle YKE$	3. __?__
4. $\triangle NKO \cong \triangle YKE$	4. (2), (3). __?__
5. $\angle ONK \cong \angle EYK$; $\overline{ON} \cong \overline{EY}$	5. (4). __?__
6. $\overline{ON} \parallel \overline{ME}$	6. (5). __?__
7. $\overline{MY} \cong \overline{EY}$	7. (1). __?__
8. $\overline{ON} \cong \overline{MY}$	8. (5), (7). __?__
9. *MONY* is a parallelogram.	9. (6), (8). __?__

18. **Given:** $\angle 1 \cong \angle 2$; $\angle 3 \cong \angle 4$

Prove: *PDES* is a parallelogram.

Statements	Reasons
1. $\angle 3 \cong \angle 4$	1. __?__
2. $\overrightarrow{SI} \parallel \overrightarrow{DR}$	2. (1). __?__
3. $\angle 2 \cong \angle S$	3. (2). __?__
4. $\angle 1 \cong \angle 2$	4. __?__
5. $\angle S \cong \angle 1$	5. (3), (4). __?__
6. $\overline{PD} \parallel \overline{SE}$	6. (5). __?__
7. *PDES* is a parallelogram.	7. (2), (6). __?__

19. Given: Parallelogram $DAGN$; $AR = NO$　　Prove: $DRGO$ is a parallelogram.

Statements	Reasons
1. $DAGN$ is a parallelogram.	1. _?_
2. $\overline{AD} \cong \overline{NG}$	2. (1). _?_
3. $AD = NG$	3. (2). _?_
4. $AR + RD = AD$; $NO + OG = NG$	4. _?_
5. $AR + RD = NO + OG$	5. (3), (4). _?_
6. $AR = NO$	6. _?_
7. $RD = OG$	7. (5), (6). _?_
8. $\overline{RD} \cong \overline{OG}$	8. (7). _?_
9. $\overline{RD} \parallel \overline{OG}$	9. (1). _?_
10. $DRGO$ is a parallelogram.	10. (8), (9). _?_

In Exercises 20–22, classify each statement as true, *T*, or false, *F*. Give the reason(s) for each answer.

20. If a quadrilateral is not a parallelogram, then the opposite sides are not congruent.

21. If the opposite sides of a quadrilateral are not congruent, then the quadrilateral is not a parallelogram.

22. A quadrilateral is a parallelogram if and only if the opposite sides are parallel.

B

23. Prove Theorem 5–7. (HINT: Refer to the table on page 213.)

24. Prove Theorem 5–8. (HINT: Refer to the table on page 213.)

In Exercises 25–26, the measures of the angles of quadrilateral *ABCD* are given. Compute the measure of each angle. Use these measures to determine whether the quadrilateral is a parallelogram.

25. $m\angle A = 5x - 1$; $m\angle B = 8x + 12$; $m\angle C = 6x - 14$; $m\angle D = 11x - 27$

26. $m\angle A = 2x + 13$; $m\angle B = 6x - 9$, $m\angle C = 3x - 10$; $m\angle D = 5x + 14$

27. In the figure for Exercise 18, $\overline{PS} \cong \overline{ED}$ and $\angle 3 \cong \angle 4$. Prove that *PDES* is a parallelogram.

28. Given: Parallelogram $DOQT$; $\angle RTD \cong \angle NOQ$

Prove: *NORT* is a parallelogram.

29. Given: Parallelogram $VKHF$; G is the midpoint of $\overline{FH}$; L is the midpoint of $\overline{VK}$.

Prove: *KGFL* is a parallelogram.

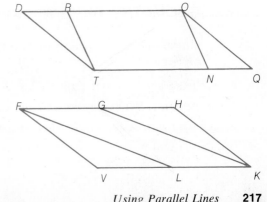

In Exercises 30–33, prove or disprove each statement. To disprove a statement, you need find only one quadrilateral to serve as a counterexample.

30. If a diagonal of a quadrilateral forms two congruent triangles, then the quadrilateral is a parallelogram.

31. If all pairs of consecutive angles of a quadrilateral are supplementary, then the quadrilateral is a parallelogram.

C

32. If the opposite angles of a quadrilateral are congruent, then the quadrilateral is a parallelogram.

33. If the diagonals of a quadrilateral are perpendicular to each other, then the quadrilateral is a parallelogram.

34. Given: $ABCD$ is a parallelogram;
$\overline{AC}$ is a diagonal;
$\overline{AP} \cong \overline{RC}$

Prove: $DPBR$ is a parallelogram.

35. Given: $DEFA$ and $FBCE$ are parallelograms.

Prove: $ABCD$ is a parallelogram.

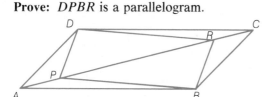

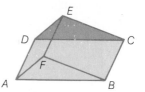

─────────────── **Puzzle** ───────────────

The two rays shown at the right are parallel.

Find m∠ 1 + m∠ 2 + m∠ 3.

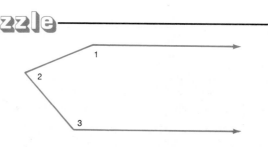

─────── **GEOMETRY REVIEW CAPSULE FOR SECTION 5-3** ───────

Match each description on the left with the name of the figure it describes on the right. *(Pages 208–210)*

1. A parallelogram with four right angles

2. A parallelogram with consecutive sides congruent

3. A rectangle with consecutive sides congruent

4. A quadrilateral with both pairs of opposite sides parallel

a. Parallelogram

b. Rectangle

c. Rhombus

d. Square

e. Trapezoid

Career Applications
Geometry and Chemistry

Chemists determine the arrangement of particles composing a crystal by a mathematical analysis of the pattern produced by x-ray photographs. This pattern is called a **crystal lattice.** Chemists identify crystals by the shape of the smallest portion of the lattice exhibiting the lattice structure, called the **unit cell.** There are seven basic crystal shapes.

Cubic	Tetragonal	Hexagonal	Trigonal
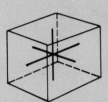	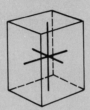	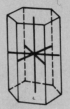	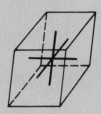
Axes: 3 Equal length. All are perpendicular.	**Axes:** 3 Two are equal. All are perpendicular.	**Axes:** 4 Three are equal and meet at a 60°–angle; one is perpendicular.	**Axes:** 3 Equal length. Meet *obliquely* at equal (not right) angles.

Orthorhombic	Monoclinic	Triclinic
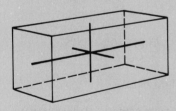	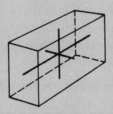	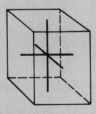
Axes: 3 All unequal. All are perpendicular.	**Axes:** 3 All unequal. Two perpendicular; one meets obliquely.	**Axes:** 3 All unequal. Meet obliquely at unequal angles.

EXERCISES

In Exercises 1–7:
   a. Give the shape of the sides of each crystal.
   b. Give the shape of the top and bottom of each crystal.

1. Cubic   **2.** Tetragonal   **3.** Hexagonal   **4.** Trigonal
5. Orthorhombic   **6.** Monoclinic   **7.** Triclinic

5-3 Rectangles, Rhombuses, Squares

Since rectangles, rhombuses, and squares are special kinds of parallelograms (see the table on page 208), all the properties of parallelograms may be used as reasons in proofs that involve these figures. However, rectangles, rhombuses, and squares also have special properties. Theorem 5–10 states a special property of rectangles. The proof of this theorem is asked for in the Written Exercises.

Theorem 5–10

> The diagonals of a rectangle are congruent.

Theorem 5–11 states a special property of a rhombus.

Theorem 5–11

> The diagonals of a rhombus are perpendicular to each other.

EXAMPLE 1 Write the *Given*, the *Prove*, and a *Plan of Proof* for Theorem 5–11.

Given: Rhombus $MQRS$

Prove: $\overline{MR} \perp \overline{SQ}$

Plan: By the definition of rhombus, $\overline{MS} \cong \overline{MQ}$ and $MQRS$ is a parallelogram. Then $\overline{ST} \cong \overline{QT}$, $\overline{MT} \cong \overline{MT}$, and $\triangle MTS \cong \triangle MTQ$ by the SSS Postulate. Thus, $\angle 1 \cong \angle 2$ and $\overline{MR} \perp \overline{SQ}$.

Theorem 5–12 states another special property of a rhombus. The proof of this theorem is asked for in the Written Exercises.

Theorem 5–12

> Each diagonal of a rhombus bisects a pair of opposite angles.

The plan of the proof of Theorem 5–12 is outlined below.

EXAMPLE 2 Write the *Given*, the *Prove*, and a *Plan of Proof* for Theorem 5–12.

Given: Rhombus $LTKE$

Prove: $\overline{ET}$ bisects $\angle KEL$ and $\angle LTK$;

$\overline{LK}$ bisects $\angle ELT$ and $\angle TKE$.

Plan: Draw diagonal ET. By definition, $LTKE$ is a parallelogram and a diagonal of a parallelogram forms two congruent triangles. Thus, $\triangle ELT \cong \triangle EKT$, $\angle 1 \cong \angle 2$, and $\angle 3 \cong \angle 4$. Therefore, $\overline{ET}$ bisects $\angle KEL$ and $\angle LTK$. Follow a similar plan to prove that diagonal LK bisects $\angle ELT$ and $\angle TKE$.

By definition, a square is a rectangle. Thus, the diagonals of a square are congruent. Also, since a square has four congruent sides, it is a rhombus. Thus, it follows that the diagonals of a square are perpendicular to each other and each diagonal bisects a pair of opposite angles.

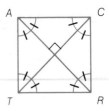

CLASSROOM EXERCISES

Complete each statement in Exercises 1–6. Use the words *parallelogram, rhombus, rectangle,* or *square.*

1. Every rectangle is also a __?__ .

2. Every rhombus is also a __?__ .

3. Every square is also a __?__ , a __?__ , and a __?__ .

4. A parallelogram with congruent diagonals is a __?__ or a __?__ .

5. A parallelogram with perpendicular diagonals is a __?__ or a __?__ .

6. A parallelogram whose diagonals are the perpendicular bisectors of each other is a __?__ or a __?__ .

7. In rectangle *DASH*, diagonals *DS* and *AH* intersect at *P* and *DP* = 2.8 centimeters. Find *DS*, *AP*, *PH*, and *AH*.

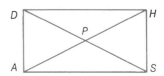

WRITTEN EXERCISES

A   In Exercises 1–6, refer to rectangle *ADCB*.

1. If *AE* = 3 meters, find *AC*, *BE*, *BD*, and *DE*.

2. Name the angles congruent to ∠*ABE*.

3. If m∠*BAE* = 30, find m∠*ABE*, m∠*AEB*, m∠*BEC*, m∠*EBC*, m∠*BCE*, m∠*CDE*, and m∠*EDA*.

4. Name four isosceles triangles in the figure.

5. Are the diagonals of the rectangle congruent?

6. Are the diagonals of the rectangle perpendicular to each other?

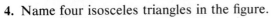

In Exercises 7–12, refer to square *FPHG*.

7. Give the measure of each acute angle.

8. Name eight triangles in the figure. State which of these are right triangles and which are isosceles triangles.

9. If *HJ* = 14 cm, find *FH* and *GP*.

10. The perimeter of *FPHG* is 18 units. Find *HG*.

11. Give the measure of angle *FJG*.

12. Give the measure of angle *GJH*.

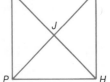

In Exercises 13–18, refer to rhombus *KOMS*.

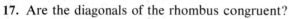

13. If m∠ *KOS* = 25, find m∠ *KOM*.

14. Name four isosceles triangles in the figure.

15. State three properties of diagonals *KM* and *OS*.

16. If m∠ *SKP* = 50, find the measures of the remaining seven acute angles.

17. Are the diagonals of the rhombus congruent?

18. Are the diagonals of the rhombus perpendicular to each other?

19. Name the properties that a rhombus and a rectangle have in common.

20. Name properties of a rhombus that are not properties of every parallelogram.

21. Name properties of a square that are not properties of every rectangle.

22. Name properties of a square that are not properties of every rhombus.

23. Name 2 parallelograms that are equilateral and 2 that are equiangular.

B

24. Prove Theorem 5–10. (HINT: Draw the diagonals and prove one pair of overlapping triangles congruent.)

25. Prove Theorem 5–12. (HINT: Refer to Example 2 on page 220.)

26. **Given:** Rhombus *TAJK*; diagonal *TJ*

    Prove: ∠1 ≅ ∠2 ≅ ∠3 ≅ ∠4

27. **Given:** Parallelogram *DSCK*; ∠1 ≅ ∠2

    Prove: *DSCK* is a rhombus.

28. **Given:** Parallelogram *CBTR*; $\overline{CT} \cong \overline{BR}$

    Prove: *CBTR* is a rectangle.

In Exercises 29–35, use the figure at the right to classify each statement as true, *T*, or false, *F*. Give the reason(s) for each answer.

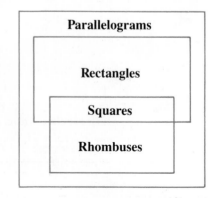

29. All rhombuses are parallelograms.

30. Some rectangles are squares.

31. All parallelograms are rectangles.

32. Some rhombuses are rectangles.

33. All rectangles are squares.

34. All squares are rectangles.

35. Some squares are rectangles.

In Exercises 36–39, prove each statement.

36. If a quadrilateral is a square, then it is a parallelogram.

37. If a quadrilateral is a square, then it is a rhombus.

38. If a parallelogram has one right angle, then it has four right angles.

39. If a parallelogram has congruent diagonals, then it is a rectangle.

40. A quadrilateral has four congruent sides. Must it be a rhombus? Prove your answer.

41. A parallelogram has its diagonals perpendicular to each other. Must it be a rhombus? Prove your answer.

ⓒ

42. Prove that the base angles of an isosceles trapezoid are congruent. (HINT: Draw segments from T and R perpendicular to $\overline{PA}$).

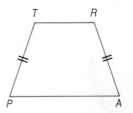

43. Using the theorem proved in Exercise 42, prove that the diagonals of an isosceles trapezoid are congruent.

In Exercises 44–46, $KETQ$ is a kite with $\overline{KQ} \cong \overline{KE}$ and $\overline{QT} \cong \overline{ET}$. (See page 213.)

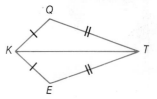

44. Prove that diagonal KT bisects $\angle QKE$ and $\angle QTE$.

45. Prove that $\angle Q \cong \angle E$.

46. In quadrilateral $KETQ$, draw $\overline{QE}$ intersecting $\overline{KT}$ at M. Prove that $\overline{KT}$ is the perpendicular bisector of $\overline{QE}$.

Puzzle

The rectangle below is divided into squares. The two largest are 69 and 72 units on a side. How long is each side of each square?

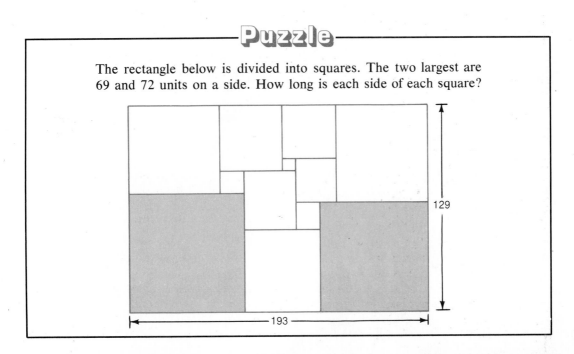

SUMMARY: Aids in Proof

The following summary lists the properties of quadrilaterals you have studied up to this point. This summary will help you to plan and write proofs involving quadrilaterals.

Quadrilateral	Sides		Angles		Diagonals
	Opposite	Consecutive	Opposite	Consecutive	
Trapezoid	One pair is parallel.				
Parallelogram	Parallel; Congruent		Congruent	Supplementary	Bisect each other
Rectangle	Parallel; Congruent	Perpendicular	Four right angles		Congruent; bisect each other
Rhombus	Parallel; Congruent	Congruent	Congruent	Supplementary	Perpendicular; bisect each other and opposite angles
Square	Parallel; Congruent	Perpendicular; Congruent	Four right angles		Congruent; Perpendicular; bisect each other and opposite angles

ALGEBRA REVIEW CAPSULE FOR SECTION 5–4

Solve and check.

Example: $2(n + 3) = 3n + 1$

Solution:
$$2(n + 3) = 3n + 1$$
$$2n + 6 = 3n + 1$$
$$2n + 6 - 2n = 3n + 1 - 2n$$
$$6 = n + 1$$
$$\mathbf{5 = n, \text{ or } n = 5}$$

1. $2(3x + 4) = 4x + 16$

2. $3p - 3 = 2(5p - 12)$

3. $2y = \frac{1}{2}(3y + 5)$

4. $\frac{1}{2}(2c + 10) = 2c$

5. $4n - 4 = 2(5n + 5)$

6. $2(2t + 2) = 3t + 15$

7. $d + 2 = \frac{1}{2}(4d - 6)$

8. $\frac{1}{2}(6w - 7) = 2w$

9. $4q - 2 = 2(3q - 6)$

5-4 Midpoints and Parallel Lines

The properties of parallelograms can be used to prove theorems about triangles and parallel lines.

<table>
<tr><td>Theorem
5–13</td><td>If a segment joins the midpoints of two sides of a triangle, then it is parallel to the third side and its length is one-half the length of the third side.</td></tr>
</table>

EXAMPLE 1   Write the *Given*, the *Prove*, and a *Plan of Proof* for Theorem 5–13.

Given: In $\triangle ABC$, D and E are the midpoints of $\overline{AC}$ and $\overline{BC}$, respectively.

Prove: $\overline{DE} \parallel \overline{AB}$ and $DE = \frac{1}{2}AB$.

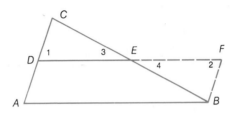

Plan: $\boxed{1}$ Extend $\overline{DE}$ its own length to F. Draw $\overline{BF}$. Show that $\triangle DEC \cong \triangle FEB$ by the SAS Postulate.

$\boxed{2}$ Prove that $\overline{AD} \parallel \overline{BF}$ and that $\overline{AD} \cong \overline{BF}$. Thus, by Theorem 5–8, $ABFD$ is a parallelogram.

$\boxed{3}$ Show that $\overline{DE}$ is parallel to $\overline{AB}$, and that $DF = AB$. Use the Midpoint Theorem to show that $DE = \frac{1}{2}DF$. Then, by substitution, $DE = \frac{1}{2}AB$.

The proof is asked for in the Written Exercises.

EXAMPLE 2   In $\triangle PQR$ at the right, A is the midpoint of $\overline{PR}$ and B is the midpoint of $\overline{QR}$.

a. If $AB = 5$ feet, find PQ.

b. Name the parallel segments.

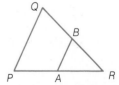

Solution: a. $AB = \frac{1}{2}PQ$ ← The length of the segment joining the midpoints of two sides of a triangle is half the length of the third side.

$5 = \frac{1}{2}PQ$ ← Solve for **PQ**.

$10 = PQ$ ← **PQ = 10 feet**

b. $\overline{AB} \parallel \overline{PQ}$ ← If a segment joins the midpoints of two sides of a triangle, it is parallel to the third side.

CLASSROOM EXERCISES

Draw △ABC so that the lengths of the sides are 8, 6, and 5. Join the midpoints of the sides of the triangle. Use this figure for Exercises 1–2.

1. Give the lengths of the sides of each triangle formed.
2. Are the four triangles congruent?

In quadrilateral *ADCB*, *E*, *F*, *H*, and *G* are midpoints of the sides. In Exercises 3–5, write a statement comparing the given measures.

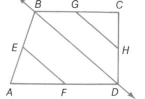

3. *EF* and *BD*   4. *GH* and *BD*   5. *EF* and *GH*
6. Is $\overline{EF} \parallel \overline{GH}$? Give the reason(s) for your answer.

WRITTEN EXERCISES

A   In △*RUS*, *A* is the midpoint of $\overline{UR}$, *E* is the midpoint of $\overline{RS}$, and *Q* is the midpoint of $\overline{SU}$. Use this information for Exercises 1–6.

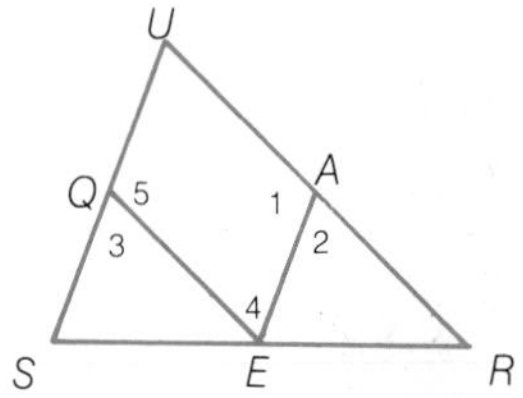

1. If *QE* = 6.8, find *UR*.
2. If m∠2 = 64, find m∠4.
3. If m∠1 = 116, find m∠5.
4. If m∠*U* = 64, find m∠3.
5. If *US* = 23, find *AE*.
6. If *UR* = 25, *US* = 12, and
   SR = 19, find the perimeter of △*QSE*.

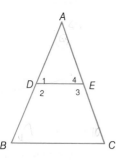

7. In △*ABC* below, *D* and *E* are the midpoints of the sides, m∠*A* = 43, and m∠*B* = 67. Find m∠1, m∠2, m∠3, m∠4, and m∠*C*.

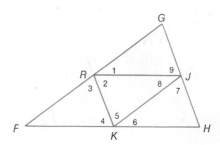

8. In △*FHG* above, *R*, *J*, and *K* are the midpoints of the sides, m∠*F* = 37, and m∠*G* = 73. Find m∠*H* and the measure of each numbered angle.

9. In the figure for Exercise 7, if *BC* = 3, find *DE*.

10. In the figure for Exercise 8, if the perimeter of △*FGH* is 18 centimeters, find the perimeter of △*JKR*.

11. In triangle ZAP, D is the midpoint of $\overline{ZA}$ and E is the midpoint of $\overline{ZP}$. If $DE = 3t - 2$ and $AP = 4t + 4$, find DE and AP.

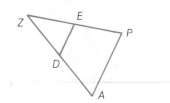

12. In the figure for Exercise 11, if $AP = 4x + 2$ and $DE = 3x - 4$, find DE.

13. In the figure for Exercise 11, if $AP = 2x$ and $DE = 3x - 8$, find AP.

14. In triangle ABC at the right, X, Y, and Z are the midpoints of $\overline{AB}$, $\overline{BC}$, and $\overline{CA}$ respectively. Find the perimeter of $\triangle XYZ$ when $AB = 12$ meters, $BC = 11$ meters, and $AC = 3$ meters.

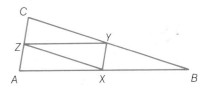

15. Each side of an equilateral triangle is 12 meters long. Segments join the midpoints of the sides. What is the perimeter of each triangle formed?

B   In Exercises 16–18, exactly one of the lengths marked x, y, or z can be found from the given information. Find that length.

16.
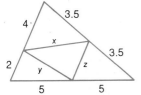

17.
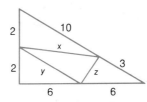

18.
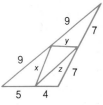

19. **Given:** Quadrilateral $ABCD$; E, F, G, and H are the midpoints of $\overline{AB}$, $\overline{BC}$, $\overline{CD}$, and $\overline{DA}$, respectively.

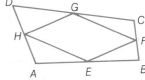

Prove: $EFGH$ is a parallelogram.

Plan: Draw diagonal AC. Show that $\overline{HG} \parallel \overline{AC}$ and $\overline{EF} \parallel \overline{AC}$. Therefore, $\overline{HG} \parallel \overline{EF}$. Then, by Theorem 5–13, $HG = \frac{1}{2}AC$ and $EF = \frac{1}{2}AC$. Thus, $HG = EF$. Complete the proof.

20. The diagonals of quadrilateral $ABCD$ are 6 inches and 10 inches long. The midpoints of $\overline{AB}$, $\overline{BC}$, $\overline{CD}$, and $\overline{DA}$ are connected in that order. Find the length of each side of the new quadrilateral.

C
21. Prove Theorem 5–13. (HINT: See the Plan in Example 1 on page 225.)

22. Prove that the quadrilateral formed by joining the midpoints of the sides of a rectangle is a rhombus.

23. The midpoints of the sides of pentagon $PENTA$ are V, W, X, Y, and Z, where V is the midpoint of $\overline{PE}$, W is the midpoint of $\overline{EN}$, and so on. Prove that the perimeter of $VWXYZ$ is one–half the sum of the lengths of the diagonals of $PENTA$.

24. In regular pentagon $ABCDE$, P is the midpoint of $\overline{BC}$ and Q is the midpoint of $\overline{CD}$. Prove that $\overline{PQ} \parallel \overline{AE}$.

Simplify. *(Pages 44–45)*

1. $(3n + 4) + (6n - 3)$
2. $(2p - 3) + (3p + 6)$
3. $(4y - 1) + (5y + 7)$
4. $(8r - 3) + (r + 9)$
5. $\frac{1}{2}(2w - 4 + 2w + 5)$
6. $\frac{1}{2}(4z - 6 + 2z + 12)$

Solve and check. *(Page 224)*

7. $4d - 6 = \frac{1}{2}(2d + 3 + 3d - 6)$
8. $\frac{1}{2}(3b - 4 + 7b - 8) = 2b + 12$
9. $2h = \frac{1}{2}(5h + 1 + h - 5)$
10. $\frac{1}{2}(2k + 5 + 3k - 4) = 4k - 9$

5-5 Parallel Lines and Congruent Segments

A trapezoid has exactly two parallel sides (see the table on page 208). In trapezoid $BARO$ at the right, $\overline{TQ}$ is the *median*. This means that T is the midpoint of $\overline{OB}$ and Q is the midpoint of $\overline{RA}$.

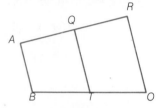

Definition	The **median of a trapezoid** is the segment joining the midpoints of the nonparallel sides.

Theorem 5–14 relates the length of the median of a trapezoid to the lengths of its bases. You are asked to prove this theorem in the Written Exercises.

Theorem 5–14	The median of a trapezoid is parallel to the bases and its length is one-half the sum of the lengths of the bases.

EXAMPLE

In trapezoid $PFQR$, shown at the right, $\overline{DE}$ is the median. If $PF = 85.2$ centimeters and $RQ = 135.4$ centimeters, find DE.

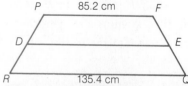

Solution:

$DE = \frac{1}{2}(PF + RQ)$ ⟵ By Theorem 5–14, the length of the median is one-half the sum of the lengths of the bases.

$DE = \frac{1}{2}(85.2 + 135.4)$

$DE = \frac{1}{2}(220.6)$, or **110.3 centimeters**

Theorem 5–15 deals with three or more parallel lines and congruent segments on two or more transversals. The proof of this theorem is based on properties of parallelograms. The proof is asked for in the Written Exercises.

<table>
<tr><td>Theorem
5-15</td><td>If three or more parallel lines cut off congruent segments on one transversal, they cut off congruent segments on any transversal.</td></tr>
</table>

The following two corollaries follow from Theorem 5-15. You are asked to prove them in the Written Exercises.

<table>
<tr><td>Corollary
5-16</td><td>If a line is parallel to one side of a triangle and bisects a second side, then it bisects the third side also.</td></tr>
<tr><td>Corollary
5-17</td><td>If a line is parallel to the bases of a trapezoid and bisects one of the nonparallel sides, then it bisects the other side also.</td></tr>
</table>

CLASSROOM EXERCISES

Find the length of the median of each trapezoid.

1.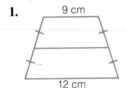
9 cm
12 cm

2.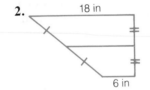
18 in
6 in

3.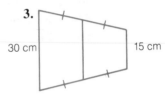
30 cm   15 cm

4. In the figure at the right, $\overline{SO} \parallel \overline{DQ} \parallel \overline{EV}$, $OQ = QV = 7$, and $SD = 4$. Find ED.

5. In the figure for Exercise 4, $\angle OQD \cong \angle V$, $\angle EDQ \cong \angle S$, $QV = 8$, and D is the midpoint of $\overline{ES}$. Find QO and VO.

6. One base of a trapezoid measures 23 and its median measures 20. Find the length of the other base.

7. In the figure at the right, $AD = DB = 6$, $AC = 18$, and $\overline{DE} \parallel \overline{BC}$. Find AE and EC.

8. In the figure for Exercise 7, $\angle AED \cong \angle C$, $AE = EC = 15$ and $AD = 10$. Find DB and AB.

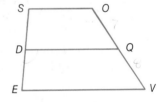

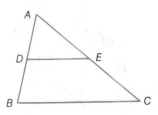

WRITTEN EXERCISES

A   In Exercises 1–10, find the unknown lengths for each trapezoid.

	One Base	Other Base	Median		One Base	Other Base	Median
1.	15	25	?	**2.**	17	8	?
3.	9	$4\frac{1}{2}$	?	**4.**	$12 + 3x$	$16 - 3x$	?
5.	$3t + 8$	$5t - 6$	?	**6.**	r	s	?
7.	54	?	36	**8.**	23	?	15
9.	?	12.5	20	**10.**	?	a	m

Segments *AB*, *CD*, and *EF* are drawn on ruled paper as shown with $AB = 2\frac{1}{4}$, $CD = 2\frac{7}{8}$, and $EF = 3\frac{3}{8}$. The rules are equally spaced.

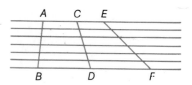

11. How long is each smaller segment of $\overline{AB}$?

12. How long is each smaller segment of $\overline{CD}$?

13. How long is each smaller segment of $\overline{EF}$?

14. Supply the missing reasons for this proof of Theorem 5–14.

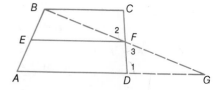

Given: Trapezoid *ABCD* with median *EF*.

Prove: $\overline{EF} \parallel \overline{AD} \parallel \overline{BC}$; $EF = \frac{1}{2}(AD + BC)$

Statements	Reasons
1. Join *B* and *F* and extend $\overline{BF}$ to intersect $\overline{AD}$ extended to *G*.	1. Two points determine a line.
2. In triangles *BCF* and *GDF*, $\overline{CF} \cong \overline{FD}$.	2. Definition of median
3. $\overline{BC} \parallel \overline{AG}$	3. Definition of trapezoid
4. $\angle C \cong \angle 1$	4. (3). __?__
5. $\angle 2 \cong \angle 3$	5. (1). __?__
6. $\triangle BCF \cong \triangle GDF$	6. (2), (4), (5). __?__
7. In $\triangle ABG$, $\overline{BF} \cong \overline{FG}$.	7. (6). __?__
8. $\overline{BE} \cong \overline{EA}$	8. __?__
9. $\overline{EF} \parallel \overline{AD}$, $EF = \frac{1}{2}(AD + DG)$	9. (7), (8). Theorem 5–13
10. $\overline{BC} \cong \overline{DG}$	10. (6). __?__
11. $BC = DG$	11. (10). __?__
12. $EF = \frac{1}{2}(AD + BC)$	12. (9), (11). __?__
13. $\overline{EF} \parallel \overline{AD} \parallel \overline{BC}$	13. (3), (9). __?__

B

15. Prove Theorem 5–15.

Given: $\overleftrightarrow{AE} \parallel \overleftrightarrow{BF} \parallel \overleftrightarrow{CG} \parallel \overleftrightarrow{DH}$; $\overline{AB} \cong \overline{BC} \cong \overline{CD}$

Prove: $\overline{EF} \cong \overline{FG} \cong \overline{GH}$

Plan: From point *E*, draw a segment parallel to $\overleftrightarrow{AB}$ and intersecting $\overleftrightarrow{BF}$ at *X*; from point *F*, draw a segment parallel to $\overleftrightarrow{AB}$ and intersecting $\overleftrightarrow{CG}$ at *Y*; from point *G*, draw a segment parallel to $\overleftrightarrow{AB}$ and intersecting $\overleftrightarrow{DH}$ at *Z*. Show that quadrilaterals *AEXB*, *BFYC*, and *CGZD* are parallelograms. Since $\overline{AB} \cong \overline{EX}$, $\overline{BC} \cong \overline{FY}$, $\overline{CD} \cong \overline{GZ}$, and $\overline{AB} \cong \overline{BC} \cong \overline{CD}$, then $\overline{EX} \cong \overline{FY} \cong \overline{GZ}$. Also, $\angle 4 \cong \angle 5 \cong \angle 6$ and $\angle 1 \cong \angle 2 \cong \angle 3$. Therefore, $\triangle EXF \cong \triangle FYG \cong \triangle GZH$ by the SAA Corollary and $\overline{EF} \cong \overline{FG} \cong \overline{GH}$.

16. Prove Corollary 5–16.

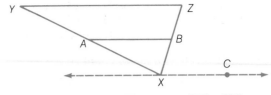

Given: In $\triangle XYZ$, $\overline{AB} \parallel \overline{YZ}$;
$\overline{AB}$ bisects $\overline{XY}$.

Prove: $\overline{AB}$ bisects $\overline{XZ}$.

Plan: Through point X, draw a line XC parallel to $\overline{AB}$. Since $\overline{AB} \parallel \overline{YZ}$, then $\overleftrightarrow{XC} \parallel \overline{YZ}$. Since $\overline{AB}$ bisects $\overline{XY}$, then $\overline{XA} \cong \overline{AY}$. Thus, $\overline{XB} \cong \overline{BZ}$ by Theorem 5–15 and $\overline{AB}$ bisects $\overline{XZ}$.

17. Given: $ABCD$ is an isosceles trapezoid
with bases DC and AB;
$\overline{DE} \perp \overline{AB}$; $\overline{CF} \perp \overline{AB}$

Prove: $\triangle EAD \cong \triangle FBC$

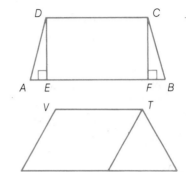

18. Given: $TVXZ$ is a trapezoid
with bases VT and XZ;
$\overline{TY} \parallel \overline{VX}$; $\angle VTY \cong \angle TZY$

Prove: a. $\angle TZX \cong \angle ZXV$
b. $\overline{TZ} \cong \overline{VX}$

19. Prove Corollary 5–17. (HINT: Draw a diagonal of the trapezoid. Then use Corollary 5–16.)

20. Write the formula for the length of the median, m, of a trapezoid whose bases have lengths of b_1 and b_2. Solve this formula for b_1.

In Exercises 21–23, find the measure of each base and the measure of the median of each trapezoid.

21.

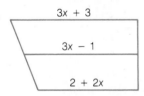

22.

23.

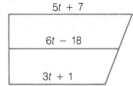

In Exercises 24–29, tell whether each statement is true for every trapezoid, E, for isosceles trapezoids only, I, or is false, F.

REMEMBER: In an isosceles trapezoid, the nonparallel sides are congruent.

24. When a diagonal of a trapezoid is drawn, two congruent triangles are formed.

25. All trapezoids have two pairs of base angles.

26. The diagonals of a trapezoid are congruent.

27. In a trapezoid, opposite angles are congruent.

28. In a trapezoid, opposite angles are supplementary.

29. The base angles of a trapezoid are congruent.

30. In isosceles trapezoid $SQTB$ at the left below, m$\angle S = 58$.

Find the measures of the remaining angles.

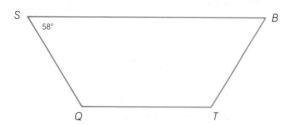 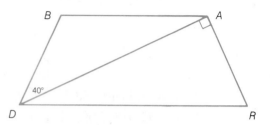

31. In isosceles trapezoid $DRAB$, $\triangle DAR$ is a right triangle and m$\angle ADB = 40$. Find m$\angle ADR$, m$\angle DAB$, m$\angle R$, m$\angle RDB$, m$\angle B$, and m$\angle RAB$.

32. In isosceles trapezoid $HTRC$, m$\angle HTC = 98$ and $\angle HRT = 26$.

Find the measure of each numbered angle.

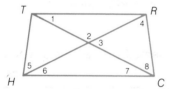

33. Given: $ABCD$ is a parallelogram with $\overline{AB}$ extended to E; Angles ADC and CEB are supplementary.

Prove: $AECD$ is an isosceles trapezoid.

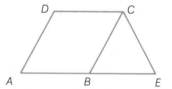

C

34. Refer to the figure at the right to write an alternative proof of this theorem. (See Exercise 42 on page 223.)

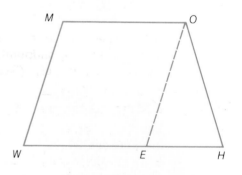

The base angles of an isosceles trapezoid are congruent.

Plan: Introduce $\overline{OE}$ with E on $\overline{WH}$ such that $\overline{WM} \parallel \overline{OE}$. Prove that $WEOM$ is a parallelogram. Then use the properties of a parallelogram and of parallel lines to complete the proof.

35. Trapezoid $ABCD$ has bases AD and BC. Median XY intersects $\overline{AB}$ in X and $\overline{CD}$ in Y. The intersection of $\overline{XY}$ and diagonal AC is R; the intersection of $\overline{XY}$ and diagonal BD is S. If $BC = 23$ and $AD = 45$, find RS.

36. Use the figure for Exercise 35 to prove that $RS = \frac{1}{2}(AD - BC)$.

37. The midpoints of the sides of an isosceles trapezoid are joined in order. Prove that the quadrilateral thus formed is a rhombus.

Review

Refer to ▱ *PARW* for Exercises 1–10.
(Section 5–1)

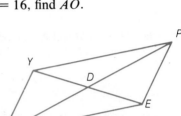

1. $\overline{WR} \parallel$ __?__
2. $\overline{WP} \cong$ __?__
3. $\angle RAP \cong \angle$ __?__
4. $\overline{PO} \cong$ __?__
5. $\triangle WPR \cong \triangle$ __?__
6. $\triangle ARW \cong \triangle$ __?__
7. If $m\angle WPA = 60$, find $m\angle WRA$.
8. If $m\angle WPA = 60$, find $m\angle PAR$.
9. If $AR = 12$, find PW.
10. If $AW = 16$, find AO.

Refer to ▱ *TEPY* for Exercises 11–14.
Use the given information to complete each statement. *(Section 5–2)*

11. If $\overline{YT} \cong \overline{PE}$, then $\overline{YP} \cong$ __?__ .
12. If $\overline{YT} \cong \overline{PE}$, then $\overline{YT} \parallel$ __?__ .
13. *D* is the midpoint of __?__ and __?__ .
14. If $\angle PYT$ is supplementary to $\angle YTE$ and $\angle PYT \cong \angle PET$, then $\angle YTE$ is supplementary to __?__ .

In Exercises 15–18, match the property named with all the quadrilaterals in the box that have the property. *(Section 5–3)*

15. The diagonals are congruent.
16. Opposite sides are parallel.
17. Adjacent sides are perpendicular.
18. The diagonals bisect the angles.

Quadrilateral	Rectangle
Trapezoid	Rhombus
Parallelogram	Square

In Exercises 19–22, refer to $\triangle DMW$. *Y*, *A*, and *O* are the midpoints of *DW*, *WM*, and $\overline{DM}$, respectively. *(Section 5–4)*

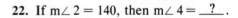

19. If $YA = 2.3$, then $DM =$ __?__ .
20. If $m\angle M = 127$, then $m\angle 1 =$ __?__ .
21. If $DW = 8.8$, then $AO =$ __?__ .
22. If $m\angle 2 = 140$, then $m\angle 4 =$ __?__ .

In the figure at the right, $\overline{AB}$ joins the midpoints of $\overline{RT}$ and $\overline{ST}$, and $\overline{DE}$ is the median of trapezoid *RABS*. *(Section 5–5)*

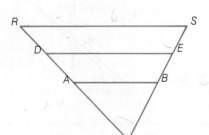

23. If $RT = 12$, then $RA =$ __?__ .
24. If $RS = 24$, then $AB =$ __?__ .
25. If $m\angle S = 60$, then $m\angle ABT =$ __?__ .
26. If $RS = 6.8$, $ST = 4.2$, and $RT = 5.6$, find the perimeter of trapezoid *DABE*.

APPLICATIONS

USING QUADRILATERALS

A   These problems apply geometric concepts studied in Sections 5–1 through 5–5.

1. When the trapeze shown in the figure is pulled to one side and held taut as shown, $\square ABCD$ is formed. If m$\angle A =$ 125, find m$\angle B$, m$\angle C$, and m$\angle D$.

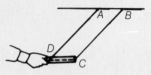

2. In the two-seater bicycle shown at the left below, quadrilateral *BIKE* represents part of the frame of the bicycle. If $\overline{BI}$ is parallel to $\overline{KE}$ and $\overline{IK}$ is parallel to $\overline{EB}$, explain why quadrilateral *BIKE* is a parallelogram.

3. An adjustable ironing board is built so that $BR = OR$ and $AR = DR$. Thus, when leg *BD* is locked in one of the adjustable positions, the top of the board remains parallel to the floor. Explain why this is true.

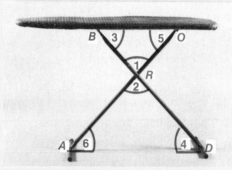

B

4. A portion of the fence shown below consists of four parallel posts anchored in concrete at equally-spaced points. If $TE = 1\frac{1}{3}$ yards, find *TA* in inches. Give the reason(s) for your answer. (HINT: 36 inches = 1 yard.)

5. In the signal light shown below, *D* is the midpoint of $\overline{BC}$ and *E* is the midpoint of $\overline{AC}$. If $ED = 7$ centimeters, find *AB*. Give the reason(s) for your answer.

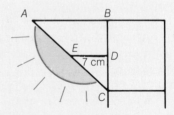

6. In the electrocardiogram reading below, $a \parallel b \parallel c \parallel d \parallel e \parallel f \parallel g$. Points A, B, C, D and points $E, F, G,$ and H are collinear, and $\overline{AB} \cong \overline{BC} \cong \overline{CD}$. State the theorem you would use to prove that $\overline{EF} \cong \overline{FG} \cong \overline{GH}$.

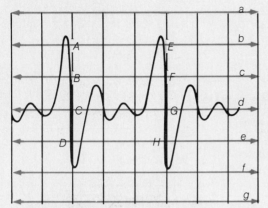

7. The figure below represents the first four floors of a department store, with $\overline{AB}$, $\overline{BC}$, and $\overline{CD}$ representing segments of line u, the "up" escalator. Explain why these segments are congruent. (Assume that ceiling heights of the floors are the same.)

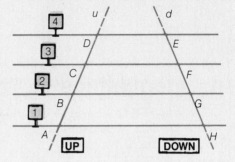

8. The side of an "in-and-out" tray in an office has the shape of a trapezoid. If the length of the lower base is 33.5 centimeters and the length of the median is 32.3 centimeters, find the length of the upper base.

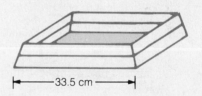

$\vdash$————33.5 cm————$\dashv$

C

9. **Given:** Envelope $BCDEA$;
   $\overline{AE} \parallel \overline{CD}$;
   $AE = CD$;
   P is the midpoint of $\overline{AB}$;
   K is the midpoint of $\overline{BC}$;
   $EM = \frac{1}{2}ED$

   Prove: $KQ = EQ$

10. When light is reflected from a smooth surface, the angle between the incoming light beam and the surface equals the angle between the reflected light beam and the surface. In the figure, m∠$NST = 75$, m∠$PNQ = 90$, and the light beam makes an angle of $35°$ with $\overrightarrow{NR}$ as it reflects from $\overrightarrow{NR}$. Then it reflects from $\overrightarrow{NS}$, from $\overrightarrow{ST}$, and from $\overrightarrow{NR}$ again. Find the angle at which the light beam reflects from $\overrightarrow{NR}$ the second time.

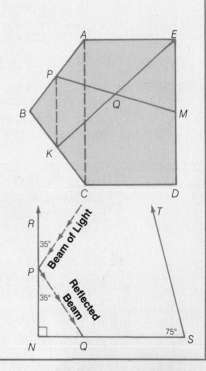

Use $>$, $<$, or $=$ to complete each statement. *(Pages 156–158)*

1. If $CD + DE = CE$, then CD __?__ CE.
2. If $HR < MP$, then $HR + YZ$ __?__ $MP + YZ$.
3. If $GL > FG$, then $2\,GL$ __?__ $2\,FG$.
4. If $PQ < RS$ and $RS < TV$, then PQ __?__ TV.
5. If $NO \neq DB$, then NO __?__ DB or NO __?__ DB.

5–6 Inequalities in Triangles

In $\triangle ABC$ at the right, side AC is opposite $\angle B$, side BC is opposite $\angle A$, and $\angle C$ is the angle opposite side AB. Further,

$$AB > BC > AC,$$

and

$$\mathrm{m}\angle C > \mathrm{m}\angle A > \mathrm{m}\angle B.$$

These inequalities suggest the following theorems.

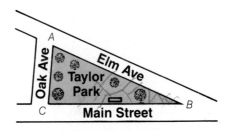

Theorem 5–18 If two sides of a triangle are not congruent, then the angles opposite these sides are not congruent, and the smaller angle is opposite the smaller side.

Theorem 5–19 If two angles of a triangle are not congruent, then the sides opposite these angles are not congruent, and the smaller side is opposite the smaller angle.

You are asked to prove these theorems in the Written Exercises.

EXAMPLE 1 Use $\triangle EFG$ and the given information to determine whether each conclusion is true, T, or false, F. Give the reason(s) for each answer.

a. $\angle F \not\cong \angle G$	$\overline{GE} \not\cong \overline{EF}$	True, by Theorem 5–19
b. $GF < EF$	$\mathrm{m}\angle E > \mathrm{m}\angle G$	False; $\mathrm{m}\angle E < \mathrm{m}\angle G$ by Theorem 5–18
c. $\mathrm{m}\angle G > \mathrm{m}\angle F$	$EF > EG$	True, by Theorem 5–19
d. $EF > EG > GF$	$\mathrm{m}\angle G > \mathrm{m}\angle F > \mathrm{m}\angle E$	True, by Theorem 5–18

Theorem 5–18 can be used to prove Theorem 5–20.

Theorem 5–20	The perpendicular segment from a point to a line is the shortest distance from the point to the line.

The proof of this theorem is given in Example 2.

EXAMPLE 2   Given: P is a point not on line m;
$\overline{PA} \perp m$;
B is any point on line m
different from A.

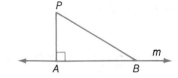

Prove: $PA < PB$

Proof:

Statements	Reasons
1. $\overline{PA} \perp m$	1. Given
2. $\angle A$ is a right angle.	2. (1). Definition of perpendicular lines
3. $m\angle A = 90$	3. (2). Definition of right angle
4. In $\triangle PAB$, $m\angle B < 90$.	4. (2). A triangle can have no more than one right angle.
5. $m\angle B < m\angle A$	5. (3), (4). Substitution property
6. $PA < PB$	6. (5). If two angles of a triangle are not congruent, then the sides opposite these angles are not congruent, and the smaller side is opposite the smaller angle.

CLASSROOM EXERCISES

1. Name an exterior angle of $\triangle ADC$.
2. Compare $m\angle 4$ and $m\angle 1$.
3. Compare $m\angle 4$ and $m\angle A$.
4. Compare $m\angle 3$ and $m\angle 2$.

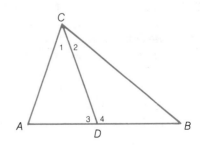

In Exercises 5–8, $\overline{CA} \cong \overline{CD}$.

5. Compare $m\angle A$ and $m\angle 3$.
6. Compare $m\angle 3$ and $m\angle B$.
7. Compare $m\angle A$ and $m\angle B$.
8. Compare BC and AC.

WRITTEN EXERCISES

A

1. In △ABC, AB < BC < AC. Compare the measures of the angles of the triangle in a similar way.

2. In △RST, m∠S < m∠T < m∠R. Compare the measures of the sides of the triangle in a similar way.

3. Complete the proof.

Given: $\overline{CD}$ bisects ∠C.

Prove: m∠3 > m∠1

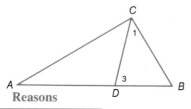

Statements	Reasons
1. $\overline{CD}$ bisects ∠C.	1. _?_
2. m∠ACD = m∠1	2. (1). _?_
3. m∠3 > m∠ACD	3. _?_
4. m∠3 > m∠1	4. (2), (3). _?_

4. Complete the proof.

Given: AB > BC; AD > DC

Prove: m∠C > m∠A

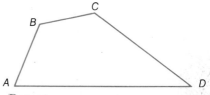

Statements	Reasons
1. In quadrilateral ABCD, draw $\overline{AC}$.	1. _?_
2. AB > BC	2. _?_
3. m∠ACB > m∠BAC	3. (2). _?_
4. AD > DC	4. _?_
5. m∠ACD > m∠CAD	5. (4). _?_
6. m∠C = m∠ACB + m∠ACD m∠A = m∠BAC + m∠CAD	6. _?_
7. m∠ACB + m∠ACD > m∠BAC + m∠CAD	7. (3), (5). (See Exercise 28, page 161.)
8. m∠C > m∠A	8. (6), (7). _?_

5. Explain why the hypotenuse of a right triangle is the longest side.

6. Complete the proof.

Given: AB = BC; AD = DC;
      AD > AB

Prove: m∠B > m∠D

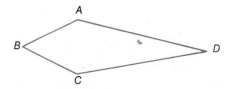

Statements	Reasons
1. Draw $\overline{BD}$.	1. ?
2. $AD > AB$	2. ?
3. $m\angle DBA > m\angle BDA$	3. (2). ?
4. $AD = DC$; $AB = BC$	4. ?
5. $DC > BC$	5. (2), (4). ?
6. $m\angle DBC > m\angle BDC$	6. (5). ?
7. $m\angle B = m\angle DBA + m\angle DBC$; $m\angle D = m\angle BDA + m\angle BDC$	7. ?
8. $m\angle DBA + m\angle DBC > m\angle BDA + m\angle BDC$	8. (3), (6). ?
9. $m\angle B > m\angle D$	9. (7), (8). ?

7. Complete the proof.

Given: $\triangle AGH$ is an isosceles triangle with base GH.

Prove: $KG < KH$

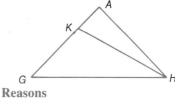

Statements	Reasons
1. Isosceles triangle AGH with base GH.	1. ?
2. $\angle G \cong \angle GHA$	2. (1). ?
3. $m\angle GHA = m\angle GHK + m\angle KHA$	3. ?
4. $m\angle KHA > 0$	4. Definition of angle measure
5. $m\angle GHK < m\angle GHA$	5. Definition of inequality
6. $m\angle G = m\angle GHA$	6. (2). ?
7. $m\angle GHK < m\angle G$	7. (5), (6). ?
8. $KG < KH$	8. (7). ?

8. In quadrilateral $BCDR$ at the left below, which segment is the shortest?

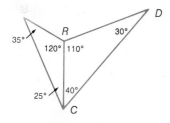

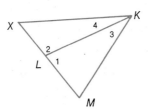

9. In the figure at the right above, $\overline{LM}$ is the base of isosceles $\triangle KLM$. If $m\angle X > m\angle 4$, prove that $KM > XL$.

10. Given: Isosceles $\triangle PQR$ with base PQ;
      $m\angle RTQ > m\angle 1$

Prove: $m\angle RTQ > m\angle 2$

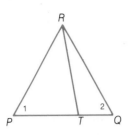

11. Given: Quadrilateral $WGNA$ with diagonals WN and AG;
      $WE + EA > WA$;
      $NE + EG > GN$

Prove: $WN + AG > WA + NG$

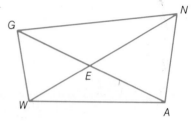

12. Given: Rhombus $QSTW$ with diagonals SW and TQ;
      $m\angle STW < m\angle QST$

Prove: $m\angle 1 < m\angle 2$

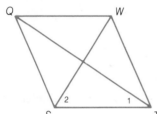

13. Given: Rectangle $GHEF$; $m\angle 1 > m\angle 2$

Prove: $m\angle 3 < m\angle 4$

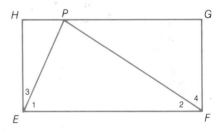

14. Prove Theorem 5–18.

   Given: $BC > AC$

   Prove: $m\angle A > m\angle B$

   Plan: Select D on $\overline{BC}$ so that $CD = CA$. Show that since $m\angle BAC > m\angle 2$, and since $m\angle 2 = m\angle 1$, then $m\angle BAC > m\angle 1$.
Since $m\angle 1 > m\angle B$ by Theorem 4–1, $m\angle A > m\angle B$.

15. Prove Theorem 5–19.

   Given: $m\angle B > m\angle A$

   Prove: $AC > BC$

   Plan: Use the indirect method.
Either $AC < BC$ or $AC = BC$ or $AC > BC$. To prove $AC > BC$, show that $AC < BC$ or $AC = BC$ leads to a contradiction. Use Theorem 5–18 to eliminate $AC < BC$, and the Isosceles Triangle Theorem to eliminate $AC = BC$. Then $AC > BC$.

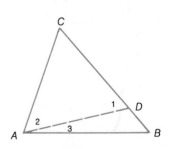

16. In the figure at the left below, $\triangle XKM$ with base XK and $\triangle KLM$ with base LM are isosceles triangles, with m$\angle X <$ m$\angle 2$. Prove that $KX > XM$.

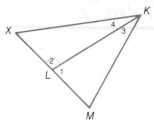

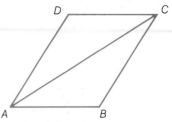

17. In the parallelogram at the right above, diagonal AC is drawn and $AB < BC$. Prove that m$\angle BAC >$ m$\angle DAC$.

18. In isosceles triangle XYZ with base XZ (see the figure at the left below), P is a point between Y and Z, and $PY < XY$. Prove that m$\angle YXZ <$ m$\angle YPX$.

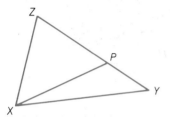

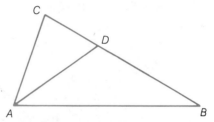

19. In $\triangle ABC$ at the right above, $\overline{AD}$ bisects angle A. If D is a point between B and C, prove that $AC > CD$.

20. In $\triangle RST$ at the left below, RX is a median and $RT > RS$. Prove that m$\angle TXR >$ m$\angle$ T.

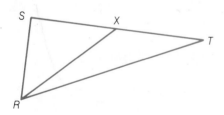

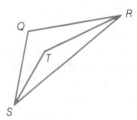

21. In $\triangle QRS$ at the right above, the bisectors of angles R and S intersect at T. Let m$\angle R = 2x$, m$\angle S = 2y$, m$\angle Q = 2z$, and m$\angle STR = w$. Show algebraically that $w > 90$.

22. In quadrilateral $TALK$, $\overline{TA}$ is the longest side and $\overline{LK}$ is the shortest side. Prove that m$\angle K >$ m$\angle A$.

23. In triangle KJL, M is a point on side KL such that $\triangle JML$ is isosceles with base ML. Prove that $KJ > JL$.

24. The diagonals of parallelogram $FGHM$ intersect at K and $MH > GH$. Prove that m$\angle FKG >$ m$\angle FGK$.

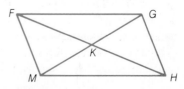

25. Prove that the length of the altitude to one side of a triangle is less than half the sum of the lengths of the other two sides.

26. In the figure at the right, $\overline{XT}$ is perpendicular to $\overline{TA}$, $\overline{XE}$ is perpendicular to $\overline{ER}$, and $\overline{XE} \cong \overline{XT}$. Explain why $m\angle 2 > m\angle 1$ and also why $m\angle TAE < 2\, m\angle 1$.

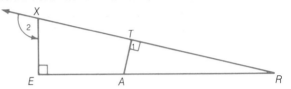

27. Prove that if a parallelogram is not a rhombus, its diagonals do not bisect the angles of the parallelogram.

28. Two given lines are cut by a transversal so that the sum of the interior angles on one side of the transversal is less than 180. Explain why the lines will intersect on that side of the transversal.

29. Prove that the length of the base of an isosceles triangle is less than twice the length of one of the equal legs.

Puzzle

One–fourth of a square has been cut away, as shown at the right. How can you divide the figure shown into four congruent parts?

(HINT: No part is a square or a triangle.)

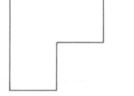

ALGEBRA REVIEW CAPSULE FOR SECTION 5–7

Solve and check.

Example: $3 - 2x > 12$

Solution: $3 - 2x > 12$

$3 - 2x - 3 > 12 - 3$ ⟵ **By the Addition Property for Inequalities**

$-2x > 9$

$(-\frac{1}{2})(-2x) < 9(-\frac{1}{2})$ ⟵ **Since you are multiplying by a negative number, replace $>$ with $<$.**

$x < -4\frac{1}{2}$

1. $m + 6 > 9$ **2.** $10 < x + 4$ **3.** $c + 2 < 4$ **4.** $n - 5 > 22$

5. $z + 4 < 6$ **6.** $p > 6 + 5$ **7.** $4 + 9 < f$ **8.** $x + 7.2 > 9.1$

9. $2q > 16$ **10.** $12 > 2t$ **11.** $3v < 30$ **12.** $25 > -5y$

13. $7 < 2p + 9$ **14.** $3t + 2 > 20$ **15.** $4 - 4r < -12$ **16.** $48 < 12 - 3m$

5-7 More Inequalities in Triangles

Try to draw a triangle with sides of 4 centimeters, 6 centimeters, and 10 centimeters. You will find that the 4–centimeter and 6–centimeter sides do not intersect to form a triangle.

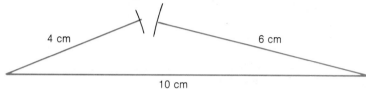

4 cm   6 cm

10 cm

The reason for this is given in the *Triangle Inequality Theorem.*

**Theorem
5–21**

Triangle Inequality Theorem
The sum of the lengths of two sides of a triangle is greater than the length of the third side.

EXAMPLE 1

Given: $\triangle RTQ$ is any triangle.

Prove: $RT + TQ > RQ$

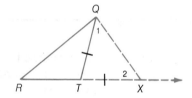

Proof:

Statements	Reasons
1. Extend $\overline{RT}$ to X so that $\overline{TX} \cong \overline{TQ}$.	1. Ruler Postulate
2. $TX = TQ$	2. (1). Congruent segments are equal.
3. Draw $\overline{QX}$.	3. Two points determine a line.
4. $\angle 1 \cong \angle 2$	4. (1). The Isosceles Triangle Theorem
5. $m\angle 1 = m\angle 2$	5. (4). Congruent angles have equal measures.
6. $RX = RT + TX$	6. Definition of betweenness of points
7. $RX = RT + TQ$	7. (2), (6). Substitution property
8. $m\angle 1 + m\angle RQT = m\angle RQX$	8. Definition of betweenness of rays
9. $m\angle RQT > 0$	9. Definition of angle measure
10. $m\angle 1 < m\angle RQX$	10. (8), (9). Definition of inequality
11. $m\angle 2 < m\angle RQX$	11. (5), (10). Substitution property
12. $RX > RQ$	12. (11). If two angles of a triangle are not congruent, then the sides opposite these angles are not congruent, and the smaller side is opposite the smaller angle.
13. $RT + TQ > RQ$	13. (7), (12). Substitution property

Example 2 shows how you can use the Triangle Inequality Theorem.

EXAMPLE 2   Which of the following sets of numbers can be the lengths of the sides of a triangle? Explain each answer.

a. 8, 8, 9   b. 11, 5, 18   c. 16, 32, 16

Solution:

Lengths of Sides	Form a Triangle?	Reason
a. 8, 8, 9	Yes	$8 + 8 > 9$ $8 + 9 > 8$
b. 11, 5, 18	No	$11 + 5 \not> 18$
c. 16, 32, 16	No	$16 + 16 \not> 32$

The *Hinge Theorem* concerns inequalities in two triangles.

Theorem 5–22

The Hinge Theorem

If two sides of one triangle are congruent to two sides of another triangle and if the included angles are not congruent, then the remaining sides are also not congruent, and the smaller side is opposite the smaller angle.

The converse of Theorem 5–22 is also a theorem. You are asked to prove both theorems in the Written Exercises.

Theorem 5–23

Converse of the Hinge Theorem

If two sides of one triangle are congruent to two sides of another triangle and if the third sides are not congruent, then the angles opposite the third sides are also not congruent, and the smaller angle is opposite the smaller side.

CLASSROOM EXERCISES

In Exercises 1–5, write the letter of the response that best completes each statement.

1. Two sides of a triangle measure 10 centimeters and 15 centimeters. Which measure is possible for the third side?

   a. 5 cm   b. 20 cm   c. 25 cm   d. 30 cm

2. In $\triangle DFE$, $DE = 4$ cm, $EF = 7$ cm, and $m\angle E = 70$. In $\triangle GJH$, $GH = 4$ cm, $HJ = 7$ cm, and $m\angle H = 60$. Then

   a. $DF > GJ$ b. $DF < GJ$ c. $DF = GJ$ d. $DF = 11$ cm

3. In $\triangle KQM$, $KM = 4$, $MQ = 5$, and $KQ = 7$. In $\triangle NPO$, $NO = 4$, $OP = 5$, and $NP = 8$. Then

    a. $m\angle M > m\angle O$ **b.** $m\angle M < m\angle O$

    c. $m\angle M = m\angle O$ **d.** $m\angle M = 90$

4. In $\triangle MNO$, $\overline{MN} \cong \overline{NO}$ and $MO > MN$. Then

    a. $m\angle M > m\angle O$ **b.** $m\angle M < m\angle O$

    c. $m\angle M = m\angle O$ **d.** $m\angle M = 90$

5. The measures of two sides of a triangle are 22 and 34. Which measure is possible for the third side?

    a. 56   **b.** 5   **c.** 51   **d.** 12

WRITTEN EXERCISES

A

1. In triangle ABC, $AB + BC > AC$. Draw triangle ABC and write two other inequalities.

> In Exercises 2–13, write *Yes* if a triangle can have sides with the given measures. Otherwise, write *No.*

2. 2, 3, and 3   **3.** 2, 3, and 4   **4.** 2, 3, and 5

5. 5, 12, and 13   **6.** 12, 13, and 21   **7.** 100, 150, and 200

8. 3, 5, and 9   **9.** 7, 9, and 14   **10.** 3, 4, and 7

11. 1, 1, and 1   **12.** 1, 2, and 3   **13.** 3, 4, and 5

> In Exercises 14 and 15, use the figures and the given information to replace ___?___ with $>$, $<$, or $=$.

14. Given: $m\angle F > m\angle C$ **15.** Given: $BC > FE$

    Conclusion: AB ___?___ DE Conclusion: $m\angle A$ ___?___ $m\angle D$

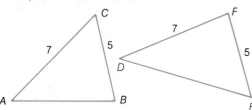 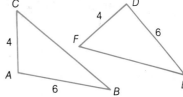

> In Exercises 16–19, use the figure below and the given information to complete each conclusion.

16. Given: $\overline{HO} \cong \overline{OP}$, $m\angle 4 > m\angle 3$

    Conclusion: $HE > $ ___?___

17. Given: $\overline{HO} \cong \overline{OP}$; $HE > EP$

    Conclusion: $m\angle 4 > m\angle$ ___?___

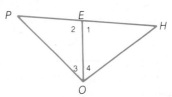

18. Given: E is the midpoint of $\overline{HP}$;
$HO > OP$

Conclusion: m∠ 1 > m∠ ___?___

19. Given: $\overline{OE}$ bisects $\overline{HP}$; $HO > OP$

Conclusion: m∠ 1 > m∠ ___?___

20. Complete the reasons in the following proof.

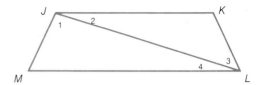

Given: $\overline{MJ} \cong \overline{KL}$; $JK < ML$

Prove: m∠ 3 < m∠ 1

Statements	Reasons
1. $\overline{MJ} \cong \overline{KL}$	1. ___?___
2. $\overline{JL} \cong \overline{JL}$	2. ___?___
3. $JK < ML$	3. ___?___
4. m∠ 3 < m∠ 1	4. (1), (2), (3). ___?___

B

21. Two rods measure 3 centimeters and 5 centimeters. They are placed as at the left below. Solve the inequality.

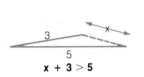

x + 3 > 5

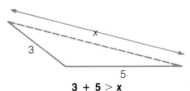

3 + 5 > x

22. The rods in Exercise 21 are placed as at the right above. Solve the inequality.

23. Use Exercises 21 and 22 to complete the following statement: If two sides of a triangle have lengths of 3 and 5, the third side must be longer than ___?___ or shorter than ___?___.

24. Write one algebraic inequality for the statement in Exercise 23.

> In Exercises 25–27, the lengths of two sides of a triangle are given. Complete this sentence for each triangle:
>
> The length of the third side, s, is such that ___?___ < s < ___?___.

25. 12 mm; 18 mm   **26.** 34 m; 17 m   **27.** 7.8 cm; 8.3 cm

28. The lengths of the sides of a triangle are 5 units and 7 units. The length of the third side, s, is such that ___?___ < s < ___?___.

29. Suppose that x and y are the lengths of two sides of a triangle with $x < y$ and that the length of the third side is z. Then ___?___ < z < ___?___.

30. In the figure at the right, O is the center of the circle, $\overline{OD} \cong \overline{OC} \cong \overline{OA} \cong \overline{OB}$, and m∠ DOC > m∠ AOB. Prove that $DC > AB$.

31. Given that O is the center of a circle, with $\overline{OD} \cong \overline{OC} \cong \overline{OB} \cong \overline{OA}$, and $DC > AB$, prove that m$\angle\, COD >$ m$\angle\, AOB$. (See the figure for Exercise 30.)

32. In triangle XZY, $\overline{XZ} \cong \overline{YZ}$ and m$\angle\, 1 >$ m$\angle\, 2$. Prove that $XW < WY$.

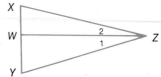

33. In the figure for Exercise 32, $\overline{XZ} \cong \overline{YZ}$ and $YW > XW$. Prove that m$\angle\, 1 >$ m$\angle\, 2$.

34. In $\triangle AKR$ at the left below, $\overline{ZR} \cong \overline{AK}$. Prove that $KR > AZ$.

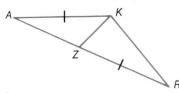
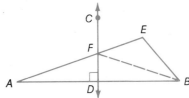

35. In the figure at the right above, $\overleftrightarrow{CD}$ is the perpendicular bisector of $\overline{AB}$, and E is not on $\overleftrightarrow{CD}$. Prove that $EA > EB$.

36. Prove Theorem 5–22. (HINT: In triangles ABC and DEF below, $\overline{AC} \cong \overline{DF}$, $\overline{CB} \cong \overline{FE}$, and m$\angle\, ACB >$ m$\angle\, F$ Draw $\overline{CH}$, $\overline{AH}$, $\overline{CG}$, and $\overline{GH}$ such that $\angle ACH \cong \angle F$, $\overline{CH} \cong \overline{FE}$, and $\overline{CG}$ bisects $\angle BCH$.)

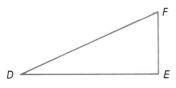
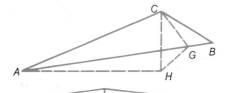

37. **Given:** A quadrilateral with sides of length q, r, s, t; One diagonal has length d.

    Prove: $q + r + s + t > 2d$

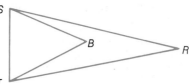

38. Prove Theorem 5–23 by the indirect method.

39. Prove that if the alternate vertices A, C, and E of regular hexagon $ABCDEF$ are joined, the perimeter of the triangle formed is less than the perimeter of the hexagon.

40. Show that the sum of the lengths of the altitudes of a triangle is less than the perimeter of the triangle.

41. Prove that for any quadrilateral whose sides have lengths a, b, c, and k and whose diagonals have lengths d_1 and d_2, the perimeter, P, of the quadrilateral is greater than $d_1 + d_2$.

42. **Given:** Triangle RST at the right is isosceles with the base ST and $TB > SB$.

    Prove: m$\angle\, RSB <$ m$\angle\, RTB$

5-8 Dihedral Angles

In the figure at the right, line p separates plane I into three sets of points.

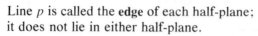

1. The **half-plane** that contains point A
2. The half-plane that contains point B
3. Line p itself

Line p is called the **edge** of each half-plane; it does not lie in either half-plane.

Each panel of the bifold door below may be thought of as a half-plane. The half-planes $ABYX$ and $DCYX$ intersect in line XY. The half-planes $ABYX$ and $DCYX$ and their edge $\overleftrightarrow{XY}$ form a *dihedral angle*.

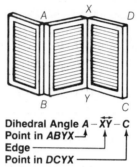

Dihedral Angle $A - \overleftrightarrow{XY} - C$
Point in $ABYX$
Edge
Point in $DCYX$

Definitions

> A **dihedral angle** is the union of two noncoplanar half-planes whose edges are the same line. The line is the **edge** of the dihedral angle and the half-planes are its **faces.**

More than one dihedral angle may have the same edge, as shown at the right. Angles $A–\overleftrightarrow{CB}–F$ and $F–\overleftrightarrow{BC}–D$ are adjacent dihedral angles.

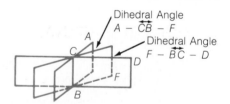

Dihedral Angle $A – \overleftrightarrow{CB} – F$

Dihedral Angle $F – \overleftrightarrow{BC} – D$

Definition

> A **plane angle** of a dihedral angle is the intersection of the dihedral angle and a plane perpendicular to its edge.

In the figure at the right, $\overleftrightarrow{EF}$ is perpendicular to plane I at S if it is perpendicular to every line in plane I that contains point S.

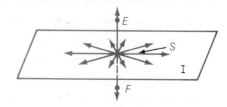

EXAMPLE

Plane I is passed through dihedral angle D-$\overleftrightarrow{EF}$-G so that it contains a point S on $\overleftrightarrow{EF}$ and is perpendicular to $\overleftrightarrow{EF}$. Describe the intersection of the plane and the dihedral angle.

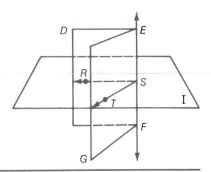

Solution: The intersection is a **plane angle**, $\angle RST$. The angle lies in plane I.

NOTE: Since an angle contains three noncollinear points, any angle determines exactly one plane.

The measure of a dihedral angle is the measure of any of its plane angles. All the plane angles of a given dihedral angle have the same measure. Dihedral angles that have the same measure are congruent. Thus, for dihedral angle C-$\overleftrightarrow{BE}$-D,

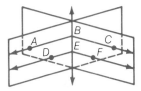

$$\angle ABC \cong \angle DEF.$$

Theorem 5-24

All plane angles of the same dihedral angle are congruent.

Acute, right, or **obtuse dihedral angles** are dihedral angles whose plane angles are acute, right, or obtuse, respectively. **Adjacent, vertical, complementary,** or **supplementary dihedral angles** are dihedral angles whose plane angles are adjacent, vertical, complementary, or supplementary, respectively.

CLASSROOM EXERCISES

For Exercises 1–6, complete each statement. Use the figure at the right in which $\overline{AQ} \perp \overline{QB}$, $\overline{AQ} \perp \overline{QC}$, and $\overline{CQ} \perp \overline{QB}$.

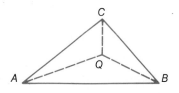

1. $\overline{CQ}$ is the edge of dihedral angle __?__ .
2. $\overline{CB}$ is the edge of dihedral angle __?__ .
3. $\overline{AB}$ is the edge of dihedral angle __?__ .
4. $\angle AQB$ is a plane angle of dihedral angle __?__ .
5. $\angle AQC$ is a plane angle of dihedral angle __?__ .
6. $\angle BQC$ is a plane angle of dihedral angle __?__ .
7. The measure of plane angle BQC is __?__ .
8. Plane angle AQB is congruent to plane angle __?__ .

WRITTEN EXERCISES

A   In the figure at the right, $\overleftrightarrow{BC}$ is the edge of half-planes AB, DB, and EB. Q is a point on $\overleftrightarrow{BC}$. $\overline{KQ}$, $\overline{MQ}$, and $\overline{OQ}$ lie in half-planes AB, DB, and EB respectively.

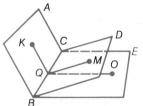

1. If $\angle KQM$ is a plane angle of dihedral angle $A\text{-}\overleftrightarrow{BC}\text{-}D$, are $\overline{KQ}$ and $\overline{MQ}$ each perpendicular to $\overleftrightarrow{BC}$? Give a reason for your answer.

2. If $\overline{MQ}$ and $\overline{OQ}$ are each perpendicular to $\overleftrightarrow{BC}$ at Q, is $\angle MQO$ a plane angle of angle $D\text{-}\overleftrightarrow{BC}\text{-}E$? Give a reason for your answer.

3. Is $\angle KQM \cong \angle MQO$? Give a reason for your answer.

     Choose the best answer. Choose a, b, c, or d.

     The figure at the right is a pyramid made up of four equilateral triangles. E and F are the midpoints of $\overline{BC}$ and $\overline{AX}$ respectively. $\overline{AE}$, $\overline{FE}$, and $\overline{XE}$ are drawn. $\overline{AD}$ is a median of $\triangle AXE$.

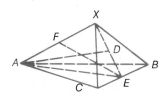

4. The number of dihedral angles in pyramid $X\text{-}ABC$ is
   a. 4.   **b.** 3.   **c.** 6.   **d.** 5.

5. The plane angle of dihedral angle $X\text{-}\overleftrightarrow{BC}\text{-}A$ is
   a. $\angle ACX$.   **b.** $\angle XEB$.   **c.** $\angle AEF$.   **d.** $\angle AEX$.

6. A plane angle of dihedral angle $C\text{-}\overleftrightarrow{AE}\text{-}X$ is
   a. $\angle XEC$.   **b.** Not shown.   **c.** $\angle XAC$.   **d.** $\angle CEF$.

7. Identify which of the following are right angles.
   a. $\angle BXE$ **b.** $\angle AEX$ **c.** $\angle AEC$ **d.** $\angle BEF$

8. Identify the pairs that are congruent dihedral angles.
   a. $\angle X\text{-}\overleftrightarrow{AB}\text{-}C$, $\angle A\text{-}\overleftrightarrow{BC}\text{-}X$ **b.** $\angle C\text{-}\overleftrightarrow{AX}\text{-}E$, $\angle F\text{-}\overleftrightarrow{AE}\text{-}C$
   c. $\angle B\text{-}\overleftrightarrow{AE}\text{-}D$, $\angle D\text{-}\overleftrightarrow{AX}\text{-}C$ **d.** $\angle B\text{-}\overleftrightarrow{AE}\text{-}X$, $\angle D\text{-}\overleftrightarrow{AE}\text{-}C$

9. Identify the pairs that are congruent segments.
   a. $\overline{CX}$, $\overline{AE}$ **b.** $\overline{ED}$, $\overline{DX}$ **c.** $\overline{EX}$, $\overline{EA}$ **d.** $\overline{AD}$, $\overline{FE}$

10. Identify the pairs that are congruent angles.
   a. $\angle FAE$, $\angle FXE$ **b.** $\angle ADE$, $\angle BXA$
   c. $\angle FEA$, $\angle BXE$ **d.** $\angle BXE$, $\angle EAC$

B   In the cube at the right, a plane is passed through the vertices A, C, and H forming $\triangle ACH$. In a cube, length, width, and height have the same measure, that is, $HG = GF = FB$. Use this figure for Exercises 11–24.

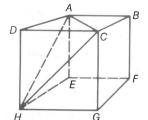

11. How many dihedral angles are there in the cube?

12. How many dihedral angles are there in pyramid $D\text{-}ACH$?

Find the measure of each angle.

13. $\angle DCH$ **14.** $\angle CHD$ **15.** $\angle CAD$ **16.** $\angle DCA$

17. $\angle HAD$ **18.** $\angle DHA$ **19.** $\angle GHC$ **20.** $\angle EHA$

21. What kind of triangle is $\triangle ACH$? Find the measure of each of its angles.

22. Find the measure of dihedral angle $C\text{-}\overleftrightarrow{DH}\text{-}A$.

23. Find the measure of dihedral angle $A\text{-}\overleftrightarrow{BC}\text{-}G$.

24. Explain how to get a plane angle of dihedral angle $D\text{-}\overleftrightarrow{HC}\text{-}A$.

The figure at the right shows two planes intersecting so that four dihedral angles are formed. Also, plane angle $CXD < 90$ and plane angle $DXE > 90$. Use this information for Exercises 25–28.

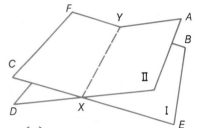

25. Name two acute dihedral angles.

26. Name two obtuse dihedral angles.

27. Name the dihedral angles that are supplementary to $\angle A\text{-}\overleftrightarrow{YX}\text{-}E$.

28. Name two pairs of vertical dihedral angles.

C Use the figure below for Exercises 29–30. Planes I and II are each perpendicular to plane III.

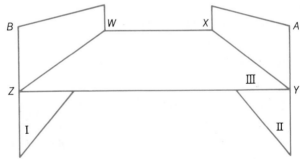

29. Name two right dihedral angles.

30. Are planes I and II necessarily parallel? Explain.

In this figure, planes I and II are parallel. Angles 1 and 2 are the plane angles of their respective dihedral angles.

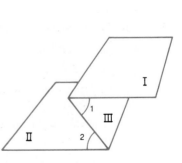

31. How would you describe plane III?

32. How would you describe $\angle 1$ and $\angle 2$?

33. What would you assume to be true of $\angle 1$ and $\angle 2$?

34. Write a definition for the interior of a dihedral angle.

35. Prove: *Two dihedral angles are congruent if their plane angles are congruent.*

36. Prove the converse of the statement in Exercise 35.

APPLICATIONS

USING INEQUALITIES AND DIHEDRAL ANGLES

These exercises apply geometric concepts studied in Sections 5–6 through 5–8.

A   In Exercises 1–5, state whether each conclusion follows from the given information. Answer *Yes* or *No*. Give the reason(s) for each answer.

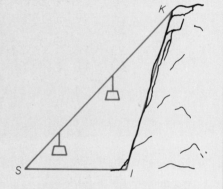

Given	**Conclusion**
1. $\angle S \cong \angle K$	$\overline{KI} \cong \overline{SI}$
2. $SK > KI$	$m\angle I > m\angle S$
3. $SK > SI$	$m\angle I < m\angle K$
4. $m\angle K < m\angle S$	$KI > SI$
5. $m\angle I > m\angle S > m\angle K$	$SI < KI < SK$

6. The door on a freezer (see the figure below) can be propped open in two different positions. State the theorem that gives the reason why $AC < DF$.

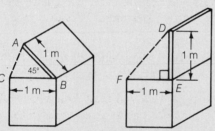

7. The doors at a kennel are all equal in size and are hinged to the wall as shown. The angle at which a door opens depends on the size of the animal passing through. Refer to the figure to explain why $AB < DE$.

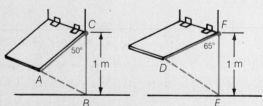

The figures below show the four congruent sections of a revolving door.

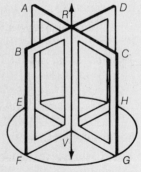

8. Name the dihedral angle formed by each section of the door.

9. Name two congruent angles of each dihedral angle.

10. Name two adjacent dihedral angles.

11. Name the edge of the dihedral angles.

BASIC: TRIANGLES

Problem: *Given the measure of three line segments, decide whether they can be used to form a triangle. Let* A, B, *and* C *represent the measures.*

Program:
```
10   READ A, B, C
20   IF A + B <= C THEN 70
30   IF A + C <= B THEN 70
40   IF B + C <= A THEN 70
50   PRINT "THE SEGMENTS CAN FORM A TRIANGLE."
60   GO TO 10
70   PRINT "THE SEGMENTS CANNOT FORM A TRIANGLE."
80   GO TO 10
90   DATA 5,6,7,13,3,5,12,6,8
100  END
```

Analysis:

Statements 10 and 90: READ A, B, C means to find three values for the measures of the segments from the DATA statement (Statement 90).

Statements 20 to 40 and 70: These statements test whether the segments are long enough to form a triangle. If any of these statements is true, Statement 70 is executed.

Statement 50: The computer gets to Statement 50 only if Statements 20 to 40 are false, in which case the segments can form a triangle.

Statements 60 and 80: These statements tell the computer to go back and read three more values from the data statement. Thus, the process repeats itself until all the data is used.

EXERCISES

A Run the program above with the given DATA statement and then by substituting the following DATA statements.

1. 90 DATA 6,4,8,12,7,20,13,3,4
2. 90 DATA 3,2,5,4,8,10,7,9,3
3. 90 DATA 24,36,59,3,21,18,54,25,75

B Write a BASIC program for each of the following.

4. Given the measures of three line segments, determine whether they form an isosceles triangle. (Assume that they form a triangle.)

5. Given the measures of three line segments, determine whether they form an equilateral triangle. (Assume that they form a triangle.)

Review

In this figure, $m\angle K > m\angle G$, and $LH > HK$. *(Section 5-6)*

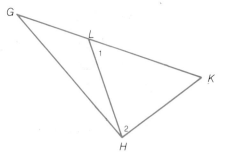

1. Name an exterior angle of $\triangle KHL$.
2. Name an exterior angle of $\triangle GHL$.
3. Compare the measures of $\angle 1$ and $\angle G$.
4. Compare the measures of $\angle 1$ and $\angle K$.
5. Compare the measures of $\overline{HK}$ and $\overline{HG}$.
6. Complete the following proof. *(Section 5-7)*

   Given: Quadrilateral $ABCD$; $AD = BC$

   Prove: $AB + AD > AC$

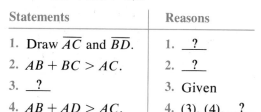

Statements	Reasons
1. Draw $\overline{AC}$ and $\overline{BD}$.	1. ___?___
2. $AB + BC > AC$.	2. ___?___
3. ___?___	3. Given
4. $AB + AD > AC$.	4. (3), (4). ___?___

Complete each statement. Use the figure at the right in which $\overline{RS} \perp \overline{ST}$, $\overline{RS} \perp \overline{VS}$ and $\overline{VS} \perp \overline{ST}$. *(Section 5-8)*

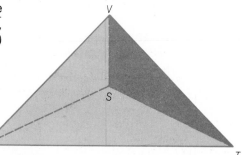

7. $\overline{VS}$ is the edge of dihedral angle ___?___.
8. $\angle RST$ is a plane angle of dihedral angle ___?___.
9. The edge of dihedral angle $R\text{-}\overleftrightarrow{SV}\text{-}T$ is ___?___.
10. $\overleftrightarrow{RS}$ is the edge of dihedral angle ___?___.
11. The plane angle for dihedral angle $V\text{-}\overleftrightarrow{SR}\text{-}T$ is ___?___.

Chapter Summary

IMPORTANT TERMS

Consecutive angles of a quadrilateral (p. 210)
Consecutive sides of a quadrilateral (p. 210)
Dihedral angle (p. 248)
Half-plane (p. 248)
Kite (p. 213)

Median of a trapezoid (p. 228)
Opposite angles of a quadrilateral (p. 208)
Opposite sides of a quadrilateral (p. 208)
Plane angle (p. 248)

IMPORTANT IDEAS

1. **Properties of a Parallelogram:** See page 210.

2. Two parallel lines are equidistant at all points.

3. The diagonals of a rectangle are congruent.

4. The diagonals of a rhombus are perpendicular to each other.

5. Each diagonal of a rhombus bisects a pair of opposite angles.

6. If a segment joins the midpoints of two sides of a triangle, then it is parallel to the third side and its length is one-half that of the third side.

7. The median of a trapezoid is parallel to the bases and its length is one-half the sum of the lengths of the bases.

8. If three or more parallel lines cut off congruent segments on one transversal, then they cut off congruent segments on any transversal.

9. The perpendicular segment from a point to a line is the shortest distance from the point to the line.

10. **Triangle Inequality Theorem:** The sum of the lengths of two sides of a triangle is greater than the length of the third side.

11. All plane angles of the same dihedral angle are congruent.

Chapter Objectives and Review

Objective: *To identify a quadrilateral as a trapezoid, parallelogram, rectangle, rhombus, or square (Section 5–1)*

Use the information about quadrilateral *ABCD* to identify it as a *trapezoid, parallelogram, rectangle, rhombus,* or *square.* More than one answer is possible.

1. $\overline{AB} \parallel \overline{CD}$, $\overline{AD} \parallel \overline{BC}$, $\angle A \cong \angle B \cong \angle C \cong \angle D$
2. $\overline{AB} \parallel \overline{CD}$, $\overline{AD} \parallel \overline{BC}$, $AB = BC = CD = DA$
3. $\overline{AB} \parallel \overline{CD}$, $\overline{BC}$ is not parallel to $\overline{AD}$.
4. $\overline{AB} \parallel \overline{CD}$, $\overline{BC} \parallel \overline{AD}$
5. $\overline{AB} \parallel \overline{CD}$, $\overline{AD} \parallel \overline{BC}$, $\overline{AB} \perp \overline{AD}$, $AB = BC$

Objective: *To identify the properties of a parallelogram (Section 5–1)*

Refer to ▱ *QRST* at the right below to complete each statement.

6. If m∠ *QTS* = 105, then m∠ ___?___ = 105.
7. If m∠ *QTS* = 120, then m∠ ___?___ = m∠ ___?___ = 60.
8. If m∠ 1 = 68, then m∠ ___?___ = 68.
9. If *TW* = 6, then ___?___ = 12.
10. If *QS* = 15, then ___?___ = 7.5 and ___?___ = 7.5.

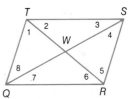

Objective: *To identify the conditions that determine a parallelogram (Section 5-2)*

In Exercises 11–16, determine whether *ABCD* is a parallelogram. Give the the reason(s) for each answer.

11.

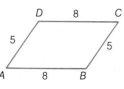

12.

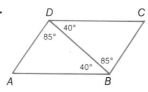

13.

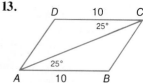

14.

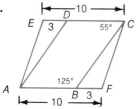

15.

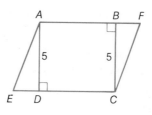

16.

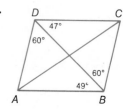

Objective: *To identify the special properties of a rectangle, a rhombus, and a square (Section 5-3)*

Refer to □*BCDE* to complete each statement.

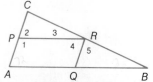

17. If $\overline{BF} \cong \overline{DF}$ but $\angle BCD \not\cong \angle CDE$, then *BCDE* is a ___?___ .

18. If $\overline{EC} \perp \overline{BD}$ and $\overline{EC} \cong \overline{BD}$, then *BCDE* is a ___?___ .

19. If $\overline{BC} \perp \overline{BE}$ and $EB > BC$, then *BCDE* is a ___?___ .

20. If $\overline{BE} \cong \overline{BC}$, and $BD > EC$, then □*BCDE* can only be a ___?___ .

Objective: *To relate midpoints and parallel lines by applying Theorem 5-13 (Section 5-4)*

In Exercises 21–24, refer to $\triangle ABC$. *P*, *R*, and *Q* are the midpoints of $\overline{AC}$, $\overline{BC}$, and $\overline{AB}$, respectively.

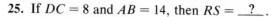

21. If $m\angle A = 72$ and $m\angle B = 25$, find $m\angle C$ and the measure of each numbered angle.

22. If $PR = 9$, find the length of $\overline{AB}$.   23. If $AC = 11$, find the length of $\overline{QR}$.

24. If $AB = 12.4$ and $AC = 5.2$, find the perimeter of □*AQRP*.

Objective: *To apply theorems that relate to parallel lines cut by more than one transversal (Section 5-5)*

ADCB is a trapezoid with median *RS*. Complete each statement.

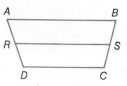

25. If $DC = 8$ and $AB = 14$, then $RS = $ ___?___ .

26. If $DC = 18$ and $RS = 20$, then $AB = $ ___?___ .

27. If $CD = x$ and $AB = y$, then $RS = $ ___?___ .

28. If $DR = 3n$ and $RA = n + 6$, then $DA = $ ___?___ .

Objective: *To identify inequality relationships in triangles (Sections 5–6 and 5–7)*

In △ *GHP*, $\overline{HG} \cong \overline{HP}$. Replace each ___?___ with <, >, or =.

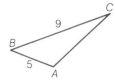

29. m∠ 1 ___?___ m∠ 2

30. m∠ 3 ___?___ m∠ 1

31. m∠ 3 ___?___ m∠ 2

32. *HN* ___?___ *HP*

In triangle *ABC*, *AB* = 5 and *BC* = 9. Classify each statement as *True* or *False*. Give a reason for each answer.

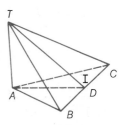

33. *AC* = 14

34. *AC* > 14

35. *AC* < 14

36. *AC* = 4

37. *AC* > 4

38. *AC* < 4

Objective: *To identify dihedral angles and their plane angles (Section 5–8)*

In the figure at the right below, △ *ABC* is in plane I, and $\overline{TA}$ is perpendicular to $\overline{AB}$, $\overline{AD}$, and $\overline{AC}$.

39. Name the dihedral angle formed by the planes containing △*ABT* and △*ADT*.

40. Name the plane angle that can be used to measure dihedral angle B–$\overleftrightarrow{AT}$–C.

41. Name the two triangles whose planes form dihedral angle A–$\overleftrightarrow{BT}$–D.

Objective: *To solve word problems that involve quadrilaterals (Pages 233–234)*

42. The address plate shown at the right is a parallelogram. If m∠ *F* = 70, find m∠ *E*, m∠ *G*, and m∠ *H*.

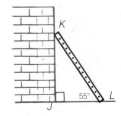

Objective: *To solve word problems that involve inequalities and dihedral angles (Page 252)*

43. A ladder is placed against a wall as shown. If m∠ *KLJ* = 55, which length is greater, *KJ* or *KL*. Give the reason(s) for your answer.

A dihedral angle is formed by the bookend shown at the right.

44. Name two dihedral angles.

45. Name the edge of the dihedral angles.

46. Name a plane angle in one of the dihedral angles.

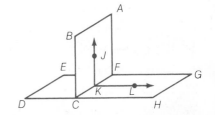

Chapter Test

Match each statement in Exercises 1–5 with all the quadrilaterals in the box that exhibit the property.

1. The diagonals bisect each other.
2. Exactly one pair of sides is parallel.
3. The diagonals are perpendicular.
4. The four sides are congruent.
5. Three angles are right angles.

Quadrilateral	Rectangle
Trapezoid	Rhombus
Parallelogram	Square

In Exercises 6–9, refer to quadrilateral ABCD to complete each statement.

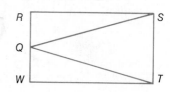

6. If $ABCD$ is a parallelogram, then $\overline{AB} \parallel$ __?__ .
7. If $\overline{AC} \cong \overline{BD}$ and $\overline{AC} \perp \overline{BD}$, then $ABCD$ is a __?__ .
8. If $ABCD$ is a rhombus, then $AB = CD =$ __?__ = __?__ .
9. If $ABCD$ is a trapezoid and $\overline{BC} \parallel \overline{AD}$, $\angle DAB$ __?__ $\angle ABC$.
10. In $\triangle RMP$, E is the midpoint of $\overline{RM}$, F is the midpoint of $\overline{RP}$, and $MP = 9$ centimeters. Find EF.
11. The lengths of the bases of a trapezoid are 7 and 16. Find the length of the median.
12. The length of the median of a trapezoid is 4. The length of one of the bases is 3. Find the length of the other base.
13. In isosceles triangle PRG, $PR = 6$ and $PG = 15$. Which side is the base?
14. In $\triangle KRM$, $KR > RM > KM$. Which angle of the triangle is the largest?
15. **Given:** Rectangle $RSTW$ with Q the midpoint of $\overline{RW}$.

   Prove: $\triangle QWT \cong \triangle QRS$

CHAPTER **6** Similarity

Sections

6-1 **Ratio and Proportion**

Applications: Using Ratio and Proportion

6-2 **Other Properties of Proportions**

Applications: Using the Geometric Mean

6-3 **Proprotional Segments**

6-4 **Other Corollaries on Proportional Segments**

6-5 **Similar Polygons**

6-6 **Similar Triangles**

6-7 **More on Similar Triangles**

Applications: Using Similar Polygons

Features

Consumer Application: Ratios and Banking

Computer Application: Similarity

Calculator Application: Finding the Geometric Mean

Calculator Application: Similar Polygons

Puzzle

Review and Testing

Algebra Review Capsule

Geometry Review Capsules

Review: Sections 6–1 through 6–4

Review: Sections 6–5 through 6–7

Chapter Summary

Chapter Objectives and Review

Chapter Test

Cumulative Review: Chapters 1–6

Preparing for College Entrance Tests

6-1 Ratio and Proportion

A **ratio** is the comparison of two numbers by division. Since division by zero is not defined, a number is never compared to zero. Ratios expressed as fractions are usually written in lowest terms.

The ratio of 9 to 15 equals $\frac{9}{15}$, or $\frac{3}{5}$.

NOTE: The ratio of 9 to 15, or $\frac{3}{5}$, is *not the same* as the ratio of 15 to 9, or $\frac{5}{3}$.

EXAMPLE 1 In the figure at the right, $PR = 24$ and $QR = 6$. Compute these ratios.

$\overset{\bullet}{P} \qquad\qquad\qquad\qquad \overset{\bullet}{Q} \quad \overset{\bullet}{R}$

a. $\dfrac{PQ}{QR}$ b. $\dfrac{PR}{PQ}$ c. $\dfrac{QR}{PR}$ d. $\dfrac{PR}{QR}$

Solutions: a. $\dfrac{PQ}{QR} = \dfrac{18}{6} = \dfrac{3}{1}$ ⟵ $PQ = PR - QR$ b. $\dfrac{PR}{PQ} = \dfrac{24}{18} = \dfrac{4}{3}$

c. $\dfrac{QR}{PR} = \dfrac{6}{24} = \dfrac{1}{4}$ d. $\dfrac{PR}{QR} = \dfrac{24}{6} = \dfrac{4}{1}$

An equation such as the one below states that two ratios are equal. Such an equation is called a **proportion.**

First Term ⟶ ⟶ Third Term

$$\frac{3}{5} = \frac{24}{40}$$

Second Term ⟶ ⟵ Fourth Term

The proportion is read: "3 is to 5 as 24 is to 40."

Theorem 6-1

$$\frac{a}{b} = \frac{c}{d} \text{ if and only if } ad = bc \ (b \neq 0, d \neq 0).$$

NOTE: Theorem 6-1 is a biconditional. You are asked to prove this theorem in the Written Exercises.

EXAMPLE 2 Test whether each pair of ratios can be written as a proportion. Answer *Yes* or *No*.

a. $\dfrac{4}{5}; \dfrac{16}{25}$ b. $\dfrac{12}{9}; \dfrac{4}{3}$

Solutions: a. $\dfrac{4}{5} \overset{?}{\times} \dfrac{16}{25}$ b. $\dfrac{12}{9} \overset{?}{\times} \dfrac{4}{3}$

$4 \times 25 \overset{?}{=} 5 \times 16$ $12 \times 3 \overset{?}{=} 9 \times 4$

$100 \overset{?}{=} 80$ **No** $36 \overset{?}{=} 36$ **Yes** ✔

When you know three terms in a proportion, you can use Theorem 6–1 to find the fourth term.

EXAMPLE 3 Find x if $\dfrac{5}{6} = \dfrac{15}{x}$.

Solution: $\dfrac{5}{6} \diagup\!\!\!\!\diagdown \dfrac{15}{x}$

$5x = (6)(15)$ ◄——— Solve for x.

$x = \dfrac{(6)(15)}{5} = 18$ ◄——— The fourth term is 18.

Given that $\dfrac{a}{b} = \dfrac{c}{d}$, you can write the proportion in other ways. For example, using c as the first term and b as the fourth term,

$\dfrac{c}{d} = \dfrac{a}{b}$ ◄——— Check: $cb = da$, or $ad = bc$

EXAMPLE 4 Given $\dfrac{5}{7} = \dfrac{15}{21}$, write the proportion in three other ways. Check each answer.

Solution: **a.** Let 7 be the first term. $\dfrac{7}{5} = \dfrac{21}{15}$ Check: $7(15) \overset{?}{=} 5(21)$

$105 = 105$ ✔

b. Let 15 be the first term. $\dfrac{15}{5} = \dfrac{21}{7}$ Check: $15(7) \overset{?}{=} 5(21)$

$105 = 105$ ✔

c. Let 21 be the first term. $\dfrac{21}{7} = \dfrac{15}{5}$ Check: $21(5) \overset{?}{=} 7(15)$

$105 = 105$ ✔

CLASSROOM EXERCISES

In Exercises 1–8, write the ratio of the given numbers as a fraction in lowest terms.

1. 9 to 12

2. 8 to 24

3. $4x$ to $5x$

4. $10x^2$ to $4x$

5. $90y$ to $270y$

6. 25 cm to 100 cm

7. 20 m to 4 m

8. 9 yd to 108 yd

9. Solve for y: $\dfrac{2}{y} = \dfrac{5}{20}$

10. Solve for x: $\dfrac{6}{5} = \dfrac{108}{x}$

11. Given the proportion $\dfrac{18}{3} = \dfrac{12}{2}$, write it in three other ways.

12. Write Theorem 6–1 as a conditional and its converse.

WRITTEN EXERCISES

A   In the figure at the right, $AB = 21$ and $BC = 7$. Write these ratios in lowest terms.

1. $\dfrac{AC}{AB}$

2. $\dfrac{BC}{AB}$

3. $\dfrac{BC}{AC}$

4. $\dfrac{AB}{AC}$

5. $\dfrac{AC}{BC}$

In the figure for Exercises 1–5, let $AC = 21$ and $CB = 7$. Write these ratios in lowest terms.

6. $\dfrac{AC}{CB}$

7. $\dfrac{CB}{AC}$

8. $\dfrac{AC}{AB}$

9. $\dfrac{AC}{AC}$

10. $\dfrac{AB}{CB}$

In the figure at the right, $AB = 5a$ and $AC = 5b$. Write these ratios in lowest terms.

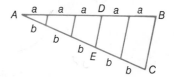

11. $\dfrac{AB}{AC}$

12. $\dfrac{AD}{DB}$

13. $\dfrac{AE}{EC}$

Test whether each pair of ratios can be written as a proportion.

14. $\dfrac{5}{8}; \dfrac{10}{16}$

15. $\dfrac{12}{27}; \dfrac{24}{54}$

16. $\dfrac{7}{19}; \dfrac{21}{57}$

17. $\dfrac{4}{11}; \dfrac{12}{32}$

18. $\dfrac{7}{21}; \dfrac{17}{51}$

19. $\dfrac{19}{18}; \dfrac{7}{6}$

20. $\dfrac{1}{5}; \dfrac{3}{15}$

21. $\dfrac{3}{2}; \dfrac{108}{72}$

In Exercises 22–29, solve for x. No denominator equals zero.

22. $\dfrac{3}{5} = \dfrac{4}{x}$

23. $\dfrac{2}{x} = \dfrac{3}{7}$

24. $\dfrac{4}{7} = \dfrac{x}{6}$

25. $\dfrac{x}{10} = \dfrac{6}{5}$

26. $\dfrac{1}{7} = \dfrac{4}{x}$

27. $\dfrac{7}{21} = \dfrac{x}{6}$

28. $\dfrac{4}{x} = \dfrac{5}{7}$

29. $\dfrac{2x}{3} = \dfrac{7}{8}$

In Exercises 30–33, write the given proportions in three other ways.

30. $\dfrac{2}{3} = \dfrac{10}{15}$

31. $\dfrac{3}{7} = \dfrac{9}{21}$

32. $\dfrac{4}{7} = \dfrac{24}{42}$

33. $\dfrac{9}{2} = \dfrac{225}{50}$

B   In Exercises 34–39, use Theorem 6–1 to find the unknown terms of each proportion.

34. If $6x = 5y$, then $\dfrac{x}{y} = \dfrac{?}{?}$.

35. If $4x = 7y$, then $\dfrac{x}{y} = \dfrac{?}{?}$.

36. If $9x = 2y$, then $\dfrac{y}{x} = \dfrac{?}{?}$.

37. If $10x = 15y$, then $\dfrac{y}{x} = \dfrac{?}{?}$.

38. If $3u = 10d$, then $\dfrac{10}{u} = \dfrac{?}{?}$.

39. If $7w = 4q$, then $\dfrac{q}{7} = \dfrac{?}{?}$.

In Exercises 40–43, use the given proportion $\frac{a}{m} = \frac{b}{r}$ to write two proportions satisfying the additional condition.

40. The first term is b.

41. The third term is r.

42. The first term is m.

43. The third term is a.

44. Prove Theorem 6–1. (Plan: Multiply each side of $\frac{a}{b} = \frac{c}{d}$ by bd. For the converse, divide each side by bd.)

> **Example:** Find the measures of the angles of a triangle if the measures are in the ratio of 1:2:3.
>
> **Solution:** Represent the measures by x, $2x$, and $3x$.
>
> $\qquad x + 2x + 3x = 180$ ⟵——— **By the Triangle–Sum Theorem**
>
> $\qquad\qquad\qquad 6x = 180$
>
> $\qquad\qquad x = \textbf{30};\ 2x = \textbf{60};\ 3x = \textbf{90}$

45. Find two numbers whose sum is 21 and whose ratio is 3 to 4.

46. Find two numbers whose sum is 80 and whose ratio is 5 to 11.

47. Find the measures of two complementary angles whose ratio is 2 to 3.

48. Find the measures of the angles of a triangle if the measures are in the ratio of 2:3:4.

49. Find the measures of the angles of a quadrilateral if the measures are in the ratio of 1:2:4:5.

In Exercises 50–58, solve for x. No denominator equals zero.

50. $\dfrac{21 - x}{x} = \dfrac{1}{2}$

51. $\dfrac{20 - x}{x} = \dfrac{2}{3}$

52. $\dfrac{a}{b} = \dfrac{c}{x}$

C

53. $\dfrac{x + 1}{x - 2} = \dfrac{x + 5}{x - 6}$

54. $\dfrac{x - 4}{x + 2} = \dfrac{x - 6}{x + 4}$

55. $\dfrac{x + 3}{x + 5} = \dfrac{x - 1}{x - 5}$

56. $\dfrac{x}{3} = \dfrac{2}{5 - x}$

57. $\dfrac{2x}{4} = \dfrac{-2}{x - 4}$

58. $\dfrac{x}{6} = \dfrac{4}{x + 5}$

Puzzle

Draw $\triangle ABC$. Mark any point A_1 on $\overline{BC}$. Draw $\overline{A_1B_1}$ parallel to $\overline{BA}$ as shown, then $\overline{B_1C_1}$ parallel to $\overline{BC}$, and $\overline{C_1A_2}$ parallel to $\overline{AC}$. If you continue angle, A_3 must equal A_1. Explain why.

What difference will it make if A_1 is the midpoint of $\overline{BC}$?

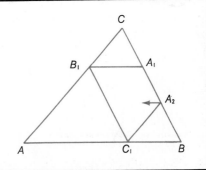

APPLICATIONS

USING RATIO AND PROPORTION

These exercises apply geometric concepts studied in Section 6–1.

A

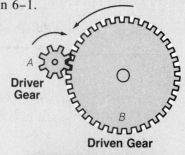

Driver Gear

Driven Gear

1. In the figure at the right, gear A drives gear B.

$$\text{Gear Ratio} = \frac{\text{Number of Teeth in Driven Gear}}{\text{Number of Teeth in Driver Gear}}$$

If there are 8 teeth in Gear A and 40 in Gear B, determine the gear ratio. Write the answer as a fraction in lowest terms.

2. **Tip-speed ratio** compares the speed of the blade-tips of a windmill to the speed of the wind. In this windmill near Sandusky, Ohio, the blade-tip speed is 180 mph in a 20 mph wind. What is the tip-speed ratio?

3. The blade-tip speed of a windmill is 120 mph in a 15 mph wind. What is the tip-speed ratio?

4. According to Federal law, the ratio of the length to the width of an official United States flag must be 1.9 to 1. What should be the length of a flag that is 18 meters wide (nearest tenth of a meter)?

The plans for this house are drawn to the following scale.

$\frac{1}{8}$ **inch represents 1 foot.**

Refer to this information in Exercises 5–6.

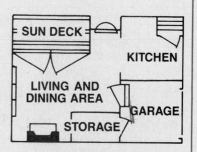

SUN DECK

KITCHEN

LIVING AND DINING AREA

GARAGE

STORAGE

5. On the plan, the width of the dining room is $\frac{3}{4}$ inch. Calculate the actual width.

6. On the plan, the length of the sun deck is $1\frac{1}{8}$ inches. Calculate the actual length.

When a photograph is reduced or enlarged, the length of the reduced or enlarged copy can be found by using a proportion.

$$\frac{\text{Length of Original}}{\text{Width of Original}} = \frac{\text{Length of Copy}}{\text{Width of Copy}}$$

7. A photograph 12 centimeters long and 8 centimeters wide is to be reduced to fit a space 7 centimeters long. What is the reduced width? Round the answer to the nearest tenth.

Use the Table of Squares and Square Roots on page 568 to approximate each number to the nearest hundredth. Exercise 1 is done for you.

1. $\sqrt{30} \longrightarrow$

No.	Square	Square Root
30	900	5.477

$\sqrt{30} = 5.48$

2. $\sqrt{15}$ **3.** $\sqrt{8}$ **4.** $\sqrt{50}$

5. $\sqrt{12}$ **6.** $\sqrt{133}$ **7.** $\sqrt{41}$

In Exercises 8–21, solve for x.

In Exercises 16–21, use the Table of Squares and Square Roots to approximate the answers to the nearest hundredth. Exercises 8 and 15 are done for you.

8. $x^2 = 36$
   $x = 6$ or -6

9. $x^2 = 81$

10. $x^2 = 169$

11. $x^2 = 10,000$

12. $x^2 = 225$

13. $x^2 = 0.09$

14. $x^2 = 0.25$

15. $x^2 = 50$
   $x = \sqrt{50}$ or $-\sqrt{50}$
   $x = 7.07$ or -7.07 $\longleftarrow$ **From the Table**

16. $x^2 = 11$

17. $x^2 = 23$

18. $x^2 = 41$

19. $x^2 = 94$

20. $x^2 = 73$

21. $x^2 = 82$

6-2   Other Properties of Proportions

Given a proportion, you can add 1 to, or subtract 1 from, each side of the proportion. Recall the many different names for 1.

$$1 = \frac{9}{9} = \frac{204}{204} = \frac{a}{a} = \frac{b}{b} = \cdots, \; a \neq 0, \; b \neq 0$$

Theorem 6-2

> If $\dfrac{a}{b} = \dfrac{c}{d}$, then $\dfrac{a+b}{b} = \dfrac{c+d}{d}$ and $\dfrac{a-b}{b} = \dfrac{c-d}{d}$.

EXAMPLE 1   Use Theorem 6-2 to write a new proportion for $\dfrac{3}{7} = \dfrac{12}{28}$ as indicated.

a. By addition   **b.** By subtraction

Solutions: **a.** $\dfrac{3}{7} + 1 = \dfrac{12}{28} + 1$ **b.** $\dfrac{3}{7} - 1 = \dfrac{12}{28} - 1$

$\dfrac{3+7}{7} = \dfrac{12+28}{28}$ $\dfrac{3-7}{7} = \dfrac{12-28}{28}$

Check: **a.** $\dfrac{10}{7} \overset{?}{=} \dfrac{40}{28}$ **b.** $\dfrac{-4}{7} \overset{?}{=} \dfrac{-16}{28}$

$10(28) \overset{?}{=} 7(40)$ $-4(28) \overset{?}{=} 7(-16)$

$280 = 280$ ✔ $-112 = -112$ ✔

If three numbers 4, 6, and 9 are related such that

$$\frac{4}{6} = \frac{6}{9},$$ ⟵ **NOTE: The second and third terms are the same.**

then 6 is the *geometric mean* or *mean proportional* between 4 and 9.

Definition

> If a, b, and x are positive numbers and $\frac{a}{x} = \frac{x}{b}$, then x is the **geometric mean** between a and b.

EXAMPLE 2 Find the geometric mean between 2 and 8.

Solution: Let x = the geometric mean.

Then $\dfrac{2}{x} = \dfrac{x}{8}.$ ⟵ **From the definition**

$x(x) = 2(8)$

$x^2 = 16$

$x = \sqrt{16}$, or 4 ⟵ **Geometric mean**

NOTE: In Example 2, the equation $x^2 = 16$ has two solutions, 4 and -4. Since in geometry, real numbers are associated with lengths of segments and with angle measures and these measures are always positive, only the positive square root is considered.

Finding the geometric mean often involves writing a radical in simplest form. In the expression $\sqrt{50}$, $\sqrt{}$ is the **radical symbol**, 50 is the **radicand**, and $\sqrt{50}$ is the **radical.**

Definition

> A radical is in **simplest form** when:
>
> **1** The radicand contains no factor (other than 1) that is a perfect square.
>
> **2** The radicand does not contain a fraction.
>
> **3** No radical appears in a denominator.

EXAMPLE 3 Simplify.

  a. $\sqrt{84}$ b. $\sqrt{\dfrac{9}{2}}$ c. $\sqrt{\dfrac{1}{20}}$

Solutions: a. $\sqrt{84} = \sqrt{4 \cdot 21} = \sqrt{4} \cdot \sqrt{21} = 2\sqrt{21}$

  b. $\sqrt{\dfrac{9}{2}} = \dfrac{\sqrt{9}}{\sqrt{2}} = \dfrac{3}{\sqrt{2}}$ ⟵ **Multiply by $\dfrac{\sqrt{2}}{\sqrt{2}}$ to make the denominator a perfect square.**

  $= \dfrac{3}{\sqrt{2}} \cdot \dfrac{\sqrt{2}}{\sqrt{2}}$ ⟵ $(\sqrt{2} \cdot \sqrt{2}) = (\sqrt{2})^2 = 2$

  $= \dfrac{3\sqrt{2}}{2}$

c. $\sqrt{\dfrac{1}{20}} = \dfrac{1}{\sqrt{20}} = \dfrac{1}{\sqrt{4}\sqrt{5}}$

$= \dfrac{1}{2\sqrt{5}}$ ← Multiply by $\dfrac{\sqrt{5}}{\sqrt{5}}$ to make the denominator a perfect square.

$= \dfrac{1}{2\sqrt{5}} \cdot \dfrac{\sqrt{5}}{\sqrt{5}}$ ← $(2\sqrt{5})(\sqrt{5}) = 2(\sqrt{5})^2 = 2(5)$

$= \dfrac{\sqrt{5}}{10}$

You can use the Table of Squares and Square Roots on page 568 to approximate $\dfrac{\sqrt{5}}{10}$ to the nearest hundredth. The symbol "$\approx$" means "is approximately equal to." Thus,

$$\dfrac{\sqrt{5}}{10} \approx \dfrac{2.236}{10} = 0.22 \quad \longleftarrow \text{ Nearest hundredth}$$

The proportion $\dfrac{a}{b} = \dfrac{c}{d}$ can also be written $a:b = c:d$. The fourth term, d, is sometimes called the **fourth proportional** to the other three.

EXAMPLE 4 Find the fourth proportional to 3, 5, and 7.

Solution: Let $x =$ the fourth proportional.

Then $\dfrac{3}{5} = \dfrac{7}{x}$. ← Solve for x.

$3x = 35$

$x = \dfrac{35}{3}$, or $11\frac{2}{3}$ ← Fourth proportional

CLASSROOM EXERCISES

In Exercises 1–8, write a new proportion by addition and by subtraction.

1. $\dfrac{5}{9} = \dfrac{10}{18}$

2. $\dfrac{1}{8} = \dfrac{5}{40}$

3. $\dfrac{15}{20} = \dfrac{11}{x}$

4. $\dfrac{9}{a} = \dfrac{12}{b}$

5. $\dfrac{20}{12} = \dfrac{50}{30}$

6. $\dfrac{18}{45} = \dfrac{2}{5}$

7. $\dfrac{3}{2} = \dfrac{7}{x}$

8. $\dfrac{a}{b} = \dfrac{5}{c}$

In Exercises 9–11, find the geometric mean.

9. 4 and 9

10. 2 and 18

11. $3a$ and $12a$

In Exercises 12–14, find the fourth proportional to the three given numbers.

12. 3, 4, and 7

13. 8, 10, and 6

14. 2, 1, and 5

WRITTEN EXERCISES

A Given that $\dfrac{a}{b} = \dfrac{c}{d}$, classify each statement as true, *T*, or false, *F*. No denominator equals zero.

1. $ad = bc$

2. $ac = bd$

3. $\dfrac{a}{d} = \dfrac{b}{c}$

4. $\dfrac{a+b}{b} = \dfrac{c+d}{c}$

5. $\dfrac{a}{c} = \dfrac{b}{d}$

6. $\dfrac{a-b}{c} = \dfrac{c-d}{d}$

7. $\dfrac{a+b}{b} = \dfrac{c+d}{d}$

8. $\dfrac{b}{a} = \dfrac{d}{c}$

Complete each statement.

9. If $\dfrac{2}{5} = \dfrac{x}{7}$, then $\dfrac{2+5}{5} = \dfrac{?}{7}$.

10. If $\dfrac{x}{3} = \dfrac{y}{7}$, then $\dfrac{?}{3} = \dfrac{y-7}{7}$.

In Exercises 11–14, write a new proportion by addition.

11. $\dfrac{5}{13} = \dfrac{20}{52}$

12. $\dfrac{9}{7} = \dfrac{36}{28}$

13. $\dfrac{2}{y} = \dfrac{8}{5}$

14. $\dfrac{a}{4} = \dfrac{b}{3}$

In Exercises 15–18, write a new proportion by subtraction.

15. $\dfrac{7}{9} = \dfrac{56}{72}$

16. $\dfrac{56}{8} = \dfrac{7}{1}$

17. $\dfrac{x}{3} = \dfrac{7}{2}$

18. $\dfrac{10}{z} = \dfrac{9}{y}$

In Exercises 19–26, find the geometric mean between the given numbers.

19. 4 and 100

20. 16 and 14

21. 27 and 3

22. 12 and 3

23. 2 and 50

24. $4a$ and $16a$

25. a and b

26. $2a$ and $8b$

Simplify.

27. $\sqrt{45}$

28. $\sqrt{81}$

29. $6\sqrt{8}$

30. $2\sqrt{20}$

31. $4\sqrt{75}$

32. $\sqrt{\dfrac{16}{3}}$

33. $\sqrt{\dfrac{36}{5}}$

34. $\dfrac{1}{\sqrt{5}}$

35. $\dfrac{1}{\sqrt{7}}$

36. $\sqrt{\dfrac{8}{3}}$

37. $\dfrac{1}{\sqrt{18}}$

38. $\dfrac{1}{\sqrt{32}}$

39. $\sqrt{\dfrac{6}{16}}$

40. $\sqrt{\dfrac{3}{2}}$

41. $\sqrt{\dfrac{8}{7}}$

Find the geometric mean between the given numbers. Use the Table of Square Roots on page 568 to approximate the answers to the nearest hundredth.

42. 12 and 6

43. 19 and 7

44. 13 and 11

45. 10 and 17

Find the fourth proportional to the given numbers.

46. 3; 4; 9

47. 8; 10; 6

48. $2a$; $3b$; $4a$

49. $6x$; $7y$; $18y$

50. 2; 6; 5

51. a; b; c

52. $\dfrac{1}{2}$; $\dfrac{2}{3}$; $\dfrac{3}{4}$

53. $\dfrac{1}{4}$; $\dfrac{3}{4}$; $\dfrac{3}{20}$

Find the geometric mean between each pair of numbers. Write the answers in simplified radical form.

54. $\frac{2}{3}; \frac{3}{4}$ **55.** $\frac{1}{6}; \frac{5}{3}$ **56.** $\frac{3}{2}; \frac{1}{8}$ **57.** $\frac{1}{2}; \frac{1}{8}$

58. $\frac{1}{2}; \frac{1}{6}$ **59.** $\frac{1}{4}; \frac{1}{5}$ **60.** $5\sqrt{2}; 3\sqrt{8}$ **61.** $\frac{3}{8}\sqrt{6}; \frac{2}{3}\sqrt{6}$

In the figure at the right, *CD* is the geometric mean between *AD* and *DB*.

62. If $AD = 9$ cm and $DB = 4$ cm, find *CD*.

63. If $AD = 30$ mm and $DB = 10$ mm, find *CD*.

64. If $AD = 18$ and $CD = 12$, find *DB*.

65. Prove Theorem 6–2. **Plan:** Use Theorem 6–1 to show that $ad = bc$. Then add $\pm bd$ to each side. Use the distributive property to express the left side as $(a + b)d$ and the right side as $b(c + d)$. Complete the proof.

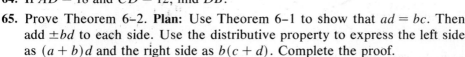

66. Given: $\dfrac{BC}{AB} = \dfrac{EF}{DE}$

   Prove: $\dfrac{AC}{AB} = \dfrac{DF}{DE}$

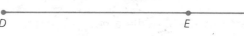

67. Prove that if $\dfrac{a}{b} = \dfrac{c}{d} = \dfrac{e}{f} = \dfrac{g}{h}$, then $\dfrac{a + c + e + g}{b + d + f + h} = \dfrac{a}{b}$.

CALCULATOR APPLICATIONS

Finding the Geometric Mean

If you have a calculator with a square root key, ☑ , you can find the geometric mean between two numbers.

EXAMPLE Find the geometric mean between 4 and 15.

SOLUTION By definition, the geometric mean between *a* and *b* is expressed as

$$\frac{a}{x} = \frac{x}{b} \longleftarrow \text{Solve for x.}$$

$$x^2 = ab \quad \text{and} \quad x = \sqrt{ab}$$

4 ⨉ 1 5 = ☑   **7.7459667**

EXERCISES

Use a calculator to find the geometric mean between the given numbers. Approximate the answers to the nearest hundredth.

1. 3 and 15   **2.** 19 and 12   **3.** 17 and 25   **4.** 32 and 50

5. 72 and 61   **6.** 155 and 101   **7.** 290 and 64   **8.** 16 and 841

APPLICATIONS

USING THE GEOMETRIC MEAN

These exercises apply geometric concepts studied in Section 6–2.

A   When the length, l, of a rectangle is the geometric mean between the width, w, and the sum of the length and width, the rectangle is called a **Golden Rectangle**.

$$\frac{w}{l} = \frac{l}{l+w}, \qquad 1$$

or $\quad l^2 = w(l+w) \qquad 2$

1. Show that when $w = 1$, Equation 2 can be written as $l^2 - l - 1 = 0$.

2. Use the quadratic formula to solve $l^2 - l - 1 = 0$.
$$\left(\text{HINT: } l = \frac{-(-1) \pm \sqrt{(-1)^2 - 4(1)(-1)}}{2} \right)$$

3. Use the Table of Squares and Square Roots on page 568 to show that, for $l = \dfrac{1 + \sqrt{5}}{2}$, $l \approx 1.618$. $\left(\text{The ratio } \dfrac{1 + \sqrt{5}}{2} \text{ is called the } \textbf{Golden Ratio.} \right)$

4. Use a calculator to compute the difference between the golden ratio and its reciprocal.

5. Write a ratio that compares your total height to the height of your waist. Express the answer as a decimal. (The answer should be close to the Golden Ratio.)

6. The Parthenon is considered the finest building of ancient Greece. The front of this building has the shape of a rectangle whose length is 110 feet and whose height is 60 feet. Write the ratio of the length to the width as a fraction in lowest terms and as a decimal.

7. How close is your answer in Exercise 6 to the Golden Ratio?

B   Index cards are sold in standard sizes (measured in inches). Three standard sizes are given below.

             3 by 5   4 by 6   5 by 8

8. Determine the ratio $\dfrac{l}{w}$ for each size. Express the ratio as a three-place decimal. (HINT: Use a calculator.)

9. For which size is the ratio closest to the Golden Ratio?

In △ABC, D and E are the midpoints of sides AC and BC, respectively. Use this information in Exercises 1–4. (Page 225)

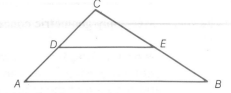

1. $\overline{DE} \parallel$ __?__   2. $DE = \frac{1}{2}$ __?__
3. If $AB = 10$, $DE = $ __?__
4. If $DE = 9$, $AB = $ __?__

5. Segments PQ and RS intersect five equally-spaced parallel lines as shown. If $PQ = 4$ and $RS = 6$, how long is each smaller segment of $\overline{PQ}$ and $\overline{RS}$? (Pages 228–229)

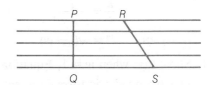

6–3 Proportional Segments

In the figure at the right, lines k, j and w are parallel, $AB = x$, $RP = y$, $BE = 3x$ and $PT = 3y$. Thus,

$$\frac{RP}{PT} = \frac{AB}{BE} = \frac{1}{3},$$

and parallel lines k, j, and w are said to *divide the transversals proportionally*.

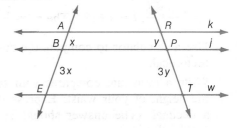

Theorem 6–3

> If three parallel lines intersect two transversals, then the lines divide the transversals proportionally.

A proof of Theorem 6–3 is not given here because it involves concepts usually studied in advanced mathematics courses.

EXAMPLE 1 In the figure, lines r, s, and t are parallel. Complete each proportion.

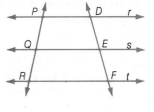

a. $\dfrac{PQ}{QR} = \dfrac{?}{EF}$ b. $\dfrac{PQ}{?} = \dfrac{DE}{DF}$ c. $\dfrac{QR}{PR} = \dfrac{?}{?}$

Solutions: a. $\dfrac{PQ}{QR} = \dfrac{DE}{EF}$ b. $\dfrac{PQ}{PR} = \dfrac{DE}{DF}$ c. $\dfrac{QR}{PR} = \dfrac{EF}{DF}$

Two corollaries of Theorem 6–3 (see page 272) apply to triangles. You are asked to prove them in the Written Exercises.

Corollary 6–4	If a line intersecting the interior of a triangle is parallel to one side, then the line divides the other two sides proportionally.

EXAMPLE 2 In $\triangle ECD$, $\overline{AB} \parallel \overline{CD}$. Find x.

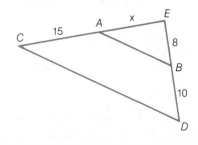

Solution: By Corollary 6–4,

$$\frac{x}{15} = \frac{8}{10} \quad \longleftarrow \quad \textbf{Solve for x.}$$

$$10x = 15(8)$$

$$10x = 120$$

$$x = 12 \quad \longleftarrow \quad \textbf{EA}$$

Corollary 6–5 also refers to the sides of a triangle.

Corollary 6–5	If a line intersecting the interior of a triangle is parallel to one side, then either side intersected by the line is to one of its segments as the other side is to its corresponding segment.

EXAMPLE 3 In $\triangle XPY$, $\overline{RS} \parallel \overline{XY}$. Write two proportions that follow from Corollary 6–5.

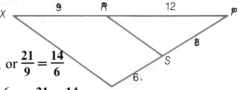

Solution: First proportion: $\dfrac{12+9}{9} = \dfrac{8+6}{6}$, or $\dfrac{21}{9} = \dfrac{14}{6}$

Second proportion: $\dfrac{12+9}{12} = \dfrac{8+6}{8}$, or $\dfrac{21}{12} = \dfrac{14}{8}$

CLASSROOM EXERCISES

In $\triangle CDE$, $\overline{AB} \parallel \overline{CD}$. Complete each proportion.

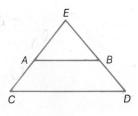

1. $\dfrac{EA}{AC} = \dfrac{EB}{?}$

2. $\dfrac{EC}{AC} = \dfrac{?}{?}$

3. $\dfrac{EB}{BD} = \dfrac{?}{?}$

4. $\dfrac{EB+BD}{EB} = \dfrac{?}{?}$

5. Use the figure to find AC if $EA = 24$, $EB = 21$, and $BD = 28$.

6. Use the figure to find BD if $EA + AC = 45$, $AC = 25$, and $EB + BD = 54$.

In the figure at the right, $\overline{AB} \parallel \overline{CD} \parallel \overline{EF}$. Complete each proportion.

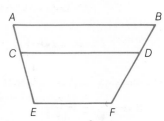

7. $\dfrac{AC}{CE} = \dfrac{?}{DF}$

8. $\dfrac{AE}{CE} = \dfrac{BF}{?}$

9. $\dfrac{BF-DF}{DF} = \dfrac{?}{CE}$

10. $\dfrac{BD+DF}{DF} = \dfrac{?}{?}$

WRITTEN EXERCISES

A In Exercises 1–3, $\overline{AB} \parallel \overline{CD}$. Find x.

1.
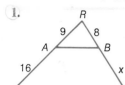

2.
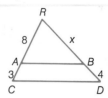

3.
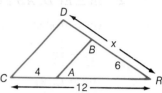

In $\triangle XYZ$, $\overline{RS} \parallel \overline{YZ}$. In Exercises 4–9, find the unknown length.

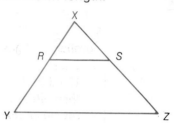

4. $XR = 2$, $RY = 4$, $XS = 3$, $SZ = $ __?__

5. $XS = 8$, $SZ = 16$, $RY = 8$, $XR = $ __?__

6. $RY = 5$, $SZ = 7$, $XR = 3$, $XS = $ __?__

7. $SZ = 9$, $XR = 5$, $XS = 4$, $RY = $ __?__

8. $XR = 5$, $XS = 4$, $SZ = 6$, $XY = $ __?__

9. $SZ = 24$, $XR = 12$, $RY = 21$, $XZ = $ __?__

In $\triangle ABC$, $\overline{DE} \parallel \overline{AB}$. Find the unknown lengths.

	AD	DC	BE	EC
10.	3	2	6	?
11.	7	3	?	5
12.	2	?	3	4
13.	$\frac{4}{3}$	$\frac{1}{2}$	4	?

	AD	DC	AC	BE	EC	BC
14.	?	8	20	?	?	15
15.	12	?	30	9	?	?
16.	10	18	?	?	?	36
17.	?	?	48	16	28	?

B

18. Prove Corollary 6–4. (Refer to the figure for Exercises 10–17.)

Given: $\triangle ABC$ with $\overline{DE} \parallel \overline{AB}$

Prove: $\dfrac{CD}{DA} = \dfrac{CE}{EB}$ or $\dfrac{DA}{CD} = \dfrac{EB}{CE}$

Plan: Through C, draw $\overleftrightarrow{CF} \parallel \overline{AB}$. Show that $\overleftrightarrow{CF} \parallel \overline{DE} \parallel \overline{AB}$. Complete the proof.

19. Prove Corollary 6–5. (HINT: Use Corollary 6–4 and Theorem 6–2)

C

20. Given: Trapezoid $LAMP$ with diagonals AP and ML intersecting at K.

Prove: $\dfrac{AK}{KP} = \dfrac{MK}{KL}$

6–4 Other Corollaries on Proportional Segments

Corollary 6–6 relates proportional segments to a line parallel to one side of a triangle and intersecting the other two sides.

Corollary 6–6	If a line divides two sides of a triangle proportionally, then the line is parallel to the third side.

The proof of this Corollary is asked for in the Written Exercises.

EXAMPLE 1 In $\triangle PTQ$, $PN = 6$, $NQ = 2$, $PR = 12$, and $RT = 4$. Is $\overline{NR} \parallel \overline{QT}$?

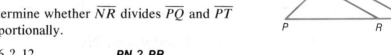

Solution: Determine whether $\overline{NR}$ divides $\overline{PQ}$ and $\overline{PT}$ proportionally.

$$\frac{6}{2} \overset{?}{=} \frac{12}{4} \quad\longleftarrow\quad \frac{PN}{NQ} \overset{?}{=} \frac{PR}{RT}$$

$$6 \cdot 4 \overset{?}{=} 2 \cdot 12 \quad\longleftarrow\quad \text{By Theorem 6–1}$$

$$24 = 24 \;\; \checkmark \qquad \text{Thus, } \overline{NR} \text{ divides } \overline{PQ} \text{ and } \overline{PT} \text{ proportionally.}$$

Since the ratios are equal, $\overline{NR} \parallel \overline{QT}$ by Corollary 6–6.

In Corollary 6–7, it is more convenient to refer to "segments that are proportional" rather than to "measures of segments that are proportional." Similar simplified language will be used. The proof of this theorem is asked for in the Written Exercises.

Corollary 6–7	The bisector of an angle of a triangle divides the opposite side into segments that are proportional to the adjacent sides of the triangle.

Example 2 shows how to use Corollary 6–7 to find the length of a segment.

EXAMPLE 2 In $\triangle ABC$, $\overrightarrow{CD}$ bisects $\angle C$ and meets $\overline{AB}$ at D. If $AC = 12$, $BC = 10$, and $AD = 5$, find BD.

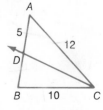

Solution: $\dfrac{10}{12} = \dfrac{BD}{5} \quad\longleftarrow\quad$ **By Corollary 6–7,** $\dfrac{BC}{CA} = \dfrac{BD}{DA}$.

$$12 \cdot BD = 10 \cdot 5 \quad\longleftarrow\quad \text{By Theorem 6–1}$$

$$BD = \frac{50}{12} = 4\frac{1}{6}$$

Parallel planes can also cut off proportional segments.

Corollary 6–8	If two lines are cut by three parallel planes, the corresponding segments are proportional.

The proof of this corollary is asked for in the Written Exercises.

CLASSROOM EXERCISES

Use the figure at the right and the given information to classify each statement as true, *T*, or false, *F*. Give a reason for each answer.

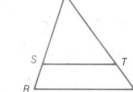

1. If $AS = 7$, $SR = 3$, $AT = 8$, and $TQ = 4$, then $\overline{ST} \parallel \overline{RQ}$.
2. If $SR = 4$, $SA = 12$, $QT = 5$, and $TA = 10$, then $\overline{ST} \parallel \overline{RQ}$.

In $\triangle RPQ$, $\overline{RS}$ bisects $\angle R$, and S is on $\overline{QP}$.

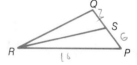

3. Find RQ if $PR = 10$, $PS = 6$ and $SQ = 3$.
4. Find PS if $PR = 12$, $RQ = 9$ and $SQ = 4$.
5. Write Corollaries 6–4 and 6–6 as a biconditional.

WRITTEN EXERCISES

A

In Exercises 1–5, use the figure and the given information to state whether $\overline{EF} \parallel \overline{HS}$. Answer *Yes* or *No*.

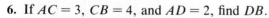

1. $HE = 3$; $EA = 6$; $AF = 8$; $FS = 4$
2. $HA = 14$; $HE = 4$; $SA = 21$; $FS = 7$
3. $HA = 18$; $EA = 12$; $AF = 20$; $FS = 10$
4. $HA = 15$; $SA = 25$; $HE = 5$; $AF = 8\frac{1}{3}$
5. $HE = 8$; $EA = 20$; $AS = 42$; $FS = 12$

In $\triangle ABC$, $\overline{CD}$ bisects $\angle C$.

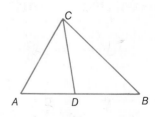

6. If $AC = 3$, $CB = 4$, and $AD = 2$, find DB.
7. If $AC = 5$, $CB = 9$, and $AD = 3$, find DB.
8. If $AC = 3$, $CB = 6$, and $AB = 7$, find AD and DB.
   (HINT: Let $AD = x$ and $DB = 7 - x$.)
9. If $AC = 16$, $CB = 20$, and $AB = 24$, find AD and DB.
10. If $AC = 12$, $CB = 15$, and $AB = 9$, find DB.

In the figure at the right, lines *k* and *t* intersect three parallel planes. Use this information in Exercises 11–16.

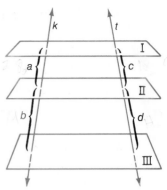

11. If $a = 6$, $b = 9$, and $c = 6\frac{1}{2}$, find d.
12. If $a = 8$, $c = 10$, and $d = 14$, find b.
13. If $b = 12$, $c = 5$, and $d = 8$, find a.
14. If $a = 2$, $b = 7$, and $d = 9$, find c.
15. If $a = 3$, $b = 8$, and $c = 5$, find d.
16. If $a = 4$, $c = 9$, and $d = 13$, find b.

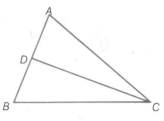

B   In $\triangle ABC$, $\overline{CD}$ bisects $\angle C$ and D is on $\overline{AB}$. Use this information in Exercises 17–20.

17. If $AC = b$, $CB = a$, and $AD = k$, find DB.
18. If $AC = b$, $CB = a$, and $AB = c$, find AD and DB.
19. If $AC = b$, $AD = k$, and $DB = t$, find CB.
20. If $CB = a$, $AB = c$, and $DB = d$, find AD and AC.

The statement $a = b = c$ is actually three statements: $a = b$, $b = c$, and $a = c$.

21. Write three statements for $\dfrac{r}{s} = \dfrac{q}{t} = \dfrac{y}{z}$.   22. Write three statements for $\dfrac{e}{m} = \dfrac{f}{n} = \dfrac{g}{k}$.

23. Prove Corollary 6–6.

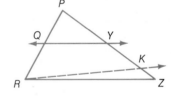

   Given: $\dfrac{PQ}{QR} = \dfrac{PY}{YZ}$ **Prove:** $\overleftrightarrow{QY} \parallel \overline{RZ}$

   Plan: Use an indirect proof. Assume that $\overleftrightarrow{QY}$ is not parallel to $\overline{RZ}$ and draw $\overrightarrow{RK} \parallel \overleftrightarrow{QY}$.

   $\therefore \dfrac{PQ}{QR} = \dfrac{PY}{YK}$ and $YK = YZ$. Complete the proof.

24. Prove Corollary 6–8.
    Plan of Proof: To show that $\dfrac{AE}{EB} = \dfrac{CF}{FG}$,

    draw $\overline{AG}$ intersecting the middle plane at D. Then draw $\overline{AC}$, $\overline{ED}$, $\overline{DF}$, and $\overline{BG}$. Use the theorem that two parallel planes cut by a third plane form parallel lines of intersection to show $\overline{ED} \parallel \overline{BG}$ and $\overline{DF} \parallel \overline{AC}$.

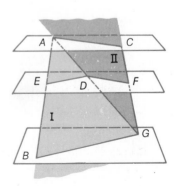

    In plane I (ABG), show that $\dfrac{AE}{EB} = \dfrac{AD}{DG}$.

    In plane II (ACG), show that $\dfrac{AD}{DG} = \dfrac{CF}{FG}$.

    Use the property of transitivity to complete the proof.

In $\triangle SZY$, $\overline{ST}$ bisects angle ZSY. Use the given information in Exercises 25–30 to find a, b, c, d.

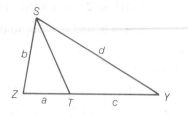

25. $a = x - 5$; $b = x - 3$; $c = x + 1$; $d = x + 6$

26. $a = x - 5$; $b = x - 3$; $c = x + 1$; $d = x + 7$

27. $a = x - 8$; $b = x - 3$; $c = x + 6$; $d = x + 16$

28. $a = x - 10$; $b = x - 4$; $c = x - 3$; $d = x + 9$

C

29. $a = x - 3$; $b = x$; $c = x + 1$; $d = 2x - 10$

30. $a = x - 5$; $b = x + 1$; $c = x + 4$; $d = 2x + 2$

31. **Given:** $\triangle GHK$;
    $\overrightarrow{HB}$ bisects the exterior angle at H.

   Prove: $\dfrac{KH}{HG} = \dfrac{KB}{BG}$

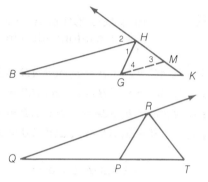

Refer to $\triangle QTR$ for Exercises 32–35. In $\triangle QRP$, $\overline{RT}$ is the bisector of the exterior angle at R. Use the results of Exercise 31 to compute each answer.

32. $QR = 12$; $RP = 9$; $QT = 16$. Find TP.

33. $QR = 16$; $RP = 12$; $TP = 15$. Find QT.

34. $QR = 18$; $QT = 27$; $TP = 21$. Find RP.

35. $QR = x + 1$; $RP = x - 3$; $QT = x + 6$; $TP = x + 1$. Find QR, RP, QT, and TP.

36. **Given:** $\overline{ME}$ bisects $\angle LMF$;
    $AL = EL$; $BF = EF$
    Prove: $\overline{AB} \parallel \overline{LF}$

37. **Given:** $\triangle XYZ$; $\overline{YR}$ bisects $\angle Y$;
    $\overline{ZP}$ bisects $\angle Z$.
    Prove: $\dfrac{a}{e} = \dfrac{b + c}{c + d}$

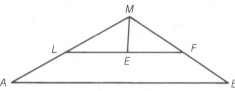

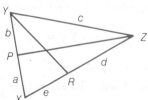

38. Prove Corollary 6–7.

   Given: $\overline{HB}$ bisects $\angle GHK$ in $\triangle GHK$;
   B is a point on $\overline{GK}$.

   Prove: $\dfrac{KH}{HG} = \dfrac{KB}{BG}$

   Plan: Through G draw $\overline{GM} \parallel \overline{BH}$.
   Extend $\overline{KH}$ to meet $\overline{GM}$. Prove $\angle 1$
   $\cong \angle 3$ and $\angle 3 \cong \angle 4$ by transitivity
   of congruence. Then prove $HM =$
   HG. Complete the proof.

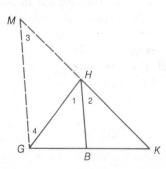

Review

Determine whether each pair of ratios can be written as a proportion. *(Section 6-1)*

1. $\dfrac{3}{8}; \dfrac{9}{21}$

2. $\dfrac{4}{9}; \dfrac{20}{45}$

3. $\dfrac{1}{2}; \dfrac{21}{42}$

4. $\dfrac{13}{4}; \dfrac{26}{9}$

Solve for *x*. No denominator equals zero. *(Section 6-1)*

5. $\dfrac{4}{7} = \dfrac{12}{x}$

6. $\dfrac{5}{8} = \dfrac{2x}{24}$

7. $\dfrac{3}{x} = \dfrac{4}{9}$

8. $\dfrac{3x}{7} = \dfrac{12}{8}$

In Exercises 9–12, write a new proportion as directed.

    a. by addition   **b.** by subtraction *(Section 6-2)*

9. $\dfrac{6}{11} = \dfrac{12}{22}$

10. $\dfrac{3}{4} = \dfrac{6}{y}$

11. $\dfrac{x}{9} = \dfrac{14}{18}$

12. $\dfrac{2a}{b} = \dfrac{3}{c}$

Find the geometric mean between the given numbers. Use the Table of Square Roots on page 568 to approximate answers to the nearest hundredth. *(Section 6-2)*

13. 5 and 12

14. 21 and 6

15. 4 and 12

16. 14 and 3

Find the fourth proportional to the given numbers. *(Section 6-2)*

17. 6; 13; 4

18. 17; 32; 51

19. $a; 2a; b$

20. $4x; 10y; 12x$

In $\triangle FGH$, $\overline{IJ} \parallel \overline{HG}$. Find the unknown lengths. *(Section 6-3)*

	FI	*IH*	*FJ*	*JG*	*FH*	*FG*
21.	4	3	6	?	7	?
22.	5	?	10	6	?	16
23.	?	5	8	$5\frac{5}{7}$	?	$13\frac{5}{7}$
24.	6	2	?	3	8	?

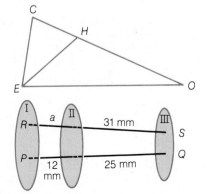

In the figure *ECHO* at the right, $\overline{EH}$ bisects angle *CEO*. Refer to this figure in Exercises 25–26 to find *x*. *(Section 6-4)*

	EC	*CH*	*HO*	*OE*
25.	12	7	*x*	18
26.	15	9	14	*x*

27. In the figure at the right, plates I, II, and III are parallel to each other. Wires run from *P* to *Q* and from *R* to *S*. Find *a*. *(Section 6-4)*

Consumer Applications

Ratios and Banking

Persons who borrow money can estimate the yearly percentage interest rate on a loan by using the constant ratio formula.

$$r = \frac{2Mi}{B(n + 1)}$$

r: yearly interest rate
M: number of payment periods per year
i: interest charge

B: amount of loan
n: number of payments

EXAMPLE A loan of $4000 was repaid in 24 monthly payments. The interest charge was $560. Estimate the yearly percentage rate of interest (nearest tenth).

Solution: $M = 12$; $i = \$560$; $B = \$4000$; $n = 24$

$$r = \frac{2(12)(560)}{(4000)(25)}$$ ⟵——— **Use a calculator.**

$$4\ 0\ 0\ 0\ \boxed{\times}\ 2\ 5\ \boxed{=}\ \boxed{\text{M+}} \qquad \boxed{\;100000.\;}$$

$$2\ \boxed{\times}\ 1\ 2\ \boxed{\times}\ 5\ 6\ 0\ \boxed{=}\ \boxed{\div}\ \boxed{\text{MR}}\ \boxed{=} \qquad \boxed{\;0.1344\;}$$

Annual percentage rate of interest: **13.4%**

NOTE: The formula can be used only when the loan is repaid in an equal number of payments.

EXERCISES

Find the approximate yearly percentage rate of interest on each loan. Round answers to the nearest tenth.

	Amount Loan	Interest Charge	Payment Periods per Year	Number of Payments
1.	$ 600.00	$ 24.00	12	6
2.	$ 800.00	$120.00	12	20
3.	$2100.00	$395.00	12	30
4.	$ 500.00	$ 7.50	12	1
5.	$ 600.00	$ 36.00	12	12

6-5 Similar Polygons

Similar polygons have the same shape. Polygons will have the same shape if corresponding angles are congruent and if the lengths of corresponding sides have the same ratio (are proportional).

Definition

> Two polygons are **similar** if corresponding angles are congruent and corresponding sides are proportional.

NOTE: The symbol for "is similar to" is "~."

EXAMPLE For similar polygons $SRQP$ and $YZTX$, the lengths of certain sides are given. Find PQ, PS, and SR.

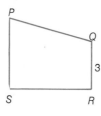 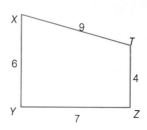

Solutions:

$$\frac{QR}{TZ} = \frac{PQ}{XT} \qquad \frac{QR}{TZ} = \frac{PS}{XY} \qquad \frac{QR}{TZ} = \frac{SR}{YZ}$$

$$\frac{3}{4} = \frac{PQ}{9} \qquad\qquad \frac{3}{4} = \frac{PS}{6} \qquad\qquad \frac{3}{4} = \frac{SR}{7}$$

$$4 \cdot PQ = 3 \cdot 9 \qquad 4 \cdot PS = 18 \qquad 4 \cdot SR = 21$$

$$PQ = \frac{27}{4} \qquad\qquad PS = \frac{18}{4} \qquad\qquad SR = \frac{21}{4}$$

$$PQ = 6\tfrac{3}{4} \qquad\qquad PS = 4\tfrac{1}{2} \qquad\qquad SR = 5\tfrac{1}{4}$$

CLASSROOM EXERCISES

State whether each pair of polygons is similar.
Give a reason for each answer.

1. Equilateral Triangles

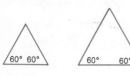

2. Isosceles Triangles

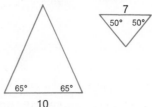

3. Rhombus and Square

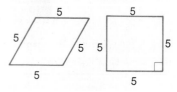

4. Parallelograms

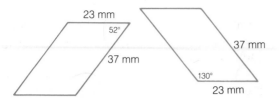

5. Rectangles

6. Rhombuses

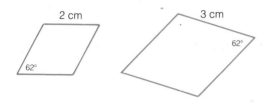

7. Parallelograms

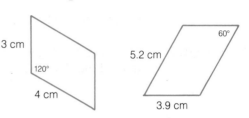

WRITTEN EXERCISES

A

1. Given that $\triangle HKM \sim \triangle RST$, name the corresponding congruent angles and write three proportions.

For Exercises 2 and 3, $\triangle ABC \cong \triangle DEF$.

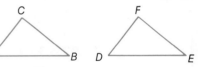

2. Is $\triangle ABC$ similar to $\triangle DEF$?

3. Give the ratio of a pair of corresponding sides.

4. If $\triangle MNQ \sim \triangle ABC$ and $\triangle ABC \sim \triangle DEF$, is $\triangle MNQ \sim \triangle DEF$?

In Exercises 5–8, the lengths of corresponding sides of two similar polygons are given. Write the ratio of the corresponding sides of the first polygon to the second.

5. 5, 6, 8;   10, 12, 16

6. 3, 6, 8, 8; $4\frac{1}{2}$, 9, 12, 12

7. 9, 11, 14; $4\frac{1}{2}$, $5\frac{1}{2}$, 7

8. 8a, 8b, 8c;   5a, 5b, 5c

In Exercises 9–18, classify each statement as true, *T*, or false, *F*. When a statement is false, give an example to show why it is false.

9. Any two squares are similar.

10. Any two triangles are similar.

11. Any two rectangles are similar.

12. Any two regular triangles are similar.

13. Any polygon is similar to itself.

14. Any two rhombuses are similar.

15. If two polygons are congruent, then they are similar.

16. If two polygons are similar, then they are congruent.

17. Any two regular hexagons are similar.

18. Any two isosceles triangles are similar.

In Exercises 19–24, the lengths of the corresponding sides of two similar triangles are given. Find the unknown lengths.

19. 6, 9, 12; 9, x, y

20. 8, 12, 16; 6, a, b

21. 15, 18, e; 45, f, 60

22. 24, 30, 36; c, 40, d

23. 1.2, 1.6, 2.4; 1.8, g, h

24. 0.75, 1.25, 1.5; 2.25, p, q

B Refer to the figure for Exercises 25–27.
In the figure, $\triangle HTR \sim \triangle HNS$.

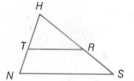

25. If m$\angle H = 50$ and m$\angle HRT = 45$, find m$\angle N$.

26. If $HT = 5$, $TN = 3$, and $HR = 7$, find RS.

27. If $HR = 9$, $RS = 4$, and $NS = 12$, find TR.

C

28. In the figure at the left below, $\triangle AXE \sim \triangle RTE$. Find EA, AR, EX, AX, and RT.

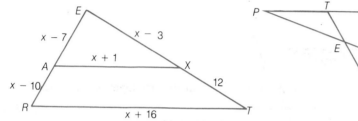

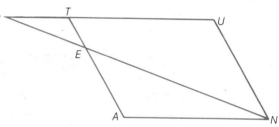

29. In parallelogram $TUNA$, $\dfrac{TP}{AN} = \dfrac{TE}{AE}$. Prove $\triangle PET \sim \triangle NEA$.

CALCULATOR APPLICATIONS

Similar Polygons

You can use the ratio of corresponding sides of two similar polygons to find the lengths of unknown sides.

EXAMPLE Suppose that the ratio of corresponding sides of similar polygons $YZTX$ and $SRQP$ on page 280 is $\frac{11}{8}$. Find XT and YZ if $PQ = 14$ and $SR = 17$.

SOLUTION Use the constant and multiplication keys (ⓚ and ⓧ) to store the ratio $\frac{11}{8}$. Then enter each known value and press ⌷= .

1 1 ⌷÷ 8 ⌷= ⌷× ⓚ 1 4 ⌷=   ⌷ 19.25 ⌷

1 7 ⌷=   ⌷ 23.375 ⌷

EXERCISES

Use a calculator to check the solutions to Exercises 19–24 above.

In the figure at the right, $\overleftrightarrow{AB} \parallel \overleftrightarrow{CD}$. Line m is a transversal. Use this information in Exercises 1–4. *(Pages 162–164, 168–169, 173–175)*

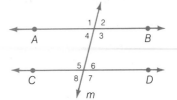

1. Name 4 pairs of congruent corresponding angles.
2. Name 2 pairs of congruent alternate interior angles.
3. What is the sum of the measures of $\angle 3$ and $\angle 6$?
4. If $m\angle 1 = 100$, find the measures of angles 2, 3, 4, 5, 6, 7, and 8.
5. In $\triangle APB$, $\overline{GH} \parallel \overline{AB}$, $m\angle PGH = 55$. Find $m\angle A$. *(Pages 173–175)*

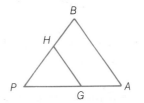

6-6 Similar Triangles

Theorem 6–9 provides a way of proving that two triangles are similar.

Theorem 6–9

> **AAA Similarity Theorem**
>
> If the angles of one triangle are congruent to the angles of another triangle, then the triangles are similar.

EXAMPLE 1   Write a plan of proof for Theorem 6–9.

Given: In $\triangle ABC$ and $\triangle DEF$,
$\angle A \cong \angle D$, $\angle B \cong \angle E$,
and $\angle C \cong \angle F$.

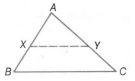

Prove: $\triangle ABC \sim \triangle DEF$

Plan:

$\boxed{1}$ Let X be a point on $\overline{AB}$ such that $\overline{AX} \cong \overline{DE}$. Let Y be a point on $\overline{AC}$ such that $\overline{AY} \cong \overline{DF}$. Show that $\triangle AXY \cong \triangle DEF$ by the SAS Postulate and that $\angle AXY \cong \angle B$ by the Transitive property of congruence.

$\boxed{2}$ Since $\overline{XY} \parallel \overline{BC}$ by Theorem 4–8, $\dfrac{AB}{AX} = \dfrac{AC}{AY}$ by Corollary 6–5.

$\boxed{3}$ Since $AX = DE$ and $AY = DF$, $\dfrac{AB}{DE} = \dfrac{AC}{DF}$.

$\boxed{4}$ To complete the proof, let R be a point on $\overline{BA}$ such that $\overline{BR} \cong \overline{ED}$ and let S be a point on $\overline{BC}$ such that $\overline{BS} \cong \overline{EF}$. Show that $\dfrac{AB}{DE} = \dfrac{CB}{FE}$.

Then $\dfrac{AB}{DE} = \dfrac{AC}{DF} = \dfrac{CB}{FE}$ and $\triangle ABC \sim \triangle DEF$.

EXAMPLE 2   Use the triangles below to show that $\triangle QGD \sim \triangle FCN$.

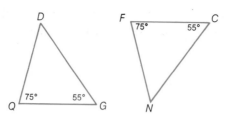

Solution: $\angle Q \cong \angle F; \angle G \cong \angle C$ ⟵——— **Given**

$\angle D \cong \angle N$ ⟵——— **By Corollary 4–13, page 183**

$\therefore \triangle QGD \sim \triangle FCN$ ⟵——— **By Theorem 6–9, page 283**

Corollary 6–10 states the results of the Example in general form.

Corollary
6–10

> **AA Similarity Corollary**
>
> If two angles of one triangle are congruent to two angles of a second triangle, then the triangles are similar.

A special case of Corollary 6–10 occurs with right triangles.

Corollary
6–11

> **Right-Triangle Similarity Corollary**
>
> If two right triangles have an acute angle of one congruent to an acute angle of the other, then the triangles are similar.

A line parallel to one side of a triangle may form another triangle with the given triangle. In these figures line YX is parallel to segment BC, and $\triangle ABC \sim \triangle AXY$ by the indicated congruence of angles.

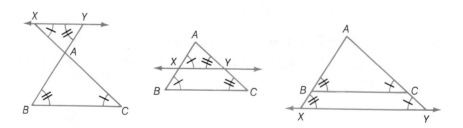

This suggests the following corollary.

Corollary
6–12

> If a line parallel to one side of a triangle determines a second triangle, then the second triangle will be similar to the original triangle.

You are asked to write a proof of the corollary in the Written Exercises.

CLASSROOM EXERCISES

Use each figure and the given information to tell whether each pair of triangles is similar. Give a reason for each answer.

1.
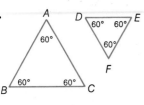

2. $\overline{KY} \parallel \overline{NO}$
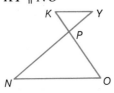

3.
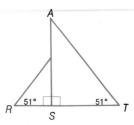

4. $\overline{KM} \parallel \overline{TS}$
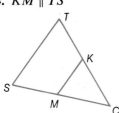

5.
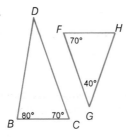

6.
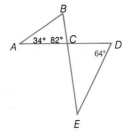

WRITTEN EXERCISES

A   Exercises 1–4 refer to △ABC in which ∠1 ≅ ∠2.

Complete each statement.

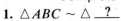

1. $\triangle ABC \sim \triangle \underline{}$

2. $\dfrac{AD}{AB} = \dfrac{?}{AC} = \dfrac{?}{BC}$

3. If $AD = 3$, $DE = 4$, and $AB = 5$, $BC = \underline{}$.

4. If $AE = 5$, $ED = 7$, and $BC = 21$, $AC = \underline{}$.

5. In figure $WATCH$, $\triangle WCT \sim \triangle WAH$. Find x and y.

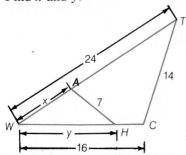

6. In the figure below, $\triangle I \sim \triangle II$. Find x and y.

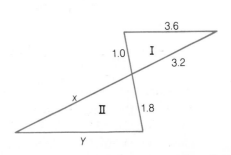

B

7. Given: $\overline{TS} \parallel \overline{PQ}$

Prove: $\triangle RTS \sim \triangle RPQ$

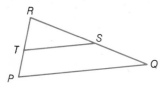

8. Given: $\triangle THE; \dfrac{EU}{UT} = \dfrac{ER}{RH}$

Prove: $\triangle URE \sim \triangle THE$

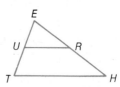

9. Given: In $\triangle MRO, \overline{TS} \perp \overline{MR}$ and $\overline{OR} \perp \overline{MR}$

Prove: $\triangle MRO \sim \triangle MST$

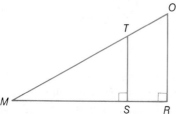

10. Given: $\triangle XYZ$, in which $m\angle Y = 90$ and $\overline{WU} \perp \overline{XZ}$

Prove: $\triangle XYZ \sim \triangle XUW$

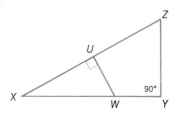

11. Given: Trapezoid $DRTC$ with bases DC and RT

Prove: $\triangle DOC \sim \triangle TOR$

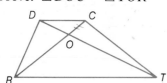

12. Given: $\triangle FDN$ in which $\angle F \cong \angle NDQ$

Prove: $\triangle NQD \sim \triangle NDF$

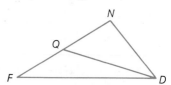

13. Complete this proof of Corollary 6–12.

Case I: $\overleftrightarrow{XY}$ is in the exterior of $\triangle ABC$.

Given: X and Y are the points of intersection of $\overleftrightarrow{XY}, \overrightarrow{CA}$, and $\overrightarrow{BA}; \overleftrightarrow{XY} \parallel \overline{BC}$

Prove: $\triangle ABC \sim \triangle AYX$

Statements	Reasons
1. X and Y are the points of intersection of $\overleftrightarrow{XY}$ and $\overrightarrow{CA}$ and $\overrightarrow{BA}$, respectively.	1. ?
2. $\overleftrightarrow{XY} \parallel \overline{BC}$	2. ?
3. $\angle B \cong \angle AYX; \angle C \cong \angle AXY$	3. (2). ?
4. $\triangle ABC \sim \triangle AYX$	4. (3). ?

14. A line is drawn parallel to the base of an isosceles triangle so that it forms a second triangle. Explain why this second triangle is also isosceles.

15. Two quadrilaterals have their corresponding angles congruent. Are the quadrilaterals similar? Explain.

16. Given: $\triangle PMT \sim \triangle RGA$;
$\overline{PS} \perp \overline{MT}$; $\overline{RQ} \perp \overline{GA}$
Prove: $\triangle STP \sim \triangle QAR$;
$\triangle SPM \sim \triangle QRG$

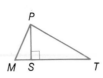
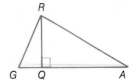

Exercises 17–19 refer to the figure at the right. $\overline{BD}$ and $\overline{AE}$ are altitudes of $\triangle ABC$.

17. Prove: $\triangle AEC \sim \triangle BDC$

18. Prove: $\triangle BFE \sim \triangle AFD$

19. Prove: $\triangle ADF \sim \triangle AEC$

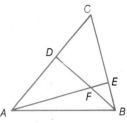

In Exercises 20–21, $\triangle ABC$ is a right triangle with the right angle at C. D is a point on $\overline{AB}$ and $\overline{CD} \perp \overline{AB}$.

20. Prove that $\dfrac{AC}{CB} = \dfrac{CD}{BD}$.

21. Prove that $AB \cdot AD = AC^2$.

22. Given: Circle O with $\angle BAE \cong \angle BDE$

Prove: $AB \cdot CD = ED \cdot AC$

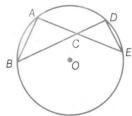

23. Scalene triangle WEF has midpoints R, T, and A. Explain why all four triangles formed by joining the midpoints are similar to triangle WEF.

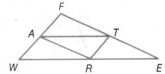

C

24. Given: $\triangle BCA \sim \triangle EFD$; $\overline{AR}$ and $\overline{DT}$ are angle bisectors.
Prove: $\triangle RCA \sim \triangle TFD$;
$\triangle RAB \sim \triangle TDE$

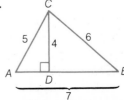

25. Two triangles have five parts (angles and sides) of the first triangle congruent to five parts of the second. The triangles are *not* congruent. Explain how this is possible.

26. Prove Theorem 6–9. (HINT: Follow the Plan in Example 1 on page 283).

GEOMETRY REVIEW CAPSULE FOR SECTION 6-7

In Exercises 1–4, refer to triangles ABC and EFG. (Pages 72, 260–261)

1. Find the perimeter of $\triangle ABC$ and of $\triangle EFG$.

2. What is the ratio of the perimeter of $\triangle ABC$ to the perimeter of $\triangle EFG$?

3. What is the ratio of AC to EG?

4. What is the ratio of AB to EF?

6-7 More on Similar Triangles

In similar triangles, *corresponding sides are opposite congruent angles.*

EXAMPLE 1 In similar triangles ABC and DEF, $\angle A \cong \angle D$ and $\angle C \cong \angle F$. Complete each statement.

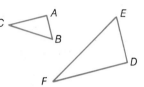

a. $\dfrac{AC}{DF} = \dfrac{?}{DE}$ b. $\dfrac{AB}{DE} = \dfrac{BC}{?}$

Solutions: a. $\dfrac{AC}{DF} = \dfrac{AB}{DE}$ ⟵ —— $\overline{DE}$ **is opposite** $\angle F$; $\overline{AB}$ **is opposite** $\angle C$.

b. $\dfrac{AB}{DE} = \dfrac{BC}{EF}$ ⟵ —— $\overline{BC}$ **is opposite** $\angle A$; $\overline{EF}$ **is opposite** $\angle D$.

The SAS Theorem for similarity corresponds to the SAS Theorem for congruence. You are asked to prove this theorem in the Written Exercises.

Theorem 6–13

> **SAS Similarity Theorem**
>
> If an angle of one triangle is congruent to an angle of another and the sides including these angles are proportional, then the triangles are similar.

There is also an SSS Theorem for similarity.

Theorem 6–14

> **SSS Similarity Theorem**
>
> If the corresponding sides of two triangles are proportional, then the triangles are similar.

You are asked to prove this theorem in the Written Exercises.

EXAMPLE 2 Determine whether each pair of triangles is similar.

a.

b.

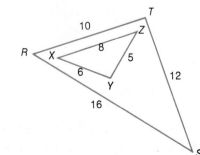

Solutions: **a.** $\angle A \cong \angle A$ ←——— **Identity**

$$\frac{AD}{AC} \overset{?}{=} \frac{AE}{AB}$$ ←——— **Test whether corresponding sides are proportional.**

$$\frac{1}{3} = \frac{2}{6}$$ ←——— **Each ratio equals $\frac{1}{3}$.**

$\therefore \triangle ADE \sim \triangle ACB$ ←——— **By the SAS Similarity Theorem**

b. $$\frac{XY}{ST} \overset{?}{=} \frac{YZ}{TR} \overset{?}{=} \frac{ZX}{SR}$$ ←——— **Test whether corresponding sides are proportional.**

$$\frac{6}{12} = \frac{5}{10} = \frac{8}{16}$$ ←——— **Each ratio equals $\frac{1}{2}$.**

$\therefore \triangle XYZ \sim \triangle STR$ ←——— **By the SSS Similarity Theorem**

The following corollaries also relate to similar triangles. Recall that "segment" refers to the "measure of segment" in theorems and corollaries about proportional segments.

Corollary 6–15	The perimeters of two similar triangles are proportional to any pair of corresponding sides.
Corollary 6–16	The altitudes of similar triangles are proportional to any pair of corresponding sides.
Corollary 6–17	The medians of similar triangles are proportional to any pair of corresponding sides.

You are asked to prove these corollaries in the Written Exercises.

EXAMPLE 3 Two similar triangles have perimeters of 63 centimeters and 49 centimeters. Find the length of the altitude of the smaller triangle if the corresponding altitude of the larger triangle is 27 centimeters long.

Solution: $$\frac{\text{Perimeter of larger triangle}}{\text{Perimeter of smaller triangle}} = \frac{63}{49} = \frac{9}{7}$$ ←—— **Ratio of any pair of corresponding sides**

Let $x =$ the length of the altitude of the smaller triangle.

$$\frac{9}{7} = \frac{27}{x}$$ ←—— **By Corollary 6–16**

$$x = \frac{7 \cdot 27}{9}$$

$$x = 21$$

Thus, the length of the altitude is **21 centimeters.**

CLASSROOM EXERCISES

In Exercises 1–3, use the given figure and information to find x.

1. $\triangle ABC \sim \triangle DEF$

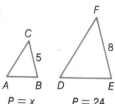

$P = x$ $P = 24$

2. $\triangle PRQ \sim \triangle TRS$

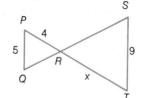

3. $\triangle PQR \sim \triangle WZT$

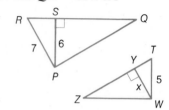

In Exercises 4–6, $\triangle LMN \sim \triangle LXY$.
Complete each statement.

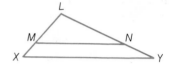

4. $\dfrac{LM}{LX} = \dfrac{?}{XY}$

5. $\dfrac{LY}{LN} = \dfrac{XY}{?}$

6. $\dfrac{MN}{XY} = \dfrac{?}{LX}$

WRITTEN EXERCISES

A In Exercises 1–3, use the given information to tell whether each pair of triangles is similar, S, or not similar, NS. Give a reason for each answer.

1.

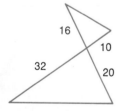

2.

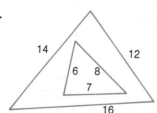

3.

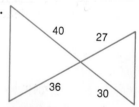

In Exercises 4–8, the lengths of the corresponding sides of two triangles are given. Tell whether each pair of triangles is similar. If the triangles are similar, determine the ratio of the corresponding sides.

4. Triangle I: $9, 5, 7\frac{1}{2}$ Triangle II: $4\frac{1}{2}, 2\frac{1}{2}, 3\frac{3}{4}$

5. Triangle I: $14, 17, 21$ Triangle II: $5, 6, 7$

6. Triangle I: $2\frac{2}{3}, 4\frac{1}{2}, 3$ Triangle II: $8, 13\frac{1}{2}, 9$

7. Triangle I: $0.14, 0.19, 0.24$ Triangle II: $0.7, 0.95, 1.2$

8. Triangle I: $7, 8, 9$ Triangle II: $17, 18, 19$

9. Two similar triangles have perimeters of 35 centimeters and 65 centimeters. Find the length of the altitude of the larger triangle if the corresponding altitude of the smaller triangle is 10 centimeters long.

10. Two corresponding medians of two similar triangles are 9 centimeters and 15 centimeters long. One side of the larger triangle is 25 centimeters long. Find the length of the corresponding side of the smaller triangle.

11. Two corresponding altitudes of two similar triangles are 12 decimeters and 16 decimeters long. A median of the larger triangle is 20 decimeters long. Find the length of the corresponding median of the smaller triangle.

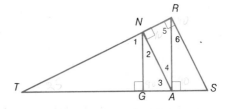

In $\triangle SRT$, $\overline{RA} \perp \overline{ST}$, $\overline{AN} \perp \overline{TR}$, $\overline{SR} \perp \overline{TR}$, $\overline{NG} \perp \overline{TA}$, *and* $m\angle T = 25$.

12. Find $m\angle S$, $m\angle 1$, $m\angle 2$, $m\angle 3$, $m\angle 4$, $m\angle 5$, and $m\angle 6$.

13. In the figure for Exercise 12, name all of the similar triangles.

14. Complete the proof of this statement.

Two right triangles are similar if the sides adjacent to the right angles are proportional.

Given: Triangles ABC and RST;
      $\angle C$ and $\angle T$ are right angles;
      $\dfrac{AC}{RT} = \dfrac{CB}{TS}$

Prove: $\triangle ABC \sim \triangle RST$

Statements	Reasons
1. Triangles ABC and RST; $\angle C$ and $\angle T$ are right angles.	1. ___?___
2. $\angle C \cong \angle T$	2. (1). ___?___
3. $\dfrac{AC}{RT} = \dfrac{CB}{TS}$	3. ___?___
4. $\triangle ABC \sim \triangle RST$	4. (2), (3). ___?___

B
15. In the figure at the left below, the lengths of the sides of each triangle are given. Prove that $\overline{XY} \parallel \overline{WU}$.

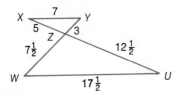
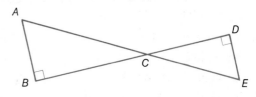

16. In the figure at the right above, $\overline{AB} \perp \overline{BD}$, $\overline{ED} \perp \overline{BD}$, and $\overline{AE}$ and $\overline{BD}$ intersect at C. Prove that $\triangle ABC \sim \triangle EDC$.

17. Write three proportions involving the sides of the triangles that you proved similar in Exercise 16.

18. Given: $\triangle MOP$ in which $\dfrac{PM}{PQ} = \dfrac{PO}{PR}$

Prove: $\triangle PMO \sim \triangle PQR$

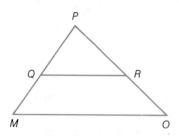

19. Given: $\angle A \cong \angle E$; $\angle B \cong \angle F$; G is the midpoint of $\overline{AB}$; H is the midpoint of $\overline{EF}$.

Prove: $\dfrac{AC}{ED} = \dfrac{CG}{DH}$.

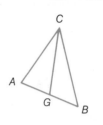 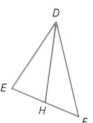

20. Prove Theorem 6–13.

Given: $\angle A \cong \angle D$; $\dfrac{AB}{DE} = \dfrac{AC}{DF}$

Prove: $\triangle ABC \sim \triangle DEF$

Plan: Mark off Q and R on $\overline{AB}$ and $\overline{AC}$, respectively, such that $\overline{AQ} \cong \overline{DE}$ and

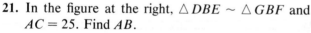

$\overline{AR} \cong \overline{DF}$. Show that $\triangle DEF \cong \triangle AQR$ and that $\dfrac{AB}{AQ} = \dfrac{AC}{AR}$.

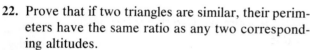

Then $\overline{QR} \parallel \overline{BC}$, and so on.

21. In the figure at the right, $\triangle DBE \sim \triangle GBF$ and $AC = 25$. Find AB.

22. Prove that if two triangles are similar, their perimeters have the same ratio as any two corresponding altitudes.

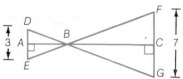

23. Prove Corollary 6–14.

24. Prove Corollary 6–15.

25. Prove Corollary 6–16.

26. Prove Corollary 6–17.

27. Prove that if two triangles are similar, the segments bisecting two corresponding angles have the same ratio as any two corresponding medians.

28. Prove that two triangles are similar if their sides are parallel to each other.

29. Given: $\angle A \cong \angle BDE$; $AB \cdot DE = AD \cdot BD$

Prove: $AB \cdot CD = AD \cdot BC$

30. In the figure below, $CRAG$ is a parallelogram.

Prove that $(AE)^2 = UE \cdot OE$.

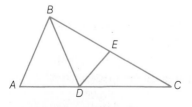

SUMMARY: Aids in Proof

The following summary lists ways of proving triangles similar that you have studied up to this point. This summary will help you to plan and write proofs involving similar triangles.

Summary

Ways of Proving Triangles Similar

1. Prove that corresponding angles are congruent and corresponding sides are proportional.

2. Prove that three angles of one are congruent to three angles of the other.

3. Prove that two angles of one are congruent to two angles of the other.

4. Prove that they are both right triangles with an acute angle of one congruent to an acute angle of the other.

5. Prove that the second triangle is formed by a line that is parallel to a side of the first triangle.

6. Prove that an angle of one triangle is congruent to an angle of the other and the sides including these angles are proportional.

7. Prove that corresponding sides are proportional.

Review

Pentagons *ABCDE* and *PQRST* are similar. Use this information for Exercises 1–4. *(Section 6–5)*

1. $\angle B \cong \angle$ __?__

2. $\angle S \cong \angle$ __?__

3. $\dfrac{CD}{RS} = \dfrac{EA}{?}$

4. $\dfrac{?}{DE} = \dfrac{PQ}{AB}$

5. **Given:** Parallelogram *ABCE*

   Prove: $\triangle BCD \sim \triangle FED$
   (Section 6–6)

6. **Given:** $\overline{AB} \perp \overline{BD}; \overline{ED} \perp \overline{BD}$

   Prove: $\triangle ABC \sim \triangle EDC$
   (Section 6–6)

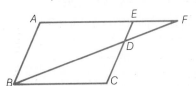

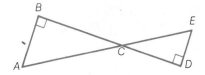

7. The perimeters of two similar triangles are 32 centimeters and 48 centimeters. What is the ratio of two corresponding sides? *(Section 6–7)*

8. Triangle *ABC* is similar to triangle *FGH*. If $AB = 4$ and $FG = \frac{8}{3}$, what is the ratio of the length of the median from $\angle A$ to the length of the median from $\angle F$? *(Section 6–7)*

APPLICATIONS

USING SIMILAR POLYGONS

These exercises apply geometric concepts studied in Sections 6–3 through 6–7.

A

1. Three building lots are located between Maple Avenue and Evergreen Avenue as shown. The lot division lines make right angles with Maple Avenue. The total frontage (front length) on Evergreen Avenue is 120 meters. Compute the frontage of each lot on Evergreen Avenue.

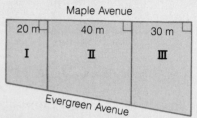

Surveyors can use the properties of similar triangles to find the distance between inaccessible points. In the figure at the right below, PQ is the distance across a lake, and $\overline{PQ} \parallel \overline{AB}$.

Use this information in Exercises 2–4.

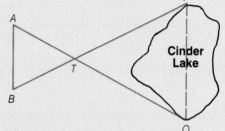

2. Prove that $\triangle ABT \sim \triangle QPT$.

3. Prove that $\dfrac{PQ}{BA} = \dfrac{PT}{BT}$.

4. If $TP = 160$ meters, $BT = 40$ meters, and $AB = 33$ meters, find PQ.

In the figure below, polygon $ABCD$ is enlarged by choosing a point P and drawing $\overrightarrow{PA}$, $\overrightarrow{PB}$, $\overrightarrow{PC}$ and $\overrightarrow{PD}$. Then points A', B', C', and D' are located so that $PA' = 2PA$, $PB' = 2PB$, $PC' = 2PC$, and $PD' = 2PD$. Finally, segments $A'B'$, $B'C'$, $C'D'$, and $D'A'$ are drawn.

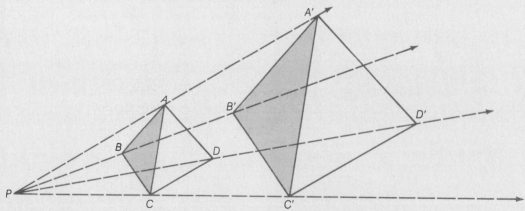

5. Prove that triangles PAB and $PA'B'$ are similar and that $\dfrac{A'B'}{AB} = \dfrac{PA'}{PA}$.

6. Prove that triangles ABC and $A'B'C'$ are similar.

7. How could the enlargement procedure be modified to draw a figure with sides one half the length of the sides of $ABCD$?

8. Draw a chair and enlarge it by this method.

9. The tallest trees in the world are the redwoods of northern California. To measure one of these giants, a forest ranger walked 520 feet from the tree and drove a stake into the ground at Q. Then, holding a small mirror at ground level and sighting in the mirror, the ranger continued to move away from the tree along the same path until the top of the tree and the top of the stake were in a direct line. If $RQ = 8$ feet and the top of the stake was 5 feet above the ground, find the height of the tree.

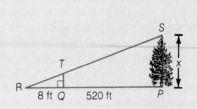

B

The pages of a book come from a printing press as a pile of flat, rectangular sheets of paper. Each sheet then passes through a series of rollers and is folded several times. Each fold is perpendicular to the longer side of the rectangle from which it is formed.

A sheet which is folded once is called a **folio**. One half a folio is a **quarto**. One half a quarto is an **octavo**.

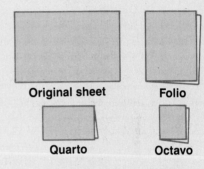

Original sheet   Folio

Quarto   Octavo

10. Fold a rectangular sheet of paper to obtain a folio, a quarto, and an octavo. Which pairs of rectangles are similar?

11. Suppose that the pattern of folding continues. Which rectangles will be similar to the original sheet?

12. A card designer wishes to make a card 6 inches long and of width x such that, when the card is folded on the dashed line as shown, it will have the same shape as when not folded. Find the width, x. Round your answer to the nearest tenth.

C

13. A tennis ball is served from a height of 7 feet. It just clears a net 3 feet high. The ball is served from a line 39 feet behind the net and travels in the straight path, $\overline{FG}$. About how far from the net will the ball hit the ground?

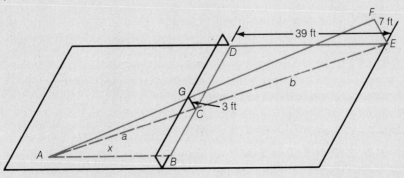

COMPUTER APPLICATIONS

BASIC: SIMILARITY

Problem: *Given the measures of the corresponding sides of two triangles, determine whether the triangles are similar:*

```
10   PRINT "ENTER THE MEASURES OF THE FIRST TRIANGLE'S
     SIDES."
20   INPUT S1, S2, S3
30   PRINT "ENTER THE MEASURES OF THE SECOND TRIANGLE'S
     SIDES."
40   INPUT T1, T2, T3
50   IF S1/T1 <> S2/T2 THEN 90
60   IF S1/T1 <> S3/T3 THEN 90
70   PRINT "THE TRIANGLES ARE SIMILAR."
80   GO TO 100
90   PRINT "THE TRIANGLES ARE NOT SIMILAR."
100  PRINT "ANY MORE TRIANGLES (1 = YES, 0 = NO)";
110  INPUT X
120  IF X = 1 THEN 10
130  END
```

Analysis:

Statements 50 and 60:   These statements test whether the ratios of the respective sides are the same, thus making the triangles similar.

EXERCISES

A   Run the program above with the following values.

1. $S1 = 5$; $S2 = 7$; $S3 = 9$;
   $T1 = 15$; $T2 = 21$; $T3 = 27$

2. $S1 = 4$; $S2 = 12$; $S3 = 10$
   $T1 = 6$; $T2 = 18$; $T3 = 15$

3. $S1 = 9$; $S2 = 15$; $S3 = 21$
   $T1 = 6$; $T2 = 10$; $T3 = 13$

4. $S1 = 45$; $S2 = 54$; $S3 = 36$
   $T1 = 10$; $T2 = 12$; $T3 = 8$

B   Write a BASIC program for each problem.

5. Given the measures of the corresponding sides of two triangles determine whether the triangles are congruent.

6. Given the measures of the corresponding sides of two quadrilaterals, determine whether the quadrilaterals are similar.

7. Given the ratio of the measures of two complementary angles, find the measures.

8. Given the ratio of the measures of two supplementary angles, find the measures.

Chapter Summary

IMPORTANT TERMS

Fourth proportional (p. 267)
Gear ratio (p. 264)
Geometric mean (p. 266)
Golden ratio (p. 270)
Golden rectangle (p. 270)

Proportion (p. 260)
Ratio (p. 260)
Similar polygons (p. 280)
Simplest form of a radical (p. 266)

IMPORTANT IDEAS

1. Three or more parallel lines divide transversals proportionally.
2. A line divides two sides of a triangle proportionally.
3. The properties of proportions can be used to determine the lengths of unknown segments in similar polygons.
4. **Ways of Proving Triangles Similar:** See p. 295.

Chapter Objectives and Review

Objective: *To solve problems using proportions (Section 6-1)*

Solve for x. No denominator equals 0.

1. $\dfrac{3}{8} = \dfrac{4}{x}$

2. $\dfrac{5}{7} = \dfrac{1}{x}$

3. $\dfrac{x-2}{x} = \dfrac{9}{12}$

4. $\dfrac{x}{x+9} = \dfrac{5}{8}$

Find the unknown terms in each proportion.

5. If $3x = 7y$, then $\dfrac{x}{y} = \dfrac{?}{?}$.

6. If $9x = 5y$, then $\dfrac{y}{x} = \dfrac{?}{?}$.

7. Find two numbers whose sum is 48 and whose ratio is 1 to 2.

8. Find the measures of two complementary angles whose ratio is 1 to 5.

Objective: *To write a new proportion from a given proportion by addition and by subtraction (Section 6-2)*

In Exercises 9–12, write a new proportion.

a. by addition   **b.** by subtraction

9. $\dfrac{3}{5} = \dfrac{12}{20}$

10. $\dfrac{4}{b} = \dfrac{6}{9}$

11. $\dfrac{x}{5} = \dfrac{7}{35}$

12. $\dfrac{x+3}{y} = \dfrac{9}{11}$

Objective: *To find the geometric mean between two numbers (Section 6-2)*

13. Find the geometric mean between 4 and 25.

14. Find the geometric mean between $6n$ and $24n$.

Objective: *To find the fourth proportional to three given numbers (Section 6-2)*

15. Find the fourth proportional to 5, 35, and 9.

16. Find the fourth proportional to 16, 20, and 24.

Objective: *To use proportional segments to solve problems (Sections 6–3 and 6–4)*

In Exercises 17–19, $\overline{EB} \parallel \overline{DC}$ and three lengths are given. Find the missing length.

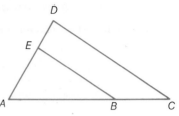

17. $AB = 6$, $BC = 4$, $AE = 3$, $ED =$ __?__
18. $AB = 9$, $BC = 6$, $ED = 4$, $AE =$ __?__
19. $BC = 3$, $AC = 10$, $AE = 2\frac{1}{3}$, $ED =$ __?__
20. In triangle RST, $\overleftrightarrow{DE}$ intersects $\overline{RT}$ at D and $\overline{ST}$ at E. $TD = 15$, $DR = 18$, $TE = 20$, and $ES = 24$. Is $\overleftrightarrow{DE}$ parallel to $\overleftrightarrow{RS}$? Give a reason for your answer.

In the figure at the right, $\overline{HW}$ bisects $\angle H$.

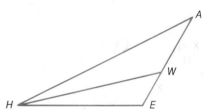

21. If $HE = 10$, $EW = 4$, $HA = 14$, find WA.

22. If $HE = 8$, $HA = 12$, and $EA = 10$, find EW and WA. (HINT: Let $EW = x$ and $WA = 10 - x$.)

Objective: *To apply the definition of similar polygons (Section 6–5)*

23. The sides of a pentagon are 10, 6, 20, 16, and 18. The corresponding sides of a similar pentagon are 35, a, b, c, and d. Find a, b, c, and d.

Objective: *To use the AAA Similarity Theorem and its corollaries to determine whether two triangles are similar (Section 6–6)*

In Exercises 24–25, refer to triangle GHK below.

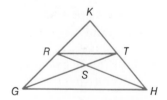

24. **Given:** R is the midpoint of $\overline{GK}$; T is the midpoint of $\overline{HK}$.
    Prove: $\triangle RKT \sim \triangle GKH$
25. **Given:** $RK = a$; $TK = b$; $GR = 2a$; $HT = 2b$
    Prove: $\triangle RST \sim \triangle HSG$

Objective: *To apply the SAS and SSS Similarity Theorems (Section 6–7)*

In Exercises 26–27, use the given information to tell why each pair of triangles is similar.

26. $\triangle RSY$; $\triangle PTW$

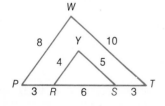

27. $\triangle AED$; $\triangle ACB$

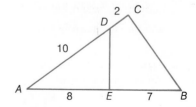

Objective: *To apply the corollaries about corresponding perimeters, altitudes, angle bisectors, and medians of similar triangles (Section 6-7)*

28. The sides of a triangle are 8, 9, and 13 units long. The shortest side of a similar triangle is 12 units long. What is the perimeter of the second triangle?

29. Corresponding sides of two similar triangles have the ratio $\frac{3}{8}$. A median of the larger triangle is 24 centimeters long. How long is the corresponding median of the smaller triangle?

Objective: *To solve word problems that involve ratio (Page 264)*

30. The blade-tip speed of a windmill is 110 mph in a 15 mph wind. What is the tip-speed ratio?

Objective: *To solve word problems that involve the geometric mean (Page 270)*

31. Picture frames are sold in standard sizes. Three of the sizes are 5 by 7, 8 by 10, and 11 by 14. Determine the ratio $\frac{l}{w}$ for each size. For which size is the ratio closest to the Golden Ratio (1.618)?

Objective: *To solve word problems that involve similar polygons (Pages 293–294)*

Sarah found the height of a tree by placing a mirror on the ground and walking backwards until she could see the top of the tree in the mirror. Use this information and the given figure in Exercises 32–33.

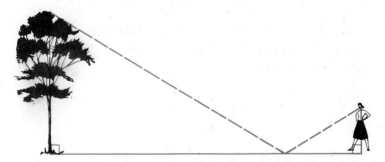

32. Sarah's eyes are 1.3 meters from the ground when her feet are 1.8 meters from the mirror and the tree is 12.8 meters from the mirror. What is the height of the tree? Round your answer to the nearest tenth.

33. Explain why Sarah's method works.

Chapter Test

Solve for *x*. No denominator is 0.

1. $\dfrac{3}{7} = \dfrac{4}{x}$ **2.** $\dfrac{x-10}{x} = \dfrac{4}{9}$ **3.** $\dfrac{x}{x+5} = \dfrac{24}{34}$

4. Find the geometric mean between 4 and 25.

5. Find the fourth proportional to 2, 6, and 7.

6. Find the fourth proportional to 4*a*, 5*c*, and 8*a*.

In Exercises 7–9, $\overline{DE} \parallel \overline{AB}$. Find *x*.

7.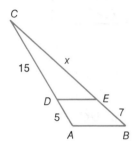

8.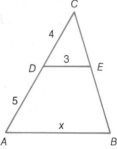

9.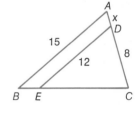

10. In $\triangle ABC$ at the right, $AC = 8$, $BC = 12$, and $AB = 10$. $\overline{CD}$ bisects $\angle C$, and D is between A and B.

Find AD and DB.

(HINT: Let $AD = x$ and $DB = 10 - x$.)

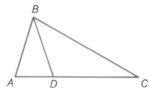

In Exercises 11–12, classify each statement as true, *T*, or false, *F*.

11. All rectangles are similar.   **12.** All squares are similar.

13. In the figure at the left below, $\overline{EA} \perp \overline{AB}$ and $\overline{DB} \perp \overline{AB}$. $\overline{EB}$ and $\overline{AD}$ intersect at C. Name two triangles that are similar.

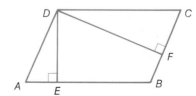

14. In the figure at the right above, $\overline{AC} \cong \overline{BC}$ and $\overline{AB} \cong \overline{BD}$. Name two similar triangles.

15. Given: $\square ABCD$ with $\overline{DE} \perp \overline{AB}$ and $\overline{DF} \perp \overline{BC}$.
Prove: $\triangle AED \sim \triangle CFD$

Cumulative Review: Chapters 1–6

Choose the best answer. Choose *a, b, c,* or *d.*

In the figure at the right, $\triangle DEC \cong \triangle BFA$ and $\triangle DAF \cong \triangle BCE$. Refer to this information and the given figure in Exercises 1–5.

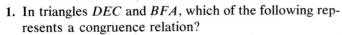

1. In triangles *DEC* and *BFA*, which of the following represents a congruence relation?
   a. $\triangle CDE \cong \triangle AFB$ b. $\triangle DCE \cong \triangle FBA$
   c. $\triangle ECD \cong \triangle FAB$ d. $\triangle EDC \cong \triangle BFA$

2. Which angle in $\triangle BFA$ corresponds to $\angle CED$ in $\triangle DEC$?
   a. $\angle FAB$ b. $\angle BFA$ c. $\angle BAF$ d. $\angle ABF$

3. Which side of $\triangle DCE$ corresponds to $\overline{FA}$ in $\triangle BAF$?
   a. $\overline{EC}$ b. $\overline{CD}$ c. $\overline{ED}$ d. $\overline{DC}$

4. Which angle in $\triangle DFA$ corresponds to $\angle BEC$ in $\triangle BEC$?
   a. $\angle DAF$ b. $\angle FDA$ c. $\angle FAD$ d. $\angle DFA$

5. Which side in $\triangle FAD$ corresponds to $\overline{EB}$ in $\triangle ECB$?
   a. $\overline{DA}$ b. $\overline{AF}$ c. $\overline{FD}$ d. $\overline{FA}$

In Exercises 6–10, refer to the figure at the right.

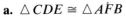

6. Name a pair of corresponding angles.
   a. $\angle 2; \angle A$ b. $\angle C; \angle 2$
   c. $\angle 1; \angle C$ d. $\angle 1; \angle A$

7. Name a pair of alternate interior angles.
   a. $\angle 1; \angle C$ b. $\angle 2; \angle C$
   c. $\angle 2; \angle A$ d. $\angle 1; \angle A$

8. If $\overrightarrow{BE} \parallel \overline{AC}$ and $m\angle ABE = 150$, find $m\angle A$.
   a. 30   b. 90   c. 105   d. 150

9. If $AB = BC$, $\overrightarrow{BE} \parallel \overleftrightarrow{AC}$, and $m\angle 2 = 40$, find $m\angle A$.
   a. 20   b. 40   c. 50   d. 140

10. If $\overrightarrow{BE}$ bisects $\angle DBC$, $\overrightarrow{BE} \parallel \overleftrightarrow{AC}$, and $\overline{CB} \perp \overleftrightarrow{AD}$, which of the following best describes $\triangle ABC$?
    a. acute   b. right isosceles   c. obtuse   d. equilateral

11. In parallelogram $ABCD$, $m\angle D = 3x - 30$ and $m\angle B = x + 90$. Find x.
    a. 30   b. 60   c. 120   d. 150

12. Find the measure of each angle of $\triangle FGH$ if $m\angle F = x$, $m\angle G = 4x$, and $m\angle H = x + 30$.

   a. 5; 35; 140   **b.** 20; 40; 120   **c.** 25; 55; 100   **d.** 30; 30; 120

13. In the figure at the right, $m\angle A = 60$, $m\angle C = 80$, and $\overrightarrow{DB}$ bisects $\angle ABE$. Find $m\angle ABD$.

   a. 40   **b.** 60.

   c. 70   **d.** 80

14. Find the sum of the measures of the angles of a seven-sided polygon.

   a. 720   **b.** 900   **c.** 1080   **d.** 1260

15. Find the measure of each angle of a regular hexagon.

   a. 60   **b.** 120   **c.** 180   **d.** 720

16. Find the number of sides in a regular polygon if the measure of each exterior angle is 40.

   a. 6   **b.** 7   **c.** 8   **d.** 9

In Exercises 17–19, refer to quadrilateral *ABCD*.

17. If $ABCD$ is a parallelogram, which conclusion can be drawn?

   a. $\overline{AD} \cong \overline{CD}$ **b.** $BC = AD$

   c. $DB = AC$ **d.** $\triangle AEB \cong \triangle AED$

18. If $ABCD$ is a rhombus, which conclusion can be drawn?

   a. $\overline{AC} \perp \overline{BD}$ **b.** $\overline{AC} \cong \overline{BD}$ **c.** $AC = BD$ **d.** $m\angle BAD = 90$

19. If $ABCD$ is a rectangle, diagonals AC and BD meet at E, $AE = 3x - 1$, and $BE = 2x + 7$, find x.

   a. 8   **b.** 10   **c.** 16   **d.** 34

In Exercises 20 and 21, refer to $\triangle ABC$ in which $\overline{DE} \parallel \overline{AB}$.

20. If $AD = 6$, $DC = 9$, $BC = 10$, find EC.

   a. 3   **b.** 5

   c. 6   **d.** 15

21. If $AB = 15$, $AD = 6$, $DC = 4$, find DE.

   a. 6   **b.** 10   **c.** $22\frac{1}{2}$ **d.** 30

22. Find the geometric mean between 4 and 16.

   a. 8   **b.** 10   **c.** 20   **d.** 64

Preparing for College Entrance Tests

Drawing auxiliary lines is a useful technique to apply to solving problems that involve parallel lines.

REMEMBER: Look for ways of extending a given segment or ray so that alternate interior angles or corresponding angles are formed.

EXAMPLE: In the figure at the right, line $k \parallel$ line t.
Find $m\angle RBC$.

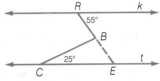

    a. 30   **b.** 80   **c.** 90

    d. 100   **e.** 180

Extend $\overline{RB}$ to intersect line t at E. Since $k \parallel t$, alternate interior angles are congruent and $m\angle BEC = 55$.

Solution: Since $\angle RBC$ is an exterior angle of $\triangle BCE$, $m\angle RBC = 25 + 55 = 80$.

Answer: b

Choose the best answer. Choose a, b, c, d, or e.

1. In the figure, line $r \parallel$ line m.
   Find x.

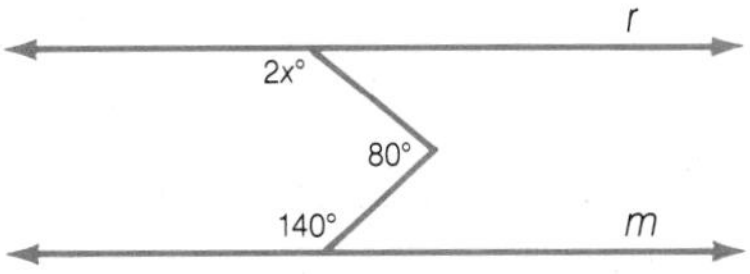

       a. 10   **b.** 30   **c.** 70

       d. 80   **e.** 140

2. In the figure, line $p \parallel$ line q.
   Find y.

       a. 10   **b.** 70   **c.** 110

       d. 140   **e.** 170

3. If lines m and t meet when extended to the right, which inequality best expresses the relationship between x and y?

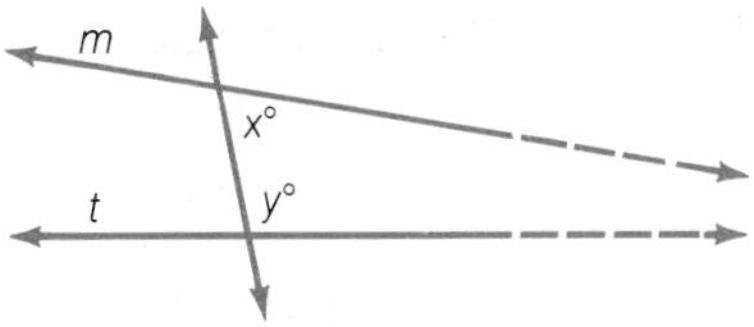

       a. $x = y$ **b.** $x + y < 180$ **c.** $x + y = 180$

       d. $x - y > 0$ **e.** $y - x > 0$

4. In this figure, $\overrightarrow{DE} \parallel \overrightarrow{BA}$, $m\angle C = 60$, and $m\angle B = 40$. Find r.

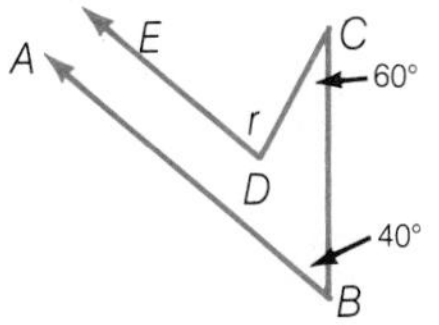

       a. 20   **b.** 80   **c.** 100

       d. 110   **e.** 120

5. In the figure at the right, all segments meet at right angles. Find the perimeter in terms of r and s.

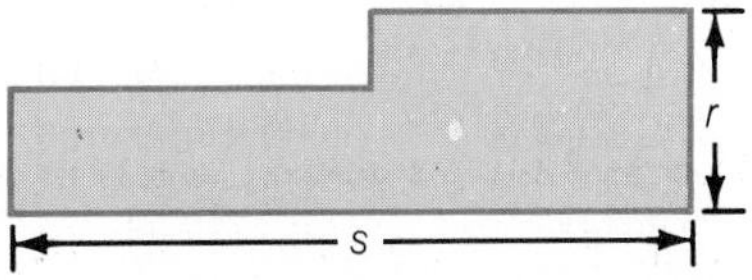

       a. $r + s$ **b.** $2r + s$ **c.** $2s + r$

       d. $r^2 + s^2$ **e.** $2r + 2s$

Preparing for College Entrance Tests

To answer questions such as the type illustrated in the Example:

1. Read the "Directions" carefully.
2. Use the given figure and information to draw a conclusion, if possible.
3. Write the letter of the statement, *a*, *b*, or *c* that identifies your conclusion. If no conclusion is possible, write *d*.

Directions: Each question consists of two quantities, one in Column A and one in Column B.
You are to compare the two quantities and determine whether

    a. the quantity in Column A is greater;

    b. the quantity in Column B is greater;

    c. the two quantities are equal;

    d. the relationship cannot be determined from the information given.

EXAMPLE:

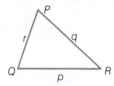

Given: $q > p$

Column A	Column B
$\angle P$	$\angle Q$

Solution: Since $q > p$, $m\angle Q > m\angle P$, because if two sides of a triangle are not congruent, the larger angle lies opposite the longer side.

Answer: b

Choose the best answer. Choose *a, b, c,* or *d.* Refer to the "Directions."

1.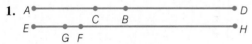

Given: $AB < CD$ and $EF < GH$

Column A	Column B
$AB + EF$	$CD + GH$

2.

Given: $AY > XZ$

Column A	Column B
AX	YZ

3.

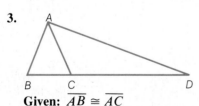

Given: $\overline{AB} \cong \overline{AC}$

Column A	Column B
AD	$AC + CD$

4.

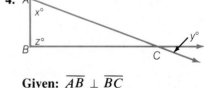

Given: $\overline{AB} \perp \overline{BC}$

Column A	Column B
$x + y$	z

CHAPTER **7** Right Triangles

Sections

7-1 Similarity Properties in Right Triangles

7-2 The Pythagorean Theorem

Applications: Using the Pythagorean Theorem

7-3 Special Right Triangles

7-4 The Tangent Ratio

Applications: Using the Tangent Ratio

7-5 The Sine and Cosine Ratios

Applications: Using the Sine and Cosine Ratios

7-6 Angle of Elevation/Angle of Depression

Features

Career Application: Geometry and Astronomy

Computer Application: Right Triangles

Calculator Application: Trigonometric Functions

Review and Testing

Algebra Review Capsules

Review: Sections 7–1 through 7–3

Review: Sections 7–4 through 7–6

Chapter Summary

Chapter Objectives and Review

Chapter Test

7–1 Similarity Properties in Right Triangles

When the altitude to the hypotenuse of a right triangle is drawn, two right triangles are formed.

EXAMPLE 1 Triangle ABC has a right angle at C. $\overline{CD}$ is the altitude to $\overline{AB}$ and m$\angle A = 40$.

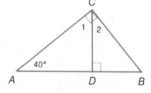

  a. Find m$\angle 1$, m$\angle 2$, and m$\angle B$.
  b. Tell which triangles are similar.

Solutions: **a.** In $\triangle ADC$, m$\angle 1 = 50$. ◄──── **m$\angle A$ + m$\angle 1 = 90$**

  In $\triangle BDC$, m$\angle 2 = 40$, ◄──── **m$\angle 1$ + m$\angle 2 = 90$**

  and   m$\angle B = 50$. ◄──── **m$\angle 2$ + m$\angle B = 90$**

  b. $\triangle ABC \sim \triangle ACD \sim \triangle CBD$ ◄──── **If the angles of one triangle are congruent to the angles of another triangle, the triangles are similar.**

Theorem 7–1 expresses the results of Example 1 in a more general form.

Theorem 7–1 | The altitude to the hypotenuse of a right triangle forms two triangles that are similar to each other and to the original triangle.

You are asked to prove this theorem in the Written Exercises. Two corollaries follow from Theorem 7–1.

Corollary 7–2 | The altitude to the hypotenuse of a right triangle is the geometric mean between the segments of the hypotenuse.

EXAMPLE 2 In $\triangle DEF$, $\angle D$ is a right angle, $\overline{DR}$ is the altitude to $\overline{EF}$, $ER = 9$, and $RF = 4$. Find DR.

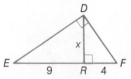

Solution: $\dfrac{ER}{DR} = \dfrac{DR}{FR}$ ◄──── **By Corollary 7–2**

  $\dfrac{9}{x} = \dfrac{x}{4}$ ◄──── **$ER = 9$; $DR = x$; $FR = 4$**

  $x^2 = 36$

  $x = 6$ ◄──── **DR**

By Corollary 7–3, either leg of a right triangle is also a geometric mean.

Corollary 7–3

> If the altitude to the hypotenuse of a right triangle is drawn, either leg is the geometric mean between the hypotenuse and the segment of the hypotenuse adjacent to the leg.

EXAMPLE 3 Right triangle BNA has altitude AD drawn to hypotenuse BN. If $AB = 8$ and $BN = 12$, find BD.

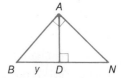

Solution: $\dfrac{BD}{BA} = \dfrac{BA}{BN}$ ⟵ **By Corollary 7-3**

$\dfrac{y}{8} = \dfrac{8}{12}$ ⟵ **BD = y; BA = 8; BN = 12**

$12y = 64$

$y = 5\frac{1}{3}$ ⟵ **BD**

You are asked to prove both corollaries in the Written Exercises.

CLASSROOM EXERCISES

Find the measure of each segment marked *x* or *y*.

1.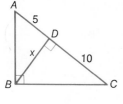

2.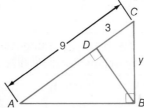

3.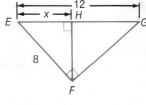

4.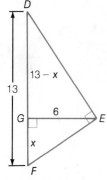

5.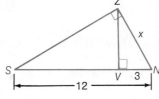

6.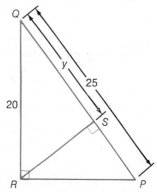

WRITTEN EXERCISES

Use Figures 1–3 for Exercises 1–8. Each figure represents a right triangle in which there is an altitude to the hypotenuse.

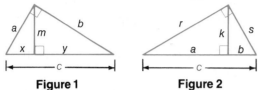

| Figure 1 | Figure 2 | Figure 3 |

1. For each figure, write the proportion of Corollary 7–2.
2. For each figure, write both proportions of Corollary 7–3.

In Exercises 3–8, state the corollary represented by each proportion.

3. For Figure 1, $\dfrac{c}{b} = \dfrac{b}{y}$.

4. For Figure 3, $\dfrac{h}{q} = \dfrac{q}{k}$.

5. For Figure 2, $\dfrac{c}{r} = \dfrac{r}{a}$.

6. For Figure 3, $\dfrac{h}{a} = \dfrac{a}{c}$.

7. For Figure 2, $\dfrac{b}{k} = \dfrac{k}{a}$.

8. For Figure 1, $\dfrac{c}{a} = \dfrac{a}{x}$.

In right triangle ABC, $\overline{CD}$ is the altitude to base AB. Use this figure for Exercises 9–14. Express any radicals in your answers in simplest form.

9. If $AD = 9$ and $DB = 4$, find DC.
10. If $AB = 12$ and $DB = 3$, how long is $\overline{BC}$?
11. Find AC if $AB = 16$ and $AD = 4$.
12. How long is $\overline{DB}$ if $AD = 20$ and $DC = 10$?
13. If $AD = 9$ and $AC = 16$, find DB. (HINT: First find AB.)
14. If $AD = 9$ and $DB = 4$, find AC and BC.
15. In right triangle ABC, altitude CD is drawn to hypotenuse AB. If $DB = 10$ and $CD = 20$, find AB.
16. In right triangle ABC, altitude CD is drawn to hypotenuse AB. If $AD = 4.5$ and $DB = 13.5$, find AC.
17. The altitude to the hypotenuse DF of right triangle DEF divides the hypotenuse into segments that are 4 centimeters and 5 centimeters long. Find the length of the shorter leg of $\triangle DEF$.

18. Prove Theorem 7–1.

Given: Right triangle ACB; $\angle ACB$ is a right angle; $\overline{CD} \perp \overline{AB}$

Prove: $\triangle ADC \sim \triangle ACB$
$\triangle CDB \sim \triangle ACB$
$\triangle ADC \sim \triangle CDB$

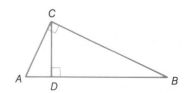

19. Prove Corollary 7–2. **Plan:** (Refer to the figure for Example 2 on page 306.) Prove $\triangle RDE \sim \triangle RFD$. Complete the proof.

20. Prove Corollary 7–3.

21. The altitude to the hypotenuse of a right triangle is 8 meters long. If the lengths of the segments of the hypotenuse are represented by y and $4y$, find the length of the hypotenuse.

22. ABC is a right triangle with $\overline{CD}$ the altitude to hypotenuse AB. If $AC = 20$ and $AB = 25$, find AD, CD, and BC.

23. In right triangle XYZ, the right angle is at Z and the altitude from Z meets the hypotenuse at F. If $ZF = 6$, $XF = 3$, and $FY = 5x - 3$, find x.

24. $\overline{CD}$ is the altitude to the hypotenuse of right triangle ABC. If $AC = 6$, $AD = 3$, and $BD = x$, write a proportion that can be used to find x. Solve the proportion for x.

25. In right triangle ABC, $\overline{BD}$ is the altitude to hypotenuse AC. If $BD = 2$, $AC = 5$, and $CD = x$, write a proportion that can be used to find x. Solve the proportion for x.

26. If x is the geometric mean between a and b, solve for x in terms of a and b.

C

27. If $\dfrac{a}{b} = \dfrac{b}{c}$, prove that $\dfrac{ac - 1}{b - 1} = \dfrac{b + 1}{1}$.

28. If $\dfrac{a}{b} = \dfrac{c}{d}$, prove that $\dfrac{a - 1}{b} = \dfrac{bc - d}{bd}$.

29. If $\dfrac{a}{b} = \dfrac{c}{d}$, prove that $\dfrac{a + 1}{1} = \dfrac{bc + d}{d}$.

30. $\overline{BC}$ is the base in isosceles triangle ABC. D is a point on $\overleftrightarrow{BC}$ such that $\angle BAD \cong \angle B$. Prove that AB is the geometric mean between BC and BD.

31. Prove that if the lengths of two legs of a right triangle are in the ratio of 1 to 2, then the altitude to the hypotenuse divides the hypotenuse into segments which are in the ratio of 1 to 4.

—— **ALGEBRA REVIEW CAPSULE FOR SECTION 7–2** ——

Square each number.

Example: $(3\sqrt{10})^2 = (3\sqrt{10})(3\sqrt{10}) = (3 \cdot 3)(\sqrt{10} \cdot \sqrt{10}) = 9 \cdot 10 = 90$

1. $\sqrt{10}$ 2. $\sqrt{a}$ 3. $3\sqrt{b}$ 4. $4\sqrt{6}$ 5. $\dfrac{2\sqrt{5}}{3}$ 6. $\dfrac{5\sqrt{c}}{2}$

Simplify. *(Pages 265–267)*

7. $\sqrt{27}$ 8. $\sqrt{50}$ 9. $2\sqrt{8}$ 10. $\sqrt{\dfrac{1}{9}}$ 11. $\sqrt{\dfrac{4}{5}}$ 12. $\dfrac{3}{\sqrt{7}}$

7-2 The Pythagorean Theorem

The *Pythagorean Theorem* is one of the best known and most useful theorems in geometry.

Theorem 7-4

> **Pythagorean Theorem**
>
> In any right triangle, the square of the length of the hypotenuse equals the sum of the squares of the lengths of the other two sides.

EXAMPLE 1 Prove the Pythagorean Theorem.

Given: $\triangle ABC$ is a right triangle with right angle at C.

Prove: $c^2 = a^2 + b^2$

Proof:

Statements	Reasons
1. Draw a perpendicular from C to $\overline{AB}$.	1. Through a given external point, there is exactly one line perpendicular to a given line.
2. $\triangle ABC$ is a right triangle.	2. Given
3. $\dfrac{c}{a} = \dfrac{a}{y}; \dfrac{c}{b} = \dfrac{b}{x}$	3. (1). If the altitude to the hypotenuse of a right triangle is drawn, either leg is the geometric mean between the hypotenuse and the segment of the hypotenuse adjacent to the leg.
4. $cy = a^2; cx = b^2$	4. (3). Theorem 6-1, page 260
5. $cy + cx = a^2 + b^2$	5. (4). Addition property
6. $c(y + x) = a^2 + b^2$	6. (5). Distributive property
7. $c^2 = a^2 + b^2$	7. (6). Substitution property

You can use the Pythagorean Theorem to find the measure of one side of a right triangle when the measures of the other two sides are known.

EXAMPLE 2 In a right triangle, the hypotenuse is 26 centimeters long and one leg is 24 centimeters long. Find the length of the other leg.

Solution:

$a^2 + b^2 = c^2$ ⟵ **Replace a with 24 and c with 26.**

$(24)^2 + b^2 = (26)^2$

$576 + b^2 = 676$ ⟵ **Solve for b.**

$b^2 = 100$

$b = 10$ Thus, $AC = \mathbf{10\ centimeters.}$

You can use the Pythagorean Theorem and the properties of geometric figures to find unknown lengths.

EXAMPLE 3 The diagonals of a rhombus are 12 centimeters and 8 centimeters long. Find the length of a side of the rhombus. Give the answer in simplified radical form.

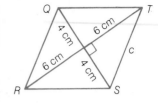

Solution: Since the diagonals of a rhombus are perpendicular bisectors of each other, the diagonals form four right triangles. Apply the Pythagorean Theorem.

$$a^2 + b^2 = c^2 \quad \longleftarrow \quad \textbf{Replace } \textit{a} \textbf{ with 6}$$
$$6^2 + 4^2 = c^2 \qquad\qquad \textbf{and } \textit{b} \textbf{ with 4.}$$
$$36 + 16 = c^2$$
$$52 = c^2$$
$$\sqrt{52} = c \quad \longleftarrow \quad \sqrt{52} = \sqrt{4 \cdot 13} = 2\sqrt{13}$$
$$c = 2\sqrt{13} \quad \longleftarrow \quad \textbf{Simplified radical form}$$

Thus, $ST = TQ = QR = RS = 2\sqrt{13}$ **centimeters.**

The converse of the Pythagorean Theorem is also a theorem.

Theorem 7–5

> **Pythagorean Theorem Converse**
>
> If the square of the length of one side of a triangle equals the sum of the squares of the lengths of the other two sides, then the triangle is a right triangle.

EXAMPLE 4 Determine whether the triangles with the given lengths for sides are right triangles.

  a. 3; 4; 5 **b.** 5; 5; $5\sqrt{2}$ **c.** 6; 8; 9

Solutions: **a.** $a^2 + b^2 = c^2$ **b.** $a^2 + b^2 = c^2$
$$3^2 + 4^2 \overset{?}{=} 5^2 \qquad\qquad 5^2 + 5^2 \overset{?}{=} (5\sqrt{2})^2$$
$$9 + 16 \overset{?}{=} 25 \qquad\qquad 25 + 25 \overset{?}{=} 25 \cdot 2$$
$$25 = 25 \quad \textbf{Yes} \; \checkmark \qquad\qquad 50 = 50 \quad \textbf{Yes} \; \checkmark$$

  c. $a^2 + b^2 = c^2$
$$6^2 + 8^2 \overset{?}{=} 9^2$$
$$36 + 64 \overset{?}{=} 81$$
$$100 \neq 81 \quad \textbf{No}$$

CLASSROOM EXERCISES

In Exercises 1–6, find *x* and *y*.

1.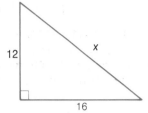

2.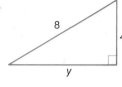

3.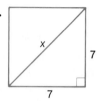

4.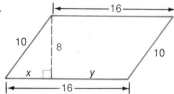

5.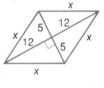

6.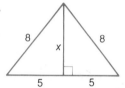

In Exercises 7–9, the lengths of three sides of a triangle are given. Determine whether the triangle is a right triangle.

7. 30; 40; 50   **8.** 12; 16; 18   **9.** 10; 24; 26

10. Write Theorems 7–4 and 7–5 as a biconditional in two ways.

WRITTEN EXERCISES

A   In these Written Exercises, express radicals in your answers in simplest form.

In Exercises 1–8, refer to right triangle *ABC* to find *c*.

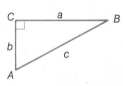

1. $a = 7; b = 24$

2. $a = 8; b = 15$

3. $a = \frac{3}{2}; b = 2$

4. $a = 0.3; b = 0.4$

5. $a = 0.6; b = \frac{4}{5}$

6. $a = \sqrt{13}; b = 6$

7. $a = 1; b = \frac{\sqrt{21}}{2}$

8. $a = 3\sqrt{3}; b = 3\sqrt{6}$

In Exercises 9–14, refer to the right triangle *ABC* with hypotenuse *c* and legs *a* and *b*. Find the unknown length.

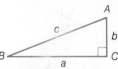

9. $c = 61; a = 60; b = \underline{?}$

10. $c = \frac{5}{12}; b = \frac{1}{3}; a = \underline{?}$

11. $c = 2.6; a = 2.4; b = \underline{?}$

12. $c = 2\sqrt{10}; a = 5; b = \underline{?}$

13. $c = 6\sqrt{5}; b = 10; a = \underline{?}$

14. $c = 10\sqrt{2}; b = 5\sqrt{3}; a = \underline{?}$

In Exercises 15–20, the lengths of the three sides of a triangle are given. Determine whether the triangle is a right triangle.

15. 7; 8; 10

16. 5; 12; 13

17. 51; 24; 45

18. 24; 8; 25

19. 2; 4.8; 5.2

20. 4; 0.9; 4.1

21. Triangle *JKM* is isosceles with *JK* = *JM* = 6, and base *KM* = 4. Find the length of altitude *JP*. (HINT: The altitude to the base of an isosceles triangle bisects the base.)

22. The base of an isosceles triangle is 24 centimeters long and the length of the altitude to the base is 5 centimeters. Find the lengths of the two congruent sides.

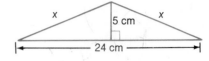

23. Each of the congruent sides of an isosceles triangle is 17 decimeters long. The length of the altitude to the base is 8 decimeters. Find the length of the base.

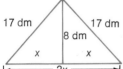

24. The length of a side of an equilateral triangle is 8 centimeters. Find the length of the altitude.

25. In an isosceles triangle, the base is 4 centimeters long and the altitude to the base is 4 centimeters long. How long is each leg?

26. Find the length of an altitude in an equilateral triangle each of whose sides is 6 centimeters long.

27. If the legs of an isosceles right triangle are each 8 units long, find the length of the hypotenuse.

28. The hypotenuse of an isosceles right triangle is 20 cm long. Find the length of each leg.

B

29. Write a formula that can be used to find the altitude of an equilateral triangle with side *s*.

(HINT: Refer to the figure at the right to solve for *h* in terms of *s*.)

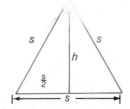

In Exercises 30–33, use your answer to Exercise 29 to determine the length *h*, of the altitude of an equilateral triangle with a side of given length, *s*. Write the answers in simplified radical form.

30. *s* = 10

31. *s* = 12

32. *s* = 5

33. *s* = 16

34. Prove the converse of the Pythagorean Theorem.

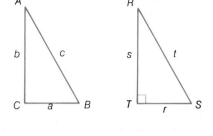

> **Given:** In $\triangle ABC$, $c^2 = a^2 + b^2$.
>
> **Prove:** $\triangle ABC$ is a right triangle, with right angle at C.
>
> **Plan:** Construct $\triangle RST$ with $m\angle T = 90$, $ST = a$, and $RT = b$. Show that $c = t$, and, therefore, that $\triangle ABC \cong \triangle RST$ by SSS. Then, since $\angle T$ is a right angle, $\angle C$ is also a right angle.

35. There are many ways to prove the Pythagorean Theorem.

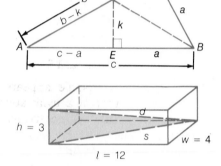

> **Given:** $\triangle ABC$ with right angle at C; $\overline{BE} \cong \overline{BC}$; $\overline{DE} \perp \overline{AB}$; $\overline{BD}$ is drawn.
>
> **Prove:** $c^2 = a^2 + b^2$

36. The dimensions of a rectangular box are 3, 4, and 12. Find the length, d, of a diagonal of the box. (HINT: In the figure at the right, solve $s^2 = 4^2 + 12^2$ for s^2. Then solve $h^2 + s^2 = d^2$ for d.)

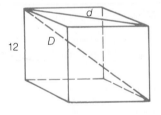

37. The dimensions of a rectangular box are 6, 8, and 10. Find the length of the diagonal, d.

38. One side of a cube is 12. (All sides of a cube have the same measure.) Compute the length, d, of a diagonal of one face of the cube.

39. Use the information and figure in Exercise 38 to compute the length, D, of a diagonal of the cube.

40. For a right triangle with legs of lengths a and b and with hypotenuse of length c, prove that $(c + a)(c - a) = b^2$.

C

41. An isosceles triangle has legs of length 25 and a base of length 30. Find the length of an altitude to one of the equal sides.

42. Compute the length of the altitude to the shortest side of a triangle whose sides are 17, 25, and 26 centimeters long.

43. Compute the length of the altitude to the longest side of a triangle whose sides are 10, 6, and 12 decimeters long.

44. Find the length of the altitude to the 28-centimeter side of a triangle whose sides are 26 centimeters, 28 centimeters, and 30 centimeters long.

APPLICATIONS

USING THE PYTHAGOREAN THEOREM

These exercises apply geometric concepts studied in Sections 7–1 and 7–2.

A   In these exercises, round answers to the nearest tenth.

1. A baseball diamond is shaped like a square. Each side is 90 feet long. How far is it from home plate to second base?

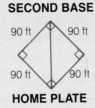

2. The front wall of an A-frame house is in the shape of an equilateral triangle. The base of the house is 8 meters long. How tall is the front of the house?

3. An equilateral triangle appears on a billboard as part of a bank advertisement. Each side of the triangle is 4 meters long. Find the length of the altitude of the triangle.

4. The two sides of a tent are each 2 meters long. If the tent is pitched so that the sides meet at a right angle at the top, find w, the width of the tent, and p, the height of center pole.

B

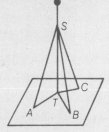

5. A tower 45 feet high is supported by three cables, each of which is attached to the tower at a point, S, five feet from the top of the tower. The cables are anchored to the ground at points A, B, and C. Each of these points is 30 feet from T, the base of the tower which is perpendicular to the ground. Find the total length of cable used to support the tower.

6. A fence based on the design shown is being constructed to enclose a plot of land. Lumber is needed for the diagonal pieces only. The fence is 1.3 meters high and runs for 200 meters. If each section is a square, how many meters of lumber are needed?

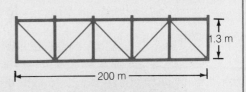

Simplify. *(Pages 265–267)*

1. $\sqrt{8}$ 2. $\sqrt{40}$ 3. $\sqrt{200}$ 4. $\sqrt{125}$ 5. $\sqrt{98}$ 6. $2\sqrt{32}$

7. $\dfrac{5}{\sqrt{2}}$ 8. $\dfrac{4}{\sqrt{3}}$ 9. $\dfrac{8}{\sqrt{2}}$ 10. $\dfrac{7}{\sqrt{2}}$ 11. $\dfrac{15}{\sqrt{3}}$ 12. $\dfrac{10}{\sqrt{5}}$

Multiply. Express radicals in your answers in simplest form.

Example: $5\sqrt{2} \cdot \sqrt{6} = 5\sqrt{12} = 5\sqrt{4 \cdot 3} = 10\sqrt{3}$

13. $3\sqrt{3} \cdot \sqrt{3}$ 14. $4\sqrt{2} \cdot \sqrt{3}$ 15. $5\sqrt{3} \cdot \sqrt{2}$ 16. $3\sqrt{6} \cdot \sqrt{2}$

17. $3\sqrt{6} \cdot \sqrt{10}$ 18. $5\sqrt{8} \cdot \sqrt{2}$ 19. $7\sqrt{8} \cdot \sqrt{3}$ 20. $5\sqrt{20} \cdot \sqrt{5}$

21. $\sqrt{6} \cdot 2\sqrt{3}$ 22. $\sqrt{5} \cdot 4\sqrt{5}$ 23. $\sqrt{10} \cdot 2\sqrt{2}$ 24. $\sqrt{7} \cdot 2\sqrt{12}$

7–3 Special Right Triangles

You can use the Pythagorean Theorem to find useful relationships in an isosceles right triangle. Such a triangle is often called a 45-45 right triangle. The table shows how to determine two relationships.

Triangle	Computation	Rule
	$c^2 = a^2 + a^2$ $c^2 = 2a^2$ $c = a\sqrt{2}$	Given the length of a leg of a 45-45 right triangle, multiply the length by $\sqrt{2}$ to find the length of the hypotenuse.
	$a^2 + a^2 = c^2$ $2a^2 = c^2$ $a^2 = \dfrac{c^2}{2}$ $a = \dfrac{c}{2}\sqrt{2}$	Given the length of the hypotenuse of a 45-45 right triangle, multiply the length by $\dfrac{\sqrt{2}}{2}$ to find the length of a leg.

Theorem 7–6 states these relationships as the Isosceles Right Triangle Theorem.

Theorem 7–6

> ### Isosceles Right Triangle Theorem
> In an isosceles right triangle with legs of length a and hypotenuse of length c,
> $$a = \frac{c}{2}\sqrt{2} \quad \text{and} \quad c = a\sqrt{2}.$$

EXAMPLE 1 Find the length of the diagonal of a square with sides of 15 centimeters.

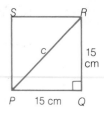

Solution: Since PQR is a 45-45 right triangle, use Theorem 7–6 to find c.

$c = a\sqrt{2}$ ⟵ **Replace *a* with 15.**

$c = 15\sqrt{2}$

The Pythagorean Theorem can also be used to determine useful relationships in a 30-60 right triangle.

Theorem 7–7

> **30-60 Right Triangle Theorem**
>
> In any right triangle with acute angle measures of 30 and 60 and with hypotenuse of length s, the length of the leg opposite the angle with measure 30 (shorter leg) is $\frac{s}{2}$ and the length of the leg opposite the angle with measure 60 (longer leg) is $\frac{s}{2}\sqrt{3}$.

EXAMPLE 2 Write the *Given*, the *Prove*, and a *Plan of Proof* for Theorem 7–7.

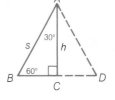

Given: A 30-60 right triangle

Prove: BC (shorter leg) $= \dfrac{s}{2}$;

$h = \dfrac{s}{2}\sqrt{3}$ (shorter leg $\cdot \sqrt{3}$)

Plan: ⟦1⟧ Draw $\overline{AD}$ forming $\triangle ADC \cong \triangle ABC$. Then $\triangle ABD$ is equilateral. Thus, $BC = CD$ and $BC = \frac{1}{2} \cdot s$, or $\frac{1}{2}s$.

⟦2⟧ By the Pythagorean Theorem, $h^2 + (\frac{1}{2}s)^2 = s^2$. Solving for h, $h = \frac{s}{2}\sqrt{3}$.

The proof of this theorem is asked for in the Written Exercises.

EXAMPLE 3 The length of the hypotenuse of a 30-60 right triangle is 14. Find the lengths of the legs.

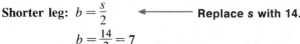

Solutions: Since the given figure is a 30-60 right triangle, use Theorem 7–7.

Shorter leg: $b = \dfrac{s}{2}$ ⟵ **Replace *s* with 14.**

$b = \dfrac{14}{2} = 7$

Longer leg: $a = \dfrac{s}{2}\sqrt{3}$ ⟵ **Replace *s* with 14.**

$a = \dfrac{14}{2}\sqrt{3}$

$a = 7\sqrt{3}$

REMEMBER: To apply the theorems of this section, you need to know the length of only one side of a right triangle in order to find the lengths of the other two sides.

CLASSROOM EXERCISES

In Exercises 1–8, refer to the figure at the right below to find the required length.

1. $a = 8$; $c =$ __?__
2. $a = 15$; $c =$ __?__
3. $a = \frac{3}{4}$; $c =$ __?__
4. $a = 6\sqrt{2}$; $c =$ __?__
5. $c = 10$; $a =$ __?__
6. $c = 12$; $a =$ __?__
7. $c = 5\frac{1}{4}$; $a =$ __?__
8. $c = 18\sqrt{2}$; $a =$ __?__

In Exercises 9–16, refer to this figure to find the required lengths.

9. $r = 2$; $s =$ __?__ ; $t =$ __?__
10. $r = 6$; $s =$ __?__ ; $t =$ __?__
11. $r =$ __?__ ; $s = \sqrt{3}$; $t =$ __?__
12. $r =$ __?__ ; $s = 2\sqrt{3}$; $t =$ __?__
13. $r =$ __?__ ; $s = 7\sqrt{3}$; $t =$ __?__   14. $r =$ __?__ ; $s =$ __?__ ; $t = 20$
15. $r =$ __?__ ; $s =$ __?__ ; $t = 24$ 16. $r =$ __?__ ; $s =$ __?__ ; $t = 8\sqrt{3}$

WRITTEN EXERCISES

A   Refer to the figure at the right to find c.

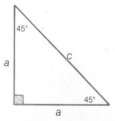

1. $a = 12$; $c =$ __?__
2. $a = 17$; $c =$ __?__
3. $a = 4.63$; $c =$ __?__
4. $a = 1\frac{3}{4}$; $c =$ __?__

Refer to the figure for Exercises 1–4 to find a.

5. $c = 24$; $a =$ __?__
6. $c = 2.8$; $a =$ __?__
7. $c = 3\frac{1}{3}$; $a =$ __?__
8. $c = \sqrt{3}$; $a =$ __?__
9. $c = 9\sqrt{2}$; $a =$ __?__
10. $c = \sqrt{2}$; $a =$ __?__

In Exercises 11–26, use the figure at the right to find the unknown measures.

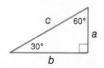

	a	b	c
11.	8	?	?
12.	4	?	?
13.	15	?	?
14.	2.75	?	?

	a	b	c
15.	$4\sqrt{3}$	?	?
16.	?	$6\sqrt{3}$	?
17.	?	$11\sqrt{3}$	?
18.	?	$\frac{13}{4}\sqrt{3}$	?

	a	b	c
19.	?	9	?
20.	?	25	?
21.	?	?	18
22.	?	?	10

	a	b	c
23.	?	?	5.6
24.	?	?	$12\sqrt{3}$
25.	?	?	$8\frac{1}{2}$
26.	?	?	1

27. Find the length of one side of a square with a 16-centimeter diagonal.

28. Find the perimeter of a square that has a diagonal of length 10 meters.

29. Find the length of the diagonal of a square with a 15-decimeter side.

30. The perimeter of a square is 48 meters. Find the length of a side and the length of a diagonal.

In Exercises 31–36, refer to right triangle *MED* with the right angle at *M*, altitude *MA*, and m∠ *D* = 30. Find the unknown measures.

	MA	*MD*	*AD*	*ME*	*EA*	*ED*
31.	?	10	?	?	?	?
32.	6	?	?	?	?	?
33.	?	?	?	4	?	?
34.	8	?	?	?	?	?
35.	?	?	?	?	?	24
36.	?	?	?	?	6	?

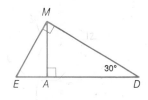

B In Exercises 37–39, the length of side *ZY* in parallelogram *XYZW* is 20 centimeters. Find the length of altitude *ZP* for each measure of ∠ *Y*.

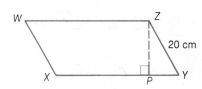

37. 30   38. 45   39. 60

In Exercises 40–42, isosceles triangle *HJK* has congruent sides that are each 12 meters long, and $\overline{HM}$ is the altitude to $\overline{JK}$. Find *HM* for each measure of ∠ *K*.

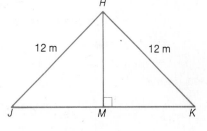

40. 30   41. 45   42. 60

43. Prove Theorem 7–7. (HINT: Refer to Example 2 on page 317.)

C

44. In trapezoid *ONTW*, $\overline{OY}$ and $\overline{WR}$ are altitudes, m∠ *N* = 45, m∠ *T* = 30, *WR* = 8, and *OW* = 10. Find *WT*, *RT*, *OY*, *NY*, *NO*, *YR*, and the perimeter.

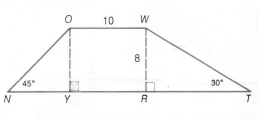

45. Derive a formula for the length *d* of a diagonal of a square in terms of *P*, the perimeter of the square.

Career Applications

Geometry and Astronomy

Astronomers usually specialize in one of the many branches of their science such as instruments and techniques. This includes devices involved with *image formation.*

The figures at the right show that a **convex lens** (a lens that is thicker at the middle than at the edges) can bring parallel light rays together to form an image on the opposite side of the lens from an object. Rays that strike the edge of a lens bend by a certain amount. Rays that pass through the center of a lens are not bent. Thus, two similar triangles. $\triangle ABC$ and $\triangle AB'C'$ are formed, and

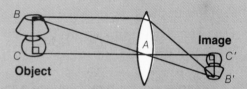

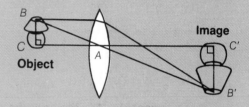

$$\frac{BC}{B'C'} = \frac{AC}{AC'}, \quad \text{or}$$

$$\frac{\textbf{object size}}{\textbf{image size}} = \frac{\textbf{object distance}}{\textbf{image distance}}.$$

EXERCISES

1. If an object 6 centimeters from a lens forms an image 15 centimeters on the other side of the lens, what is the ratio of the object size to the image size?

2. Rosa placed a lens 25 centimeters from an object 10 centimeters tall. An image was formed at a distance of 5 centimeters from the lens. How tall was the image?

3. In the given figures above, prove that $\triangle ABC \sim \triangle AB'C'$.

4. How could you arrange an object, a lens, and an image so that the image is 20 times as tall as the object to which it corresponds?

5. How would you arrange an object, a lens, and an image so that the object and the image are the same size?

Review

In $\triangle CAP$ at the right, angle CAP is a right angle and $\overline{AE} \perp \overline{CP}$. Use this figure for Exercises 1–4. Express any radicals in your answers in simplest form. *(Section 7–1)*

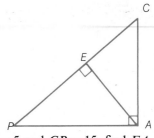

1. If $CE = 8$ and $EP = 5$, find EA.
2. If $EA = 6$ and $EP = 4$, find CE.
3. If $CP = 12$ and $CE = 9$, find EA.   4. If $EP = 5$ and $CP = 15$, find EA.

In Exercises 5–10, refer to right triangle ABC with hypotenuse c and legs a and b. Find the unknown length. Express any radicals in simplest form. *(Section 7–2)*

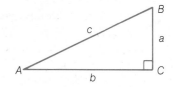

5. $a = 5;\ b = 12;\ c = \underline{\ ?\ }$ 6. $a = 8;\ b = 10;\ c = \underline{\ ?\ }$
7. $a = 12;\ b = \underline{\ ?\ };\ c = 20$ 8. $a = 4;\ b = \underline{\ ?\ };\ c = 15$
9. $a = \underline{\ ?\ };\ b = 14;\ c = 21$ 10. $a = \underline{\ ?\ };\ b = 9;\ c = 12$

In Exercises 11–14, the lengths of the three sides of a triangle are given. Determine whether the triangle is a right triangle. *(Section 7–2)*

11. 6; 8; 10   12. 5; 6; 7   13. 4; 8; 11   14. 8; 15; 17

$\triangle ABC$ is an isosceles right triangle with right angle ABC, and $\overline{BD} \perp \overline{AC}$. Use this figure and the given information to find the unknown lengths. *(Section 7–3)*

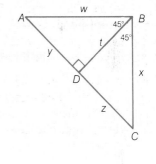

	t	w	x	y	z
15.	4	?	?	?	?
16.	?	?	6	?	?
17.	?	?	?	?	10

Use the 30-60 right triangle at the right for Exercises 18–20. Compute the unknown measures. *(Section 7–3)*

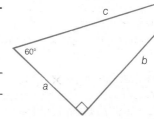

	a	b	c
18.	13	?	?
19.	?	9	?
20.	?	?	23

Find x to the nearest whole number. *(Pages 260–261)*

1. $1.0952 = \dfrac{x}{21}$ **2.** $0.7142 = \dfrac{x}{14}$ **3.** $0.3000 = \dfrac{x}{20}$

4. $0.4228 = \dfrac{63}{x}$ **5.** $0.5647 = \dfrac{48}{x}$ **6.** $1.3061 = \dfrac{64}{x}$

7. $\dfrac{x}{15} = 0.4040$ **8.** $\dfrac{x}{74} = 3.4874$ **9.** $\dfrac{31}{x} = 1.1504$

7-4 The Tangent Ratio

These three triangles are *similar*.

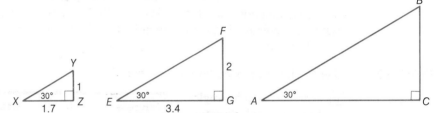

Thus, you can write the following statement.

$$\frac{1}{1.7} = \frac{2}{3.4} = \frac{BC}{AC}$$

The ratio $\dfrac{BC}{AC}$ in *any* right triangle ABC, where C is a right angle, is the *tangent of angle A*.

Definition

> In a right triangle, the **tangent of an acute angle** is the ratio
> $$\frac{\textbf{length of the opposite leg}}{\textbf{length of the adjacent leg}}.$$

Thus, the tangent of angle B, or *tan B*, is written as follows.

$$\tan B = \frac{AC}{BC} \longleftarrow \quad \begin{array}{l} \textbf{length of opposite leg} \\ \textbf{length of adjacent leg} \end{array}$$

EXAMPLE 1 Use right triangle ABC to find each ratio.

    a. $\tan A$ **b.** $\tan B$

Solutions: **a.** $\tan A = \dfrac{BC}{AC} \longleftarrow \quad \begin{array}{l} \overline{BC} \text{ is opposite } \angle A \\ \overline{AC} \text{ is adjacent to } \angle A \end{array}$

        $\tan A = \dfrac{5}{12}$

        $\tan A \approx .4167 \longleftarrow$ **Write as a four-place decimal.**

b. $\tan B = \dfrac{AC}{BC}$ ← $\overline{AC}$ **is opposite** $\angle B$

$\overline{BC}$ **is adjacent to** $\angle B$

$\tan B = \dfrac{12}{5}$

$\tan B = \mathbf{2.4}$

A ratio of the lengths of two sides of a right triangle is a **trigonometric ratio.** Such ratios are the basis for *trigonometry,* the study of the relationships between the sides and angles of triangles.

A trigonometric ratio depends only on the measure of an acute angle, *not* on the size of the right triangle. Thus, for the three similar triangles on page 322, tan 30° is always the same number.

The Tables of Sine, Cosine, and Tangent Values on page 569 give the values of the trigonometric ratios for acute angles. Although most values are approximations for the ratios, the "=" symbol is used because it is more convenient. Thus, in Example 1, write "tan A = .4167" instead of "tan $A \approx$ .4167."

EXAMPLE 2   Use the table on page 569 to find tan 67°.

Solution: **1** Find 67 in the Angle-column. Look directly to the right under the Tan-column.

2 Read: tan 67° = **2.3559**

Angle	Sin	Cos	Tan
65	.9063	.4226	2.1445
66	.9135	.4067	2.2460
67	.9205	.3907	2.3559
68	.9272	.3746	2.4751
69	.9336	.3584	2.6051

When the value of the tangent of an angle is known, you can use the table to find the angle.

EXAMPLE 3   If tan y = .4247, find y to the nearest degree.

Solution: **1** Find the number closest to .4247 in the Tan-column. Look directly to the left under the Angle-column. (.4247 is closer to .4245 than to .4040 or to .4452)

Angle	Sin	Cos	Tan
20	.3420	.9397	.3640
21	.3584	.9336	.3839
22	.3746	.9272	.4040
23	.3907	.9205	.4245
24	.4067	.9135	.4452

2 Read: 23   Thus, y is about **23°**.

The equation $\tan A = \dfrac{BC}{AC}$ has three variables. They are tan A, BC, and AC. If you know any two of them, you can find the third.

EXAMPLE 4 In $\triangle PQR$, $PQ = 95$ cm and $m\angle R = 17$. Find QR to the nearest centimeter.

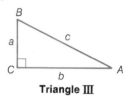

Solution: $\tan 17° = \dfrac{95}{QR}$ ← Find tan 17° in the table on page 569.

$.3057 = \dfrac{95}{QR}$ ← Solve for **QR**.

$QR = \dfrac{95}{.3057}$ ← Use paper and pencil or use a calculator.

$QR = 310.7$ Rounded to the nearest centimeter, $QR = $ **311 cm.**

CLASSROOM EXERCISES

Use the right triangles below in Exercises 1–3.

Triangle I   **Triangle II**   **Triangle III**

1. What is the length of the leg opposite $\angle A$?
2. What is the length of the leg adjacent to $\angle B$?
3. Find tan A and tan B for each triangle.

Use the table on page 569 to find x.

4. $\tan 73° = x$ 5. $\tan 8° = x$ 6. $\tan x = .5095$ 7. $\tan x = 1.1509$

In right triangle ABC, $m\angle B$ and a are given. Find b to the nearest whole number.

8. $a = 142$, $m\angle B = 36$
9. $a = 385$, $m\angle B = 24$
10. $a = 556$, $m\angle B = 62$

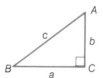

WRITTEN EXERCISES

A   Use the right triangles below in Exercises 1–3.

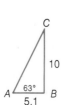
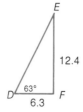
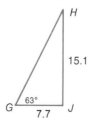

	Length of leg opposite 63°-angle	Length of leg adjacent to 63°-angle	tan 63°
1. Triangle *ABC*	?	?	?
2. Triangle *DFE*	?	?	?
3. Triangle *GJH*	?	?	?

4. Compare the values of tan 63° found in Exercises 1–3 with the value from the table on page 569. Do they agree to two decimal places?

In Exercises 5–7, find tan *A* and tan *B*.
Write each answer as a four-place decimal.

5.
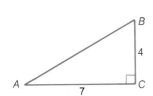

6.
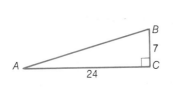

7.
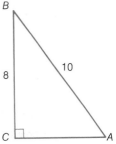

In Exercises 8–15, use the table on page 569 to find each ratio.

8. tan 25°   **9.** tan 29°   **10.** tan 38°   **11.** tan 78°

12. tan 14°   **13.** tan 28°   **14.** tan 62°   **15.** tan 85°

In Exercises 16–23, use the table on page 569 to find *x*.

16. tan *x* = .1228   **17.** tan *x* = .5774   **18.** tan *x* = 11.4301   **19.** tan *x* = 4.7046

20. tan *x* = 57.2900   **21.** tan *x* = .9657   **22.** tan *x* = 2.2460   **23.** tan *x* = .0175

In Exercises 24–29, write an equation involving the given measures and the unknown measure *x*.

24.
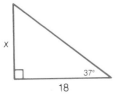

25.

26.
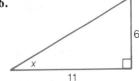

27.
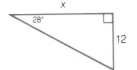

28.

29.
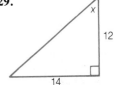

Find *a* to the nearest tenth.

30. $b = 16.5$, m∠$A = 32$

31. $b = 98.3$, m∠$A = 70$

32. $b = 19.7$, m∠$A = 38$

Find *a* to the nearest hundredth. (HINT: Use tan *B*.)

33. $b = 3.24$, m∠$B = 25$

34. $b = 8.62$, m∠$B = 60$

35. $b = 5.91$, m∠$B = 72$

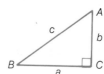

Find *A* to the nearest degree.

36. $a = 13$, $b = 6$

37. $a = 3$, $b = 7$

38. $a = 24$, $b = 19$

B   In Exercises 39–44, solve for *x* in the equation you wrote for the given exercise on page 325. Round the measures of segments to the nearest hundredth and angle measures to the nearest degree.

39. Exercise 24   **40.** Exercise 25   **41.** Exercise 26

42. Exercise 27   **43.** Exercise 28   **44.** Exercise 29

45. In right triangle *RST*, angles *R* and *T* are complementary. Solve each equation below for *x*.

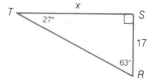

$$\tan 27° = \frac{17}{x} \qquad \tan 63° = \frac{x}{17}$$

46. Which equation in Exercise 45 do you find easier to work with?

47. In right triangle *XYZ* at the left below, compute the measure of each acute angle to the nearest degree.

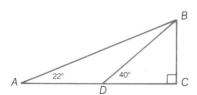

C

48. In right triangle *ABC* above, $BC = 114$, m∠$BAC = 22$ and m∠$BDC = 40$. Find *AD* to the nearest tenth.

49. In the figure for Exercise 48, suppose that $CD = 88$, m∠$BAC = 22$, and m∠$BDC = 40$. Find *AD* to the nearest tenth.

APPLICATIONS

USING THE TANGENT RATIO

These exercises apply geometric concepts studied in Section 7–4.

A   In these exercises, express answers to the nearest tenth or to the nearest degree.

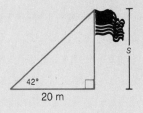

1. Determine the height of the flagpole shown in the figure at the right.

2. The **angle of inclination** of a highway or railroad is the angle formed by the roadbed and the horizontal line XY. Find the angle of inclination of the railroad that runs to the top of Pike's Peak in Colorado at its steepest point where $ZY = 182$ meters when $XY = 356$ meters. Express the angle measure to the nearest degree.

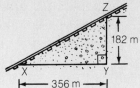

3. In order to construct a bridge across a lake, an engineer wishes to determine AB. A surveyor found that $AC = 530$ meters and m$\angle C = 43$. If angle A is a right angle, find AB, the distance across the lake.

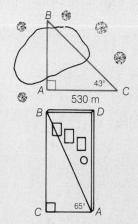

4. Find the height of the door shown at the right if m$\angle CAB = 65$ and $CA = 3$ feet.

5. In the figure for Exercise 4, if $BC = 7$ feet and $AC = 3$ feet, find m$\angle BAC$ to the nearest degree.

B

6. Points P and Q are on the north and south rims, respectively, of the Grand Canyon, with Q directly south of P (see the figure at the right). Point R is located 780 meters west of P. The measure of $\angle PRQ$ is 84. Find PQ, the width of the canyon.

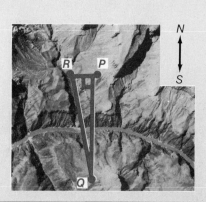

7-5 The Sine and Cosine Ratios

You cannot use the tangent ratio to find BC and AC in the figures below, because the side that is known, the hypotenuse, is not a side used in the definition of tangent.

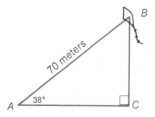

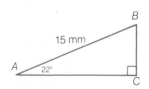

Two trigonometric ratios, the *sine* (abbreviated: *sin*) and the *cosine* (abbreviated: *cos*) are defined in terms of one leg and the hypotenuse of a right triangle.

Definitions

> In a right triangle, the **sine of an acute angle** is the ratio
>
> $$\frac{\text{length of the opposite leg}}{\text{length of the hypotenuse}}.$$
>
> In a right triangle, the **cosine of an acute angle** is the ratio
>
> $$\frac{\text{length of the adjacent side}}{\text{length of the hypotenuse}}.$$

Applying the definitions of the sine and cosine of an acute angle to triangle ABC at the right,

$$\sin 38° = \frac{BC}{70}$$

and $\cos 38° = \dfrac{AC}{70}.$

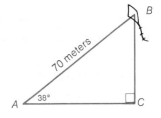

EXAMPLE 1 Use right triangle ABC to find BC to the nearest whole number.

Solution: Since m$\angle A$ and AB, the hypotenuse, are known and you are asked to find BC, the side opposite $\angle A$, use the sine ratio.

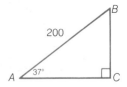

$\sin 37° = \dfrac{BC}{200}$ ⟵ **From the table, sin 37° = .6018.**

$.6018 = \dfrac{BC}{200}$ ⟵ **Solve for BC.**

$BC = 200(.6018) = 120.36$ Thus, $BC = \mathbf{120}$ (nearest whole number).

Follow a similar procedure in Example 2 to find AC.

EXAMPLE 2   Use right triangle ABC in Example 1 to find AC.

Solution: Since $m\angle A$ and AB, the hypotenuse, are known and you are asked to find AC, the side adjacent to $\angle A$, use the cosine ratio.

$$\cos 37° = \frac{AC}{200} \longleftarrow \text{ From the table, } \cos 37° = .7986$$

$$.7986 = \frac{AC}{200}$$

$$AC = 200(.7986) = 159.72 \quad \text{Thus, } AC = \mathbf{160} \text{ (nearest whole number).}$$

To decide which trigonometric ratio to use, make a sketch of the triangle first. Label the parts of the triangle that are known and those that are to be found. Use the trigonometric ratio for which you know two of the three parts.

Known and Unknown Parts of the Right Triangle	Ratio to Use
acute angle, opposite side, adjacent side	tangent
acute angle, opposite side, hypotenuse	sine
acute angle, adjacent side, hypotenuse	cosine

CLASSROOM EXERCISES

Write each ratio in Exercises 1–6 as a fraction.

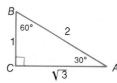

1. $\sin 30°$ **2.** $\cos 30°$ **3.** $\sin 60°$

4. $\cos 60°$ **5.** $\sin 45°$ **6.** $\cos 45°$

7. Write the answers to Exercises 1–6 as four-place decimals. Then compare these decimals with the values found in the table.

Write the equation that you would use to solve for the unknown measure.

8.

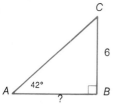

9.

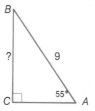

10.

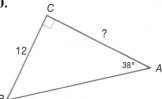

11.

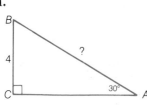

12.

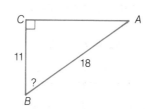

13.

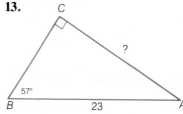

Right Triangles   **329**

WRITTEN EXERCISES

A   Use right triangle *ABC* in Exercises 1–12.

In Exercise 1–2, find *b* to the nearest whole number.

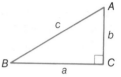

1. $c = 462$; m∠ $B = 49$

2. $c = 215$; m∠ $B = 57$

In Exercises 3–4, find *a* to the nearest whole number.

3. $c = 485$; m∠ $B = 62$ **4.** $c = 12.3$; m∠ $B = 55$

In Exercises 5–8, find *a* to the nearest tenth.

5. $c = 21.2$; m∠ $A = 18$ **6.** $c = 93.2$; m∠ $A = 68$

7. $c = 45.3$; m∠ $A = 27$ **8.** $c = 48.9$ m∠ $A = 37$

In Exercises 9–12, find *b* to the nearest tenth.

9. $c = 200$; m∠ $A = 14$ **10.** $c = 12.5$; m∠ $A = 60$

11. $c = 300$; m∠ $A = 35$ **12.** $c = 762$; m∠ $A = 84$

In Exercises 13–18, *a* and *c* or *b* and *c* are given. Find m∠ *A* to the nearest degree.

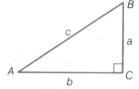

13. $a = 2$; $c = 4$

14. $b = 5$; $c = 10$

15. $b = 4$; $c = 5$ **16.** $a = 6$; $c = 8$

17. $b = 9$; $c = 10$ **18.** $a = 3$; $c = 9$

In Exercises 19–30, △ *ABC* is an isosceles right triangle and △ *DEF* is a 30–60 right triangle.

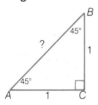   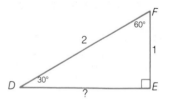

Use your knowledge of these special triangles to compute the indicated trigonometric ratios. Express answers in simplified radical form.

19. sin *A*   **20.** cos *B*   **21.** tan *A*   **22.** cos *D*

23. sin *F*   **24.** sin *B*   **25.** tan *B*   **26.** cos *A*

27. tan *F*   **28.** sin *D*   **29.** cos *F*   **30.** tan *D*

To "**solve a triangle**" means to find the measures of all sides and angles of the triangle that are not given.

In Exercises 31–36, solve each triangle. Refer to right triangle ABC with right angle at C. Compute angle measures to the nearest degree and the measures of segments to the nearest tenth.

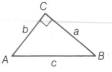

31. $b = 8$; $c = 10$ **32.** $a = 1$; $b = 1$ **33.** $b = 27$; $m\angle B = 60$

34. $a = 12$; $c = 18$ **35.** $a = 14$; $b = 9$ **36.** $a = 8$; $m\angle A = 61$

37. Use the triangle for Exercises 31–36 to show that $\tan a = \dfrac{\sin A}{\cos A}$.

38. Each edge of a cube measures 10 centimeters. Find the smallest angle formed by the intersection of two diagonals of the cube. Express your answer to the nearest degree.

39. An acute angle of a right triangle measures y. Prove that $(\sin y)^2 + (\cos y)^2 = 1$.

40. Use $\triangle ABC$ at the right to show that $\dfrac{\sin A}{\sin B} = \dfrac{a}{b}$.

(HINT: Draw the altitude to $\overline{AB}$ from C.)

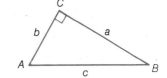

CALCULATOR APPLICATIONS

Trigonometric Functions

You can use a scientific calculator instead of a table to find the value of trigonometric functions, given the angle measures. You can also use the inverse key ("[INV]") to find an unknown angle measure, given the value of the trigonometric ratio.

EXAMPLE 1 Find each ratio.   **a.** tan 42°   **b.** cos 87°

SOLUTIONS   **a.** 4 2 [tan] $\boxed{0.900404}$ **b.** 8 7 [cos] $\boxed{0.052335}$

EXAMPLE 2 Find x if $\sin x = \frac{7}{9}$.

SOLUTION   7 9 [INV] [sin] $\boxed{51.057559}$

EXERCISES

Use a calculator to check your answers to Exercises 8–23 on page 325 and Exercises 13–18 on page 330.

APPLICATIONS

USING THE SINE AND COSINE RATIOS

These exercises apply geometric concepts studied in Section 7–5.

A In these exercises, express lengths to the nearest tenth and angles to the nearest degree.

1. A kite has 70 meters of string out. The string makes an angle of 38° with the ground. How far above the ground is the kite?

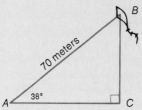

2. A scout troop built a frame for a lean-to as shown below. In the right triangle formed by one side of the lean-to, $BC = 26$ and $AB = 35$. Find $m\angle B$.

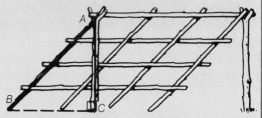

3. The ancient Egyptians constructed hoes in the shape shown below. If $m\angle O = 90$, $HO = 42$, and $HE = 54$, find $m\angle E$.

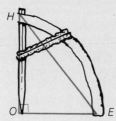

4. Find the angle that a 30-foot ladder leaning against a wall makes with the ground, if the bottom of the ladder is 9 feet from the base of the wall.

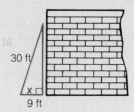

B

5. Lighthouse C is due west from a ship at A. Lighthouse B, which is due north of C, is so situated that $m\angle CAB = 26$ and $CB = 13$ kilometers. How far is the ship from B?

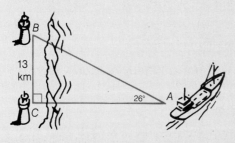

6. A tree is broken by the wind. The top of the tree touches the ground at a point 13 meters from the center of its trunk and makes an angle of 29° with the ground. What was the tree's original height?

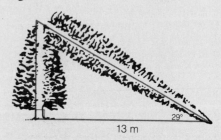

7–6 Angle of Elevation/Angle of Depression

For some problems in trigonometry, you need to know the *angles of elevation* and *depression*.

When an observer at point P sights upward to an object at A, the angle the line of sight, $\overleftrightarrow{PA}$, makes with the horizontal, $\overleftrightarrow{PH}$, is called the **angle of elevation.** Thus, in the figure, $\angle P$ is the angle of elevation.

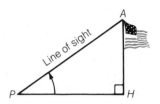

EXAMPLE 1 Find, to the nearest degree, the angle of elevation of the top of a tower from a point 90 meters from the base of the tower. The tower is 56 meters high.

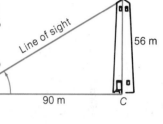

Solution: Since BC and AC are known and you wish to find $m\angle A$, use the tangent ratio.

$$\tan A = \frac{56}{90}$$

$$\tan A = .6222$$

$m\angle A = 32 \longleftarrow$ **Nearest degree**

When an observer at point P sights downward to an object at B, the angle the line of sight, $\overleftrightarrow{PH}$, makes with the horizontal $\overleftrightarrow{AB}$ is called the **angle of depression.** Thus, in the figure, $\angle HPB$ is the angle of depression.

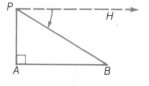

Since $\overrightarrow{PH} \perp \overline{AP}$ and $\overline{AB} \perp \overline{AP}$, $\overrightarrow{PH} \parallel \overline{AB}$. Therefore, $m\angle HPB = m\angle PBA$ since they are alternate interior angles.

EXAMPLE 2 An airplane pilot notes that the angle of depression to an airport at A is 28° when the plane is 8.5 kilometers from the airport. Find the altitude, h, of the plane to the nearest kilometer.

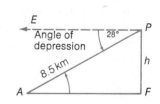

Solution: Since $m\angle EPA = m\angle A$, $m\angle A$ and AP are known. Thus, to find h or PF, use the sine ratio.

$$\sin 28° = \frac{h}{8.5} \longleftarrow \begin{array}{l}\angle \textbf{\textit{EPA}}\textbf{ and }\angle \textbf{\textit{FAP}}\textbf{ are alternate interior angles.} \\ \textbf{Thus, m}\angle \textbf{\textit{FAP}}\textbf{ = 28.}\end{array}$$

$$.4695 = \frac{h}{8.5} \longleftarrow \textbf{Solve for \textit{h}.}$$

$$h = 8.5(.4695) = 3.99075, \text{ or about 4 km} \longleftarrow \textbf{Nearest kilometer}$$

CLASSROOM EXERCISES

In Exercises 1–6:
a. Express each ratio as the sine, cosine, or tangent of an angle measure.
b. Find x to the nearest whole number or to the nearest degree.

1. $\dfrac{x}{100} = \underline{\ ?\ }$

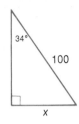

2. $\dfrac{20}{x} = \underline{\ ?\ }$

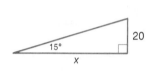

3. $\dfrac{x}{162} = \underline{\ ?\ }$

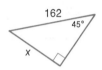

4. $\dfrac{90}{50} = \underline{\ ?\ }$

5. $\dfrac{16}{17} = \underline{\ ?\ }$

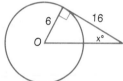

6. $\dfrac{8}{11} = \underline{\ ?\ }$

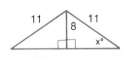

WRITTEN EXERCISES

A In Exercises 1–12, give answers to the nearest whole number or to the nearest degree.

1. In the figure at the left below, the angle of elevation of a monument is 53° from a point on level ground that is 35 meters from the base. Find the height of the monument.

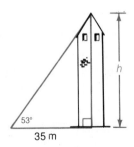

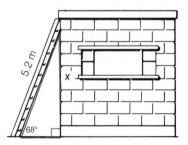

2. In the figure at the right above, a ladder 5.2 meters long leans against a building and makes an angle of 68° with the ground. How far up the building does the ladder reach?

Chapter Summary

IMPORTANT IDEAS

1. The altitude to the hypotenuse of a right triangle forms two triangles similar to each other and to the original triangle.

   Thus, $\dfrac{x}{h} = \dfrac{h}{y}$, $\dfrac{c}{a} = \dfrac{a}{y}$, and $\dfrac{c}{b} = \dfrac{b}{x}$.

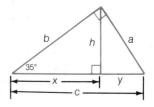

2. A triangle with sides of lengths a, b, and c is a right triangle if and only if $c^2 = a^2 + b^2$.

3. In a 45-45 right triangle with legs of length a, the hypotenuse has a length of
   $$a\sqrt{2}.$$

4. In a 30-60 right triangle with a hypotenuse of length s, the legs have the lengths shown at the right.

5. In right triangle ABC with right angle at C:

   $$\tan A = \frac{a}{b}$$

   $$\sin A = \frac{a}{c}$$

   $$\cos A = \frac{b}{c}$$

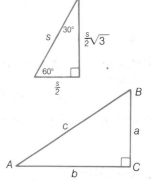

Chapter Objectives and Review

Objective: *To apply the theorem and corollaries about similar right triangles (Section 7–1)*

In right $\triangle ABC$, $\overline{AD}$ is the altitude to the hypotenuse $\overline{BC}$. Refer to this figure for Exercises 1–4. Express any radicals in answers in simplest form.

1. If $CD = 3$ and $AD = 9$, find BD.
2. If $CD = 1$ and $CB = 12$, find AC.
3. If $AB = 8$ and $BD = 6$, find BC.
4. If $CD = 4$ and $DB = 16$, find AC, AD, and AB.

Objective: *To apply the Pythagorean Theorem (Section 7–2)*

In Exercises 5–8, refer to right triangle
ABC with hypotenuse *c*. Find the length
of the unknown side.

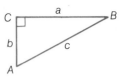

5. $a = 8; b = 6; c =$ __?__
6. $a = 12; c = 13; b =$ __?__
7. $b = 2\sqrt{6}; c = 7; a =$ __?__   8. $a = 35; c = 37; b =$ __?__

Objective: *To use the converse of the Pythagorean Theorem to determine whether a triangle is a right triangle (Section 7–2)*

The lengths of three sides of a triangle are given. Determine whether the triangle is a right triangle.

9. 5; 10; 12   10. 16; 30; 34   11. 60; 80; 100   12. 0.7; 2.4; 2.5

Objective: *To apply the relationships in special right triangles (Section 7–3)*

In Exercises 13–17, refer to right triangle
ABC.

13. If $BC = 8$, find AB.
14. If $BC = 5$, find AC.
15. If $AC = 3\sqrt{3}$, find BC.
16. If $BC = 8\sqrt{3}$, find AC and AB.
17. If $AB = 18$, find BC and AC.

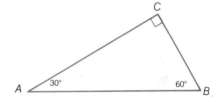

Objective: *To use a Table of Sines, Cosines, and Tangents (Sections 7–4 and 7–5)*

Use the table on page 569 to find *x*.

18. $\sin 27° = x$ 19. $\cos 88° = x$ 20. $\tan x = 1.8040$

Objective: *To use the tangent ratio to solve problems with right triangles (Section 7–4)*

Refer to △ *ABC* below. Give answers
to the nearest whole number.

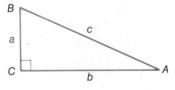

21. If m∠$A = 28$ and $b = 82$, find a.
22. If m∠$B = 65$ and $b = 104$, find a.
23. If $a = 75$ and $b = 52$, find m∠A and m∠B.

Objective: *To use the sine and cosine ratios to solve problems with right triangles (Section 7–5)*

24. In right triangle *ABC*, the hypotenuse *AB* is 15 centimeters long and m∠A = 37. Find *AC* and *BC* to the nearest centimeter.

25. In isosceles triangle *RST*, the length of the altitude to base *RS* is 18 and the length of each leg is 26. Find m∠R to the nearest degree.

In Exercises 26–28, express each ratio as the sine, cosine, or tangent of an angle measure.

26. $\dfrac{a}{8} = $? _____

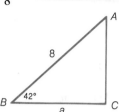

27. $\dfrac{7}{12} = $? _____

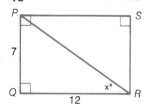

28. $\dfrac{h}{15} = $? _____

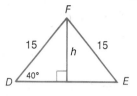

29. The base of an isosceles triangle is 26 and one of the base angles has a measure of 28. Find the length of the altitude to the base.

Objective: *To use the angle of elevation and the angle of depression in solving problems (Section 7–6)*

30. The angle of elevation of the top of a tower from a point 150 meters from its base is 8°. Find the height of the tower to the nearest meter.

Objective: *To solve word problems that involve the Pythagorean Theorem (Page 315)*

31. A surveyor wants to know the distance from point *C* to point *B* across the lake. Use the measurements given in the figure to find *CB*.

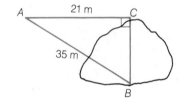

Objective: *To solve word problems that involve the tangent ratio (Page 327)*

32. A jet airplane takes off at an angle of 20° to the runway. How high is the jet when it is above a point that is 200 meters from the point of takeoff?

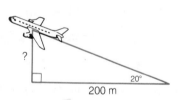

Objective: *To solve word problems that involve the sine and cosine ratios (Page 332)*

33. Two pieces of metal are to be welded into a wall bracket as shown below. At what angle should they be joined?

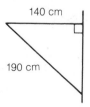

34. How far from the landing pad is the helicopter in the picture below?

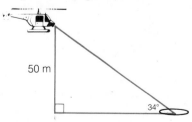

Chapter Test

In △ABC at the right, ∠ACB is a right angle and $\overline{CD} \perp \overline{AB}$. Find the unknown length.

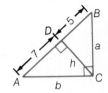

1. $h =$ ___?___   **2.** $a =$ ___?___   **3.** $b =$ ___?___

In Exercises 4–6, refer to △ABC above.

4. If $a = 5, b = 12, AB =$ ___?___   **5.** If $AB = 16, a = 6, b =$ ___?___

6. If $a = 9$, $b = 12$, and $AB = 15$, is △ABC a right triangle?

7. If $a = 4$, $b = 7$, and $AB = 10$, is △ABC a right triangle?

△ABC is a right triangle. Refer to this figure for Exercises 8–10.

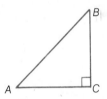

8. $m\angle A = 45$; $AC = 16$; $BC =$ ___?___; $AB =$ ___?___

9. $m\angle B = 30$; $AC = 8$; $BC =$ ___?___; $AB =$ ___?___

10. $m\angle A = 60$; $AB = 14$; $AC =$ ___?___; $BC =$ ___?___

In Exercises 11–13, compute the value of x to the nearest tenth or to the nearest degree.

11.

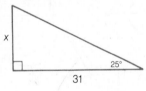

12.

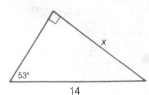

13.

14. A ladder 6 meters long is leaning against a vertical wall. It reaches a point 5.5 meters high on the wall. Find the measure of the angle formed by the foot of the ladder and the ground.

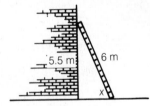

15. The angle of elevation from a speed-boat in a river to a bridge over the river is 40°. The boat is 58 meters from a point directly under the bridge. At that point, how high is the bridge above the water?

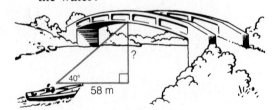

CHAPTER **8** Circles

Sections   8-1   **The Circle: Related Lines and Segments**

8-2   **Central Angles and Arcs**

Applications: Using Angles and Arcs

8-3   **Congruent Chords and Arcs**

8-4   **Chords and Inscribed Polygons**

8-5   **Tangents to a Circle**

8-6   **Inscribed Angles**

8-7   **Inscribed Angle Corollaries**

8-8   **More Angles and Arcs**

8-9   **Lengths of Segments**

Applications: Using Chords and Arcs

8-10   **The Sphere**

Features   **Career Application: Other Geometries and Mathematics**

Computer Applications: Angles in Circles

Puzzles

Review and Testing   **Algebra Review Capsule**

Geometry Review Capsules

Review: Sections 8–1 through 8–3

Review: Sections 8–4 through 8–6

Review: Sections 8–7 through 8–10

Chapter Summary

Chapter Objectives and Review

Chapter Test

8-1   The Circle: Related Lines and Segments

In the figure at the right, circle O is in plane I. Point O is the *center* of the circle and all points on the circle are 3 centimeters from O. $\overline{OP}$ is a *radius* of circle O.

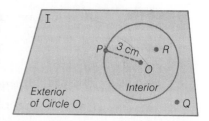

In the figure, point Q is in the exterior of the circle and point R is in the interior. Thus, $RO < PO < QO$.

Definitions

> A **circle** is the set of all points in a plane at a given distance from a fixed point of the plane. The fixed point is the **center** of the circle and the given distance is the **radius**.

The following statement follows from the definition of a circle.

All radii (plural of radius) **of the same circle are congruent.**

A line in the plane of a circle can intersect the circle in no points, one point, or two points.

No Points	**One Point**	**Two Points**
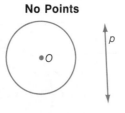	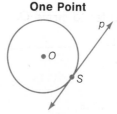	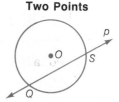
The line and the circle do **not** intersect.	A line that intersects the circle in exactly one point is a **tangent** to the circle (line p).	A line that intersects the circle in two points is a **secant** (line p).

Segments related to the circle have special names.

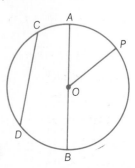

Segment	Name	Description
$\overline{OP}$	**Radius**	A segment joining the center of the circle with a point on the circle.
$\overline{CD}$	**Chord**	A segment with endpoints on the circle.
$\overline{AB}$	**Diameter**	A chord passing through the center of the circle.

EXAMPLE   In circle A, all points of the circle are 2 centimeters from A.

a. Name two radii of the circle.

b. Find the length of the radius.

c. Why is $\overline{AC}$ congruent to $\overline{AB}$?

d. Find the length of a diameter of circle A.

Solutions: a. $\overline{AC}$ and $\overline{AB}$

b. $AC = AB = 2$ **centimeters**

c. **Radii of the same circle are congruent.**

d. Length of diameter: $2AC = 2(2) = 4$ **centimeters**

The circles in the photograph at the right are *concentric*. **Concentric circles** have the same center and radii of different lengths.

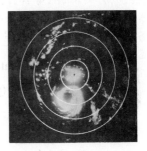

CLASSROOM EXERCISES

In Exercises 1–6, refer to circle O.

1. Name the center of the circle.

2. Name two radii of the circle.

3. Name a diameter of the circle.

4. Name three chords of the circle.

5. Name a tangent to the circle.

6. Name a secant to the circle.

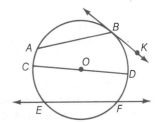

A circle has a radius of 8 centimeters. If each measure in Exercises 7–11 is the distance of a line from the center of the circle, state whether the line intersects the circle in 0, 1, or 2 points.

7. 6 cm   **8.** 8 cm   **9.** 8.5 cm   **10.** 7.5 cm   **11.** 5 cm

In Exercises 12–15, refer to circle T.

12. Give the length of $\overline{PQ}$.

13. Give the length of $\overline{PR}$.

14. Which segment is longer, $\overline{PQ}$ or $\overline{PR}$?

15. Complete: The shortest distance from P to circle T along $\overleftrightarrow{PR}$ is __?__ mm.

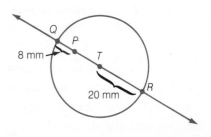

WRITTEN EXERCISES

A In Exercises 1–12, refer to the figure at the right to complete each statement.

Circle P has a radius of 3 centimeters; circle Q has a radius of 2 centimeters.

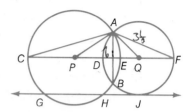

1. Three radii of circle P are $\overline{PA}$, __?__ , and __?__ .
2. Three radii of circle Q are __?__ , __?__ , and __?__ .
3. $\overline{CE}$ is a __?__ of circle P; $\overline{DF}$ is a __?__ of circle Q.
4. If $DE = 1$ centimeter, then $CF =$ __?__ .   5. $\overline{GH}$ is a __?__ of circle P.
6. $\overleftrightarrow{GH}$ is a __?__ of circle P.   7. $\overleftrightarrow{GH}$ is a __?__ to circle Q.
8. If $DE = 1$ centimeter and $AF = 3\frac{1}{2}$ centimeters, then the perimeter of $\triangle APQ =$ __?__ and the perimeter of $\triangle AQF =$ __?__ .
9. $\overline{AB}$ is a __?__ of circle P and a __?__ of circle Q.
10. $DQ = \frac{1}{2}$ __?__   11. $PA = \frac{1}{2}$ __?__   12. $\overline{QA} \cong$ __?__ $\cong$ __?__

13. Circle Q has a radius of 8 cm, P is in the plane of the circle, and $QP = 6$ cm. State whether P is inside, on, or outside the circle.

14. A circle O has a radius of 8. Find the length of the longest chord of the circle.

In Exercises 15–19, find the radius of a circle in which the longest chord has each of the following lengths.

15. 12   16. 9   17. 15|24   18. $2x$ 19. y

20. Two concentric circles have a common center P and radii of 7 centimeters and 11 centimeters respectively. Points A, B, C, D are chosen such that $PA = 5$ cm, $PB = 8$ cm, $PC = 10$ cm, and $PD = 14$ cm. State whether each of the points A, B, C, and D is in the interior or exterior of each circle.

The figure at the right below shows two circles with four common tangents. Lines p and q are common *external* tangents; lines r and s are *common internal* tangents.

Refer to this figure in Exercises 21–24. If possible, draw two circles in such a position that each condition in these exercises is satisfied.

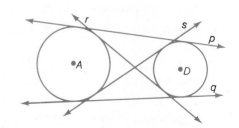

21. Exactly three common tangents can be drawn.
22. Exactly two common tangents can be drawn.
23. Exactly one common tangent can be drawn.
24. No common tangents can be drawn.

In Exercises 25–32, classify each statement as true, *T*, or false, *F*. Give the reason(s) for each answer.

25. Every diameter of a circle is also a chord of the circle.

26. Every radius of a circle is also a chord of the circle.

27. Every chord of a circle contains exactly two points of the circle.

28. A line and a circle can have exactly one point in common.

29. A circle has exactly two radii.

30. A chord of a circle can be a segment of a tangent to the circle.

31. The union of any two radii of a circle is a diameter of the circle.

32. If a line intersects a circle in one point, then it intersects the circle in two points.

B

33. Circle *O* has a radius of 4 centimeters. If radii *OA* and *OB* form a right angle, find *AB*.

34. In circle *Q*, radii *QX* and *QY* form a right angle. If *XY* = 128, find *QX*.

35. Circle *N* has a radius of 10 meters, and radii *NA* and *NB* form an angle of 120°. Find *AB*.

36. $\overline{TP}$ and $\overline{TQ}$ are radii of a circle. If m∠ *PTQ* = 120 and *PQ* = 18, find *TQ*.

37. In the figure at the left below, $\overline{AB}$ is a diameter of circle *O*, $\overline{OC}$ and $\overline{OD}$ are radii, m∠ *D* = 70, and m∠ *C* = 55. Find the measure of each of the numbered angles.

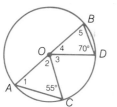

C

38. In the figure at the right above, $\overline{EU}$ is a diameter of circle *Q*. $\overline{QL}$ and $\overline{QA}$ are radii, and ∠ 1 ≅ ∠ 2. Prove that △*AQL* ≅ △*AQU* and that $\overline{AQ} \perp \overline{LU}$.

_____ **GEOMETRY REVIEW CAPSULE FOR SECTION 8–2** _____

Write each biconditional as a conditional and its converse. *(Pages 66–68)*

1. A triangle is isosceles if and only if it has two congruent angles.

2. Two triangles are similar if and only if two pairs of corresponding angles are congruent.

3. Two lines cut by a transversal are parallel if and only if two alternate interior angles are congruent.

4. Two sides of a triangle are not congruent if and only if the angles opposite these sides are not congruent.

8-2 Central Angles and Arcs

In circle B, $\angle ABC$ is a *central angle*. A **central angle** has its vertex at the center of the circle.

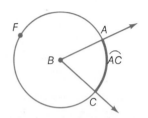

Points A and C and all points of the circle in the interior of $\angle ABC$ form a **minor arc,** called $\overarc{AC}$ (arc AC).

Points A and C and all points of the circle in the exterior of $\angle ABC$ form a **major arc,** $\overarc{AFC}$. You use three letters to name a major arc.

A **semicircle** is the union of the endpoints of a diameter and all points of the circle lying on one side of the diameter. In the figure, $\overarc{ADB}$ and $\overarc{ACB}$ are semicircles.

The measure of a major or minor arc of a circle is determined by the central angle of its minor arc.

Definitions

> The **measure of a minor arc** equals the measure of its central angle.
>
> The **measure of a semicircle** is 180.
>
> The **measure of a major arc** equals $360 - m$, where m is the measure of the central angle of its minor arc.

EXAMPLE 1 In circle E, $m\angle TEN = 70$, $m\overarc{NR} = 80$, and $\overline{CN}$ is a diameter. Find $m\overarc{TN}$, $m\overarc{TC}$, $m\overarc{TR}$, and $m\overarc{NTR}$.

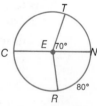

By the definition of the measure of a minor arc,

Solutions:
$m\overarc{TN} = 70$
$m\overarc{TC} = 110$ ◄─────── $m\angle TEC = 180 - 70 = 110$
$m\overarc{TR} = 150$ ◄─────── $m\angle TER = 70 + 80 = 150$
$m\overarc{NTR} = 360 - 80 = 280$ ◄─── **By the definition of the measure of a major arc**

To find $m\overarc{TR}$ in Example 1, you can use the equation

$$m\overarc{TN} + m\overarc{NR} = m\overarc{TR}.$$

This implies that T, N, and R are points on a circle with point N *between* points T and R.

Definition	**Betweenness of Points for Circles** If B is a point on $\overset{\frown}{AC}$, then $m\overset{\frown}{AB} + m\overset{\frown}{BC} = m\overset{\frown}{AC}$.

Suppose that B is a point on $\overset{\frown}{AC}$, such that B is between A and C, $m\overset{\frown}{AB} = 55$, and $m\overset{\frown}{BC} = 55$. Then $m\overset{\frown}{AB} = m\overset{\frown}{BC}$ and B is the *midpoint of* $\overset{\frown}{AC}$.

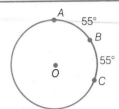

Definition	B is the **midpoint of** $\overset{\frown}{AC}$ if B is a point on $\overset{\frown}{AC}$ and $m\overset{\frown}{BA} = m\overset{\frown}{BC}$.

All circles have the same shape. Two circles are congruent if their radii are congruent. Circles O and P are congruent if $\overline{OQ} \cong \overline{PR}$.

Further, $\overset{\frown}{QS} \cong \overset{\frown}{RT}$ if $m\overset{\frown}{QS} = m\overset{\frown}{RT}$.

Definitions	Two **circles are congruent** if their radii are congruent. In the same or in congruent circles, two **arcs are congruent** if they have the same measure.

From the definition of congruent arcs, it follows that if $\overset{\frown}{AB} \cong \overset{\frown}{CB}$, then B is the bisector of $\overset{\frown}{AC}$.

EXAMPLE 2 In the figure, O is the center of the concentric circles. $\overline{AB}$ and $\overline{CD}$ are diameters of the larger circle, and $m\angle DOB = 50$.

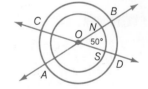

    a. Find $m\overset{\frown}{NS}$ and $m\overset{\frown}{DB}$.

    b. Is $\overset{\frown}{SN}$ congruent to $\overset{\frown}{BD}$?

Solutions: **a.** $m\overset{\frown}{NS} = 50$; $m\overset{\frown}{DB} = 50$

        b. No; because $\overset{\frown}{SN}$ and $\overset{\frown}{DB}$ are not in the same or in congruent circles.

Example 2 illustrates that arcs with equal measures are not necessarily congruent. Arcs with equal measures can be proved congruent if they are in the same or congruent circles.

Theorem 8–1	In the same circle or in congruent circles, two arcs are congruent if and only if their central angles are congruent.

Proofs of Theorems 8–1 and 8–2 are asked for in the Written Exercises.

<table>
<tr><td>Theorem
8-2</td><td colspan="2">Common Arc Theorem</td></tr>
<tr><td></td><td>If four points on a circle are,
in order,

$A, B, C, D,$ or $A, C, B, D,$

and $\overset{\frown}{AB} \cong \overset{\frown}{CD}$, then $\overset{\frown}{AC} \cong \overset{\frown}{BD}$.</td><td></td></tr>
</table>

CLASSROOM EXERCISES

In Exercises 1–6, refer to circle P. In circle P, $\overline{CD}$ and $\overline{AB}$ are diameters.

1. Name four central angles in the figure.

2. Name one diameter in the figure.

3. Name two pairs of congruent minor arcs.

4. Name four semicircles in the figure.

5. Name a major arc for each of the minor arcs $\overset{\frown}{AC}$, $\overset{\frown}{BC}$, and $\overset{\frown}{BD}$.

6. Find $m\overset{\frown}{AD}$, $m\overset{\frown}{DB}$, $m\overset{\frown}{BC}$, $m\overset{\frown}{CA}$, and $m\overset{\frown}{ADB}$.

7. In circle R at the right, the central angles have the measures shown. Find $m\angle MRS$, $m\overset{\frown}{MA}$, $m\overset{\frown}{AJ}$, $m\overset{\frown}{JS}$, $m\overset{\frown}{JSM}$, and $m\overset{\frown}{MAS}$.

8. State Theorem 8–1 as a conditional and its converse.

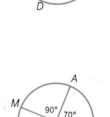

WRITTEN EXERCISES

   The measures of the central angles in circle Q are given in the figure. Find the measure of each arc.

1. $\overset{\frown}{RT}$ 2. $\overset{\frown}{UR}$ 3. $\overset{\frown}{VS}$ 4. $\overset{\frown}{US}$

5. $\overset{\frown}{RSU}$ 6. $\overset{\frown}{SUV}$ 7. $\overset{\frown}{TVR}$ 8. $\overset{\frown}{VTR}$

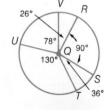

In circle P, $\overline{CE}$ is a diameter and $m\angle DPE = 70$. Find each of the following.

9. $m\overset{\frown}{DE}$ 10. $m\overset{\frown}{DFE}$ 11. $m\angle CPD$ 12. $m\overset{\frown}{CD}$

13. $m\overset{\frown}{CED}$ 14. $m\overset{\frown}{CFD}$ 15. $m\overset{\frown}{CDE}$ 16. $m\overset{\frown}{EFC}$

17. Make a drawing to show how two arcs can have the same measure but not be congruent.

18. In the figure at the right, O is the center of the circle and $m\angle AOB = m\angle DOC = 80$. Which arcs are congruent? Give a reason for each answer.

In the figure at the right, $\overline{AC}$ and $\overline{BD}$ are diameters of circle O and $m\overset{\frown}{DC} = 71$. Find each of the following.

19. $m\angle AOD$ **20.** $m\angle AOB$

21. $m\overset{\frown}{ADC}$ **22.** $m\overset{\frown}{BC}$

23. Complete this proof for Part I of Theorem 8–1.

Prove: *In the same circle or in congruent circles, if two arcs are congruent, then their central angles are congruent.*

Given: Circles O and P are congruent; $\overset{\frown}{AB} \cong \overset{\frown}{CD}$ **Prove:** $\angle O \cong \angle P$

Statements	Reasons
1. Circle $O \cong$ Circle P; $\overset{\frown}{AB} \cong \overset{\frown}{CD}$	1. Given
2. $m\overset{\frown}{AB} = m\overset{\frown}{CD}$	2. (1). __?__
3. $m\overset{\frown}{AB} = m\angle O$; $m\overset{\frown}{CD} = m\angle P$	3. (1). __?__
4. $m\angle O = m\angle P$	4. (2), (3). __?__
5. $\therefore \angle O \cong \angle P$	5. (4). __?__

24. Complete this proof of Theorem 8–2.

Given: $\overset{\frown}{AB} \cong \overset{\frown}{CD}$

Prove: $\overset{\frown}{AC} \cong \overset{\frown}{BD}$

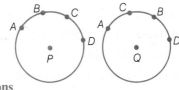

Statements	Reasons
1. Draw $\overline{AP}, \overline{BP}, \overline{CP}, \overline{DP}, \overline{AQ},$ $\overline{BQ}, \overline{CQ},$ and $\overline{DQ}$.	1. __?__
2. $\overset{\frown}{AB} \cong \overset{\frown}{CD}$	2. __?__
3. $\angle APB \cong \angle CPD$; $\angle AQB \cong \angle CQD$	3. (2). Theorem 8–1, Part I
4. $\angle APC \cong \angle BPD$; $\angle AQC \cong \angle BQD$	4. (1), (3). __?__
5. $\overset{\frown}{AC} \cong \overset{\frown}{BD}$	5. (4). Theorem 8–1, Part __?__

B

25. Given: $\overline{AB}$ and $\overline{CD}$ are diameters of circle O.

    Prove: $\overset{\frown}{AD} \cong \overset{\frown}{BC}$

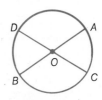

26. Given: $\overline{AB}$ and $\overline{CD}$ are diameters of circle O.

    Prove: $\overset{\frown}{AC} \cong \overset{\frown}{DB}$

27. Given: Circle R;

    $\overset{\frown}{TM} \cong \overset{\frown}{AE}$

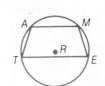

    Prove: $\overset{\frown}{TA} \cong \overset{\frown}{EM}$

In the figure at the right, *H* is the center of concentric circles with radii *HM* and *HT*.

If m∠ *JHK* = 51 and m∠ *KHT* = 77, find each of the following.

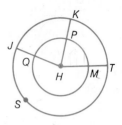

28. m$\overset{\frown}{JK}$
29. m$\overset{\frown}{QP}$
30. m$\overset{\frown}{KT}$
31. m$\overset{\frown}{PM}$
32. m$\overset{\frown}{JSK}$
33. m$\overset{\frown}{QMP}$
34. m$\overset{\frown}{JST}$
35. m$\overset{\frown}{KST}$

36. In the figure for Exercises 28–35, which arcs have the same measure?

37. Write a proof for Part II of Theorem 8–1.

> **Prove:** *In the same or in congruent circles, if two central angles are congruent, then their arcs are congruent.*
>
> (HINT: Refer to the figure for Exercise 23 on page 351.)

38. In the same circle, is the chord of a central angle of 120 twice as long as the chord of a central angle of 60? (HINT: Use a drawing to help you find the answer.)

39. Find the measure of the central angle of a chord with length equal to the length of the radius of the circle.

40. In the figure at the right, polygon *MNPQRS* is a regular hexagon. Explain why each small arc, such as $\overset{\frown}{MN}$, $\overset{\frown}{NP}$, and $\overset{\frown}{PQ}$, has a measure of 60.

41. Use the figure and the information for Exercise 40 to find m$\overset{\frown}{MSR}$, m$\overset{\frown}{SRQ}$, m$\overset{\frown}{SRP}$, and m$\overset{\frown}{NRP}$.

42. Points *A*, *B*, *C*, and *D* are placed in succession on a circle such that $\overset{\frown}{AB} \cong \overset{\frown}{CD}$ and $\overset{\frown}{BC} \cong \overset{\frown}{DA}$. Is $\overline{AC}$ a diameter? Give the reason for your answer.

43. $\overline{AB}$ and $\overline{BC}$ are congruent chords in circle *O*, and *A* and *C* are distinct points. If $\overline{BD}$ is a diameter, prove ∠ *ABD* ≅ ∠ *CBD*.

44. Point *B* on $\overset{\frown}{AB}$ is equidistant from the radii *OA* and *OB*. Prove that *P* is the midpoint of arc *AB*.

C

45. A circle is divided into three congruent arcs. Chords join the endpoints of the arcs. Prove that the triangle formed is equilateral.

46. Triangle *ABC* is inscribed in a circle (all three vertices of the triangle are on the circle) and has ∠ *A* ≅ ∠ *C*. Prove that $\overset{\frown}{AB} \cong \overset{\frown}{BC}$.

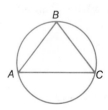

47. In circle *Q*, chord *AB* is parallel to diameter *RS*. Prove that $\overset{\frown}{RA} \cong \overset{\frown}{SB}$.

These exercises apply geometric concepts studied in Sections 8–1 and 8–2.

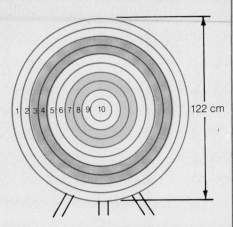

1 2 3 4 5 6 7 8 9 10   122 cm

A The target used in target archery competition has ten equally-spaced concentric circles as shown. The space between two circles is called a scoring ring. The total height of the target is 122 centimeters.

Use this information in Exercises 1–8.

1. What is the diameter of the target?

2. What is the radius of the target?

3. What is the radius of the circle that forms the outer boundary of scoring ring 1?

4. What is the radius of the circle that forms the outer boundary of scoring ring 9?

5. What is the diameter of the circle that forms scoring ring 10?

6. What is the diameter of the circle that forms the outer boundary of scoring ring 3?

7. The four spokes of an ancient Egyptian chariot wheel form equal central angles. What is the measure of each angle?

8. The eight spokes of a Roman chariot wheel form equal central angles. Find the measure of an arc cut off on the rim by two consecutive spokes.

1400 BC
Egyptian
Chariot wheel

60 AD
Roman
Chariot wheel

9. The spokes of a wagon wheel in use in 1750 form 12 equal central angles. Use this information and the figure below to find the measures of minor arc *AB* and of major arc *AFB*.

10. The spokes of a 1906 automobile wheel form 12 equal central angles. Use this information and the figure below to show that arcs *AC* and *DE* are congruent.

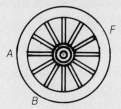

1750
Wagon wheel

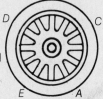

1906
Automobile wheel

In Exercises 1–6, write one or more conclusions that follow from the *Given*. Justify your answer with a definition, theorem or corollary. *(Pages 49–50)*

1. Given: $m\angle 1 = 90$
   Conclusion: ___?___

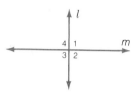

2. Given: $p \parallel q$;
      $m\angle 6 = 90$
   Conclusion: ___?___

3. Given: Isosceles $\triangle ABC$;
      $BD \perp AC$
   Conclusion: ___?___

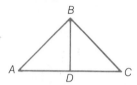

4. Given: $\overline{FE} \cong \overline{FG}$;
      $\overline{EH} \cong \overline{HG}$
   Conclusion: ___?___

5. Given: $ABCD$ is a
      square.
   Conclusion: ___?___

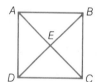

6. Given: $ABCD$ is a
      rhombus.
   Conclusion: ___?___

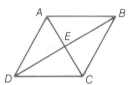

8-3 Congruent Chords and Arcs

In circle O at the right, there are two arcs with endpoints A and B, $\overset{\frown}{AB}$ and $\overset{\frown}{AEB}$. Unless otherwise stated, the arc of chord AB is $\overset{\frown}{AB}$, the smaller of the two arcs with endpoint A and B.

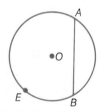

Theorem 8-3

In the same or in congruent circles, if two arcs are congruent, then their chords are congruent.

Theorem 8-4 is the converse of Theorem 8-3. The proofs for both theorems are asked for in the Written Exercises.

Theorem 8-4

In the same or in congruent circles, if two chords are congruent, then their arcs are congruent.

Consider two chords that intersect in the interior of a circle. When any two of the conditions stated by each of the four cases in the table on page 355 exist, the other two can be proved.

Case I: One chord bisects the other.	Case II: One chord is perpendicular to the other.	Case III: One chord is a diameter.	Case IV: One chord bisects the arc of the other.
$CE = ED$	$\overline{AB} \perp \overline{CD}$	$\overline{AB}$ is a diameter.	$\overparen{CA} \cong \overparen{DA}$
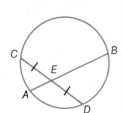	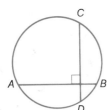	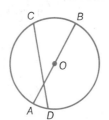	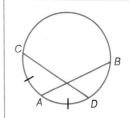

Cases II and III in the table can be combined as Theorem 8–5.

Theorem 8–5

If a diameter of a circle is perpendicular to a chord, then the diameter bisects the chord and its arc.

EXAMPLE

Write a Plan of Proof for Theorem 8–5.

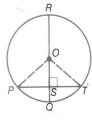

Given: $\overline{RQ}$ is a diameter of circle O; $\overline{RQ} \perp \overline{PT}$ at S.

Prove: **a.** S is the midpoint of $\overline{PT}$.
b. Q is the midpoint of $\overparen{PT}$.

Plan: 1. Draw $\overline{OP}$ and $\overline{OT}$. Prove that $\triangle OPS \cong \triangle OTS$ by the Hypotenuse-Leg Theorem.
2. Since $\overline{PS} \cong \overline{TS}$ by CPCTC, S is the midpoint of $\overline{PT}$ by definition.
3. Since $\angle POQ \cong \angle TOQ$ by CPCTC, $m\overparen{PQ} = m\overparen{TQ}$, and Q is the midpoint of $\overparen{PT}$.

Cases I and IV in the table lead to Theorem 8–6.

Theorem 8–6

If a chord of a circle bisects a second chord and its arc, then the first chord is a diameter and is perpendicular to the second chord.

In Theorem 8–7, it is given that a diameter of a circle bisects a chord that is not a diameter.

Theorem 8–7

If a diameter bisects a chord that is not a diameter, then it is perpendicular to the chord and bisects its arc.

The proofs of Theorems 8–6 and 8–7 are asked for in the Exercises.

CLASSROOM EXERCISES

In Exercises 1–10, give the reason
for each statement.

1. If $RS = PQ = 1$, then $\overset{\frown}{RS} \cong \overset{\frown}{PQ}$.
2. If $\overset{\frown}{RS} \cong \overset{\frown}{PQ}$ and $RS = 5$, then $PQ = 5$.
3. If $\angle ROS \cong \angle POQ$, then $\overset{\frown}{RS} \cong \overset{\frown}{PQ}$.
4. If $\overset{\frown}{RS} \cong \overset{\frown}{PQ}$, then $m\angle ROS = m\angle POQ$.

In circle O at the right, $\overline{OC} \perp \overline{AB}$,
$AB = 24$, and $OC = 5$.

5. $\overline{AC} \cong \overline{CB}$ 6. $AC = 12$
7. $(AO)^2 = (AC)^2 + (OC)^2$ 8. $AO = 13$

In the figure at the right, $AE = EB$,
and $m\overset{\frown}{AD} = m\overset{\frown}{DB}$

9. $m\angle CEA = 90$ 10. $\overline{CD}$ is a diameter.
11. Write Theorems 8–3 and 8–4 as a biconditional.

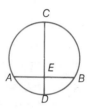

WRITTEN EXERCISES

In Exercises 1–6, write the conclusions that can be drawn from the
given information and figure. Give the reason(s) for each conclusion.

1. $\overline{AB} \cong \overline{CD}$ 2. $\overline{AB}$ is a diameter; $\overline{AB} \perp \overline{PQ}$ 3. $\overline{AP} \cong \overline{BR}$; $\overset{\frown}{PQ} \cong \overset{\frown}{RS}$

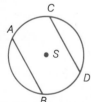

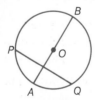

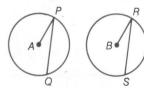

4. $\overline{PQ}$ is a diameter;   5. $TW = WV$;   6. $\overline{PD} \perp \overline{AB}$; $AP = 5$;
$AE = EB$ $m\overset{\frown}{TS} = m\overset{\frown}{SV}$ $PD = 4$

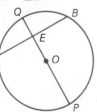

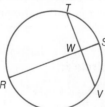

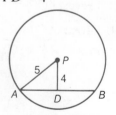

7. In semicircle O at the right, $\overline{OB}$ bisects $\angle AOC$
and $\angle 1 \cong \angle 2$.
Explain why $\overline{BC} \cong \overline{DE}$.

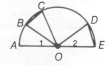

8. Five points on a circle divide it into five congruent arcs. Explain why the chords of these arcs form an equilateral pentagon.

9. Complete the following proof.

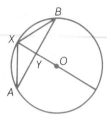

Given: $\overline{XA} \cong \overline{XB}$; $\overline{YA} \cong \overline{YB}$

Prove: $\overline{XO} \perp \overline{AB}$

Statements	Reasons
1. __?__	1. __?__
2. $\overset{\frown}{AX} \cong \overset{\frown}{XB}$	2. (1). __?__
3. X bisects $\overset{\frown}{AB}$.	3. (2). __?__
4. $\overline{YA} \cong \overline{YB}$	4. __?__
5. Y bisects $\overset{\frown}{AB}$.	5. (4). __?__
6. $\overline{XO} \perp \overline{AB}$	6. (3), (5). __?__

10. Prove Theorem 8–3.

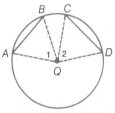

Given: In circle Q, $\overset{\frown}{AB} \cong \overset{\frown}{CD}$.   **Prove:** $\overline{AB} \cong \overline{CD}$

Plan: Draw $\overline{AQ}$, $\overline{BQ}$, $\overline{CQ}$, and $\overline{DQ}$.
Then $\overline{AQ} \cong \overline{BQ} \cong \overline{CQ} \cong \overline{DQ}$ because radii of the same circle are congruent.
Since $\overset{\frown}{AB} \cong \overset{\frown}{CD}$, $\angle 1 \cong \angle 2$.
Prove $\triangle ABQ \cong \triangle CDQ$ by the SAS Postulate. Thus, $\overline{AB} \cong \overline{CD}$.

11. Prove Theorem 8–4. Refer to the figure for Exercise 10.

Given: In circle Q, $\overline{AB} \cong \overline{CD}$.

Prove: $\overset{\frown}{AB} \cong \overset{\frown}{CD}$

Plan: Draw the radii as in the proof for Theorem 8–3.
Prove $\triangle ABQ \cong \triangle CDQ$ by the SSS Postulate.
Then $\angle 1 \cong \angle 2$ and $\overset{\frown}{AB} \cong \overset{\frown}{CD}$ by Theorem 8–1.

12. Prove Theorem 8–5. Refer to the Plan of Proof in the Example on page 355.

In Exercises 13–14, refer to circle O.

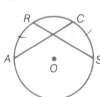

13. **Given:** $\overset{\frown}{AR} \cong \overset{\frown}{CS}$
    Prove: $\overline{AC} \cong \overline{RS}$

14. **Given:** $\overline{AC} \cong \overline{RS}$
    Prove: $\overset{\frown}{AR} \cong \overset{\frown}{CS}$

In Exercises 15–16, refer to circle R.

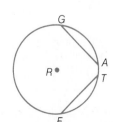

15. **Given:** $\overline{GA} \cong \overline{TE}$
    Prove: $\overset{\frown}{GT} \cong \overset{\frown}{AE}$

16. **Given:** $\overset{\frown}{GT} \cong \overset{\frown}{AE}$
    Prove: $\overline{GA} \cong \overline{TE}$

17. In circle S at the left below, $\overline{RX}$ bisects $\overline{DO}$ and $\overparen{DO}$. If $DO = 12$ and $PY = 9$, find DY, PD and PO.

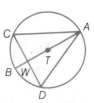

18. In circle T at the right above, $\overline{AB}$ is a diameter and $AB = 22$. $\overline{AB}$ bisects $\overline{CD}$, $CD = 16$, and $BW = 4$. Find AC.

19. Given: $\overline{AD} \perp \overline{AB}$; $\overline{DC} \perp \overline{BC}$;   **20. Given:** $\overline{PQ} \cong \overline{RS}$
        $\overline{BD}$ bisects $\angle ABC$.   **Prove:** $m\overparen{PQR} = m\overparen{SRQ}$
   Prove: $m\overparen{AB} = m\overparen{BC}$

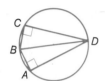

21. In circle O, diameter QR is perpendicular to chord AC. Prove that $\angle RAC \cong \angle RCA$ without proving triangles congruent.

22. In circle S below, $\overline{AB}$ and $\overline{BC}$ are congruent chords, $\overline{SV} \perp \overline{AB}$, and $\overline{SU} \perp \overline{BC}$. Prove that B is the midpoint of $\overparen{VU}$.

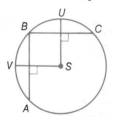

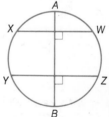

23. In the figure at the right above, diameter AB is perpendicular to chords XW and YZ. Prove that $\overparen{XB} \cong \overparen{WB}$.

24. Prove Theorem 8–6.

   Given: In circle O, $\overleftrightarrow{DE}$ intersects chord AB
          and arc AB such that $\overline{AC} \cong \overline{CB}$ and
          $\overparen{AD} \cong \overparen{DB}$.

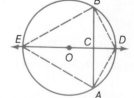

   Prove: $\overleftrightarrow{DE} \perp \overline{AB}$; $\overleftrightarrow{DE}$ contains O.

    Plan: Draw $\overline{DA}$, $\overline{DB}$, $\overline{EA}$, and $\overline{EB}$. Show that C and D are equidistant from A and B. Then C and D must lie on the perpendicular bisector of $\overline{AB}$ and $\overleftrightarrow{ED} \perp \overline{AB}$. Then show that $\overparen{DAE} \cong \overparen{DBE}$, and that $\overparen{DAE}$ and $\overparen{DBE}$ are semicircles. Complete the proof.

25. Prove Theorem 8–7. (HINT: Draw the radii to the endpoints of the chord.)

26. Given: Diameter AB bisects chord CD.
   Prove: $\triangle ABC \cong \triangle ABD$

27. Given: In circle M, $\overline{AB} \cong \overline{CD}$.
   Prove: $\triangle DBE$ is isosceles.
   (HINT: Draw $\overline{AD}$ and $\overline{BC}$.)

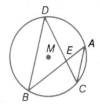

Review

In Exercises 1–5, refer to circle P. *(Section 8–1)*

1. Name two radii.
2. Name a tangent.
3. Name a secant.
4. Name three chords.
5. Name a diameter.

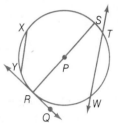

The measures of the central angles in circle K are given. Find the measure of each arc.
(Section 8–2)

6. $\overset{\frown}{AE}$ 7. $\overset{\frown}{AB}$ 8. $\overset{\frown}{DC}$ 9. $\overset{\frown}{DCB}$
10. $\overset{\frown}{ABC}$ 11. $\overset{\frown}{EDC}$ 12. $\overset{\frown}{CBA}$ 13. $\overset{\frown}{AED}$

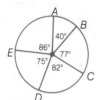

In the figure at the right, P is the center of concentric circles with radii PQ and PR. If $m\angle JPS = 62$ and $m\angle SPR = 84$, find each of the following. *(Section 8–2)*

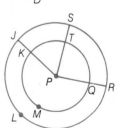

14. $m\overset{\frown}{KT}$ 15. $m\overset{\frown}{TQ}$ 16. $m\overset{\frown}{JS}$ 17. $m\overset{\frown}{SR}$
18. $m\overset{\frown}{JLR}$ 19. $m\overset{\frown}{KTQ}$ 20. $m\overset{\frown}{KMQ}$ 21. $m\overset{\frown}{JLS}$

Complete each statement. *(Section 8–3)*

22. In the same or in congruent circles, if two chords are __?__ , then their arcs are congruent.
23. If a chord of a circle bisects a second chord and its arc, then it is a __?__ and is perpendicular to the second chord.
24. If a diameter bisects a chord that is not a diameter, then it is perpendicular to the __?__ and bisects its __?__ .
25. In the same circle, if two __?__ are congruent, then their chords are __?__ .
26. If a diameter is perpendicular to a chord, then it bisects the __?__ and its __?__ .

Simplify. *(Pages 265–267)*

1. $\sqrt{36}$ 2. $\sqrt{8}$ 3. $\sqrt{27}$ 4. $\sqrt{50}$ 5. $\sqrt{12}$ 6. $\sqrt{75}$

7. $\sqrt{72}$ 8. $\sqrt{64}$ 9. $\sqrt{196}$ 10. $\sqrt{300}$ 11. $\sqrt{117}$ 12. $\sqrt{242}$

8-4 Chords and Inscribed Polygons

Recall that the distance from a point to a line is the length of the perpendicular segment from the point to the line.

Theorem 8-8	In the same or in congruent circles, two chords are congruent if and only if they are equidistant from the center.

You are asked to prove this biconditional in the Written Exercises.

EXAMPLE

Circle C has a radius of 10.
Chord QT is 5 units from C
and chord PR is 8 units from C.

a. Compare the lengths of $\overline{PR}$ and $\overline{QT}$.

b. Compare the distances of $\overline{PR}$ and $\overline{QT}$ from C.

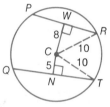

Solutions: Use the Pythagorean Theorem to compute NT and WR.

a. $(NT)^2 + (NC)^2 = (CT)^2$ $(WR)^2 + (WC)^2 = (RC)^2$

$\quad (NT)^2 + (5)^2 = (10)^2$ $\quad (WR)^2 + (8)^2 = (10)^2$

$\quad\quad\quad (NT)^2 = 100 - 25$ $\quad\quad\quad (WR)^2 = 100 - 64$

$\quad\quad\quad (NT)^2 = 75$ $\quad\quad\quad (WR)^2 = 36$

$\quad\quad\quad NT = 5\sqrt{3}$ $\quad\quad\quad WR = 6$

$\quad QT = 2(NT) = 10\sqrt{3}$ $\quad PR = 2(WR) = 12$

From the Table of Square Roots, $\sqrt{3} \approx 1.73$.

Thus, $10\sqrt{3} \approx 10\,(1.73) = 17.3$.

Since $17.3 > 12$, $QT > PR$.

b. Since $CW > CN$, $\overline{PR}$ is **farther** from C than $\overline{QT}$.

The results of Example 2 are generalized in the following two theorems.

Theorem 8-9	In the same or in congruent circles, if two chords are not congruent, then their distances from the center of the circle are not equal, and the longer chord is closer to the center.

Theorem 8–10	In the same or in congruent circles, if the distances of two chords from the center of the circle are not equal, then the chords are not congruent, and the chord that is closer to the center is the longer chord.

Theorems 8–9 and 8–10 are converses of each other. Thus, the theorems can be stated as a biconditional. You are asked to prove these theorems in the Written Exercises.

Polygons are sometimes drawn with their vertices on a circle. Polygon *ABCD* at the left below is an inscribed quadrilateral. Polygon *KEFGHJ* at the right is an inscribed hexagon.

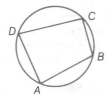
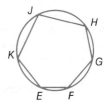

Definition	A polygon is **inscribed in a circle** if all its vertices are on the circle.

CLASSROOM EXERCISES

In Exercises 1–5, choose the best answer. Choose a, b, or c.

1. In a circle, two chords are equally distant from the center of the circle. The chords are
   a. congruent.   **b.** not congruent.   **c.** parallel.

2. $\overline{AB}$ and $\overline{CD}$ are two chords of the same circle O and $AB < CD$. Then
   a. $\overline{AB}$ is closer to O.   **b.** $\overline{CD}$ is closer to O.   **c.** $\overline{AB}$ is a diameter.

3. A chord is 5 centimeters from the center of a circle of radius 13 centimeters. The length of the chord is
   a. 6 centimeters.   **b.** 12 centimeters.   **c.** 24 centimeters.

4. A chord 40 units long is contained in a circle of radius 25. The distance of the chord from the center of the circle is
   a. 15 units.   **b.** 31.2 units.   **c.** 47.1 units.

5. A chord $8\sqrt{3}$ units long is 4 units from the center of a circle. The length of the radius of the circle is
   a. 14.4 units.   **b.** 8 units.   **c.** $4\sqrt{2}$ units.

6. Write Theorem 8–8 as a conditional and its converse.

WRITTEN EXERCISES

A   In circle O, $\overline{AB}$ is a chord, $\overline{OA}$ is a radius, and $\overline{AB} \perp \overline{OC}$. Refer to this figure in Exercises 1–6. Express answers in simplified radical form.

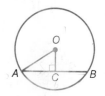

1. If $AO = 13$ and $OC = 5$, find AC and AB.

2. If $\overline{AB}$ is 16 centimeters long and is 6 centimeters from O, find the radius and diameter of the circle.

3. If the diameter of circle O is 34 centimeters, how far from the center is a chord 30 centimeters long?

4. The radius of circle O is 25 units long. How long is $\overline{AB}$ if it is 7 units from point O?

5. If m $\angle AOC = 60$ and $AO = 12$, find OC, AC, and AB.

6. Chord AB is 10 meters long and is 5 meters from O. Find OA.

7. In circle Q, $\overline{QW} \perp \overline{XY}$, $\overline{QT} \perp \overline{YZ}$, $QW = 5$, $QT = 5$, and $YT = 12$. Find XY.

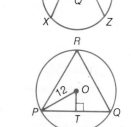

8. An equilateral triangle is inscribed in a circle of radius 12 centimeters. Find the distance from the center of the circle to each side of the triangle.

9. In Exercise 8, find the length of each side of $\triangle PQR$.

     Square $ABCD$ is inscribed in a circle with center O and radius 8 centimeters.

10. Find m$\angle AOB$.

11. What kind of triangle is $\triangle AOB$?

12. Find the length of $\overline{AB}$.

13. How far is $\overline{AB}$ from O?

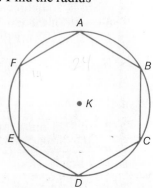

14. A square whose side is 20 centimeters is inscribed in a circle. Find the radius of the circle. (Use the figure for Exercises 10–13.)

     A regular hexagon is inscribed in a circle of radius 14.

15. Find the length of each side of the hexagon.

16. Find the distance of each side of the hexagon from the center of the circle.

17. A regular hexagon is inscribed in a circle. Each side of the hexagon is $5\sqrt{3}$ units from the center of the circle. Find the radius of the circle.

18. A, B, and C are three points on circle T. A, B, and C are joined to form $\triangle ABC$ and $m\angle A < m\angle C$. Prove that the distance from T to $\overline{AB}$ is less than the distance from T to $\overline{BC}$.

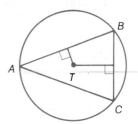

19. Prove Theorem 8–8.

   Part I **Given:** In circle O, $\overline{AB} \cong \overline{CD}$, $\overline{OE} \perp \overline{AB}$, and $\overline{OF} \perp \overline{CD}$.

   Prove: $OE = OF$

   Plan: Draw $\overline{OA}$ and $\overline{OC}$. Prove that $\triangle AEO \cong \triangle CFO$.

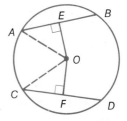

   Part II **Given:** In circle O, $\overline{OE} \perp \overline{AB}$, $\overline{OF} \perp \overline{CD}$, and $\overline{OE} \cong \overline{OF}$.

   Prove: $\overline{AB} \cong \overline{CD}$

   Plan: Draw $\overline{OA}$ and $\overline{OC}$. Prove that $\triangle AEO \cong \triangle CFO$, and $\overline{AE} \cong \overline{CF}$ by CPCTC. Use Theorem 8–5 to show that $AB = 2AE$ and $CD = 2CF$. Thus, $\overline{AB} \cong \overline{CD}$.

20. Prove Theorem 8–9.

   Given: In circle O, $AB > CD$, $\overline{OG} \perp \overline{AB}$, and $\overline{OH} \perp \overline{CD}$.

   Prove: $OG < OH$

   Plan: Draw chord AE so that $\overline{AE} \cong \overline{CD}$. Let $\overline{OF}$ be perpendicular to $\overline{AE}$ and draw $\overline{FG}$. Show that $AB > AE$ and that $AG > AF$. It follows that $m\angle 2 > m\angle 4$ and, by the properties of order, $m\angle 1 < m\angle 3$, which makes $OG < OF$. Since $OH = OF$, $OG < OH$.

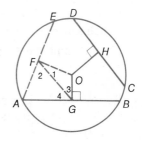

21. Prove Theorem 8–10. (Use the figure for Exercise 20.)

   Given: In circle O, $OG < OH$, $\overline{OG} \perp \overline{AB}$, and $\overline{OH} \perp \overline{CD}$.

   Prove: $AB > CD$

   Plan: Draw the same auxiliary segments as in Exercise 20. Reverse the order of the reasons given in the proof of Exercise 20.

22. Prove that if the vertices of a square are on a circle, then the diagonals of the square intersect at the center of the circle.

23. Equilateral triangle ABC is inscribed in a circle of radius h. The altitude of equilateral triangle DEF has length h. What is the ratio of the perimeter of $\triangle ABC$ to the perimeter of $\triangle DEF$?

24. Triangle ABC is inscribed in circle O and $m\angle A < m\angle B < m\angle C$. Prove that $m\angle BOC < m\angle COA < m\angle AOB$.

Choose the word(s) from the box at the right that best completes each statement. *(Pages 127–128)*

1. To begin an indirect proof, you assume the __?__ of what you want to prove.

2. The second step in an indirect proof is to reason until you reach a __?__ .

3. The third step is to state that your assumption must be __?__ .

4. This leads to the conclusion that what you set out to prove must be __?__ .

| Contradiction |
| True |
| Negation |
| Assumption |
| Unequal |
| False |

8-5 Tangents to a Circle

When a line and a circle lie in the same plane and the line and the circle have exactly one point in common, the line is **tangent** to the circle.

Thus, in circle O at the right, line t is tangent at C, the **point of tangency**. Theorem 8–11 states an important relationship between a tangent line and the radius drawn to the point of tangency.

Theorem 8–11

> If a line in the plane of a circle is tangent to a circle, then the line is perpendicular to the radius drawn to the point of tangency.

Theorem 8–11 is proved by the indirect method.

EXAMPLE 1 Prove Theorem 8–11.

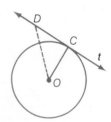

Given: Line t is tangent to circle O at C.

Prove: $\overline{OC} \perp t$ at C

Proof: Assume $\overline{OC}$ is not perpendicular to t.
Let $\overline{OD}$ be perpendicular to t.

If $\overline{OD} \perp t$, then $OD < OC$ because a perpendicular segment is the shortest distance from a point to a line.

Since it is given that C is the point of tangency, D must be in the exterior of the circle. If D is in the exterior, then $OC < OD$ because $\overline{OC}$ is a radius.

But $OD < OC$ and $OD \not< OC$ is a contradiction.

$\therefore \overline{OC} \perp t$ at C.

The converse of Theorem 8–11 is also a theorem.

Theorem 8–12

> If a line in the plane of a circle is perpendicular to a radius at its outer endpoint, then the line is tangent to the circle.

Theorem 8–12 is also proved by the indirect method. You are asked to complete this proof in the Written Exercises.

In the figure at the right, $\overrightarrow{XY}$ and $\overrightarrow{XZ}$ are tangents to circle O. Segments XY and XZ are called *tangent segments*.

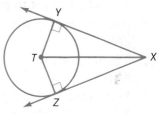

Definition

> A **tangent segment** is a segment from a point in the exterior of a circle to the point of tangency.

Theorem 8–13 concerns tangent segments drawn from the same exterior exterior point.

Theorem 8–13

> The two tangent segments from the same exterior point of a circle are congruent.

You are asked to prove this theorem in the Written Exercises.

EXAMPLE 2 $\overline{QT}$ and $\overline{QS}$ are tangent segments to circle R, $TR = 5$, and $RQ = 13$. Find QT and QS.

Solution: QRT is a right triangle.   ◀— **By Theorem 8–11**

$(QR)^2 = (QT)^2 + (TR)^2$

$(13)^2 = (QT)^2 + 5^2$

$169 = (QT)^2 + 25$

$(QT)^2 = 169 - 25$

$QT = 12$

By Theorem 8–13, $\overline{QT} \cong \overline{QS}$.   Thus, $QT = QS = \mathbf{12}$.

In Example 2, $\triangle QTR \cong \triangle QSR$ and $\angle 1 \cong \angle 2$. Thus, $\overline{QR}$ bisects $\angle TQS$. Corollary 8–14 states these results in general form.

Corollary 8–14

> Two tangents to a circle from a given point in the exterior of the circle determine an angle that is bisected by the segment joining the given point to the center of the circle.

You are asked to prove this corollary in the Written Exercises.

CLASSROOM EXERCISES

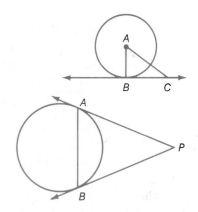

In Exercises 1 and 2, refer to circle *A*.

1. Given that $\overline{AB}$ is a radius and $\overleftrightarrow{BC}$ is a tangent, classify triangle *ABC* as an acute, obtuse, or right triangle.
2. Given that $\overline{AB}$ is a radius and $\overline{AB} \perp \overleftrightarrow{BC}$, what conclusion can be drawn? Give a reason for your answer.
3. In the figure at the right, $\overrightarrow{PA}$ and $\overrightarrow{PB}$ are tangents. Classify $\triangle PAB$ as a scalene, isosceles, or equilateral triangle.
4. In the figure, if m∠ *PAB* = 65, find m∠ *P*.
5. In the figure, if m∠ *P* = 48, find m∠ *PBA*.

WRITTEN EXERCISES

A

1. In the figure at the right, m∠ *C* = 40 and $\overleftrightarrow{AC}$ is a tangent to circle *O*. Find m∠ *O*.

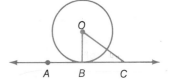

2. In the figure for Exercise 1, if *B* is a point on circle *O* and $\overline{AC} \perp \overline{OB}$, is $\overleftrightarrow{AC}$ a tangent? Why?

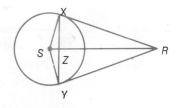

In the figure at the right, $\overline{RX}$ and $\overline{RY}$ are tangent segments to circle *S*. $\overline{XY}$ joins the points of tangency and $\overline{SR}$ is drawn.

Classify each triangle as *right, isosceles, equilateral, right isosceles,* or *right scalene*.

3. $\triangle SXZ$
4. $\triangle RZY$
5. $\triangle SXY$
6. $\triangle RXY$

In Exercises 7–14, refer to the figure for Exercises 3–6. If m∠ *RSX* = 80, find the measure of each angle.

7. ∠ *RSY*
8. ∠ *SXZ*
9. ∠ *SYX*
10. ∠ *XZR*
11. ∠ *ZXR*
12. ∠ *XRZ*
13. ∠ *YRZ*
14. ∠ *RYZ*

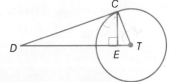

In the figure at the right, $\overline{CD}$ is a tangent segment to circle *T*, $\overline{CE} \perp \overline{TD}$, and m∠ *T* = *a*.

Find the measure of each angle.

15. ∠ *TCE*
16. ∠ *ECD*
17. ∠ *D*

18. Refer to the figure for Exercises 15–17 and use m∠ *DCE* = 56 to find m∠ *T*.

B
19. Prove: Two tangents to a circle from a given external point form an isosceles triangle with the segment joining their points of tangency.

20. In the figure at the right, $\overline{AP}$ and $\overline{BP}$ are tangent segments to circle *O* from *P*, and m∠ *ABO* = 12. Find m∠ *P*.

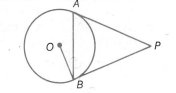

21. In the figure for Exercise 20, prove that m∠ *P* = 2m∠ *ABO*.

22. Prove Theorem 8–13.

23. Prove Corollary 8–14.

24. In the figure at the left below, the distance from point *C* to circle *A* is *BC*, where points *A*, *B*, and *C* are collinear. Prove that if any other point *D* of the circle is chosen, then *CD* > *CB*.

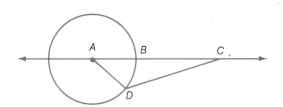

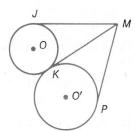

25. Segments *MJ*, *MK*, and *MP* are each tangent to circles *O* and *O'* as shown at the right above. Prove that $\overline{MJ} \cong \overline{MP}$.

26. Prove that if the vertices of a quadrilateral lie on a circle, then the opposite angles of the quadrilateral are supplementary.

27. In the figure at the left below, $\overline{CE}$ and $\overline{NE}$ are tangent segments to circle *O*. Prove that ∠ *CON* and ∠ *E* are supplementary.

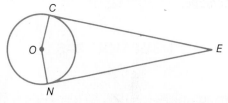

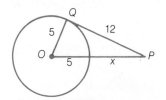

28. In the figure at the right above, the tangent segment from a point is 12 units and the radius of the circle is 5 units. Find the distance from the point to the circle.

C
29. In the figure at the right, *A* is the center of the smaller circle, and $\overline{AB}$ is a diameter of the larger circle. The circles intersect at *C*. $\overleftrightarrow{AC}$ and $\overleftrightarrow{BC}$ are drawn. Prove that $\overleftrightarrow{BC}$ is tangent to circle *A*.

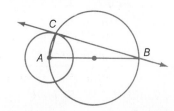

30. Prove Theorem 8–12. (HINT: Use the indirect method.)

> Points O and O' trisect $\overline{AB}$. O is the center of a circle with radius AO, and O' is the center of a circle with radius $O'B$. The circles intersect at points X and Y. Use this information to prove the statements in Exercises 31 and 32.

31. $AXBY$ is a rhombus with $m\angle A = 60$.

32. $\overline{AX}$ and $\overline{AY}$ are tangent segments to circle O' from A.

Puzzle

Sixteen disks are arranged in a square, as shown in Figure 1 below. Two players alternately remove 1, 2, 3, or 4 disks from the square. The disks removed in each turn must come from a single row or column. The disks must also be adjacent. The player who takes the final disk on the square loses the game.

Two games in progress are shown in Figures 2 and 3. For each game, find the next move that guarantees that you will win.

Figure 1

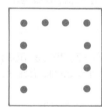

Figure 2

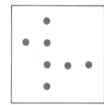

Figure 3

GEOMETRY REVIEW CAPSULE FOR SECTION 8–6

In circle O at the right, $\overline{AB}$ is a diameter. Use this figure in Exercises 1–6 to name the arc cut off by the given angle. *(Pages 348–350)*

1. $\angle AOF$ **2.** $\angle FOE$ **3.** $\angle COD$

4. $\angle DOB$ **5.** $\angle COA$ **6.** $\angle AOD$

In Exercises 7–12, refer to circle O to compute the measure of each arc. *(Pages 348–350)*

7. $m\overset{\frown}{DB}$ **8.** $m\overset{\frown}{DC}$ **9.** $m\overset{\frown}{CA}$ **10.** $m\overset{\frown}{FE}$ **11.** $m\overset{\frown}{DBF}$ **12.** $m\overset{\frown}{ACD}$

8-6 Inscribed Angles

In each figure, $\angle BAC$ is an *inscribed angle*. $\overset{\frown}{BC}$ is the *intercepted arc*.

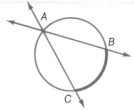

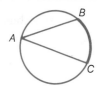

Secants *AB* and *AC* intersect at *A*.   **Chords *AB* and *AC* intersect at *A*.**

Definition	An **inscribed angle** is an angle whose vertex lies on the circle and whose sides contain chords of the circle.

Theorem 8–15 tells how to determine the measure of an inscribed angle, given the measure of its intercepted arc.

Theorem 8–15	The measure of an inscribed angle is one–half the measure of its intercepted arc.

To prove Theorem 8–15, three possible cases must be considered. In Case 1, the center of the circle lies on one side of the inscribed angle.

EXAMPLE 1   Prove Case 1 of Theorem 8–15.

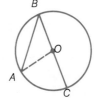

Given: $\angle ABC$ is inscribed in circle O; point O lies on $\angle ABC$.

Prove: $m\angle ABC = \frac{1}{2}m\overset{\frown}{AC}$

Proof:

Statements	Reasons
1. Draw $\overline{OA}$.	1. Two points determine a line.
2. $\overline{OB} \cong \overline{OA}$	2. (1). Radii of the same circle are congruent.
3. $\angle A \cong \angle B$	3. (2). Isosceles Triangle Theorem
4. $m\angle A = m\angle B$	4. (3). Definition of congruent angles
5. $m\angle A + m\angle B = m\angle AOC$	5. Corollary 4–18, page 188
6. $m\angle B + m\angle B = m\angle AOC$, or $2m\angle B = m\angle AOC$	6. (4), (5). Substitution property
7. $m\angle B = \frac{1}{2}m\angle AOC$	7. (6). Multiplication property
8. $m\overset{\frown}{AC} = m\angle AOC$	8. Definition of arc measure
9. $m\angle B = \frac{1}{2}m\overset{\frown}{AC}$	9. (7), (8). Substitution property

You are asked to prove Case 2 and Case 3 in the Written Exercises.

Case 2: Point *O* lies in the interior of ∠ *ABC*.

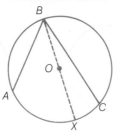

Case 3: Point *O* lies in the exterior of ∠ *ABC*.

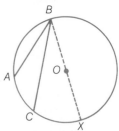

EXAMPLE 2 In the circle at the right, m$\widehat{TN}$ = 120. Find m∠ *A*, m∠ *E*, and m∠ *O*.

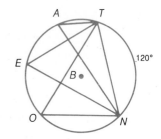

Solutions: m∠ *A* = $\frac{1}{2}$(120) = **60** ⟵ **By Theorem 8–15**

m∠ *E* = $\frac{1}{2}$(120) = **60**

m∠ *O* = $\frac{1}{2}$(120) = **60**

In Example 2, inscribed angles *A*, *E*, and *O* intercept the same arc. Thus, angles *A*, *E*, and *O* are congruent.

Theorem 8–16

> If inscribed angles intercept the same arc or congruent arcs, the angles are congruent.

CLASSROOM EXERCISES

In Exercises 1–3, refer to circle *O* at the right. In circle *O*, $\overline{BC}$ is a diameter and m∠ *A* = 22.

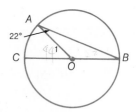

1. Find m∠ 1.

2. Find m$\widehat{AC}$.

3. Name an inscribed angle in circle *O*.

In Exercises 4–7, refer to the circle at the right.

4. m$\widehat{AB}$ = 60   m∠ *C* = __?__   m∠ *D* = __?__

5. m∠ *D* = 22   m$\widehat{AB}$ = __?__   m∠ *C* = __?__

6. m$\widehat{CD}$ = 85   m∠ *B* = __?__   m∠ *A* = __?__

7. m∠ *B* = a   m$\widehat{DC}$ = __?__   m∠ *A* = __?__

WRITTEN EXERCISES

A   In Exercises 1–23, refer to the three circles below.

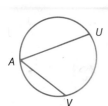 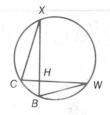 

In Exercises 1–6, name the arc intercepted (cut off) by each angle.

1. $\angle A$ **2.** $\angle B$ **3.** $\angle C$ **4.** $\angle D$ **5.** $\angle E$ **6.** $\angle F$

In Exercises 7–12, m$\overset{\frown}{UV}$ = 80, m$\overset{\frown}{XW}$ = 170, and m$\overset{\frown}{YZ}$ = 36. Find the measure of each angle.

7. $\angle A$ **8.** $\angle B$ **9.** $\angle C$ **10.** $\angle D$ **11.** $\angle E$ **12.** $\angle F$

13. If m$\overset{\frown}{UAV}$ = 236, find m$\angle A$.

14. If m$\overset{\frown}{UAV}$ = 5(m$\overset{\frown}{UV}$), find m$\angle A$.

15. Is $\angle C$ congruent to $\angle B$? Is $\angle X$ congruent to $\angle W$? Is $\triangle XHC$ similar to $\triangle WHB$?

In Exercises 16–20, m$\overset{\frown}{CX}$ = 100, m$\overset{\frown}{CB}$ = 40, and m$\overset{\frown}{BW}$ = 55. Find each of the following.

16. m$\overset{\frown}{WX}$ **17.** m$\angle X$ **18.** m$\angle C$ **19.** m$\angle B$ **20.** m$\angle W$

21. Are angles D, E, and F congruent? Why or why not?

22. Name two inscribed angles that intercept $\overset{\frown}{DE}$. Are they congruent?

23. Name two inscribed angles that intercept $\overset{\frown}{EF}$. Are they congruent?

24. In the figure at the right, angles X and Y are inscribed angles and $\overset{\frown}{AB} \cong \overset{\frown}{CD}$. Is $\angle X$ congruent to $\angle Y$? Give a reason for your answer.

An angle is sometimes described as being inscribed in an arc. In the figure at the right, $\angle MAK$ is *inscribed in* major arc *MAK*. The angle *intercepts* arc *MK*.

Use the figures for Exercises 1–23 to name the arc in which each angle is inscribed.

25. $\angle A$ **26.** $\angle B$ **27.** $\angle C$ **28.** $\angle D$ **29.** $\angle E$ **30.** $\angle F$

31. In the figures for Exercises 1–23, name the angles inscribed in $\overset{\frown}{XBW}$, $\overset{\frown}{YEZ}$, and $\overset{\frown}{DZE}$.

In the figure at the right, $\overline{AB}$, $\overline{BC}$, and $\overline{CD}$ are chords, $m\overset{\frown}{ADC} = 136$, and $m\overset{\frown}{BAD} = 148$.

32. Find m∠ B.   **33.** Find m∠ C.

34. In the figure at the left below, E is *not* the center of the circle. Find m∠ B, m∠ C, and m∠ AEC.

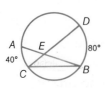
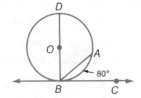

35. In the figure at the right above, $\overleftrightarrow{DB}$ is a diameter, $\overleftrightarrow{BC}$ is a tangent, and $m\overset{\frown}{AB} = 80$. Find $m\overset{\frown}{BAD}$, $m\overset{\frown}{AD}$, m∠ DBA, m∠ DBC, and m∠ ABC.

36. In the figure at the left below, $m\overset{\frown}{PT} = 40$ and $m\overset{\frown}{MQ} = 100$. Find m∠ MTQ, m∠ M, and m∠ R.

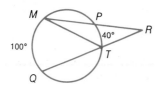

B

37. In the figure at the right above, $m\overset{\frown}{KM} = 2x + 8$, $m\overset{\frown}{KS} = 4x - 20$, and $m\overset{\frown}{SM} = 3x + 12$. Find m∠ K, m∠ S, and m∠ M.

38. In circle R below, $\overline{TP}$, $\overline{JM}$, $\overline{MP}$, and $\overline{JT}$ are chords. Prove that ∠ T ≅ ∠ M, ∠ J ≅ ∠ P, and △ JAT ~ △ PAM.

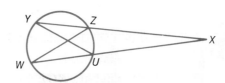

39. Use the figure at the right above to prove △ XYU ~ △ XWZ.

40. Prove Case 2 for Theorem 8–15. **Case 2:** Point O lies in the interior of ∠ ABC. (See the figure on page 370.) (HINT: Draw diameter BX.)

41. Prove Case 3 for Theorem 8–15. **Case 3:** The center of the circle lies in the exterior of ∠ ABC. (See the figure on page 370.) (HINT: Draw diameter BX.)

42. Prove Theorem 8–16. (HINT: The steps of the proof will be similar to the procedure in Example 2.)

Review

Refer to the figure at the right for Exercises 1–3. *(Section 8–4)*

1. In circle X, $AB = 48$ and $\overline{AB} \cong \overline{CD}$. If $BX = 26$, how far is $\overline{CD}$ from X?

2. If $AB = 28$ and $EX = 8$, find the length of a diameter of circle X.

3. If $EX = XF = 7$, and $XB = 15$, find AB and CD.

4. Rectangle $ABCD$ is inscribed in a circle with center at O, $AB = 24$, and $BC = 7$. Find OB. *(Section 8–4)*

5. In the figure at the left below, $\overline{AB}$ is a tangent segment to circle C. If $AB = 12$ and $BC = 8$, find AC and AD. *(Section 8–5)*

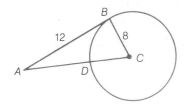 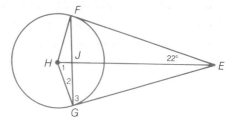

6. In the figure at the right above, $\overline{EF}$ and $\overline{EG}$ are tangent segments to circle H. If $m\angle JEF = 22$, find $m\angle 1$, $m\angle 2$, and $m\angle 3$. *(Section 8–5)*

Refer to the figures below for Exercises 7–13. *(Section 8–6)*

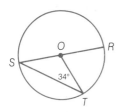 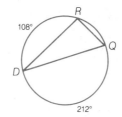 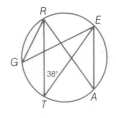

7. $\overline{SR}$ is a diameter in circle O. If $m\angle T = 34$, find $m\angle S$ and $m\angle TOR$.

8. Find $m\overarc{RQ}$.   9. Find $m\angle D$.   10. Find $m\angle Q$.

11. Find $m\overarc{RE}$.   12. Find $m\angle RGE$.   13. Find $m\angle RAE$.

Puzzle

Point B is the center of the circle shown at the right. The radius of the circle is 5 centimeters long. The figure $EGBF$ is a rectangle. Find GF.

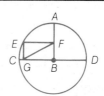

BASIC: ANGLES IN CIRCLES

Problem: *Given the measure of an angle and of the arc it cuts off on a circle, determine if the angle is a central angle, an inscribed angle, or neither of these.*

```
10   PRINT "ENTER THE MEASURES OF THE ANGLE AND THE ARC."
20   INPUT X, Y
30   IF X = Y THEN 90
40   IF X = .5* Y THEN 70
50   PRINT "THE ANGLE IS NOT A CENTRAL OR AN INSCRIBED
     ANGLE."
60   GO TO 100
70   PRINT "THE ANGLE IS AN INSCRIBED ANGLE."
80   GO TO 100
90   PRINT "THE ANGLE IS A CENTRAL ANGLE."
100  INPUT "ANY MORE ANGLES AND ARCS (1 = YES, 0 = NO)"; Z
110  IF Z = 1 THEN 10
120  END
```

Analysis:

Statement 100: On many systems a message can be put in an INPUT statement as is done here. The message will be printed with a question mark at the end. The computer will wait for you to input a 1 or a 0. If your system will not accept this statement, substitute the following statements for Statement 100.

```
100  PRINT "ANY MORE ANGLES AND ARCS (1 = YES,
     0 = NO)";
105  INPUT Z
```

EXERCISES

A   Run the program above with the following angle and arc measures.

1. 50, 25	2. 50, 100	3. 50, 50	4. 60, 120
5. 29, 38	6. 46, 92	7. 65, 65	8. 28, 14

B   Write a BASIC program for each problem.

9. Given the measure of a central angle in a circle, compute the measure of the arc it cuts off on the circle.

10. Given the measure of an inscribed angle in a circle, compute the measure of the arc it cuts off on the circle.

11. Given the diameter of a circle, compute the circle's circumference and area.

8-7 Inscribed Angle Corollaries

In the figure at the right, angles AEB, ADB, and ACB are each inscribed in circle O. Since the arc intercepted by each angle is a semicircle, the measure of each angle equals $\frac{1}{2}(180)$. Thus, each of these angles is a right angle.

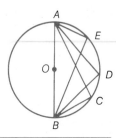

Corollary 8–17

> An inscribed angle is a right angle if and only if it is inscribed in a semicircle.

You are asked to prove this corollary in the Written Exercises.

When two parallel secants intersect a circle as shown, chords AB and RY will also be parallel and arcs AR and BY will be congruent.

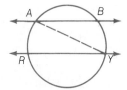

Corollary 8–18

> If two secants of the same circle are parallel, then the arcs between them are congruent.

A third corollary also follows from Theorem 8–15. You are asked to prove these corollaries in the Written Exercises.

Corollary 8–19

> The opposite angles of an inscribed quadrilateral are supplementary.

EXAMPLE

Quadrilateral $ABCD$ is inscribed in a circle, $\overline{AB} \parallel \overline{CD}$, $m\widehat{AB} = 130$, and $m\angle D = 110$. Find $m\widehat{BC}$, $m\widehat{AD}$, $m\angle B$, $m\angle C$, and $m\angle A$. Give the reason(s) for each answer.

Solution:

Arc or Angle	Measure	Reason
$\widehat{BC}$	90	Since $m\angle D = 110$, $m\widehat{ABC} = 220$. Since $m\widehat{BC} = m\widehat{ABC} - m\widehat{AB}$, $m\widehat{BC} = 220 - 130 = 90$.
$\widehat{AD}$	90	Since $\overline{AB} \parallel \overline{CD}$, $m\widehat{AD} = m\widehat{BC}$ by Corollary 8–18.
$m\angle B$	70	By Corollary 8–19, $\angle B$ is supplementary to $\angle D$, and $m\angle D = 110$.
$m\angle C$	110	$m\angle C = \frac{1}{2}m\widehat{DAB} = \frac{1}{2}(220) = 110$
$m\angle A$	70	By Corollary 8–19, $\angle C$ and $\angle A$ are supplementary.

CLASSROOM EXERCISES

In circle O, $\overline{XZ}$ is a diameter and $\overline{YZ} \parallel \overline{XR}$. Use this information in Exercises 1–10 to classify each statement as true, T, or false, F. Give the reason(s) for each answer.

1. $m\angle XYZ = 90$.

2. $\triangle XRZ$ is an obtuse triangle.

3. $m\overset{\frown}{XY} = m\overset{\frown}{ZR}$

4. $m\angle YZX = m\angle ZXR$

5. $m\angle YXZ + m\angle RZX = 180$

6. $m\angle Y + m\angle R = 180$

7. $m\angle YZR + m\angle YXR = 180$

8. If $m\angle RZX = 58$, then $m\angle YXZ = 58$.

9. Angles RXZ and RZX are complementary.

10. Quadrilateral $RXYZ$ is a square.

11. Write Corollary 8–17 as a conditional and its converse.

WRITTEN EXERCISES

In circle O, $\overline{WT}$ is a diameter, points Q and S are on the circle, $m\overset{\frown}{ST} = 60$, and $m\angle QWT = 50$. Find the measure of each of the following.

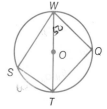

1. $\angle S$ 2. $\angle Q$ 3. $\overset{\frown}{WS}$ 4. $\angle SWT$

5. $\angle WTS$ 6. $\overset{\frown}{QT}$ 7. $\overset{\frown}{WQ}$ 8. $\angle WTQ$

In Exercises 9–12, O is the center of the circle and $\overline{ZY} \parallel \overline{TR}$. Find x.

9.

10.
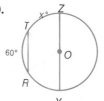

11.
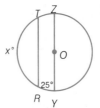

12.
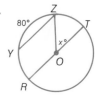

13. In the figure at the right, $PQRS$ is an inscribed quadrilateral, and $m\overset{\frown}{RSP} = 206$. Find $m\angle PST$.

14. In inscribed quadrilateral $ABCD$,
$m\overset{\frown}{AB} = 90$, $m\overset{\frown}{BC} = 110$, and $m\overset{\frown}{CD} = 70$.
Find the measures of the angles of the quadrilateral.

15. Refer to the figure at the left below to prove that $\overset{\frown}{CAB} \cong \overset{\frown}{DBA}$ if $\overleftrightarrow{AB} \parallel \overleftrightarrow{CD}$.

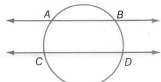 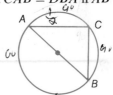

16. In the figure at the right above, $\overline{AB}$ is a diameter of the circle and $m\overset{\frown}{AC} = \frac{1}{2}m\overset{\frown}{AB}$. Find $m\angle C$, $m\angle A$, and $m\angle B$.

B

17. Prove: If a right triangle is inscribed in a circle, then the hypotenuse of the triangle is a diameter of the circle.

18. Prove Corollary 8–17. 19. Prove Corollary 8–18.

20. Prove Corollary 8–19.

Given: $m\overset{\frown}{AB} = w$; $m\overset{\frown}{BC} = x$; $m\overset{\frown}{CD} = y$; $m\overset{\frown}{DA} = z$

Prove: $m\angle B + m\angle D = 180$; $m\angle A + m\angle C = 180$

Plan: Show that $m\angle B = \frac{1}{2}(z + y)$ and $m\angle D = \frac{1}{2}(w + x)$. Then show that $m\angle B + m\angle D = \frac{1}{2}(z + y + w + x) = \frac{1}{2}(360)$. Follow a similar plan to prove that $m\angle A + m\angle C = 180$.

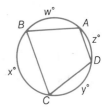

21. In the figure at the right, $\overline{AB}$ is a diameter and $\overline{DC} \perp \overline{AC}$. Points E, B, and D are collinear. Prove that $\triangle AEB \sim \triangle DCB$.

22. Quadrilateral $ABCD$ is inscribed in a circle, $m\angle A + m\angle B = 180$, and $AD \neq BC$. Prove that the quadrilateral is an isosceles trapezoid.

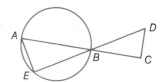

23. In the figure at the left below, $\overline{CD}$ is a diameter, X is the midpoint of $\overline{EF}$ and Y is the midpoint of $\overline{GH}$. Prove that $\overset{\frown}{EG} \cong \overset{\frown}{FH}$.

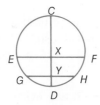

24. In the figure at the right above, $\overline{QM} \parallel \overline{KT}$, $m\overset{\frown}{QK} = 87$, and $m\angle K = 62$. Find $m\angle Q$, $m\angle T$, $m\angle M$, $m\overset{\frown}{QM}$, $m\overset{\frown}{MT}$, and $m\overset{\frown}{TK}$.

In the figure at the right, $\overline{BE}$ bisects $\angle ABC$ of inscribed $\triangle ABC$.

25. Prove $\triangle ABD \sim \triangle EBC$.

26. Prove $\triangle EDC \sim \triangle ECB$.

Complete each statement. *(Pages 182, 193, 348–350, 369–370, 375)*

1. The sum of the measures of the angles of a triangle is __?__ .
2. The measure of a minor arc of a circle equals the measure of __?__ .
3. The measure of a major arc of a circle equals __?__ .
4. The sum of the measures of the angles of a quadrilateral is __?__ .
5. The measure of an inscribed angle of a circle equals __?__ .
6. The measure of an angle inscribed in a semicircle equals __?__ .

8–8   More Angles and Arcs

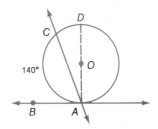

In circle O shown at the right, secant AC and tangent BA intersect at point A on the circle, forming angle BAC. Theorem 8–20 states the relationship between the measure of this angle and the degree measure of the intercepted arc, $\overparen{AC}$.

Theorem 8–20	If a tangent and a secant (or chord) intersect in a point on a circle, the measure of the angle formed is one half the measure of the intercepted arc.

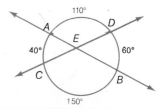

When two secants intersect in the interior of a circle (see the figure at the right), two pairs of vertical angles are formed. Theorem 8–21 tells how to find the measure of each of these angles.

Theorem 8–21	If two secants (or chords) intersect in the interior of a circle, the measure of an angle formed is one-half the sum of the measures of the arcs intercepted by the angle and its vertical angle.

The proofs of Theorems 8–20 and 8–21 are asked for in the Written Exercises.

EXAMPLE 1   Chords ST and QR intersect at P,
$\overleftrightarrow{SN}$ is tangent to the circle at S,
$m\overparen{SQ} = 112$, $m\overparen{TR} = 38$, and $m\overparen{RS} = 75$.

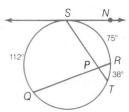

a. Find m∠ TSN.

b. Find m∠ SPQ.

Solutions: **a.** By Theorem 8–20,

$$m\angle TSN = \tfrac{1}{2}m\widehat{ST}.$$
$$= \tfrac{1}{2}(m\widehat{SR} + m\widehat{RT})$$
$$= \tfrac{1}{2}(75 + 38)$$
$$= \tfrac{1}{2}(113) = 56\tfrac{1}{2}$$

b. By Theorem 8–21,

$$m\angle SPQ = \tfrac{1}{2}(m\widehat{SQ} + m\widehat{RT}).$$
$$= \tfrac{1}{2}(112 + 38)$$
$$= \tfrac{1}{2}(150)$$
$$= 75$$

Two secants, a secant and a tangent, or two tangents can intersect in the exterior of a circle as shown in Example 2. Theorem 8–22 tells how to determine the measure of the angle formed in each of these cases.

Theorem 8–22

If two secants, a tangent and a secant, or two tangents intersect in the exterior of a circle, the measure of the angle formed is one-half the difference of the measures of the intercepted arcs.

You are asked to prove this theorem in the Written Exercises.

EXAMPLE 2 In each case, find $m\angle D$.

a. Two Secants   **b. One Secant; One Tangent**   **c. Two Tangents**

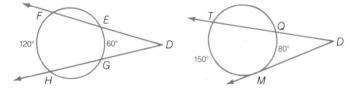 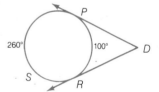

Solutions: Apply Theorem 8–22.

a. $m\angle D = \tfrac{1}{2}(m\widehat{FH} - m\widehat{EG})$ **b.** $m\angle D = \tfrac{1}{2}(m\widehat{TM} - m\widehat{QM})$ **c.** $m\angle D = \tfrac{1}{2}(m\widehat{PSR} - m\widehat{PR})$

$= \tfrac{1}{2}(120 - 60)$ $= \tfrac{1}{2}(150 - 80)$ $= \tfrac{1}{2}(260 - 100)$

$= \tfrac{1}{2}(60) = 30$ $= \tfrac{1}{2}(70) = 35$ $= \tfrac{1}{2}(160) = 80$

CLASSROOM EXERCISES

In Exercises 1–4, use the given circle to complete each statement.

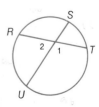

1. If $m\widehat{RS} = 140$ and $m\widehat{TU} = 96$, then $m\angle 1 = \underline{\ \ ?\ \ }$.

2. If $m\widehat{ST} = 70$ and $m\widehat{RU} = 88$, then $m\angle 2 = \underline{\ \ ?\ \ }$.

3. If $m\widehat{RU} = 95$ and $m\widehat{ST} = 63$, then $m\angle 2 = \underline{\ \ ?\ \ }$.

4. If $m\widehat{RS} = 157$ and $m\widehat{TU} = 106$, then $m\angle 1 = \underline{\ \ ?\ \ }$.

In Exercises 5–7, use the given circle to complete each statement.

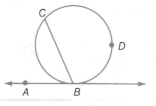

5. If m$\overparen{BC}$ = 82, then m∠ABC = ___?___ .
6. If m$\overparen{BC}$ = 148, then m∠ABC = ___?___ .
7. If m$\overparen{BDC}$ = 226, then m∠ABC = ___?___ .

In Exercises 8–10, find x.

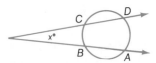

8. m$\overparen{AD}$ = 108 and m$\overparen{BC}$ = 42
9. m$\overparen{AD}$ = 130 and m$\overparen{BC}$ = 28
10. m$\overparen{AD}$ = 117 and m$\overparen{BC}$ = 35

WRITTEN EXERCISES

A

1. Given that $\overleftrightarrow{AB}$, $\overleftrightarrow{BC}$, $\overleftrightarrow{FY}$, and $\overleftrightarrow{RS}$ are tangents, name the angles formed by a tangent and a secant or by a tangent and a chord intersecting on the circle.

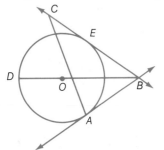
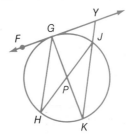
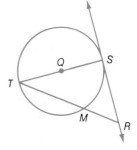

Use circle P above to name the arcs intercepted by each angle.

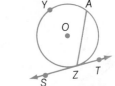

2. ∠HJK   3. ∠HGK   4. ∠FGH   5. ∠JPK

6. $\overline{AZ}$ is a chord in circle O, and $\overleftrightarrow{ST}$ is tangent at Z. If m$\overparen{AZ}$ = 146, find m∠AZT, m$\overparen{AYZ}$, and m∠AZS.

7. In the figure for Exercise 6, if m∠AZT = 81, find m$\overparen{AZ}$, m$\overparen{AYZ}$, and m∠AZS.

8. In the figure at the left below, $\overleftrightarrow{VU}$ is tangent at y, $\overline{WY}$ and $\overline{XY}$ are chords such that m$\overparen{WY}$ = 72 and m$\overparen{XW}$ = 88. Find m∠UYW, m∠UYX, and m∠WYX.

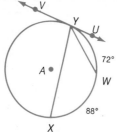
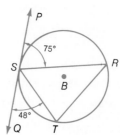

9. In the figure at the right above, $\overleftrightarrow{PQ}$ is tangent at S to circle B, m∠RSP = 75, and m∠TSQ = 48. Find the measure of each angle of △RST.

10. Use the figure and *Given* for Exercise 8 to find m∠ *VYX* and m∠ *VYW*.

In Exercises 11–14, refer to the figure to complete each statement.

11. If m$\widehat{AC}$ = 50 and m$\widehat{DB}$ = 80, m∠ *AEC* = __?__.

12. If m$\widehat{AC}$ = 40 and m$\widehat{DB}$ = 80, m∠ *AEC* = __?__.

13. If m$\widehat{AC}$ = 60 and m$\widehat{DB}$ = 100, m∠ *AED* = __?__.

14. If m$\widehat{AC}$ = 70, m$\widehat{AD}$ = 100, and m$\widehat{DB}$ = 90, m∠ *BEC* = __?__.

In the figure at the right, $\overline{AB}$ and $\overline{CD}$ intersect at *E*.
Find m$\widehat{BD}$ in Exercises 15–17.

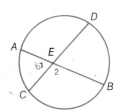

15. m∠ 1 = 80, m$\widehat{AC}$ = 100

16. m∠ 1 = 67, m$\widehat{AC}$ = 98

17. m∠ 1 = $46\frac{1}{2}$, m$\widehat{AC}$ = $62\frac{3}{4}$

Refer to the figure at the right for Exercises 18–21.

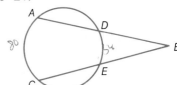

18. m$\widehat{AC}$ = 80, m$\widehat{DE}$ = 50, m∠ *B* = __?__

19. m$\widehat{AC}$ = 94, m$\widehat{DE}$ = 57, m∠ *B* = __?__

20. m∠ *B* = 20, m$\widehat{AC}$ = 100, m$\widehat{DE}$ = __?__

21. m∠ *B* = 31, m$\widehat{DE}$ = 40, m$\widehat{AC}$ = __?__

In the figure at the right, $\overleftrightarrow{MS}$ and $\overleftrightarrow{QS}$ are tangents that intersect at *S*. Use this information in Exercises 22–24.

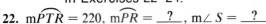

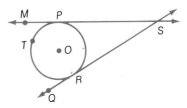

22. m$\widehat{PTR}$ = 220, m$\widehat{PR}$ = __?__, m∠ *S* = __?__

23. m$\widehat{PR}$ = 78, m$\widehat{PTR}$ = __?__, m∠ *S* = __?__

24. m$\widehat{PTR}$ = *b*, m$\widehat{PR}$ = __?__, m∠ *S* = __?__

In Exercises 25–28, find m$\widehat{AC}$.

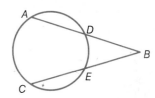

25. m∠ *B* = 30, m$\widehat{DE}$ = 40

26. m∠ *B* = 37, m$\widehat{DE}$ = 64

27. m∠ *B* = $\frac{3a}{4}$, m$\widehat{DE}$ = *a*

28. m∠ *B* = 90 − *a*, m$\widehat{DE}$ = 90 + *a*

B

29. Prove Theorem 8-21.

Given: Chords *AC* and *BD* intersect at *E*.

Prove: m∠ *AEB* = $\frac{1}{2}$(m$\widehat{AB}$ + m$\widehat{CD}$)

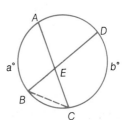

Plan: Let m$\widehat{AB}$ = *a* and m$\widehat{CD}$ = *b*. Draw $\overline{BC}$.
Then m∠ *C* = $\frac{1}{2}a$, m∠ *B* = $\frac{1}{2}b$, and
m∠ *AEB* = m∠ *B* + m∠ *C*. Complete the proof.

30. Prove Theorem 8–20.

Given: $\overleftrightarrow{AB}$ is tangent to the circle at C;
$\overleftrightarrow{CD}$ is a secant.

Prove: $m\angle ACD = \frac{1}{2}m\widehat{CD}$

Plan: Let $m\widehat{CD} = a$. Draw diameter CE.
Then $m\widehat{CD} + m\widehat{DE} = 180$, or $a + m\widehat{DE} = 180$.
Thus, $m\angle 3 = \frac{1}{2}(180 - a)$. Since $\overleftrightarrow{CE} \perp \overleftrightarrow{AB}$,
$m\angle 1 + m\angle 3 = 90$, and $m\angle 1 = 90 - m\angle 3$. Complete the proof.

31. Prove Theorem 8–22.

Given: $\overleftrightarrow{XP}$ and $\overleftrightarrow{XQ}$ secants or tangents to a circle as shown.

Prove: $m\angle X = \frac{1}{2}(a - b)$ (HINT: Draw $\overline{PQ}$. Then $\angle 1$ is an exterior angle of $\triangle PQX$.)

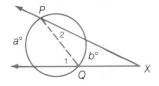
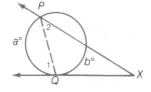
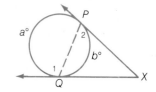

$\overrightarrow{EA}$ is tangent to circle O at A and secant ED intersects the circle at B and D. Diameter AC intersects $\overline{BD}$ at F, $m\angle E = 26$, and $m\widehat{AD} = 108$. Find each of the following.

32. $m\widehat{AB}$ **33.** $m\widehat{BC}$ **34.** $m\angle DFC$

35. $m\angle EAB$ **36.** $m\angle ABE$ **37.** $m\angle DOC$

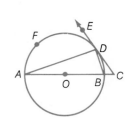

Secant AC passes through the center of circle O and $\overrightarrow{CE}$ is tangent to the circle at D. The ratio of $m\widehat{BD}$ to $m\widehat{AFD}$ is 1:4. $\overline{BD}$ and $\overline{AD}$ are chords. Find each of the following.

38. $m\widehat{BD}$ **39.** $m\angle BAD$ **40.** $m\angle ADE$

41. $m\angle C$ **42.** $m\angle DBC$ **43.** $m\angle ADB$

44. $\overleftrightarrow{AB}$ is tangent to circle Q at B, $\overline{AE} \perp \overline{AD}$, and segment DE contains B. Prove that $\triangle AEB$ is isosceles with base BE.

45. $\overline{BA}$, $\overline{BC}$, $\overline{BE}$, $\overline{CA}$ and $\overline{CE}$ are chords, and $\overline{BE}$ bisects angle ABC. Prove that the angles of $\triangle ABD$ are congruent to the angles of $\triangle EBC$.

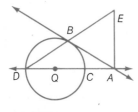

Find the geometric mean between each pair of numbers. *(Pages 265–267)*

1. 3 and 27   **2.** 16 and 4   **3.** 25 and 4   **4.** 3 and 8

5. a and b **6.** $8a$ and $6a$ **7.** $\sqrt{2}$ and $3\sqrt{2}$ **8.** $\sqrt{3}$ and $5\sqrt{3}$

In the figure at the right, $\triangle ABE \sim \triangle DBC$.
Complete the following.
(Pages 280–281)

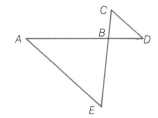

9. $\angle A \cong \angle \underline{\ ?\ }$ **10.** $\angle E \cong \angle \underline{\ ?\ }$

11. $\dfrac{AE}{AB} = \dfrac{?}{DB}$ **12.** $\dfrac{CB}{EB} = \dfrac{CD}{?}$

8-9   Lengths of Segments

When the endpoints of two chords that intersect in the interior of a circle are joined, two similar triangles are formed.

Theorem 8-23

> If two chords intersect in the interior of a circle, the product of the lengths of the segments of the first chord equals the product of the lengths of the segments of the second chord.

EXAMPLE 1   Write the *Given*, the *Prove*, and a *Plan of Proof* for Theorem 8–23.

Solution: **Given:** In circle O, chords AB and CD intersect at E.

Prove: $AE \cdot EB = CE \cdot ED$

Plan: Draw $\overline{AC}$ and $\overline{BD}$. Prove $\triangle AEC$ similar to $\triangle DEB$ by showing that $\text{m}\angle A$ and $\text{m}\angle D = \frac{1}{2}\text{m}\overset{\frown}{BC}$ and that $\text{m}\angle C$ and $\text{m}\angle B = \frac{1}{2}\text{m}\overset{\frown}{AD}$.

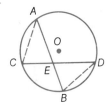

Since corresponding sides of similar triangles are proportional, $\dfrac{AE}{DE} = \dfrac{CE}{BE}$.

Then $AE \cdot EB = CE \cdot ED$ by Theorem 6–1, page 260.

Theorem 8–23 can be used to find the measures of segments.

EXAMPLE 2   In circle A, chords QR and ST intersect at P.
If $SP = 8$, $TP = 3$, and $RP = 6$, find QP.

Solution: $RP \cdot QP = SP \cdot TP$ ←——— **By Theorem 8-23**

$6\,(QP) = 8 \cdot 3$

$QP = \dfrac{24}{6} = 4$

In the figure at the right, $\overleftrightarrow{AC}$ and $\overleftrightarrow{AE}$ are secants, $\overline{AC}$ and $\overline{AE}$ are **secant segments**, and $\overline{AB}$ and $\overline{AD}$ are **external secant segments**.

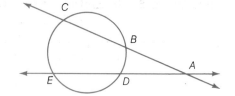

Theorem 8–24	If a tangent and a secant intersect in the exterior of a circle, the square of the tangent segment equals the product of the secant segment and the external secant segment.

EXAMPLE 3   Write the *Given*, the *Prove*, and a *Plan of Proof* for Theorem 8–24.

Solution: **Given:** Tangent line XR and secant line XP as shown.

Prove: $(XR)^2 = XP \cdot XQ$

Plan: Draw $\overline{RP}$ and $\overline{RQ}$. In triangles XRQ and XPR, $\angle X \cong \angle X$ and $\angle P \cong \angle QRX$. Thus, $\triangle XRQ \sim \triangle XPR$ by the AA Similarity Corollary.

Then $\dfrac{XP}{XR} = \dfrac{XR}{XQ}$, and $(XR)^2 = XP \cdot XQ$.

In the figure in Example 3, $\overleftrightarrow{XP}$ is any secant. Thus, $XP \cdot XQ$ is a constant for each given secant length. This length depends only on the locations of the given circle and the given exterior point.

EXAMPLE 4   In the figure, $WZ = 5$ and $WT = 4$. Find TE.

Solution:
$(TE)^2 = TZ \cdot TW$ ◄——— **By Theorem 8–24**
$y^2 = 9 \cdot 4$
$y^2 = 36$
$y = 6$ ◄——— **TE**

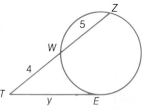

Corollary 8–25 is concerned with two secants that intersect in the exterior of a circle.

Corollary 8–25	If two secants intersect in the exterior of a circle, the product of the lengths of one secant segment and its external segment equals the product of the lengths of the other secant segment and its external segment.

Example 5 shows how to use this corollary to find the lengths of segments.

EXAMPLE 5 In circle O, $AB = 10$, $CB = 6$, and $CF = 8$. Find JF.

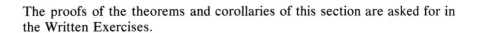

Solution: Let $JF = x$. Then $JC = x + 8$.
By Corollary 8–25, $JC \cdot CF = CA \cdot CB$

$$(x + 8) \cdot 8 = 16 \cdot 6$$
$$8x + 64 = 96 \quad \longleftarrow \quad \text{Solve for } x.$$
$$8x = 32$$
$$x = 4 \quad \longleftarrow \quad FJ = 4$$

The proofs of the theorems and corollaries of this section are asked for in the Written Exercises.

CLASSROOM EXERCISES

Refer to the figure at the right in Exercises 1–3.

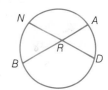

1. $BR = 12$, $RA = 4$, and $NR = 6$. Find RD.
2. $NR = 4$, $RD = 5$, and $BR = 8$. Find RA.
3. $AR = 2$, $RB = 8$, and R is the midpoint of $\overline{ND}$.
   Find NR, RD, and ND.

In Exercises 4–6, refer to this figure.

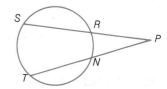

4. $PS = 12$, $PR = 3$, and $PT = 18$. Find PN.
5. $PN = 3$, $NT = 7$, and $PR = 4$. Find RS.
6. $PR = 4$, $RS = 8$, and $PN = 3$. Find NT.

In Exercises 7–9, refer to circle O.

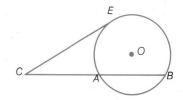

7. $CA = 5$ and $BA = 15$. Find CE.
8. $CA = 4$ and $BA = 12$. Find CE.
9. $CE = 6$ and $CA = 4$. Find AB.

WRITTEN EXERCISES

A   In Exercises 1–4, refer to this circle.

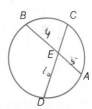

1. $AE = 4$, $EB = 3$, and $CE = 2$. Find ED.
2. $AE = 5$, $EB = 4$, and $ED = 10$. Find CE.
3. $AE = 2\frac{1}{2}$, $EB = 3\frac{1}{3}$, and $ED = 6$. Find CE.
4. $AE = 6.4$, $EB = 5.3$, and $CE = 3.2$. Find ED.

In Exercises 5–9, refer to this figure.

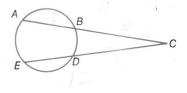

5. $AC = 9$, $BC = 4$, and $DC = 2$. Find EC.

6. $AC = 9$, $BC = 3$, and $EC = 12$. Find DC.

7. $AB = 5$, $BC = 4$, and $DC = 2$. Find EC.
(HINT: $AC = \underline{\ ?\ }$)

8. $AB = 6$, $BC = 3$, and $DC = 2$. Find ED.
(HINT: First find EC.)

9. $AB = 8$, $BC = 6$, and $DC = 4$. Find ED.

In Exercises 10–14, refer to the figure at the right.

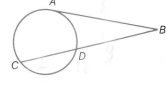

10. $AB = 8$ and $CB = 16$. Find BD.

11. $CB = 9$ and $DB = 4$. Find AB.

12. $CD = 5$ and $DB = 4$. Find AB.

13. $CD = 6$ and $DB = 3$. Find AB. Leave your answer in simplified radical form.

14. $CD = 2$ and $DB = 3$. Find AB to the nearest hundredth.

B

15. Prove Theorem 8–23. Follow the *Plan of Proof* in Example 1.

16. Prove Theorem 8–24. Follow the *Plan of Proof* in Example 3.

Example: In the figure at the right, $AE = 8$, $EB = 3$, and $CD = 10$. Find CE and ED.

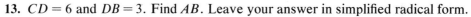

Solution: Let $CE = x$. Then $ED = 10 - x$.

$CE \cdot ED = AE \cdot EB$ ⟵ **By Theorem 8–23**
$x(10 - x) = 8 \cdot 3$
$10x - x^2 = 24$ or $x^2 - 10x + 24 = 0$
$(x - 6)(x - 4) = 0$
$x = \textbf{6 or } x = \textbf{4}$ ⟵ **CE**
$10 - x = \textbf{4 or 6}$ ⟵ **DE**

Refer to the circle in the Example above to find CE and DE for the given values of AE, EB, and CD.

	AE	EB	CD
17.	8	6	16
19.	10	3	11

	AE	EB	CD
18.	9	4	15
20.	12	6	22

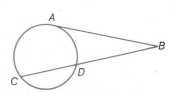

In the figure at the right, $\overline{AB}$ is a tangent segment, and $\overline{BC}$ is a secant segment.

Use this information in Exercises 21–24 to find BD and BC for the given values of AB and CD.

21. $AB = 12$; $CD = 7$
22. $AB = 8$; $CD = 12$
23. $AB = 9$; $CD = 24$
24. $AB = 10$; $CD = 15$

25. Prove Corollary 8–25.

26. When the product of two quantities is a constant, they are said to *vary inversely*. For example, if $xy=k$, where k is a constant, then x varies inversely as y and y varies inversely as x. Write Theorem 8–23 and Corollary 8–25 in terms of inverse variation.

27. Given: Triangle ABC is inscribed in a circle; $\overline{CD}$ is drawn to D, the midpoint of $\overset{\frown}{ADB}$.

Prove: $AC{:}CD=AE{:}BD$.

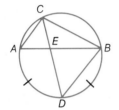

28. Given: X is a point exterior to circle O; secant segment XP with external segment XQ; secant segment XR with external segment XS.

Prove: $XP{:}XR=XS{:}XQ$

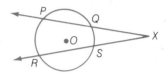

C

29. In the figure at the left below, $\triangle ABC$ is inscribed in a circle, $\overline{BE}$ is a diameter, and $\overline{BD} \perp \overline{AC}$. Prove that $AB \cdot BC = DB \cdot BE$.

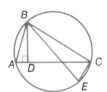
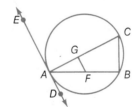

30. In the figure at the right above, $\overleftrightarrow{DE}$ is tangent to the circle at A and $\overline{FG} \parallel \overleftrightarrow{DE}$. Prove that $AF \cdot AB = AG \cdot AC$.

31. In circle A of radius 8, $\overline{XY}$ and $\overline{RS}$ are perpendicular bisectors of each other. Chord BX intersects $\overline{RS}$ in C, and $BX = 12$. Find the lengths of the segments into which $\overline{RS}$ is divided by C.

In Exercises 32–34, prove each statement.

32. In any triangle, the product of the measures of any altitude and the side to which it is drawn is equal to the product of the measures of any other altitude and the side to which it is drawn.

33. In any parallelogram, the product of the measures of any altitude and the side to which it is drawn is equal to the product of the measures of any other altitude and the side to which it is drawn.

34. The product of the measures of the two legs of a right triangle is equal to the product of the measures of the hypotenuse and the altitude to the hypotenuse.

APPLICATIONS

USING CHORDS AND ARCS

These exercises apply geometric concepts studied in Sections 8–4 through 8–9.

A A wheel is broken so that only part of the rim remains. To find the diameter of the wheel, Susan marked three points *F*, *P*, and *R* such that chord *FP* = chord *PR* = 15 inches and chord *RF* = 24 inches. Then she drew a line from *P* through *T*, the midpoint of $\overline{RF}$. Use this information and the given figure to give the reason(s) for each statement in Exercises 1–4.

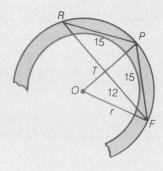

1. $\overleftrightarrow{TP} \perp \overline{RF}$ 2. $\triangle PTF$ is a right triangle.
3. $(PT)^2 + 12^2 = 15^2$
4. $\overleftrightarrow{PT}$ passes through the center of the wheel.
5. Use the equation in Exercise 3 to find *PT*.
6. If *O* is the center of the wheel, why does *OP* = *OF*?
7. Let *OF* = *r*. Represent *OT* in terms of *r* and your answer to Exercise 5.
8. Use your answer to Exercise 7 to write an equation you can use to find *r*. (HINT: Apply Theorem 8–23.)
9. What is the length of a diameter of the wheel?

B

10. A hole 40 inches in diameter is cut in a sheet of plywood. A sphere 50 inches in diameter is set in the hole. How far below the surface of the board will the sphere sink? (HINT: Study the given figure. Find *x*. Then find 25 − *x*.)

11. A pipeline, supported by an arch, crosses a river that is 20 meters wide. Halfway across the river, a cable, 5 meters long, is suspended from the arch to help support the pipe. Find the radius of the arch. (HINT: Extend $\overline{CD}$ through *O*, the center of the circle of which *ACB* is an arc.)

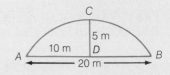

C

12. Assume that the earth is a sphere having a radius of 4000 miles. A straight tunnel $\overline{AB}$ connects two points *A* and *B* on the earth's surface. The tunnel is 200 miles long. A ventilation shaft, $\overline{CD}$, is constructed at the center of the tunnel. What is the height of the shaft to the nearest quarter mile? (HINT: Use a calculator to compute *OD* and *DC*.)

8-10 The Sphere

A **sphere** is the set of all points in space at a given distance from a fixed point in space.

In the figure at the right, $\overline{AO}$ and $\overline{DO}$ are *radii* of the sphere and O, the *center* of the sphere, is the fixed point in space. $\overline{BC}$ is a *diameter* of the sphere. It is a chord of the sphere that also passes through its center. A *chord* is a segment whose endpoints are points of the sphere.

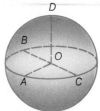

EXAMPLE   A sphere has a radius of 10 centimeters. Describe the intersection of the sphere with a plane for each given distance of the center of the sphere from the plane.

a. 12 cm   **b.** 10 cm   **c.** 6 cm

Solutions:

a.

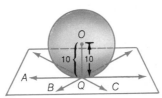

They do not intersect. Thus, the intersection is the empty set.

b.

They intersect in one point. That is, the plane is tangent to the sphere.

c.

They intersect in a circle.

The results of the Example are summarized in Theorem 8–26.

Theorem 8–26   If a plane intersects a sphere, the intersection is either a point or a circle.

Many of the terms connected with circles are also used with spheres. Thus, in the figure at the right, C is the center of the sphere, A and B are points on the sphere, and $\angle ACB$ is a *central angle*. Points A, B, and C determine a plane that intersects the sphere in a *great circle*. $\overset{\frown}{AB}$ of this great circle is a *minor arc*.

Definition | A **great circle** of a sphere is the circle formed by the intersection of the sphere and a plane passing through its center.

Each great circle of a sphere separates it into two *hemispheres* (half-spheres). On the surface of a sphere, the shortest distance from any point A to any other point B is along $\overset{\frown}{AB}$, an arc of a great circle.

CLASSROOM EXERCISES

In Exercises 1–11, refer to this sphere with center Q.

Identify each of the following.

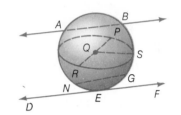

1. Eight points that lie on the sphere
2. Two points that lie in the exterior of the sphere
3. One point that lies in the interior of the sphere
4. Three radii of the sphere
5. A diameter of the sphere
6. Three chords of the sphere
7. A secant of the sphere
8. A line tangent to the sphere
9. A great circle of the sphere
10. Two minor arcs of the sphere
11. Two central angles of the sphere

WRITTEN EXERCISES

A In Exercises 1–9, classify each statement as true, *T*, or false, *F*. Give the reason(s) for each answer.

1. Two spheres are congruent if they have the same center.
2. All great circles of a sphere are congruent.
3. All radii of a sphere are congruent.
4. Every diameter of a sphere is a diameter of a great circle.
5. A secant of a sphere intersects the sphere in exactly one point.
6. Two spheres always intersect in exactly one point.
7. A line tangent to one endpoint of a diameter of a sphere is parallel to a line tangent to the other endpoint of the diameter.
8. If a plane is tangent to a sphere, it is perpendicular to a radius of the sphere drawn to the point of tangency.
9. If two chords of a sphere are congruent, they are equally distant from the center of the sphere.

Two spheres have radii of 4 centimeters and 8 centimeters. Describe their intersection for each distance (given in centimeters) between their centers.

10. 16 **11.** 12 **12.** 10 **13.** 4 **14.** 2 **15.** 0

Two spheres have radii of 3 centimeters and 5 centimeters and their centers are 12 centimeters apart.

16. How many lines can be tangent to both spheres?

17. How many planes can be tangent to both spheres?

18. Chord AB of a sphere is shorter than chord CD of the same sphere. Which chord is closer to the center of the sphere?

19. Two arcs lie on the surface of the sphere. When are the arcs congruent?

20. Two tangent segments are drawn to a sphere from the same point in the exterior of the sphere. Compare the lengths of the tangent segments.

21. A diameter of a sphere is perpendicular to a chord of the sphere. Does the diameter bisect the chord?

22. A diameter of a sphere bisects a chord of the sphere. Is the diameter always perpendicular to the chord?

23. A plane intersects a sphere and a diameter of the sphere is perpendicular to the plane. Does the diameter pass through the center of the circle formed by this intersection?

In the figure at the right, a plane intersects sphere O in circle A. Points B, C, and D are on circle A and $\overline{OA}$ is perpendicular to the plane. (Circle A is a small circle of the sphere.) Tell which statements in Exercises 24–32 are *always* true.

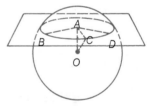

24. $\overline{AB} \cong \overline{AD}$ **25.** $\overline{AB} \cong \overline{AO}$ **26.** $\overline{AB} \cong \overline{OB}$

27. $\overline{AC} \cong \overline{AB}$ **28.** $\overline{OA} \perp \overline{AD}$ **29.** $\overline{AB} \perp \overline{AD}$

30. $\triangle ADO \cong \triangle ABO$ **31.** $\overline{OA} \cong \overline{AC}$ **32.** $\overline{AC} \cong \overline{AD}$

33. If a sphere is inscribed in a cube, how many faces of the cube are tangent to the sphere?

34. If a cube is inscribed in a sphere, how many points do the cube and the sphere have in common?

35. A plane is passed through a sphere 6 centimeters from its center. The radius of the sphere is 10 centimeters. Find the radius of the circle formed by the intersection of the plane and the sphere. (HINT: Use the figure for Exercises 24–32 with $CO = 10$ cm and $AO = 6$ cm. Find AC.)

36. A sphere has a radius of 26 centimeters. How far from the center of the sphere must a plane pass for the circle formed by the intersection to have a radius of 24 centimeters? (Refer to the figure for Exercise 35.)

37. Describe the figure you would get by drawing all possible tangent lines to a sphere from an external point. What figure is determined by all of the points of tangency?

38. In circle O, $\overset{\frown}{ABC}$ is a semicircle, and point D on $\overset{\frown}{ABC}$ is so located that $\overset{\frown}{BD} \cong \overset{\frown}{DC}$. Prove that $\overline{AB} \parallel \overline{OD}$.

39. Prove Theorem 8–26.

   Given: Sphere O and plane I intersect in Section BCD.

   Prove: Section BCD is a circle.

   Plan: If center O is not in plane I, then let C and B be any two distinct points of section BCD. Prove that $\overline{AB} \cong \overline{AC}$ and that all points of section BCD are equidistant from A. If center O is in plane I, $\overline{OB} \cong \overline{OC}$.

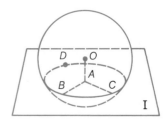

40. Spheres A and B are tangent externally at C. Prove that the lengths of any two tangents to each of the two spheres from a common point in the plane that is the common internal tangent are congruent.

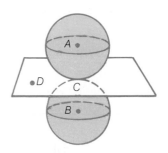

Review

Refer to the figures below for Exercises 1–8. *(Section 8–7)*

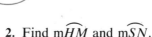

1. If $\overline{SN} \parallel \overline{HM}$, find $m\overset{\frown}{MN}$.
2. Find $m\overset{\frown}{HM}$ and $m\overset{\frown}{SN}$.
3. Find $m\overset{\frown}{RIA}$.
4. Find $m\angle RFA$.
5. Find $m\angle RFI$.
6. Find $m\angle AIR$.
7. If $\overline{BD} \parallel \overline{LG}$, find $m\overset{\frown}{BL}$.
8. Find $m\overset{\frown}{LG}$.

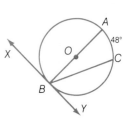

In Exercises 9–10, refer to the circle at the right.
In the circle, $\overline{AB}$ is a diameter. *(Section 8–7)*

9. Find $m\angle CBY$.
10. Find $m\angle CBX$.

Use the figures below in Exercises 11–13. *(Section 8-8)*

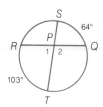
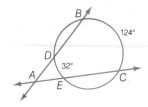
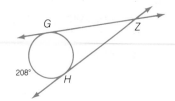

11. $\overline{RQ}$ and $\overline{ST}$ are chords intersecting at P. Find m∠1 and m∠2.

12. $\overleftrightarrow{AB}$ and $\overleftrightarrow{AC}$ are secants intersecting at A. Find m∠A.

13. $\overleftrightarrow{ZG}$ and $\overleftrightarrow{ZH}$ are tangents intersecting at Z. Find m∠Z.

14. In the circle at the left below, $\overline{AB}$ and $\overline{CD}$ are chords intersecting at E. If $AE = 15$, $BE = 4$, and $CE = 5$, find DE. *(Section 8-9)*

15. $\overline{FG}$ is a diameter of circle H at the right above. Chord JK intersects $\overline{FG}$ at M. If $FM = 2$, $JM = 4$, and $MK = 7$, find MG, and the radius of the circle. *(Section 8-9)*

16. In the circle at the right, $\overline{AX}$ and $\overline{AY}$ are secant segments. If $AW = 8$, $AT = 6$, and $TX = 12$, find AY. *(Section 8-9)*

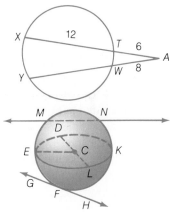

The figure at the right shows a sphere with center C. Identify each of the following. *(Section 8-10)*

17. Five points that lie on the sphere

18. Two minor arcs of the sphere

19. A secant of the sphere

20. A great circle of the sphere

Puzzle

Find the sum of the angle measures at the five points of the star shown at the right.

Career Applications

Other Geometries and Mathematics

Mathematicians often deal with problems that seem unrelated to real-life situations. Later, applications are found in the real world in areas such as science, medicine, space technology, and so on. For example, the study of non-Euclidean geometry is useful in solving certain problems related to space travel.

The geometry you are studying is **Euclidean;** that is, it is based on the postulates of Euclid (about 300 B.C.). In a **non-Euclidean geometry,** Euclid's Parallel Postulate (Postulate 15, page 162) does not hold. The following example of hyperbolic geometry illustrates this.

Model	Description
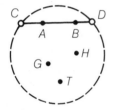	The plane consists of points in the interior of a circle, such as *A* and *B* but not *C* and *D*. Two points in the interior determine a chord, and each chord is thought of as a "line", such as "line" *AB*.

In hyperbolic geometry, lines *TG* and *TH* are parallel to line *AB* because they do not intersect line *AB*. (Recall that points *C* and *D* are not in the interior of the circle.) Further, there are *infinitely many* lines through *T* that are parallel to line *AB*; that is, they do not intersect line *AB*, but they are coplanar with line *AB*. One of these is line *TK*.

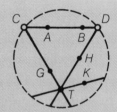

EXERCISES

1. Write a parallel postulate for hyperbolic geometry.
2. The model for **elliptic geometry** is a sphere. In this geometry, a "line" is a great circle of the sphere, such as line *AB*. Can a line be drawn through *G* that will be parallel to line *AB*? Explain.
3. Write a parallel postulate for elliptic geometry.
4. Are Postulates 1, 2, and 4 on page 10 true in hyperbolic geometry?   in elliptic geometry?

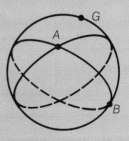

Chapter Summary

IMPORTANT TERMS

Central angle (p. 348)
Chord (p. 344)
Circle (p. 344)
Concentric circles (p. 345)
Congruent arcs (p. 349)
Congruent circles (p. 349)
Diameter (p. 344)
Great circle (p. 390)
Inscribed angle (p. 369)
Inscribed polygon (p. 361)

Intercepted arc (p. 369)
Major arc (p. 348)
Midpoint of an arc (p. 349)
Minor arc (p. 348)
Radius (p. 344)
Secant (p. 344)
Secant segment (p. 384)
Semicircle (p. 348)
Sphere (p. 389)
Tangent (p. 344)
Tangent segment (p. 365)

IMPORTANT IDEAS

1. **Measures of angles in a circle**

   a. The measure of a central angle equals the measure of its intercepted arc.

   b. The measure of an inscribed angle equals one-half the measure of its intercepted arc.

   c. The measure of an angle formed by a tangent and a chord drawn at the point of tangency equals one-half the measure of the intercepted arc.

   d. The measure of an angle formed by two chords intersecting in the interior of a circle equals one-half the sum of the measures of the intercepted arcs.

   e. The measure of an angle formed by two secants, a secant and a tangent, or two tangents drawn to a circle from an outside point equals one-half the difference of the measures of the intercepted arcs.

2. **Congruence of arcs in a circle**

   In a circle or in congruent circles, arcs are congruent if:

   a. they have the same measure.

   b. they have congruent central angles.

   c. they have congruent chords.

   d. they are intercepted between two parallel lines.

   e. they are intercepted by congruent inscribed angles.

3. **Congruence of chords in a circle.**

   In a circle or in congruent circles, chords are congruent if:

   a. they have congruent arcs.

   b. they are equidistant from the center.

4. **Product relationships in a circle**

a. If two chords intersect in the interior of a circle, the product of the lengths of the segments of one chord equals the product of the lengths of the segments of the other chord.

b. If a tangent and a secant intersect in the exterior of a circle, the square of the tangent segment equals the product of the secant segment and the external secant segment.

c. If two secants intersect in the exterior of a circle, the product of the lengths of one secant segment and its external segment equals the product of the lengths of the other secant segment and its external segment.

—— **Chapter Objectives and Review** ——

Objective: *To identify the special points, lines, and line segments associated with a circle (Section 8–1)*

Use the figure at the right to identify each of the following.

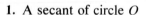

1. A secant of circle O
2. A diameter of circle P
3. A radius of circle O
4. A chord of circle P
5. A common external tangent to circles O and P
6. A common internal tangent to circles O and P

Objective: *To compute the distance from a point P to a circle (Section 8–1)*

Refer to the figure at the right for Exercises 7–9.

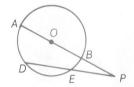

7. If $AB = 10$ and $OP = 8$, find BP.
8. If $DE = 7$ and $DP = 9.8$, find EP.
9. If $AO = 6$ and $OP = 10$, find BP.

Objective: *To find the measures of a central angle and its major and minor arcs (Section 8–2)*

In circle A, $\overline{BD}$ is a diameter and $m\angle DAE = 85$. Find each of the following.

10. $m\widehat{DE}$ 11. $m\widehat{DBE}$ 12. $m\angle BAE$ 13. $m\widehat{EB}$ 14. $m\widehat{DFB}$

Objective: *To identify congruent chords and the relationships between chords and arcs (Section 8-3)*

Classify each statement as true, *T*, or false, *F*.

15. If two arcs of a circle are congruent, the chords of these arcs are congruent.

16. The perpendicular bisector of a chord of a circle never passes through the center of the circle.

17. A line passing through the midpoint of a chord of a circle always passes through the center of the circle.

18. Two chords of the same circle intersect at *M*, and *M* is the midpoint of each chord. Then the chords are perpendicular to each other and one chord is a diameter of the circle.

Objective: *To identify the relationship between the length of a chord and its distance from the center of a circle (Section 8-4)*

19. Chords *AB* and *CD* are in the same circle and *AB* > *CD*. Which chord is closer to the center of the circle?

20. An equilateral triangle is inscribed in a circle of radius 10.

    a. Find *x*, the distance of a side of the triangle from the center of the circle.

    b. Find the perimeter of the triangle.

Objective: *To identify and apply tangent relationships (Section 8-5)*

21. In the figure at the right, $\overline{PX}$ and $\overline{PY}$ are tangent segments to circle *O* and m∠ *XYO* = 20. Find m∠ *P*.

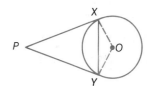

Objective: *To identify and apply relationships between inscribed angles and their intercepted arcs (Sections 8-6, 8-7)*

Refer to the figure at the right for Exercises 22-24.

22. m∠ *M* = 30; m$\overarc{OP}$ = __?__ ; m∠ *N* = __?__

23. m∠ *MOQ* = 40; m$\overarc{QM}$ = __?__ ; m∠ *MPQ* = __?__

24. m$\overarc{QMN}$ = 120; m∠ *QPN* = __?__ ; m∠ *NOQ* = __?__

Refer to the figure at the right.

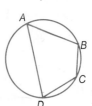

25. If m$\overarc{BAD}$ = 260, find m∠ *BAD*.

26. *ABCD* is an inscribed quadrilateral. If m∠ *A* = 45, find m∠ *C*.

Objective: *To find the measures of angles formed by a tangent and a secant or by two secants (or chords) intersecting in the interior of a circle (Section 8–8)*

27. In the circle at the left below, $\overleftrightarrow{AY}$ is a tangent at A and $\overleftrightarrow{XA}$ is a secant. If $m\angle XAY = 50$, find $m\widehat{AX}$.

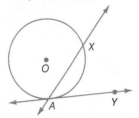
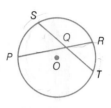

28. In circle O at the right above, $m\widehat{PS} = 60$ and $m\widehat{RT} = 40$. Find $m\angle SQR$.

Objective: *To find the measures of angles formed by two secants or a·tangent and a secant (Section 8–8)*

29. In Figure 1 below, $\overleftrightarrow{PQ}$ is a tangent, $\overleftrightarrow{PS}$ is a secant, R is the midpoint of $\widehat{QRS}$, and $m\widehat{QS} = 160$. Find $m\angle P$.

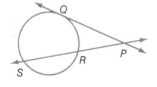
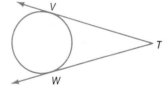
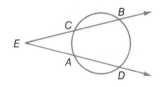

Figure 1   **Figure 2**   **Figure 3**

30. In Figure 2 above, $\overrightarrow{TV}$ and $\overrightarrow{TW}$ are tangents, and $m\widehat{VW} = 95$. Find $m\angle T$.
31. In Figure 3 above, $m\widehat{DB} = 110$ and $m\widehat{AC} = 44$. Find $m\angle E$.

Objective: *To find the lengths of segments formed by intersecting chords, secant segments, and tangent segments (Section 8–9)*

32. $AE = 5$, $EB = 4$, $CE = 2$, $x = \underline{\ ?\ }$

33. $ST = 6$, $TV = 4$, $SQ = 5$, $x = \underline{\ ?\ }$

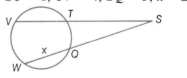

Objective: *To identify the special points, lines, and line segments associated with a sphere (Section 8–10)*

Identify each of the following.

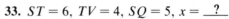
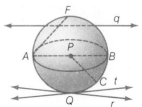

34. A diameter of the sphere
35. A radius of the sphere
36. A secant to the sphere
37. A chord of the sphere

38. A great circle of the sphere

39. A minor arc of the sphere

40. A central angle of the sphere

41. Two intersecting lines tangent to the sphere

Objective: *To solve word problems that involve central angles and arcs (Page 353)*

42. The spokes on the wheels of Pierre Lallement's pedal-powered bicycle, patented in 1866, form eight congruent central angles. What is the measure of each central angle in circle *O*? In circle *P*?

Objective: *To solve word problems that involve chords and arcs of circles (Page 388)*

43. Maria Toms, an archaeologist, discovers a broken plate similar to the one shown at the right. She wishes to find the diameter of the plate so she marks off three equally-spaced points *A*, *B*, *C* and draws the given segments. Find the length of a diameter of the plate.

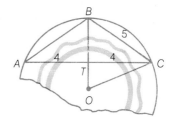

—— Chapter Test ——

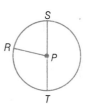

1. In the figure at the right, $\overline{ST}$ is a diameter of the circle and m$\widehat{TR}$ = 105. Find m∠ *RPS*.

2. An equilateral triangle is inscribed in a circle whose radius is 8 centimeters. Find the length of a side of the triangle.

3. In circle *O*, chord *ST* measures 7 and chord *QR* measures 5. Which chord is closer to the center of the circle?

4. In circle *O* at the left below, $\overline{PX}$ and $\overline{PY}$ are tangent segments, *OX* = 5 and *OP* = 13. Find *PX*.

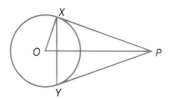

5. Use the figure at the right above to name two inscribed angles that intercept $\widehat{ZX}$.

6. In the figure for Exercise 5, m$\widehat{WY}$ = 190. Find m∠ *X*.

7. In the figure at the left below, circles S and T are tangent at A, and $\overline{AT}$ is a diameter of circle S. If $ST = 2.4$ cm and $MT = 3$ cm, find AB.

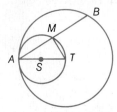
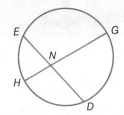

8. In the figure at the right above, chords ED and HG intersect at N, $m\widehat{EG} = 126$, and $m\widehat{HD} = 86$. Find $m\angle ENG$.

9. In the figure for Exercise 8, $ED = 13$, $HN = 12$, and $NG = 3$. Find DN and NE.

10. In the figure at the left below, $\overleftrightarrow{TN}$ is tangent to circle O at A, and $m\angle BAN = 50$. Find $m\widehat{BA}$.

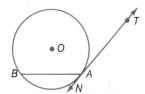
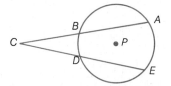

11. In the figure at the right above, $CB = 4$, $CD = 6$, and $DE = 7$. Find BA.

12. In the circle at the left below, PT is a tangent segment, $PR = 4$, and $RS = 12$. Find PT.

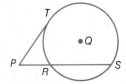

13. In the figure at the right above, quadrilateral $PQRS$ is inscribed in a circle, $m\angle P = 85$, and $m\angle Q = 100$. Find $m\angle S$ and $m\angle R$.

14. Two spheres have radii of 5 centimeters and 9 centimeters and the distance between their centers is 11 centimeters. Describe the figure determined by their intersection.

15. How many lines can be tangent to both spheres in Exercise 14?

CHAPTER **9**

Constructions and Loci

Sections

9-1 **Congruent Segments, Angles, and Triangles**

9-2 **Perpendicular and Parallel Lines**

9-3 **Circles**

9-4 **Special Segments**

9-5 **Meaning of Locus**

9-6 **Intersection of Loci**

9-7 **Constructions and Loci**

Applications: Constructions and Loci

Features

Career Application: Geometry and Geology

Puzzles

Review and Testing

Geometry Review Capsules

Review: Sections 9–1 through 9–4

Review: Sections 9–5 through 9–7

Chapter Summary

Chapter Objectives and Review

Chapter Test

Cumulative Review: Chapters 1–9

Preparing for College Entrance Tests

Construction Applications

9–1 Congruent Segments, Angles, Triangles

In geometry, only two tools may be used to construct a geometric figure, a *straightedge* (unmarked ruler) and a *compass*.

Construction 1 applies the definition of congruent segments.

CONSTRUCTION 1   **Constructing a Segment Congruent to a Given Segment**

Given: Segment XY

Construct: A segment congruent to $\overline{XY}$

Procedure: ① Draw any ray AB.

② Adjust the compass to correspond to the length of $\overline{XY}$. Place the tip of the compass at A. Mark off $AC = XY$.

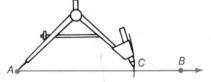

Analysis: The radius of a circle with center X and length XY has the same measure as the radius of a circle with center A and length XY. Thus, $\overline{AC} \cong \overline{XY}$.

Construction 2 applies the definition of congruent angles.

CONSTRUCTION 2   **Constructing an Angle Congruent to a Given Angle**

Given: $\angle F$

Construct: An angle congruent to $\angle F$

Procedure: ① With center F and with any compass opening, draw an arc intersecting $\overrightarrow{FE}$ at H and $\overrightarrow{FG}$ at K.

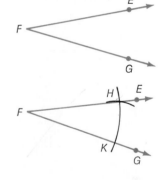

② On any ray XY with center X and radius FK, draw an arc.

Open the compass to length KH. With center J, draw an arc. Draw $\overrightarrow{XM}$. Then $\angle JXM \cong \angle EFG$.

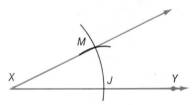

Analysis: Draw $\overline{HK}$ and $\overline{MJ}$. By construction, $\overline{HK} \cong \overline{MJ}$, $\overline{FH} \cong \overline{XM}$, and $\overline{FK} \cong \overline{XJ}$. Then $\triangle FHK \cong \triangle XMJ$ by the SSS Postulate and $\angle X \cong \angle F$ by CPCTC.

Construction 3 applies the definition of angle bisector.

CONSTRUCTION 3 **Bisecting an Angle**

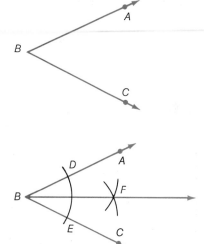

Given: ∠ABC

Construct: A ray bisecting ∠ABC

Procedure: **1** With center B, construct an arc that intersects $\overrightarrow{BA}$ and $\overrightarrow{BC}$.

2 With center E and with the compass open more than $\frac{1}{2}DE$, construct an arc in the interior of the angle. With center D and the same compass opening, repeat this procedure. Draw $\overrightarrow{BF}$.

Analysis: Draw $\overline{DF}$ and $\overline{EF}$. By construction, $\overline{DF} \cong \overline{EF}$ and $\overline{BD} \cong \overline{BE}$. Also, $\overline{BF} \cong \overline{BF}$. Then, $\triangle DBF \cong \triangle EBF$ by the SSS Postulate, and $\angle DBF \cong \angle EBF$ by CPCTC. Thus, m$\angle DBF =$ m$\angle EBF$ and $\overrightarrow{BF}$ bisects ∠ABC.

CLASSROOM EXERCISES

1. Use a ruler to draw segment PQ having a length of 4 centimeters. On $\overrightarrow{AK}$, construct $\overline{AB}$ such that $\overline{AB} \cong \overline{PQ}$.

2. Use a protractor to draw an angle of 65°. Construct ∠MOQ congruent to this angle.

3. Construct $\overrightarrow{OT}$, the bisector of ∠MOQ in Exercise 2.

CONSTRUCTION EXERCISES

A

1. Use a ruler to draw $\overline{XY}$ such that $XY = 7$ centimeters. On ray WK, construct $\overline{WR}$ such that $\overline{WR} \cong \overline{XY}$.

2. Use a protractor to draw an angle of 50°. Construct ∠ABC congruent to this angle.

3. Use a protractor to draw an angle of 90°. Construct ∠QPR congruent to this angle.

4. Use a protractor to draw an angle of 165°. Construct ∠DEF congruent to this angle.

Use a protractor to draw $\angle ACE$ such that $m\angle ACE = 140$.

5. Construct $\overrightarrow{CB}$ bisecting $\angle ACE$.　　**6.** Construct $\overrightarrow{CD}$ bisecting $\angle BCE$.

B　　In Exercises 7–14, draw $\overline{AB}$ such that $AB = 2$ centimeters and $\overline{CD}$ such that $CD = 3$ centimeters. Then construct each of the following.

7. $AB + CD$　　　　**8.** $3AB$　　　　　**9.** $AB + 2CD$　　　**10.** $3CD$

11. $2(AB + CD)$　　**12.** $2AB - CD$　　**13.** $3CD - AB$　　**14.** $4AB - 2CD$

In Exercises 15–20, use a protractor to draw angle K such that $m\angle K = 35$ and $\angle S$ such that $m\angle S = 70$. Then construct each of the following.

15. $m\angle S + m\angle K$　　　　　　**16.** $3m\angle K$　　　　　　**17.** $m\angle S + 2\,m\angle K$

18. $\frac{1}{2}(m\angle S + m\angle K)$　　　　**19.** $\frac{1}{4}m\angle S$　　　　　**20.** $2(m\angle S - \frac{1}{2}m\angle K)$

21. Draw an obtuse scalene triangle XYZ. Construct a triangle congruent to $\triangle XYZ$. Use the SSS Postulate to do this construction.

22. Draw an acute scalene triangle NPR. Construct a triangle congruent to $\triangle NPR$. Use the SAS Postulate to do this construction.

23. Draw an acute scalene triangle MVS. Construct a triangle congruent to $\triangle MVS$. Use the ASA Postulate to do this construction.

24. Draw an isosceles triangle DPR having $\overline{DP}$ as its base. Construct $\triangle GEF$ congruent to $\triangle DPR$. Use the SSS Postulate to do the construction.

25. Draw an acute scalene triangle. Bisect each angle of the triangle.

C　　Construct angles having the given measures.

26. 60　　　　**27.** 30　　　　**28.** 120　　　**29.** 15　　　**30.** 150　　　**31.** 165

32. Draw any triangle EFG. Construct $\triangle XYZ$ such that $\triangle EFG \sim \triangle XYZ$ and $EF = 2XY$.

33. Construct a triangle given two angles and the side opposite one of these angles.

GEOMETRY REVIEW CAPSULE FOR SECTION 9–2 ———

In Exercises 1–5, tell whether each statement is true, *T,* or false, *F.* When a statement is false, tell why it is false. *(Pages 29–32, 100–102, 173–175)*

1. Two congruent angles that form a linear pair are right angles.

2. If three angles of one triangle are congruent to three angles of another triangle, the triangles are congruent.

3. If three sides of one triangle are congruent to the three corresponding sides of another triangle, the triangles are congruent.

4. If two lines meet to form right angles, the lines are perpendicular.

5. If two lines are cut by a transversal such that corresponding angles are complementary, the lines are parallel.

Construction Applications

9-2 Perpendicular and Parallel Lines

Constructions 4 and 5 apply the definition of perpendicular lines.

CONSTRUCTION 4 **Constructing a Line Perpendicular to a Given Line at a Point on the Line**

Given: Line q and point C on line q.

Construct: $\overleftrightarrow{FC} \perp q$

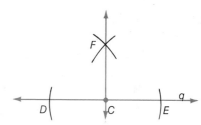

Procedure:

1. With C as center and keeping the same radius, construct arcs that intersect q at D and E.

2. With D as center and radius greater than DC, construct an arc on one side of q. Repeat the procedure, using E as center and the same radius. Label the point of intersection F. Draw line CF.

Analysis: Draw $\overline{DF}$ and $\overline{EF}$. By construction, $\overline{DF} \cong \overline{EF}$ and $\overline{CD} \cong \overline{CE}$. Also, $\overline{CF} \cong \overline{CF}$. Then $\triangle FCD \cong \triangle FCE$ by the SSS Postulate and $\angle FCD \cong \angle FCE$ by CPCTC. Since angles FCD and FCE are adjacent and congruent, $\overleftrightarrow{FC} \perp q$.

CONSTRUCTION 5 **Constructing a Line Perpendicular to a Given Line from a Given Point not on the Line**

Given: Line k and point C not on line k.

Construct: $\overleftrightarrow{CF} \perp k$

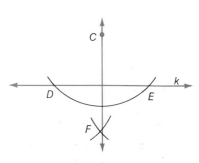

Procedure:

1. With C as center and radius greater than the distance from C to line k, construct an arc intersecting k at D and E.

2. With D as center and radius greater than $\frac{1}{2}(DE)$, construct an arc below k. With E as center and with the same radius, repeat the procedure. Draw $\overleftrightarrow{CF}$.

Analysis: You are asked to state the reasons for key steps of this construction in the Classroom Exercises.

Construction 6 applies the definition of segment bisector together with the definition of perpendicular lines.

CONSTRUCTION 6 Constructing the Perpendicular Bisector of a Segment

Given: Segment AB

Construct: Line CD such that $\overleftrightarrow{CD} \perp \overline{AB}$ at Q, the midpoint of $\overline{AB}$

Procedure:
1. Adjust the compass so that the opening is greater than $\frac{1}{2}(AB)$.
2. With the tip of the compass at A, make arcs above and below $\overline{AB}$. With the tip of the compass at B and with the same radius, make arcs above and below $\overline{AB}$. Label the points of intersection C and D.

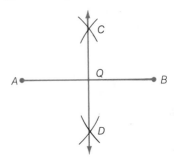

Analysis: You are asked to state the reasons for the key steps of this construction in the Classroom Exercises.

Construction 7 is an application of Theorem 4–8.

CONSTRUCTION 7 Constructing a Line Parallel to a Given Line

Given: Line q and a point P not on q

Construct: A line through P parallel to q

Procedure:
1. Draw line r through P and intersecting line q. Label $\angle 1$ as shown.
2. At P, construct $\angle 2$ such that $\angle 2 \cong \angle 1$. Draw $\overleftrightarrow{PT}$.

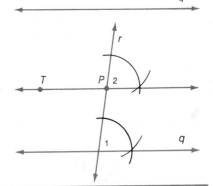

Analysis: Since $\angle 1$ and $\angle 2$ are corresponding angles and $\angle 1 \cong \angle 2$, $\overleftrightarrow{PT} \parallel q$ by Theorem 4–8.

CLASSROOM EXERCISES

Give the reason(s) for each key statement in the analysis of Construction 5.

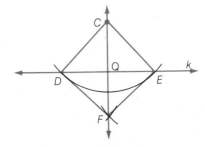

1. Draw $\overline{CD}, \overline{CE}, \overline{DF}, \overline{EF}$.
2. $\triangle CDF \cong \triangle CEF$
3. $\angle DCQ \cong \angle ECQ$
4. $\triangle CQD \cong \triangle CQE$
5. $\angle CQD \cong \angle CQE$
6. $\overleftrightarrow{CF} \perp k$

In Exercises 7–15, give the reason(s) for each key statement in the analysis of Construction 6.

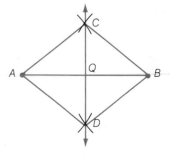

7. Draw $\overline{CA}$, $\overline{CB}$, $\overline{DA}$, and $\overline{DB}$.   8. $\triangle CAD \cong \triangle CBD$

9. $\angle ACQ \cong \angle BCQ$ 10. $\triangle ACQ \cong \triangle BCQ$

11. $\overline{AQ} \cong \overline{BQ}$ 12. Point Q bisects $\overline{AB}$.

13. $\angle CQA \cong \angle CQB$ 14. $\overleftrightarrow{CD} \perp \overline{AB}$

15. $\overleftrightarrow{CD}$ is the perpendicular bisector of $\overline{AB}$.

CONSTRUCTION EXERCISES

A

1. Use a ruler to draw a segment AB that is 6 centimeters long. At A and B, construct lines perpendicular to $\overline{AB}$.

2. Draw an acute scalene triangle ABC. Construct a segment from C perpendicular to $\overline{AB}$.

3. Draw an acute scalene triangle ABC. Construct the perpendicular bisectors of $\overline{AB}$, $\overline{BC}$, and $\overline{CA}$.

4. Draw an obtuse scalene triangle ABC with the obtuse angle at B. Construct a segment from B perpendicular to $\overline{AC}$.

5. Draw right triangle CAB with the right angle at A. From A, construct a segment perpendicular to $\overline{BC}$.

6. Use a ruler to draw a segment AE that is 7.5 centimeters long. Construct C, the midpoint of AE. Then construct D, the midpoint of AC. (HINT: Use Construction 6.)

7. Draw two acute adjacent angles, $\angle CBD$ and $\angle DBA$. Choose any point E on $\overrightarrow{BD}$. From E, construct a segment perpendicular to $\overrightarrow{BA}$ and a segment perpendicular to $\overrightarrow{BC}$.

8. Through a point A not on line r, construct line XA parallel to line r.

9. Draw an acute scalene triangle and label it ABC. Through C, construct a line parallel to $\overline{AB}$.

10. Use a protractor to draw angle XYZ with a measure of 120. Through point Z, construct line ZQ parallel to $\overrightarrow{YX}$, and through point X construct line XT parallel to $\overrightarrow{YZ}$.

11. At point T on a line TR construct right angle RTN. At point R on line TR, construct line RV parallel to $\overleftrightarrow{TN}$.

12. Draw an acute triangle. Construct the three altitudes.

13. Draw an acute triangle. Construct the three medians.

Construct angles having the following measures.

14. 90   15. 45   16. 135   17. $22\frac{1}{2}$ 18. $112\frac{1}{2}$ 19. $67\frac{1}{2}$

20. Given $\overleftrightarrow{AB}$, construct $\overleftrightarrow{EF} \parallel \overleftrightarrow{AB}$ at a distance of 2 centimeters from $\overleftrightarrow{AB}$. (HINT: Begin with $\overleftrightarrow{AB}$ and a segment of length 2 centimeters.)

21. Construct a polygon of four sides having its opposite sides parallel.

22. Draw an acute scalene triangle ABC and construct altitude BD. Then construct a line that intersects $\overline{AB}$, is parallel to $\overline{AC}$, and whose distance from $\overline{AC}$ is $\frac{1}{2} BD$.

23. Construct a parallelogram given two sides and an included angle of 60°.

24. Construct a quadrilateral, given the sides and one diagonal.

25. Construct $\triangle ABC$ so that m$\angle A = 60$, $AB = 4$ cm, and $AC = 3$ cm. Use a marked straightedge, but do not use a protractor.

26. Construct $\triangle ABC$ so that m$\angle A = 30$, m$\angle B = 45$, and $AB = 3.5$ cm.

27. Construct $\triangle ABC$ so that m$\angle A = 60$, m$\angle C = 45$, and $AB = 2.7$ cm.

28. Construct $\square ABCD$ so that $AB = 3$ cm, m$\angle A = 60$, and $AD = 2$ cm.

29. Construct a quadrilateral, given four sides and one angle.

30. Construct a rhombus, given its perimeter and one angle.

31. Construct a trapezoid, given the lengths of the two bases and the lengths of the nonparallel sides. When will this construction be impossible?

32. Construct a rhombus with one angle having a measure of 30.

33. Given that the lengths of the diagonals of a rhombus are 4 centimeters and 3 centimeters, construct the rhombus.

34. Given the positions of the midpoints of the three sides of a triangle, construct the triangle.

35. Construct a parallelogram, given its diagonals.

36. Construct a rectangle, given the perimeter and one diagonal.

37. Construct an isosceles triangle, given the measure of the vertex angle and the length of the side opposite the vertex angle.

─────── **GEOMETRY REVIEW CAPSULE FOR SECTION 9–3** ───────

In Exercises 1–4, choose from the box at the right the word that best completes each statement. *(Pages 344, 355, 365, 375)*

1. A line that intersects a circle in only one point is a __?__.

2. The perpendicular bisector of a chord of a circle passes through the __?__ of the circle.

3. If an angle is inscribed in a __?__, its measure is 90.

4. A tangent to a circle is __?__ to a radius of the circle at its point of contact.

| parallel |
| center |
| perpendicular |
| tangent |
| semicircle |

Construction Applications

9-3 Circles

Construction 8 is an application of Theorem 8–12.

CONSTRUCTION 8 **Constructing a Tangent to a Circle at a Given Point on the Circle**

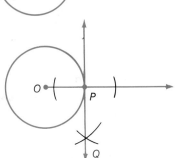

Given: Circle O and point P on circle O

Construct: Line QP tangent to circle O at P

Procedure: Draw $\overrightarrow{OP}$.
At P, construct $\overleftrightarrow{PQ} \perp \overrightarrow{OP}$ (see Construction 4, page 405).

Analysis: If a line in the plane of a circle is perpendicular to a radius at its outer endpoint, the line is tangent to the circle.
$\therefore \overleftrightarrow{PQ}$ is tangent to circle O at P.

Construction 9 is an application of Theorem 8–12 and Corollary 8–17.

CONSTRUCTION 9 **Constructing a Tangent to a Circle from a Point Outside the Circle**

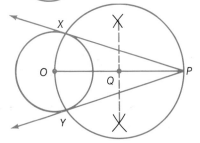

Given: Circle O and point P outside circle O

Construct: A tangent to circle O from P

Procedure: ⬚1 Draw $\overline{OP}$. Construct the perpendicular bisector of $\overline{OP}$.

⬚2 With Q as center and radius OQ construct a circle intersecting circle O at X and Y. Draw $\overrightarrow{PX}$ and $\overrightarrow{PY}$.

Analysis: Draw $\overline{OX}$. Since $\angle OXP$ is inscribed in a semicircle, $\angle OXP$ is a right angle by Corollary 8–17. Thus, $\overrightarrow{PX}$ is perpendicular to radius OX at X, and $\overrightarrow{PX}$ is tangent to circle O by Theorem 8–12. Similarly, it can be shown that $\overrightarrow{PY}$ is tangent to circle O.

Construction 10 applies the fact that a perpendicular bisector of a chord of a circle passes through the center of the circle. (See Cases I and II on page 355.)

CONSTRUCTION 10 Locating the Center of a Given Circle

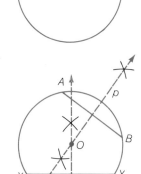

Given: Circle O

Construct: The center of circle O

Procedure: [1] Draw two chords. Call them $\overline{AB}$ and $\overline{XY}$.

[2] Construct the perpendicular bisector of each chord. Label these lines p and q.

Analysis: Since the perpendicular bisector of a chord passes through the center of a circle, lines p and q each contain O, the center of the circle. Since O is the only point which is on both lines p and q, O is the center of the circle.

Construction 11 applies the definition of perpendicular bisector.

CONSTRUCTION 11 Circumscribing a Circle About a Triangle

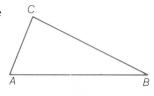

Given: Triangle ABC

Construct: Circle P passing through A, B, and C

Procedure: [1] Construct the perpendicular bisectors of any two sides of the triangle.

[2] With the point of intersection, P, as center and radius PA, construct a circle.

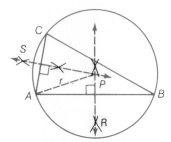

Analysis: Draw $\overline{PC}$, $\overline{PB}$, and $\overline{PA}$. Since $\overleftrightarrow{PR}$ is the perpendicular bisector of $\overline{AB}$, $PA = PB$. Similarly, since $\overleftrightarrow{PS}$ is the perpendicular bisector of $\overline{AC}$, $PA = PC$. Then $PA = PB = PC$. Thus, a circle with P as center and radius of length PA passes through A, B, and C. That is, circle P **circumscribes** $\triangle ABC$.

Construction 12 applies the definition of angle bisector and of the distance from a point to a line.

CONSTRUCTION 12 Inscribing a Circle in a Triangle

Given: $\triangle ABC$

Construct: Circle T tangent to $\overline{AB}$, $\overline{BC}$, and $\overline{AC}$

Procedure:
1. Construct the bisectors of any two angles. Name the point of intersection T. From T, construct a ray perpendicular to $\overline{AB}$. Name the point of intersection Y.

2. With T as center and TY as radius, construct a circle.

Analysis: Since $\overrightarrow{AT}$ is the bisector of $\angle CAB$, T is equidistant from $\overline{AB}$ and $\overline{AC}$. Similarly, T is equidistant from $\overline{AB}$ and $\overline{BC}$. Since $\overrightarrow{TY} \perp \overline{AB}$, TY is the measure of the distance from T to $\overline{AB}$. Thus, a circle with center T and radius of length TY will be tangent to $\overline{AC}$. $\overline{AB}$, and $\overline{BC}$. $\therefore$ Circle T is inscribed in $\triangle ABC$.

CLASSROOM EXERCISES

1. Draw a circle with radius 20 millimeters. At any point Q on the circle, construct a tangent to the circle.

2. Choose a point R outside the circle in Exercise 1. From R, construct two tangents to the circle.

In Exercises 3–4, complete each statement.

3. The perpendicular bisectors of the sides of a triangle meet at a point equidistant from the __?__ of the triangle.

4. The bisectors of the angles of a triangle meet at a point equidistant from the __?__ of the triangle.

5. Construct an equilateral triangle having a side of 4 centimeters. Construct the circumscribed and inscribed circles.

6. Construct the circumscribed circle of a right triangle with legs of 3 centimeters and 4 centimeters.

CONSTRUCTION EXERCISES

A

1. A circle of radius 2 centimeters has a point *R* located on its circumference. Construct a tangent to the circle at *R*.

2. A circle of radius 2 centimeters has point *R* located 5 centimeters from its center. From *R*, construct two tangents to the circle.

3. Draw a circle and place a point *A* outside the circle. Construct an isosceles triangle with vertex angle at *A* so that all three sides of the triangle will be tangent to the circle.

4. Given any circle, locate its center by construction.

5. Draw a large obtuse triangle. Construct the circumscribed circle.

6. Draw a large right triangle. Construct the inscribed circle.

7. Draw a large acute triangle. Inscribe a circle in the triangle.

8. Draw a large obtuse triangle. Circumscribe a circle about the triangle.

9. Draw a circle. Using the radius of the circle, mark off six equals arcs on the circle. Join the points in order. Explain why polygon *ABCDEF* is a regular hexagon.

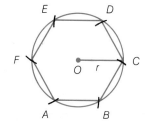

10. Given a circle, how could you use the method of Exercise 9 to inscribe an equilateral triangle in the circle?

11. Construct a square inscribed in a circle. (HINT: First draw a diameter through *C*, the center of the circle. Then construct the perpendicular bisector of the diameter.)

12. Given an arc of a circle, find the midpoint of the arc by construction.

B

13. Given two points that are 4 centimeters apart, construct a circle having a radius of 3 centimeters and passing through the given points.

14. Draw a rectangle with dimensions 3 centimeters by 4 centimeters. Then construct a circle such that the rectangle is inscribed in it.

15. Given a circle and line *q* outside the circle, construct a line *p* parallel to line *q* and tangent to the circle.

16. Given a circle and line *r* outside the circle, construct a line *t* perpendicular to *r* and tangent to the circle.

C

17. Is the construction in Exercise 13 always possible? Let the given points be *d* centimeters apart and let the radius of the circle be *r* centimeters. What must be the relationship between *d* and *r* for the construction to be possible?

18. Is the construction in Exercise 14 possible for a rectangle of any dimensions whatsoever?

19. Circumscribe a circle about a given square.

Construction Applications

9–4 Special Segments

Construction 13 is an application of Theorem 5–15.

CONSTRUCTION 13 **Dividing a Given Line Segment into Congruent Parts**

Given: Segment AB

Construct: Points H and J such that $\overline{AH} \cong \overline{HJ} \cong \overline{JB}$.

Procedure: ☐1 Draw $\overrightarrow{AK}$. Using any convenient radius, mark off three equal segments on $\overrightarrow{AK}$.

           ☐2 Draw $\overline{BE}$. At D and C, construct lines parallel to $\overline{BE}$.

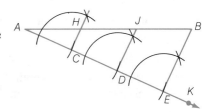

Analysis: Since the parallel lines HC, JD, and BE cut off equal segments on $\overrightarrow{AK}$, they cut off equal segments on $\overline{AB}$ by Theorem 5–15.

Construction 14 is an application of Corollary 6–4.

CONSTRUCTION 14 **Constructing Proportional Segments**

Given: Segments of lengths a, b, and c

Construct: A segment of length x such that $\dfrac{a}{b} = \dfrac{c}{x}$

Procedure: ☐1 Draw an angle ABC. On $\overline{BC}$, mark off $BD = a$ and $DE = b$. On $\overrightarrow{BA}$, mark off $BF = c$. Draw $\overline{DF}$.

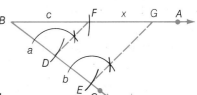

           ☐2 At E, construct a line parallel to $\overline{DF}$, intersecting $\overrightarrow{BA}$ at G. Then $FG = x$ such that $\dfrac{a}{b} = \dfrac{c}{x}$.

Analysis: In $\triangle BEG$, $\overline{DF} \parallel \overline{EG}$. By Corollary 6–4, $\dfrac{a}{b} = \dfrac{c}{x}$.

Construction 15 is an application of Corollary 7–2.

CONSTRUCTION 15 Constructing the Geometric Mean

Given: Segments of lengths r and s

Construct: A segment of length x such that
$$\frac{r}{x} = \frac{x}{s}$$

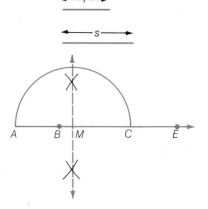

Procedure: **1** On $\overrightarrow{AE}$, mark off $AB = r$ and $BC = s$. Construct the perpendicular bisector of $\overline{AC}$. With M, the midpoint of $\overline{AC}$, as center and AM as radius, construct a semicircle.

2 At B, construct $\overline{BD} \perp \overrightarrow{AC}$ so that D is a point on the semicircle. Draw $\overline{AD}$ and $\overline{CD}$.

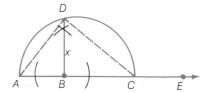

Analysis: $\triangle ADC$ is a right triangle and DB is the altitude to the hypotenuse. Thus, $\frac{r}{x} = \frac{x}{s}$ by Corollary 7–2.

CLASSROOM EXERCISES

1. Draw a segment 9 centimeters long. By construction, divide it into four congruent segments.

2. Draw three segments x, y, and z with lengths 1, 2, and 4 centimeters respectively. Construct a segment of length y such that $\frac{1}{2} = \frac{4}{y}$.

3. Given line segments of lengths 1.5 and 3 centimeters respectively. Construct a segment of length x such that $\frac{1.5}{x} = \frac{x}{3}$.

CONSTRUCTION EXERCISES

A In Exercises 1–6, divide a given segment 15 centimeters long into the given number of equal parts.

1. 3   **2.** 5   **3.** 4   **4.** 8   **5.** 7   **6.** 10

7. Draw three segments with lengths 1, 2, and 3 centimeters respectively. Construct a segment with length y, such that $\frac{1}{2} = \frac{3}{y}$.

8. Draw three segments with lengths 3, 4, and 5 centimeters, respectively. Construct a segment with length x such that $\frac{3}{4} = \frac{5}{x}$.

9. Draw three segments with lengths 5, 6, and 7 centimeters respectively. Construct a segment with length y such that $\frac{5}{6} = \frac{10}{y}$.

10. Draw three segments with lengths 4, 5, and 7 centimeters, respectively. Construct a segment with length x such that $\frac{5}{4} = \frac{7}{x}$.

11. Given segments of length 3 centimeters and 5 centimeters. Construct the geometric mean between the two segments.

12. Draw segments with length 2.5 centimeters and 3 centimeters. Construct the geometric mean between the two segments.

13. Construct a segment whose length is the fourth proportional to segments with lengths of 4.5, 3.5, and 5 centimeters, respectively.

B

14. Draw three segments whose lengths are 3, 5, and 6 centimeters, respectively. By construction, find a point on the longest segment so that it is divided in the ratio of 3 to 5. See the figure at the right. Use Corollary 6–4.

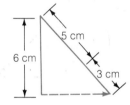

15. Draw 3 segments of lengths 3, 5, and 7 centimeters. Find a point on the longest segment so that it is divided in the ratio of 2 to 5.

16. Draw a segment having a convenient length and divide it, by construction, into two parts having the ratio of 2 to 3.

17. Given two segments with lengths s and t. Construct a segment equal to $\sqrt{st}$.

18. Given two segments with lengths s and t. Construct a segment equal to $\sqrt{6st}$.

C

Given two segments with lengths r and s, construct segments equal to each of the following.

19. $\dfrac{\sqrt{rs}}{3}$ 20. $\sqrt{\dfrac{rs}{3}}$ 21. $\sqrt{\dfrac{r^2}{2}}$ 22. $\sqrt{r^2 + s^2}$

23. Construct a segment whose length is x such that $4 \cdot 2 = 3x$.

24. Draw two segments whose lengths are a and b. Construct a segment whose length x is such that $x = \dfrac{b^2}{a}$.

25. Given a line and points P and Q on the same side of the line, construct a circle through P and Q and tangent to the given line.

Career Applications
Geometry and Geology

Geologists study the structure and composition of the earth's crust in order to locate natural resources. Some geologists, called **mineralogists,** analyze and classify minerals. Minerals consisting of three compounds can be represented by constructing **triangle graphs.** (Note that the constructed triangle is equilateral.)

EXAMPLE Refer to the graph at the right to give the composition of mineral *t*.

Solution: Mineral *t* is at the intersection of the lines representing 20% *A*, 30% *B*, and 50% *C*.

Composition of *t*: **20% compound *A*; 30% compound *B*; 50% compound *C***

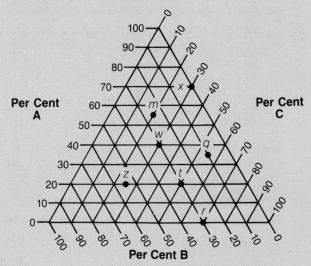

EXERCISES

Refer to the graph in the Example to give the composition of each mineral.

1. *x*   2. *w*   3. *z*   4. *r*   5. *q*   6. *m*

Construct a triangle graph similar to the one in the Example. On this triangle, graph each mineral based on its composition.

7. 50% *A*, 10% *B*, 40% *C*   8. 70% *A*, 10% *B*, 20% *C*
9. 25% *A*, 0% *B*, 75% *C*   10. 15% *A*, 5% *B*, 80% *C*

11. Triangle graphs can be used to represent the composition of other substances besides minerals. Construct a triangle graph to represent the composition of a loamy garden soil that is 25% clay, 35% sand, and the rest humus.

Review

In Exercises 1–4, draw $\overline{AB}$ such that $AB = 3$ centimeters and $\overline{CD}$ such that $CD = 4$ centimeters. Then construct each of the following. *(Section 9–1)*

1. $AB + CD$ **2.** $CD - AB$ **3.** $3CD$ **4.** $2AB - CD$

In Exercises 5–7, use a protractor to draw angle D such that $m\angle D = 30$ and angle E such that $m\angle E = 25$. Then construct each of the following. *(Section 9–1)*

5. $m\angle D + m\angle E$ **6.** $m\angle D - m\angle E$ **7.** $\frac{1}{2}m\angle D$

In Exercises 8–11, draw $\overline{XY}$ and perform the following constructions. *(Section 9–2)*

8. Choose a point C on $\overline{XY}$. Construct a line perpendicular to $\overline{XY}$ through point C.

9. Choose any point D below $\overline{XY}$. Construct a line perpendicular to $\overline{XY}$ through D.

10. Construct the perpendicular bisector of $\overline{XY}$.

11. Choose a point E above $\overline{XY}$. Construct a line parallel to $\overline{XY}$ through E.

Given circle P with a radius of 3 centimeters, perform the following constructions. *(Section 9–3)*

12. Construct a tangent to the circle at a point F on circle P.

13. Construct a tangent to the circle from a point G outside circle P.

14. Given any circle, locate its center by construction. *(Section 9–3)*

15. Given obtuse triangle ABC, construct the inscribed and circumscribed circles. *(Section 9–3)*

16. Divide a segment 10 centimeters long into 4 equal parts. *(Section 9–4)*

17. Draw three segments with lengths 3.5, 5, and 7 centimeters. Construct a segment with length x, such that $\frac{5}{3.5} = \frac{7}{x}$. *(Section 9–4)*

18. Construct the geometric mean between segments of lengths 4 centimeters and 6 centimeters. *(Section 9–4)*

Puzzle

$\overline{AB}$ is a side of square $ABCD$. It is also the diameter of a semicircle.

Locate the vertices of a square with base on $\overline{AB}$ inscribed in the semicircle. Prove your answer.

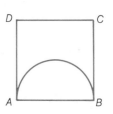

9-5   Meaning of Locus

A **locus** is a set of points (geometric figure) that satisfies certain conditions.

You have already solved two locus problems in a plane.

1 Constructing the perpendicular bisector of a segment: The locus of points equidistant from two fixed points is the *perpendicular bisector of the segment* joining the two fixed points.

2 Constructing the bisector of an angle: The locus of points equidistant from the sides of an angle is the *angle bisector*.

Example 1 shows how to determine the locus of points in a plane at a given distance from a given point.

EXAMPLE 1   Draw and describe the locus of points one centimeter from a given point P.

Solution: 1 Find as many points as necessary to give you a "picture" of the locus.

2 Then draw the figure —a circle.

Description: The locus of points one centimeter from P is a circle with its center at P and with a radius of one centimeter.

Example 2 illustrates how to determine the locus of points in a plane at a given distance from a given line.

EXAMPLE 2   Draw and describe the locus of points that are two meters from a given line k.

Solution:

1 Find as many points as necessary to give you a "picture" of the locus.

2 Draw the figure —two parallel lines.

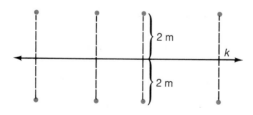
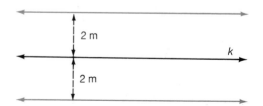

Description: The locus is a pair of lines, one on each side of k, parallel to k and 2 meters from k.

EXAMPLE 3   Draw the locus of points that are the vertices of the right angles of all right triangles with a fixed hypotenuse AB. Describe the locus.

Solution:

| 1 | Find one point that is a vertex of a right triangle. | 2 | Find as many points as necessary to give you a picture. | 3 | Draw the locus — a circle without points A and B. |

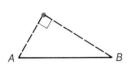   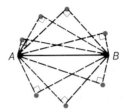   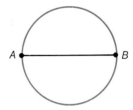

Description: The locus is two arcs of the circle having $\overline{AB}$ as a diameter and containing all points of the circle except points A and B.

The steps for finding and describing a locus are summarized below.

Summary

> **Steps in Finding and Describing a Locus**
> 1 Decide what information is given or fixed.
> 2 Locate one of the points of the locus.
> 3 Locate several other points and see whether they form a familiar shape, such as a circle or line.
> 4 Locate points of special importance such as endpoints of a segment or the center of a circle.
> 5 Describe the locus.

CLASSROOM EXERCISES

Classify each statement as true, *T*, or false, *F*.

1. A circle is determined if a given segment is its diameter.

2. A segment EF is determined if points E and G are given and G is between E and F.

3. A segment PR is determined if points P and Q are given and Q is the midpoint of $\overline{PR}$.

4. One line is determined if it is tangent to a given circle.

5. One line is determined if it is tangent to a given circle at a given point A on the circle.

6. Two parallel lines are determined if they are each perpendicular to a given segment GH at G and at H.

WRITTEN EXERCISES

In Exercises 1–19, first draw the locus. Then write its description.

1. The locus of points equidistant from R and from S in a given triangle RST.

2. The locus of vertices R and T in rectangle $QRST$ if diagonal QS is fixed in length and position.

3. The locus of points 1.5 centimeters from a given circle whose radius is 1 centimeter.

4. The locus of points 1 centimeter from a given circle whose radius is 1 centimeter.

5. The locus of points equidistant from two parallel lines.

6. The locus of the vertices, C, of all isosceles triangles that have a fixed base AB.

7. The locus of the midpoints of all chords of length 4 in a given circle with radius of length 3.

8. The locus of the centers of circles with radii 2 centimeters and passing through a given point Q.

9. The locus of the center of a circle that is tangent to a given circle O at a given point A on circle O.

10. The locus of the midpoints of all segments in a given circle if one of the endpoints is on the circle and the other endpoint is the center of the circle.

11. The locus of the centers of circles each of which is tangent to a given line at a given point of the line.

12. The locus of the centers of circles each of which is tangent to both sides of a given angle.

13. The locus of points whose distance from a given point P is less than a given distance, r.

14. The locus of vertex K in a given triangle KLM if $\overline{LM}$ is fixed in length and position and the altitude from K is 2.75 centimeters long.

15. Base AB in trapezoid $ABCD$ is fixed in length and position. The distance between the parallels $\overline{AB}$ and $\overline{CD}$ is given as d. Describe the locus of the midpoints of the medians of trapezoid $ABCD$.

16. For a given point Q and a given line k not containing Q, describe the locus of the endpoints of segments whose midpoints lie on k and whose other endpoint is Q.

17. Describe the locus of points equidistant from each of three given noncollinear points.

18. Describe the locus of the midpoint of a segment of given length s, having one endpoint on each ray of a given right angle.

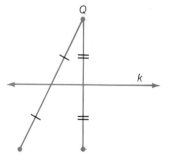

19. Segments AB and CD are segments of given lengths, and d is a given distance; $\overline{AB}$ is fixed in position, and $\frac{1}{2}AB < CD < AB$. For a trapezoid with base AB and median CD, when $\overline{AB}$ and $\overline{CD}$ are a distance d apart, describe the locus of the other base of the trapezoid.

In Exercises 20–28, write a description of each locus in space. A sketch of the figure may help you to visualize the locus. Exercises 20–23 are partly done for you.

20. The locus of points at a given distance from a given point O

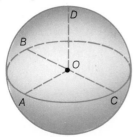

21. The locus of points at a given distance from a given line, m

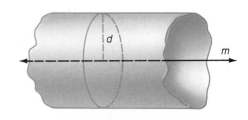

22. The locus of points equidistant from two given points, A and B

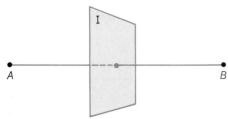

23. The locus of points equidistant from two given parallel planes

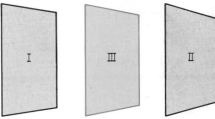

24. The locus of lines perpendicular to a given line p at a given point on p

25. The locus of the centers of spheres of given radius r that are tangent to a given plane

C

26. The locus of side RS in square $RSTU$ if side UT remains fixed in length and position. (HINT: Let the figure revolve around side UT as an axis.)

27. The locus of side UR in square $RSTU$ if side TS remains fixed in length and position

28. The locus of side UR in square $RSTU$ if side UT remains fixed in length and position

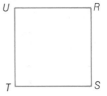

Find the locus of points for each given rotation of right triangle ABC.

29. Around $\overline{AB}$ as an axis

30. Around $\overline{AC}$ as an axis

31. Around $\overline{BC}$ as an axis

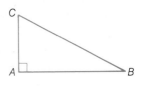

9–6 Intersection of Loci

When a set of points must satisfy each of two conditions, its location can be found from the *intersection of two loci* (plural of locus and pronounced LOW SIGH). The intersection of two loci consists of all the points they have in common.

EXAMPLE 1 Find the locus of points 2 centimeters from a circle O whose radius is 3 centimeters. The locus is also 1 centimeter from a line that is tangent to the circle.

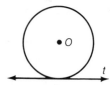

Solution:

First Condition	**Second Condition**	**Both Conditions**
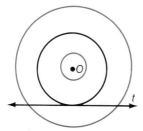	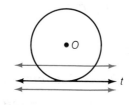	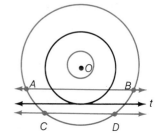
Locus: Two circles with center O, each 2 cm from circle O	**Locus:** Two lines parallel to t and 1 cm from t	**Locus:** Points A, B, C, and D

In Examples 1 and 2, only coplanar points are considered.

EXAMPLE 2 Given $\triangle ABC$, find the locus of points that are equidistant from A and B. The locus is also the same distance from $\overleftrightarrow{AC}$ that B is from $\overleftrightarrow{AC}$.

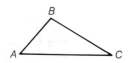

Solution:

First Condition	**Second Condition**	**Both Conditions**
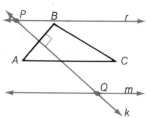		
Locus: Perpendicular bisector of $\overline{AB}$	**Locus:** Pair of lines, one on each side of $\overline{AC}$, parallel to $\overline{AC}$ and d units from $\overleftrightarrow{AC}$	**Locus:** Points P and Q

NOTE: If $\angle A$ in $\triangle ABC$ is a right angle, then the figure at the right results.

In this special case, the loci do <u>not</u> intersect. The solution is the empty set.

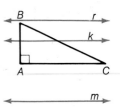

CLASSROOM EXERCISES

State the number of possible intersections of the given loci.

1. A circle and a pair of parallel lines
2. A pair of intersecting lines and a third line
3. A pair of concentric circles and a line
4. Two circles of unequal radii
5. A pair of parallel lines and a ray

WRITTEN EXERCISES

A

In Exercises 1–19, consider only coplanar points.

In Exercises 1–4, r and k are two parallel lines 1 centimeter apart. V is a given point such that V and line k are on opposite sides of r and V is 0.5 centimeter from r.

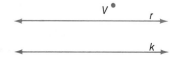

Find the locus of points that meets the given condition and is also equidistant from k and r.

1. 1.75 cm from V 2. 1 cm from V 3. 1.5 cm from V 4. 0.75 cm from V

Point X is 2 cm from the given line m. Find the locus of points that meets the given condition and is also 1 cm from m.

5. 3 cm from X 6. 3.5 cm from X
7. 1.75 cm from X 8. 1 cm from X

9. Find the locus of points $\frac{1}{2}$ inch from a given line h and equidistant from the sides of a given angle ABC. (See the figure at the left below.)

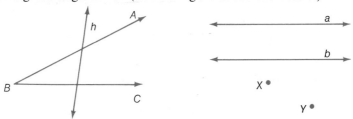

10. Find the locus of points equidistant from two given parallel lines a, b, and from two given points X, Y. (See the figure at the right above.)

11. Find the locus of points one centimeter from the vertex of a given right angle and in the interior of the angle.

12. Points A and B are 2 meters apart. Find the locus of points 3 meters from A and 2.5 meters from B.

13. Point T is 1 cm from line g. Find the locus of points 3 cm from T and 2 cm from g.

14. Find the locus of points at a given distance d from a given circle O with radius r and the same distance from a secant containing O. Discuss the special cases.

15. Find the locus of points equidistant from two given concentric circles and also equidistant from two given parallel lines. Consider special cases.

B

16. A, B, C, and D are collinear points such that $\overline{AC}$ is $1\frac{1}{2}$ cm long and $\overline{CD}$ is 1 cm long. Base AC of $\triangle XAC$ is fixed in length and position. $\overline{BX}$ is a median of length 1.5 cm. Triangle YBD is a right triangle with right angle at Y and base BD fixed in length and position. Locate a point Z that will serve as X in $\triangle XAC$ and also as Y in $\triangle YBD$.

17. Find the locus of points on a given line q and at a given distance d from a circle with radius r. Discuss the special cases.

18. Find the locus of points equidistant from two given parallel lines and a given distance d from a third line. Discuss the special cases.

19. Find the locus of points equidistant from two intersecting lines.

C   In Exercises 20–24, also consider points in space. Exercise 20 is partly done for you.

20. The locus of points that are on a line k and are also in plane I.

Case 1: The plane contains the line.	**Case 2:** The plane and the line are parallel.	**Case 3:** The plane neither contains the line nor is parallel to it.

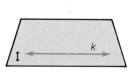 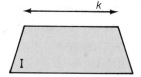 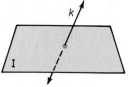

Locus: __?__   Locus: __?__   Locus: __?__

21. The locus of points equidistant from two given points and on a given line (HINT: There are three cases to consider.)

22. The locus of a point at a given distance from a given point and equidistant from two given parallel planes

23. The locus of lines tangent to a given sphere at a given point of the sphere

24. The locus of planes tangent to a given sphere at each point of a great circle of the sphere

9–7 Constructions and Loci

Sometimes constructions can be used to solve locus problems.

EXAMPLE 1 Find the locus of points equidistant from the vertices of $\triangle ABC$.

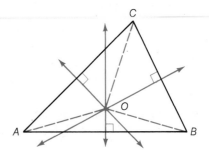

Solution: Since any point on the perpendicular bisector of a segment is equidistant from the endpoints of the segment, construct the perpendicular bisector of each side of $\triangle ABC$.

$AO = BO$ ⟵ —— **Since O is on the perpendicular bisector of $\overline{AB}$**

$AO = CO$ ⟵ —— **Since O is on the perpendicular bisector of $\overline{AC}$**

$BO = CO$ ⟵ —— **Since O is on the perpendicular bisector of $\overline{BC}$**

Since $AO = BO = CO$, the locus of points equidistant from the vertices of $\triangle ABC$ is **O**.

NOTE: To show that $AO = BO = CO$, it is sufficient to construct perpendicular bisectors of only two sides of $\triangle ABC$.

The perpendicular bisectors in $\triangle ABC$ are *concurrent*. Three or more lines are **concurrent** if they have a point in common.

Theorem 9–1 | The perpendicular bisectors of the sides of a triangle are concurrent in a point that is equidistant from the vertices of the triangle.

The point in which the perpendicular bisectors of the sides of one triangle are concurrent is the **circumcenter** of the triangle.

EXAMPLE 2 Find the locus of points equidistant from the sides of $\triangle ABC$.

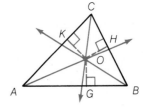

Solution: Since any point on the bisector of an angle is equidistant from the sides of the angle, construct the angle bisector of each angle of $\triangle ABC$.

$GO = KO$ ⟵ —— **Since O is on the bisector of $\angle A$**

$GO = HO$ ⟵ —— **Since O is on the bisector of $\angle B$**

$KO = HO$ ⟵ —— **Since O is on the bisector of $\angle C$**

Since $GO = KO = HO$, the locus of points equidistant from the sides of $\triangle ABC$ is **O**.

NOTE: To show that $GO = HO = KO$, it is sufficient to construct the bisectors of only two angles of $\triangle ABC$.

Example 2 shows that the bisectors of the angles of a triangle are also concurrent.

The point in which the angle bisectors of a triangle are concurrent is the **incenter** of the triangle.

Theorem 9–2 | The bisectors of the angles of a triangle are concurrent in a point that is equidistant from the sides of a triangle.

Other constructions can lead to theorems about concurrent lines. For example, the altitudes and medians of a triangle are also concurrent.

Theorem 9–3 | The altitudes of a triangle are concurrent.

Theorem 9–4 | The medians of a triangle are concurrent.

The point of concurrency of the altitudes is the **orthocenter**. The point of concurrency of the medians is the **centroid**.

CLASSROOM EXERCISES

Classify each statement as true, *T*, or false, *F*. When a statement is false, explain why it is false.

1. Concurrent lines are parallel.
2. The altitudes of a triangle meet at the circumcenter of the triangle.
3. The medians of a triangle meet at the centroid of the triangle.
4. The bisectors of the angles of a triangle meet at the incenter of the triangle.
5. The incenter of a triangle is equidistant from the sides of the triangle.

WRITTEN EXERCISES

A   In each of Exercises 1–4, copy the acute triangle shown at the right. Then perform the indicated constructions.

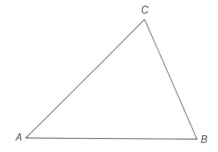

1. By construction, locate the circumcenter of $\triangle ABC$. Why is this called the circumcenter? (HINT: See Construction 11 on page 410.)
2. By construction, locate the incenter of $\triangle ABC$. Why is this called the incenter? (HINT: See Construction 12 on page 411.)

3. Construct the three altitudes. Label the point of concurrence T.

4. Construct the three medians. Label the point of concurrence R.

5. Repeat Exercises 1–4 with a triangle in which $\angle C$ is a right angle.

6. Repeat Exercises 1–4 with a triangle in which $\angle C$ is obtuse.

Use the results of Exercises 1–6 to complete the table below. Write *inside, outside, at the vertex,* or *on a side of,* the triangle.

	Acute	Right	Obtuse
7. Circumcenter	inside	?	?
8. Incenter	?	?	?
9. Orthocenter	?	?	?
10. Centroid	?	?	?

B

In the figure at the right, G is the midpoint of $\overline{OA}$ and H is the midpoint of $\overline{OB}$. $\overline{AE}$, $\overline{BF}$, and $\overline{CD}$ are medians.

Use this information in Exercises 11–14.

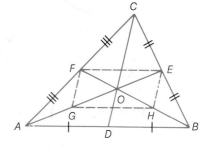

11. $AE = 6$; $AO = \frac{2}{3}AE$; $OG =$ ___?___

12. $AO = 8$; $AO = \frac{2}{3}AE$; $AE =$ ___?___

13. $BF = 7$; $BO = \frac{2}{3}BF$; $BH =$ ___?___

14. $DO = 3$; $OC = \frac{2}{3}DC$; $OC =$ ___?___

C

15. Prove Theorem 9–4. Use the figure given for Exercises 11–14, where G is the midpoint of $\overline{AO}$ and H is the midpoint of $\overline{BO}$. (HINT: Show that $EFGH$ is a parallelogram and that $\overline{AE}$ and $\overline{BF}$ are trisected. To show that $\overline{CD}$ contains O, assume that the intersection is another point. Then show that this is impossible.)

─────────────────  ─────────────────

Triangle ABC below is drawn incorrectly.

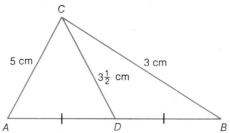

Can you construct the triangle correctly so that $AC = 5$ centimeters, $BC = 3$ centimeters, and $\overline{CD}$, the median to $\overline{AB}$, is $3\frac{1}{2}$ centimeters long?

APPLICATIONS

CONSTRUCTIONS AND LOCI

These exercises apply geometric concepts studied in Sections 9–6 and 9–7.

A

1. Fire protection experts recommend at least one smoke detector for each floor of a residence and at least one alarm near the bedroom area. If the smoke detector is installed on a wall, it should be between 6 and 12 inches from the ceiling. Explain how an installer locates the position for a smoke detector that will be placed on the wall halfway between the two bedroom doors shown.

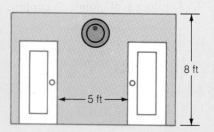

2. A city park has the shape of quadrilateral *ABCD*. The park commission plans to place a water fountain at a point equidistant from $\overline{AB}$ and $\overline{BC}$ also equidistant from points *D* and *C*.

   a. Explain how this point can be found.

   b. Copy quadrilateral *ABCD* on a piece of paper.

   By construction, locate the point.

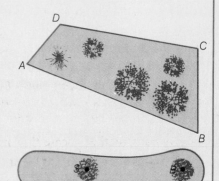

3. Within the park of Exercise 2, three large trees are positioned as shown. The city council plans to erect a monument at a spot equidistant from the three points. How can these points be found?

Copy this map on a separate piece of paper. Use this copy to show the constructions asked for in Exercises 4–5.

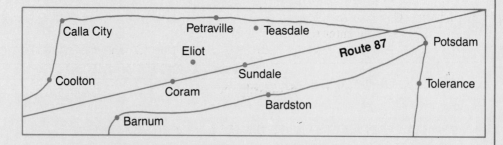

4. Philip Jona works in Sundale. He wishes to purchase a home within an area that is no less than 20 miles but no more than 30 miles from Sundale. By construction, locate the cities which satisfy Philip Jona's conditions. Use the scale: $\frac{1}{4}$ inch represents 10 miles.

5. The citizens of Potsdam and Tolerance vote to build a highway running halfway between the two cities and connecting with Route 87. By construction, locate the point where the highway will meet Route 87.

_____ Review _____

In Exercises 1–3, first draw the locus. Then write its description.
(Section 9–5)

1. The locus of points 2 centimeters from a given circle whose radius is 1.5 centimeters.

2. The locus of the centers of circles that are tangent to two parallel lines.

3. The locus of the midpoints of the radii of a circle.

In Exercises 4–7, point *Y* is 3 centimeters from the given line *q*. Find the locus that meets the given condition and is also 2 centimeters from *q*. *(Section 9–6)*

4. 4 cm from *Y*

5. 3.5 cm from *Y*

6. 4.25 cm from *Y*

7. 5 cm from *Y*

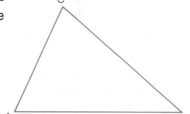

In each of Exercises 8–10, copy the acute triangle shown at the right. Then perform the indicated construction. *(Section 9–7)*

8. By construction, locate the circumcenter.

9. By construction, locate the incenter.

10. Construct the three medians. Label the point of concurrence *P*.

_____ Chapter Summary _____

IMPORTANT TERMS

Centroid (p. 426)
Circumcenter (p. 425)
Concurrent lines (p. 425)

Incenter (p. 426)
Locus (p. 418)
Orthocenter (p. 426)

IMPORTANT IDEAS

1. The only tools permissible for constructions are a compass and a straight-edge.

2. **Steps in Finding and Describing a Locus:** See p. 419.

3. When a set of points must satisfy each of two conditions, its location can be found from the intersection of two loci.

4. **Concurrent Lines or Segments in a Triangle**
   a. The perpendicular bisectors of the sides
   b. The bisectors of the angles
   c. The altitudes
   d. The medians

Chapter Objectives and Review

Objective: *To perform constructions involving segments, angles, and triangles (Section 9–1)*

1. Use a ruler to draw $\overline{AB}$ such that $AB = 6$ centimeters. Then construct $\overline{CD}$ such that $CD = AB$.

2. Construct $\overline{EF}$ such that $EF = 3AB$.

3. Use a protractor to draw an angle of 160°. Construct $\angle ABC$ congruent to this angle.

4. Construct $\overrightarrow{BD}$ bisecting the angle constructed in Exercise 3.

Objective: *To perform constructions involving perpendicular and parallel lines (Section 9–2)*

In Exercises 5–8, copy and use $\triangle ABC$.

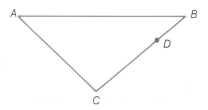

5. Construct a line through D perpendicular to $\overline{CB}$.

6. Construct a line through B perpendicular to $\overline{AC}$.

7. Construct a line through A parallel to $\overline{CB}$.

8. Construct the perpendicular bisector of $\overline{AB}$.

Objective: *To perform constructions involving circles (Section 9–3)*

In Exercises 9–10, copy and use circle P with point Q on the circle and point R in the exterior of the circle.

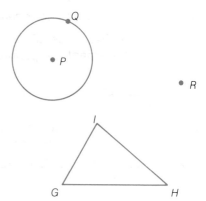

9. Construct a tangent to circle P at Q.

10. Construct tangents to circle P from point R.

11. Given any circle, locate its center by construction.

12. Given acute triangle GHI, construct a circle passing through points G, H, and I.

13. By construction, inscribe a circle in $\triangle GHI$.

Objective: *To perform constructions involving proportional segments (Section 9–4)*

14. Draw a line segment CD that is 7 centimeters long. By construction, divide this segment into three equal parts.

15. Draw three segments with lengths of 7, 9, and 14 millimeters. Construct a segment with length x such that $\dfrac{7}{9} = \dfrac{14}{x}$.

16. Given segments of length 4 centimeters and 7 centimeters; construct the geometric mean between the two segments.

Preparing for College Entrance Tests

A **Pythagorean triple** *is a set of three integers (a, b, c) that can be the lengths of the sides of a right triangle.* The following are common triples.

| 3, 4, 5 | 5, 12, 13 | 8, 15, 17 | 7, 24, 25 |

Memorizing the 4 most common triples can help save you time on College Entrance tests. Multiples of triples, such as (6, 8, 10), are also Pythagorean triples.

EXAMPLE: The diagonals of parallelogram $ABCD$ form four congruent triangles. If $DE = 3$ and $EC = 4$, find the perimeter of the parallelogram.

a. 14   **b.** 17   **c.** 20   **d.** 25   **e.** 28

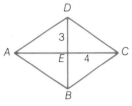

Solution: Since $m\angle DEA = m\angle DEC = m\angle CEB = m\angle BEA$, the triangles are right triangles.

$DE = EB = 3$ and $AE = EC = 4$ ⟵ **CPCTC**

Thus, $DC = CB = BA = AD = 5.$ ⟵ **3, 4, 5 is a Pythagorean triple.**

Perimeter $= 5 + 5 + 5 + 5 = 20$ **Answer: c**

Choose the best answer. Choose *a, b, c, d,* or *e*

1. Tangent $\overline{XY}$ is drawn to circle Q whose diameter is 14. If $QX = 25$, find XY.

   a. 18   **b.** 24   **c.** 32   **d.** 39   **e.** $\sqrt{719}$

2. What is the perimeter of a right triangle whose legs are 36 and 48?

   a. 144   **b.** 84   **c.** 132   **d.** 120   **e.** 225

3. In the figure at the right, $\overline{AE} \perp \overline{ED}$, $\overline{CD} \perp \overline{ED}$, and $\overline{DC} \perp \overline{CB}$. If $ED = 13$, $CD = 3$, $CB = 2$, and $AE = 11$, find AB.

   a. 8   **b.** 14   **c.** 16

   d. 17   **e.** 24

4. Triangles ABC and DBC are right triangles with the right angle at C. Find x.

   a. 10   **b.** 14   **c.** 16

   d. 20   **e.** 24

5. In the figure at the right, $ABCD$ is a square and $EHGF$ is a rectangle. Also, $\triangle DKL \cong \triangle GJC$, $\triangle EKF \cong \triangle HCL$, $DL = 3$, and $EF = 7$. Find LC.

   a. 5   **b.** 8   **c.** $\sqrt{65}$

   d. 10   **e.** 11

Preparing for College Entrance Tests

To solve problems such as the type illustrated in the Example:

1️⃣ Number the wheels as shown.

2️⃣ Determine whether each wheel, in order, is turning in a clockwise or counterclockwise direction.

REMEMBER: The arrows show the direction of turning.

Clockwise   Counter-clockwise

EXAMPLE: In the figure, a belt which runs over five wheels moves in the direction of the arrows. How many of the wheels are turning clockwise?

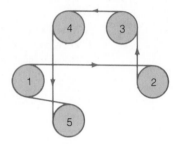

a. 1   b. 2   c. 3   d. 4   e. 5

Solution:
Wheel 1: Clockwise
Wheel 2: Clockwise
Wheel 3: Counterclockwise
Wheel 4: Counterclockwise
Wheel 5: Counterclockwise   Answer: b

In each exercise, determine how many wheels are turning clockwise. Choose the best answer. Choose a, b, c, d, or e.

a. 2   b. 3   c. 4   d. 5   e. None

1.
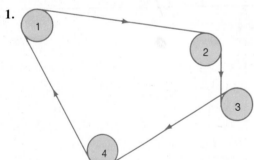

2.
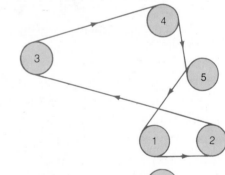

3.
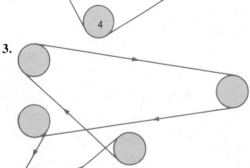

4.
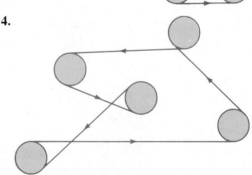

CHAPTER **10** **Area**

Sections

10-1 **Area: Rectangles and Squares**

10-2 **Area: Parallelograms and Triangles**

10-3 **Area: Rhombuses and Trapezoids**

Applications: Using Area

10-4 **Circumscribed and Inscribed Polygons**

10-5 **Area: Regular Polygons**

10-6 **Similarity and Polygons**

10-7 **Circumference and Arc Length**

10-8 **Area: Circles, Sectors, and Segments**

Applications: Using Area, Perimeter, and Circumference

Features

Consumer Application: Geometry and Wallpapering

Computer Application: Area

Calculator Application: Hero's Formula

Review and Testing

Geometry Review Capsules

Review: Sections 10–1 through 10–4

Review: Sections 10–5 through 10–8

Chapter Summary

Chapter Objectives and Review

Chapter Test

10–1 Area: Rectangles and Squares

The two figures at the left below are *polygonal regions*. The figure at the right is a *circular region*.

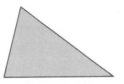 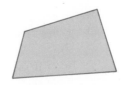

Definitions

> A **polygonal region** consists of a polygon and its interior.
>
> A **circular region** consists of a circle and its interior.

One way to measure a polygonal or circular region is to find its area. For convenience, the area of a polygonal or a circular region will be referred to as the *area of a polygon* or the *area of a circle*.

To compute areas of polygons, you use the Area Postulates.

Area Postulates

Postulate 16	To each polygon, there corresponds a positive number which is its area.
Postulate 17	Congruent triangles have the same area.
Postulate 18	The area of a polygon is the sum of the areas of the nonoverlapping triangular regions into which it can be separated.
Postulate 19	The area, A, of a rectangle is the product of its length, l, and its width, w. That is, $A = lw$.

Area is measured in *square units*. For example, if measures are given in centimeters, then area is stated in terms of square centimeters, written cm². One square centimeter is the area of a square with side of length one centimeter.

1 cm

Area: 1 cm²

EXAMPLE 1 In rectangle $ABCD$, the area of $\triangle ACD$ is 36 square units.

a. Find the area of $\triangle CAB$.

b. Find the area of rectangle $ABCD$.

Solutions: **a.** Since $\triangle ACD \cong \triangle CAB$, area $\triangle CAB$ = **36 square units.**

b. Since area rectangle $ABCD$ = area $\triangle ACD$ + area $\triangle CAB$, area rectangle $ABCD$ = **72 square units.**

Given the area of a rectangle and its length, you can use Postulate 19 to find the width.

EXAMPLE 2 The length of a rectangle is 9 centimeters and its area is 31.5 square centimeters. Find its width.

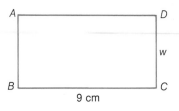

Solution: $A = lw$ ⟵ **Replace A with 31.5 and l with 9.**

$31.5 = 9w$

$3.5 = w$ The width is **3.5 centimeters.**

Since a square is a rectangle, you can use the formula $A = lw$ to find the area of any square. However, each side of a square has the same length. Thus, for a square with side of length s,

$$A = s^2.$$

CLASSROOM EXERCISES

In Exercises 1–8, the unit of measure for the sides of a rectangle or square is given. Write the corresponding unit of area.

1. meters
2. kilometers
3. centimeters
4. millimeters
5. yards
6. inches
7. feet
8. miles

9. In the polygon below, the area of $\triangle ABD$ is 12 cm² and the area of $\triangle BCD$ is 50 cm². Find the area of polygon $ABCD$.

10. In rectangle $PQST$, ST is 12 inches and TP is 5 inches. Find the area of the rectangle.

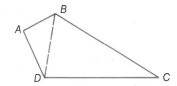

11. In the figure for Exercise 10, find ST if the area of rectangle $STPQ$ is 36 m² and $TP = 5$ meters.

12. Find the area of a square whose side is 9 centimeters long.

13. Find the side of a square whose area is 225 m².

WRITTEN EXERCISES

A

1. In the figure, the area of $\triangle MQP$ is 12 square units, the area of $\triangle SRT$ is 10 square units, and area of $\triangle PSR =$ area of $\triangle RPQ = 15$ square units. What is the area of polygon $MTSP$?

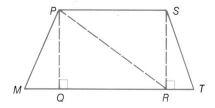

In Exercises 2–6, refer to rectangle *ABCD*. Find each unknown measure.

Length	Width	Area
2. 5 cm	3.28 cm	?
3. 3 cm	?	30 cm²
4. ?	6.25 m	1250 m²
5. $2\sqrt{5}$	?	$12\sqrt{5}$
6. ?	0.6 k	0.42 k^2

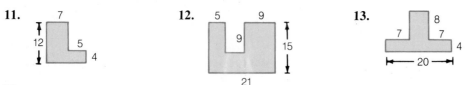

7. Find the area of a square whose side is 30 meters long.

8. Find the side of a square whose area is 144 cm².

9. Find the area of a square whose perimeter is 20 yards.

10. Find the area of a square whose perimeter is 32 centimeters.

In Exercises 11–16, consecutive sides of each figure are perpendicular. Find the area of each shaded region.

11.   **12.**   **13.**

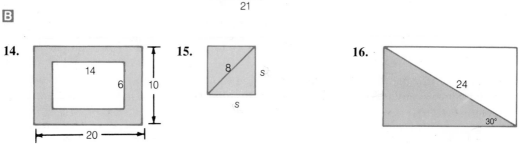

B

14.   **15.**   **16.**

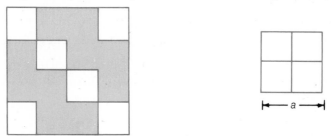

17. Find the area of the shaded part in the figure at the left below in terms of *a* if *a* is the length of a side of a square as shown on the right below.

18. If the length of a side of a square is doubled, how is the area affected?

19. If the length of the base of a rectangle is doubled and its width is tripled, how is the area affected?

20. The width of a rectangle is 10 centimeters and its area is 120 square centimeters. What is the length of a diagonal?

21. The length of a rectangle is 30 millimeters and its area is 480 square millimeters. Find the length of a diagonal.

22. A square is equal in area to a rectangle whose length is 20 feet and whose width is 5 feet. Find the length of a side of the square.

23. The area of a rectangle is 56. The length of the rectangle is $x + 5$ and its width is $x - 5$. Find the dimensions of the rectangle.

C

24. Polygon *ABCDE* at the left below is a regular pentagon with side of length s and with perimeter p. Express the area of *ABCDE* in terms of p and h if the area of $\triangle ABO$ is $\dfrac{sh}{2}$.

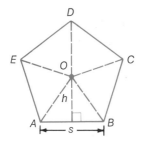 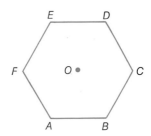

25. Express the area of the regular hexagon *ABCDEF* above in terms of the length s of one side. Assume the area of a triangle is one-half the product of the measures of the base and altitude.

26. A diagonal of a rectangle is 60 meters long and makes an angle of 30° with the base. Find the area of the rectangle.

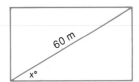

27. Find the area of the rectangle in Exercise 26 if the angle that the diagonal makes with the base is 45.

28. Find the area of the rectangle in Exercise 26 if the measure of the angle that the diagonal makes with the base is 60.

29. Find the area of a square whose diagonal is 25 inches.

30. The area of a rectangle is 12 square units and the length of a diagonal is 5 units. Find the length and width.

31. What are the length and width of a rectangle whose area is 14 square centimeters and whose perimeter is 18 centimeters?

32. Find the length and width of rectangle *ABCD*. Round your answers to the nearest whole number. Then find the area of the rectangle.

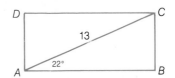

33. A rectangle is one-third as wide as it is long. Its perimeter is P. Express the area in terms of P.

34. Express the perimeter of the rectangle in Exercise 33 in terms of the area.

10-2 Area: Parallelograms and Triangles

Any side of a parallelogram may be called the **base** of the parallelogram. For each base, there is a corresponding *altitude*.

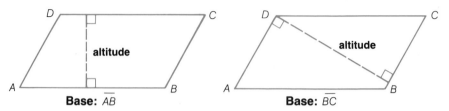

Base: $\overline{AB}$ **Base:** $\overline{BC}$

An **altitude of a parallelogram** is a perpendicular segment whose endpoints lie on opposite sides of the parallelogram. In the theorems that follow, the terms "base" and "altitude" refer to the lengths of these segments.

REMEMBER: Since parallel lines are equidistant at all points, the location of the altitude does not change its length.

Theorem 10-1	The area of a parallelogram is the product of its base, b, and the corresponding altitude, h. That is, $$A = bh.$$

EXAMPLE 1   Write the *Given*, the *Prove*, and a *Plan of Proof* for Theorem 10–1.

Solution: **Given:** Parallelogram $ABCD$ has base b and altitude h.

Prove: A (area) $= bh$.

Plan: With $\overline{EB}$ as the given altitude, $\overline{AF}$ can be constructed to intersect $\overrightarrow{CD}$ so that $ABEF$ is a rectangle whose area is bh. Prove that the area of $\triangle CBE$ equals the area of $\triangle DAF$.

The area A of parallelogram $ABCD$ is the sum of the areas of regions $ABED$ and CBE. The area of rectangle $ABEF$ is the sum of the areas of regions $ABED$ and DAF.

In this way, show that the area of parallelogram $ABCD$ equals the area, bh, of rectangle $ABEF$.

Corollary 10–2 relates parallelograms with equal bases and equal altitudes.

Corollary 10-2	Parallelograms with equal bases and equal altitudes have equal areas.

Any side of a triangle may be the base of the triangle. The corresponding altitude is the perpendicular segment from one vertex to the line that contains the base.

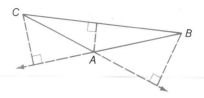

Theorem 10–3	The area, A, of a triangle is one-half the product of a base, b, and its corresponding altitude, h. That is, $$A = \tfrac{1}{2}bh.$$

EXAMPLE 2 Write the *Given*, the *Prove*, and a *Plan of Proof* for Theorem 10–3.

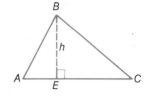

Solution: **Given:** $\triangle ABC$ has base b and altitude h.

Prove: A (area) $= \tfrac{1}{2}bh$

Plan: Through B construct a line parallel to $\overline{AC}$. Through C construct a line parallel to $\overline{AB}$ and intersecting the first line at D. Prove $\triangle ABC \cong \triangle DCB$. Use Theorem 10–1 and Postulates 17 and 18.

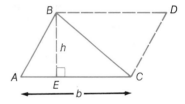

Corollary 10–4 for triangles is similar to Corollary 10–2 for parallelograms.

Corollary 10–4	Triangles with equal bases and equal altitudes have equal areas.

Any altitude of an equilateral triangle forms two 30–60–90 triangles. Recall the following relationship between the lengths of the side opposite the 60°-angle, h, and the hypotenuse, s.

$$h = \frac{s}{2}\sqrt{3}$$

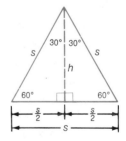

Replacing h with $\dfrac{s}{2}\sqrt{3}$ and b with s in $A = \tfrac{1}{2}bh$ leads to Corollary 10–5.

Corollary 10–5	For an equilateral triangle with side of length s, $$A(\text{area}) = \frac{s^2\sqrt{3}}{4}.$$

EXAMPLE 3 Find the area of $\triangle ABC$ and of $\triangle EFG$.

a.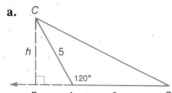

b.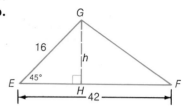

Solutions: Find h for each triangle. Then apply Theorem 10–3.

a. m$\angle DAC = 60$ ⟵ m$\angle BAC = 120$, and $180 - 120 = 60$

$\therefore \triangle CDA$ is a 30–60–90 triangle.

$h = \frac{s}{2}\sqrt{3}$ ⟵ **Relationship in a 30–60–90 triangle**

$= \frac{5}{2}\sqrt{3}$

$A = \frac{1}{2}bh$

$= \frac{1}{2}(8)\left(\frac{5}{2}\sqrt{3}\right) = 10\sqrt{3}$ ⟵ **Area is $10\sqrt{3}$ square units.**

b. $\triangle EHG$ is a 45–45–90 triangle.

$h = \frac{\sqrt{2}}{2} \cdot c$ ⟵ **Relationship in a 45–45–90 triangle**

$= \frac{\sqrt{2}}{2} \cdot 16 = 8\sqrt{2}$ ⟵ **Replace c with 16.**

$A = \frac{1}{2}bh$

$= \frac{1}{2}(42)(8\sqrt{2}) = 168\sqrt{2}$ ⟵ **Area is $168\sqrt{2}$ square units.**

CLASSROOM EXERCISES

1. In parallelogram $ABCD$, $AB = 10$ centimeters and $DE = 6$ centimeters. Find the area of the parallelogram.

2. The area of parallelogram $ABCD$ is 24 and $AB = 6$. Find DE.

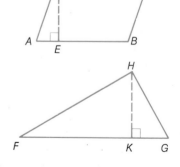

3. In triangle FGH, $FG = 15$ centimeters and $HK = 6$ centimeters. Find the area of the triangle.

4. In triangle FGH, $FG = 8$, $FH = 6$ and m$\angle F = 30$. Find the area of the triangle.

5. The legs of a right triangle are 14 centimeters and 12 centimeters long. Find the area of the triangle.

6. Each side of an equilateral triangle is 12 meters long. Find the area of the triangle.

WRITTEN EXERCISES

A   In Exercises 1–4, refer to parallelogram *ABCD*. Find each unknown measure.

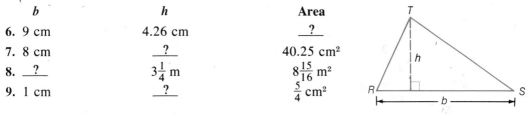

	b	*h*	Area
1.	12 cm	4.32 cm	?
2.	4 cm	?	36 cm²
3.	?	3.75 m	19.5 m²
4.	$5\sqrt{2}$ cm	?	$40\sqrt{2}$ cm²

5. In parallelogram *ABCD* above, $AB = 12$, $AD = 4$ and $m\angle A = 45$. Find the area of the parallelogram.

In Exercises 6–9, refer to triangle *RST*. Find each unknown measure.

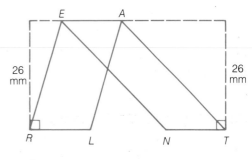

	b	*h*	Area
6.	9 cm	4.26 cm	?
7.	8 cm	?	40.25 cm²
8.	?	$3\frac{1}{4}$ m	$8\frac{15}{16}$ m²
9.	1 cm	?	$\frac{5}{4}$ cm²

10. In △*RST* above, $RS = 12$, $RT = 9$ and $m\angle R = 60$. Find the area of the triangle. (Leave your answer in radical form.)

11. Explain why parallelograms *REAL* and *NEAT* in the figure at the right have equal areas.

In Exercises 12–15, classify each statement as true, *T*, or false, *F*. When a statement is false, give a reason or an example to show why it is false.

12. If two triangles are congruent, then they have equal areas.

13. If two triangles have equal areas, then they are congruent.

14. If two parallelograms have equal areas, then they have equal bases and equal altitudes.

15. If two triangles have equal areas, then they have equal bases and equal altitudes.

In the figure at the right, *ABC* is a right triangle with the right angle at *C*.

In Exercises 16–20, find the area of △ *ABC* for each given length of $\overline{AB}$.

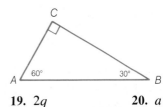

16. 10   **17.** 20   **18.** 13   **19.** 2*q*   **20.** *a*

DEF at the right is an isosceles right triangle.

In Exercises 21–25, find the area of △ *DEF* for each given length of $\overline{DF}$.

21. 16 **22.** 38 **23.** 18 **24.** 7 **25.** *a*

In right triangle *ABC*, the sides have lengths *a*, *b*, and *c*.

In Exercises 26–31, use the given information to find the area of △ *ABC*.

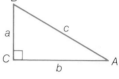

26. $a = 4$; $b = 12$ **27.** $a = 6.2$; $b = 5.4$ **28.** $c = 10$; $a = 8$

29. $c = 16$; $a = b$ **30.** $c = 20$; $b = 12$ **31.** $c = 41$; $a = 9$

32. Find the area of an equilateral triangle with a side of 20 centimeters.

33. Find the area of an equilateral triangle with an altitude of 9 millimeters.

34. The area of an equilateral triangle is $25\sqrt{3}$ square units. Find the length of one side of the triangle.

B

35. Prove Theorem 10–1. (HINT: See Example 1 on page 442.)

36. Prove Theorem 10–3. (HINT: See Example 2 on page 443.)

37. Prove Corollary 10–2. (HINT: See Exercise 11.)

38. Prove Corollary 10–4. **39.** Prove Corollary 10–5.

In parallelogram *ABCD*, *E* is the midpoint of $\overline{AB}$, and $\overline{BD}$ is a diagonal.

Refer to this figure in Exercises 40–42 to find the ratio of the areas of each pair of polygons.

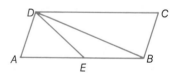

40. △ *ABD* to ▱ *ABCD* **41.** △ *AED* to △ *ABD* **42.** △ *AED* to ▱ *ABCD*

In Exercises 43–44, use the given information to sketch parallelogram *ABCD*. Then find its area.

43. $AD = 16$; $AB = 5$; $m\angle A = 30$ **44.** $AD = 14$; $AB = 5$; $m\angle A = 135$

45. The perimeter of an equilateral triangle is $5x$ centimeters. Express the altitude of the triangle in terms of *x*.

46. In △ *APC* at the right, $\angle C$ is a right angle. $\overline{HE} \perp \overline{PA}$ and *E* is the midpoint of $\overline{PA}$. If $AP = 26$ and $AC = 10$, find the area of △ *HEP*.

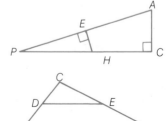

47. In △ *ABC*, $\overline{DE}$ divides the triangle into two regions that are equal in area. If the altitude to side *AB* is 18, find the distance between *DE* and *AB*.

In Exercises 1–6, classify each statement as true, *T*, or false, *F*. When a statement is false, give a reason for your answer. *(Page 224)*

1. A parallelogram with all four sides congruent is a rectangle.
2. A quadrilateral with exactly one pair of parallel sides is a trapezoid.
3. The bases of a trapezoid are the nonparallel sides.
4. The diagonals of a rhombus are congruent.
5. The diagonals of a parallelogram bisect each other.
6. The diagonals of a rhombus are perpendicular to each other.

Triangle *ABC* is a right triangle with the right angle at *C*. Refer to this triangle to find the unknown sides. *(Pages 310–311)*

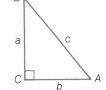

7. $a = 6$; $b = 7$; $c = \underline{\ ?\ }$
8. $a = 4$; $b = \underline{\ ?\ }$; $c = 17$
9. $a = \underline{\ ?\ }$; $b = 5$; $c = 9$
10. $a = 12$, $b = \underline{\ ?\ }$; $c = 13$

10–3   Area: Rhombuses and Trapezoids

In a rhombus, all sides are congruent and the diagonals are perpendicular to each other.

EXAMPLE 1   In rhombus *ABCD*, $AC = 8$ and $BD = 6$.

     a. Find the area.

     b. Compare the area with $AC \cdot BD$.

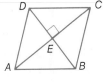

Solutions: **a.** Area of $\triangle ADC = \frac{1}{2}AC \cdot DE$ ←——— $DE = \frac{1}{2}BD$

$$= \frac{1}{2}(8)(3) = 12$$

Area of $\triangle ABC = \frac{1}{2}AC \cdot BE$ ←——— $BE = \frac{1}{2}BD$

Area rhombus $ABCD =$ Area $\triangle ADC +$ Area $\triangle ABC$

$$=\quad 12 \quad + \quad 12$$

$$= \textbf{24 square units}$$

     b. $AC \cdot BD = 8 \cdot 6 = 48$ Thus, area of rhombus $ABCD = \frac{1}{2}AC \cdot BD$.

The results of Example 1 are stated in Corollary 10–6.

Corollary 10–6

> The area *A* of a rhombus is one-half the product of the lengths of its diagonals, d_1 and d_2. That is,
>
> $$A = \frac{1}{2}d_1 d_2.$$

EXAMPLE 2   Find the area of rhombus $GAME$, where
$GM = d_1 = 32$ and $AM = 20$.

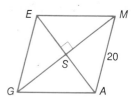

Solution: To find d_2, first find ES, which is $\frac{1}{2}d_2$.
Use the Pythagorean theorem.

$$(ES)^2 + (SM)^2 = (EM)^2$$
$$(ES)^2 + (16)^2 = (20)^2 \quad\longleftarrow\quad \textbf{SM} = \tfrac{1}{2}\textbf{GM and}$$
$$\textbf{EM} = \textbf{MA} = \textbf{20}$$
$$(ES)^2 + 256 = 400$$
$$(ES)^2 = 144$$
$$ES = 12$$
$$\therefore\ d_2 = 24 \quad\longleftarrow\quad \textbf{d}_2 = \textbf{2(ES)}$$

$$A = \tfrac{1}{2}d_1\,d_2$$
$$= \tfrac{1}{2}(32)(24)$$
$$= \textbf{384 square units}$$

The formula for the area of a trapezoid can be
found by finding the areas of the triangles formed
by drawing a diagonal.

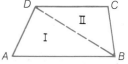

Area of $ABCD$ = Area of Triangle I + Area of Triangle II

**Theorem
10–7**

The area A of a trapezoid is one-half the product of its altitude and
the sum of its bases, b and b' (read: "b prime"). That is,

Area of trapezoid $ABCD = \tfrac{1}{2}bh + \tfrac{1}{2}b'h = \tfrac{1}{2}h(b + b')$.

The proof of this theorem is asked for in the Written Exercises.

CLASSROOM EXERCISES

1. The diagonals of rhombus are 32 centimeters and 20 centimeters long. Find
   the area.

2. The area of a rhombus is 48 and one diagonal is 12. Find the other diagonal.

3. In trapezoid $ABCD$, $AB = 32$ meters, $DC = $
   18 meters, and $DE = 20$ meters. Find the
   area.

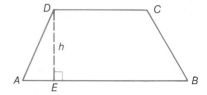

4. In trapezoid $ABCD$, $AB = 27$, $DC = 13$,
   and the area of $ABCD$ is 140. Find altitude
   DE.

5. In trapezoid $ABCD$, $AB = 12$ centimeters, $DC = 8$ centimeters, $AD = 6$ centimeters, and m$\angle A = 30$. Find the area.

WRITTEN EXERCISES

In Exercises 1–5, refer to rhombus *KATH* to find each unknown measure.

	KT	*AH*	Area
1.	20	8	?
2.	?	15	60
3.	4	?	$10\sqrt{3}$
4.	10.2	16.4	?
5.	?	$6\frac{2}{3}$	30

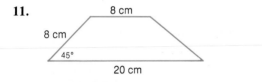

In Exercises 6–10, refer to trapezoid *WXYZ* to find each unknown measure.

	h	*b*	*b'*	Area
6.	2	6	4	?
7.	5	3	2	?
8.	?	10	8	45
9.	5	10	?	$32\frac{1}{2}$
10.	?	$5\sqrt{2}$	$3\sqrt{2}$	$4\sqrt{6}$

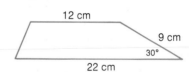

In Exercises 11–12, find the area of each figure.

11.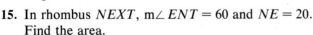

8 cm · 8 cm · 45° · 20 cm

12.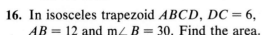

12 cm · 9 cm · 30° · 22 cm

13. In rhombus *NEXT*, $NX = 24$ and $EX = 13$. Find the area of the rhombus.

14. In rhombus *NEXT*, $NX = 10$ centimeters and the area is 120 square centimeters. Find the length of one side of the rhombus.

15. In rhombus *NEXT*, $m\angle ENT = 60$ and $NE = 20$. Find the area.

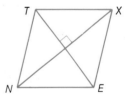

16. In isosceles trapezoid *ABCD*, $DC = 6$, $AB = 12$ and $m\angle B = 30$. Find the area.

17. Find a side of a square equal in area to a rhombus with diagonals of 10 and 12.

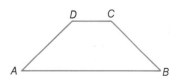

18. The perimeter of a rhombus is 60 and one of its diagonals is 18. Find the area of the rhombus.

19. Prove Corollary 10–6. (HINT: Follow the procedure of Example 1.)

20. Prove Theorem 10–7. Refer to the *Given*, the *Prove*, and the *Plan of Proof* below.

Given: Trapezoid $ABCD$ with bases b and b', altitude h and area A.

Prove: $A = \frac{1}{2}h(b + b')$

Plan: Draw $\overline{BD}$. Then, area of $ABCD$ = area of $\triangle ABD$ + area of $\triangle BCD$. Since h is the altitude of each triangle, area of $ABCD = \frac{1}{2}bh + \frac{1}{2}b'h = \frac{1}{2}h(b + b')$.

B In the figure at the right, *CLEA* is a trapezoid.

Explain why each pair of triangles is equal in area.

21. $\triangle AEC$ and $\triangle EAL$ **22.** $\triangle CLA$ and $\triangle LCE$ **23.** $\triangle CRA$ and $\triangle LRE$

24. Find the area and perimeter of a rhombus whose diagonals have lengths in the ratio of 2 to 9. The sum of the lengths of the diagonals is 22.

C First make a sketch of each figure. Then solve the problem.

25. A rhombus is equal in area to a trapezoid with an altitude of 10 centimeters. The diagonals of the rhombus are 15 cm and 20 cm long. Find the measures of the bases of the trapezoid if one base is twice the length of the other.

26. The length of one diagonal of a rhombus is three times the length of the other and the area of the rhombus is 54. Find the lengths of the diagonals.

27. The perimeter of a rhombus is 20 units and its area is 24 square units. Find the lengths of the diagonals.

CALCULATOR APPLICATIONS

Hero's Formula

When the lengths a, b, and c of the sides of a triangle are known, the area A is given by **Hero's Formula,** $A = \sqrt{s(s-a)(s-b)(s-c)}$, where $s = \dfrac{a+b+c}{2}$.

EXAMPLE The sides of a triangle are 496, 564, and 632 centimeters long. Find the area.

SOLUTION $A = \sqrt{846(350)(282)(214)}$ ⟵ Use a calculator to compute s, $s-a$, $s-b$, and $s-c$.

8 4 6 ⊠ 3 5 0 ⊠ 2 8 2 ⊠ 2 1 4 = √

$\boxed{133675.1391}$

The area is about **133,675 cm²** (nearest whole number).

EXERCISES

Find the area of each triangle. Round answers to the nearest whole number.

1. $a = 3;\ b = 25;\ c = 26$ **2.** $a = 4;\ b = 13;\ c = 15$ **3.** $a = 6;\ b = 25;\ c = 29$

4. $a = 9;\ b = 10;\ c = 17$ **5.** $a = 35;\ b = 42;\ c = 37$ **6.** $a = 212;\ b = 341;\ c = 285$

APPLICATIONS

USING AREA

These exercises apply geometric concepts studied in Sections 10–1 through 10–3.

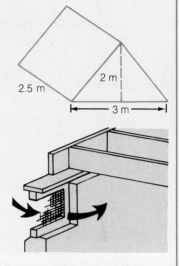

A

1. Find the number of square meters of canvas needed to make the tent shown at the right. No canvas is needed for the floor. Add 2 square meters for flaps and seams.

2. A tennis court is 20 meters wide and 40 meters long. A contractor's bid for resurfacing the court amounts to $12.65 per square meter. Find the total cost.

B   For reasons of comfort, some humidity is necessary in homes. Too much humidity can cause mold and peeling paint. Exercises 3 and 4 relate area to humidity.

3. An attic should have 900 cm² of ventilation for each 27 m² of floor area. How many square centimeters of ventilation are needed for a rectangular attic floor area with dimensions 4 meters by 12 meters?

4. A crawl space should have 900 cm² of ventilation for each 27 m² of floor area. There should be an additional 1800 cm² of ventilation for each 30 meters of perimeter around the crawl space. How many cm² are needed for a rectangular crawl space with dimensions 10 meters by 15 meters?

The dimensions of a flag are 65 feet by 39 feet. The length of each short stripe is 39 feet.

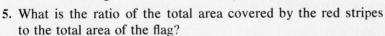

5. What is the ratio of the total area covered by the red stripes to the total area of the flag?

6. What is the ratio of the total area of the striped regions to the total area of the flag?

C In the city of Dellville, the assessment rate for determining property taxes is $189 per square meter. Use this information in Exercises 7–9 to compute the value of each one-floor dwelling.

7. Ranch style home: 8 meters by 14 meters

8. L-shaped home: 8.9 meters by 11 meters plus 8 meters by 9.5 meters

9. Suppose that the tax rate for Dellville is $62 on every $1000 of assessment value. Find the amount of taxes on the house in Exercise 7.

Find the sum of the measures of the interior angles of a polygon with the given number of sides. *(Pages 193–194)*

1. 3   **2.** 4   **3.** 6   **4.** 8   **5.** 10   **6.** 12

Find the measure of one angle of a regular polygon having the given number of sides. *(Pages 193–194)*

7. 3   **8.** 4   **9.** 5   **10.** 8   **11.** 20   **12.** 9

13. The length of one side of a regular polygon is y centimeters. Find the length of each of the other sides.

14. The measure of one angle of a regular polygon is t. Find the measure of each of the other angles.

10–4 Circumscribed and Inscribed Polygons

A circle **circumscribed** about a polygon contains each vertex of the polygon. A **radius of a regular polygon** is a radius of a circumscribed circle. The radii of pentagon *ABCDE* are $\overline{AO}$, $\overline{BO}$, $\overline{CO}$, $\overline{DO}$, and $\overline{EO}$.

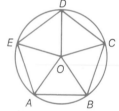

A circle **inscribed** in a polygon is tangent to each side of the polygon. An **apothem** of a regular polygon is a radius of its inscribed circle. The apothems of pentagon *ABCDE* are $\overline{FO}$, $\overline{GO}$, $\overline{HO}$, $\overline{JO}$, and $\overline{KO}$.

The **center of a regular polygon** is the common center of its inscribed and circumscribed circles.

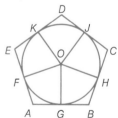

REMEMBER: If a polygon is *not* regular, *both* a circumscribed and inscribed circle with a common center cannot be drawn.

Theorem 10–8

> A polygon is regular if and only if a circle can be inscribed in the polygon and a circle with the same center can be circumscribed about the polygon.

Note that Theorem 10–8 is a biconditional.

Complete proofs of many theorems and corollaries in this chapter are lengthy and time consuming. Proofs of other theorems and corollaries are rather obvious. For these reasons, only the proofs of certain selected theorems and corollaries are asked for in the Written Exercises.

Each of the triangles formed by two consecutive radii and a side of a regular polygon are congruent. Thus, the *central angles* are congruent. A **central angle** is determined by two consecutive radii.

EXAMPLE 1
a. Name each pair of consecutive radii and the central angle each pair determines.

b. Find the measure of each central angle.

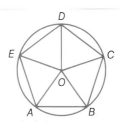

Solutions:

a.

Consecutive radii	$\overline{AO}, \overline{BO}$	$\overline{BO}, \overline{CO}$	$\overline{CO}, \overline{DO}$	$\overline{DO}, \overline{EO}$	$\overline{EO}, \overline{AO}$
Central angles	$\angle AOB$	$\angle BOC$	$\angle COD$	$\angle DOE$	$\angle EOA$

b. $m\angle AOB + m\angle BOC + m\angle COD + m\angle DOE + m\angle EOA = 360$

$m\angle AOB = m\angle BOC = m\angle COD = m\angle DOE = m\angle EOA$ ←——— The central angles are congruent.

$\therefore x + x + x + x + x = 360$ ←——— Let x represent the measure of each central angle.

$5x = 360$

$x = 72$ ←——— The measure of each central angle

The results of Example 1 are stated in general form in Corollary 10–9.

Corollary 10–9

The measure, a, of each central angle of a regular polygon of n sides is $\dfrac{360}{n}$. That is, $a = \dfrac{360}{n}$.

By the SSS Postulate, triangles formed by two consecutive radii and a side of a regular polygon are congruent.

EXAMPLE 2 In the figure at the right, circle O is circumscribed about regular pentagon $ABCDE$.

a. Find the measure of a base angle of one of the isosceles triangles.

b. Find the measure of an angle of the regular polygon.

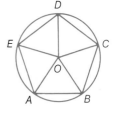

Solutions:
a. In $\triangle AOB$, $m\angle OAB + m\angle OBA + m\angle AOB = 180$.

$m\angle AOB = 72$ ←——— From Example 1

$m\angle OAB = m\angle OBA$ ←——— Since $\angle OAB \cong \angle OBA$

$y + y + 72 = 180$ ←——— Let $y = m\angle OAB = m\angle OBA$.

$2y = 108$

$y = 54$ ←——— $m\angle OAB$ and $m\angle OBA$

b. $m\angle EAB = m\angle OAE + m\angle OAB$

$m\angle OAE = m\angle OAB \longleftarrow$ **Since** $\angle OAE \cong \angle OAB$

$m\angle OAE = 54$

$\therefore m\angle EAB = m\angle OAE + m\angle OAB = 54 + 54 = \mathbf{108}$

In Example 2b, $m\angle OAE = m\angle OAB$. This result can be stated as a corollary.

Corollary 10–10

> A radius of a regular polygon bisects an angle of the polygon.

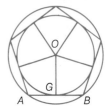

In this figure, $\overline{AB}$ is a tangent to the inscribed circle, and apothem OG is perpendicular to $\overline{AB}$. Further, $\overline{AB}$ is a chord of the circumscribed circle. Therefore, apothem OG also bisects $\overline{AB}$ (Theorem 8–5).

Corollary 10–11

> The apothem of a regular polygon is the perpendicular bisector of a side of the polygon.

CLASSROOM EXERCISES

In Exercises 1–8, complete each statement.

1. A regular polygon of n sides has __?__ central angles.
2. The measure of each central angle of a regular polygon of nine sides is __?__ .
3. Each central angle of a regular polygon has a measure of 45. The polygon has __?__ sides.
4. In Exercise 3, the name of the regular polygon is __?__ .
5. The central angles of a regular polygon are __?__ .
6. A central angle of a regular polygon is formed by two __?__ .
7. The radii of a regular hexagon are drawn and the length of each radius is 9. Then the length of a side of the regular hexagon is __?__ .
8. Apothem OG is drawn to side AB of regular pentagon $ABCDE$. Then, $\overline{OG}$ __?__ $\overline{AB}$ and $\overline{OG}$ bisects __?__ .
9. Write Theorem 10–8 as a conditional and its converse.

WRITTEN EXERCISES

A In Exercises 1–5, the number of sides of a regular polygon is given. Find the measure of a central angle of the polygon.

1. 5   2. 8   3. 10   4. 12   5. 20

In Exercises 6–10, the measure of a central angle of a regular polygon is given. Find the number of sides of the polygon.

6. 18   **7.** 40   **8.** 120   **9.** 30   **10.** 72

In Exercises 11–15, the number of sides of a regular polygon is given. Find the measure of each angle of the polygon.

11. 18   **12.** 12   **13.** 20   **14.** 30   **15.** 10

In Exercises 16–18, refer to the 30–60 right triangle below.

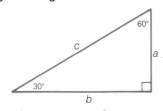

	c	*a*	*b*
16.	8	?	?
17.	?	5	?
18.	?	?	6

In Exercises 19–21, refer to regular triangle *ABC* inscribed in circle *O*.

	r	*a*	*AD*	*AB*
19.	8	?	?	?
20.	?	5	?	?
21.	?	?	6	?

In Exercises 22–24, refer to the 30–60 right triangle below.

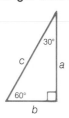

	c	*a*	*b*
22.	2	?	?
23.	?	$\sqrt{7}$	?
24.	?	?	$6\sqrt{3}$

In Exercises 25–27, refer to the regular hexagon inscribed in circle *O*.

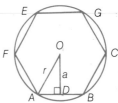

	r	*a*	*AD*	*AB*
25.	2	?	?	?
26.	?	$\sqrt{7}$	?	?
27.	?	?	$6\sqrt{3}$	?

28. A radius of a regular hexagon is 9 centimeters long. Find the length of a side of the hexagon.

29. The length of one side of a regular hexagon is 7 centimeters. What is the length of a radius?

30. A radius of a regular triangle is 12. Find the length of one side of the triangle.

31. The length of one side of a regular triangle is 30. Find the length of a radius of the triangle.

32. The length of a radius of a regular quadrilateral is 16 units. Find the length of one side.

33. The length of one side of a regular quadrilateral is 48. What is the length of a radius of the quadrilateral?

In Exercises 34–39, the radius of a regular hexagon is given. Find the length of the apothem.

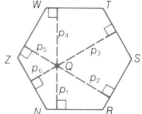

34. 2 meters

35. 3 meters

36. 4 decimeters

37. 6 centimeters

38. 5.5 millimeters

39. y meters

40. A regular hexagon is inscribed in a circle whose radius is 10 centimeters. What is the length of the apothem?

41. In the figure at the left below, an equilateral triangle is inscribed in a circle whose radius is 12. Find the length of the apothem.

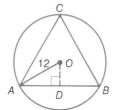

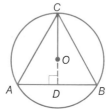

B

42. In the figure at the right above, equilateral triangle ABC is inscribed in circle O whose radius is 8. Find the length of altitude CD. (HINT: Draw $OA = 8$ and find apothem OD. Then $CO + OD = CD$.)

43. What is the ratio of the radius of a circle circumscribed about an equilateral triangle to an altitude of the triangle?

C

44. In regular hexagon $ABCDEF$, diagonals AC and AD are drawn. Find m$\angle DAC$.

45. Explain why the measure of an exterior angle of a regular polygon equals the measure of a central angle.

46. In regular hexagon $WZNRST$, Q is any interior point and p_1, p_2, p_3, p_4, p_5, and p_6 are perpendicular segments from Q to the sides of the hexagon. Compare the sum of the lengths of these six segments to an apothem, a, of the hexagon.

47. Write a formula that expresses the length of a side of a regular hexagon in terms of the radius, r, of the inscribed circle.

48. Write a formula that expresses the length of a side of a regular octagon in terms of a radius, r, of the octagon. (HINT: Use the sine ratio.)

—— Review ——

In Exercises 1–2, refer to rectangle *ABCD*. *(Section 10–1)*

1. If the area of rectangle *ABCD* is 450 cm² and *AD* = 12.5 centimeters, find *DC*.

2. If *BC* = 8 millimeters and *BD* = 8√3 millimeters, find the area of rectangle *ABCD*.

Use the given figure for Exercises 3–6. *(Section 10–2)*

3. Find the measure of one altitude of parallelogram *EFGH* if *HG* = 25 centimeters and the area is 250 cm².

4. If *EF* = 33 millimeters and the altitude to $\overline{EF}$ is 27 millimeters long, what is the area of parallelogram *EFGH*?

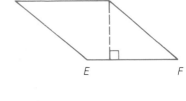

5. In △*ABC*, $\overline{CD}$ is a median. The area of △*ADC* is 18.5 square units. Find the area of △*ABC*.

6. In equilateral triangle *ABC*, *AC* = 2 millimeters. Find the area of △*ABC*.

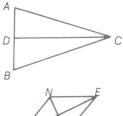

In Exercises 7–10, refer to rhombus *RAEN* to compute each unknown measure. *(Section 10–3)*

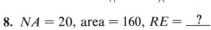

7. *NA* = 16, *RE* = 20, area = __?__   8. *NA* = 20, area = 160, *RE* = __?__

9. *NA* = 5, *RP* = 6, area = __?__   10. *NE* = 10, *RE* = 16, area = __?__

In Exercises 11–13, refer to trapezoid *LINE* to find each unknown measure. *(Section 10–3)*

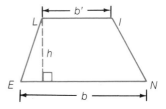

	h	*b*	*b′*	**Area**
11.	3	7	5	__?__
12.	4	6	__?__	60
13.	6	__?__	9	270

Complete each statement. *(Section 10–4)*

14. The measure of each central angle of a regular polygon of 12 sides equals __?__ .

15. If the measure of a central angle of a regular polygon is 20, the polygon has __?__ sides.

16. The perimeter of an inscribed regular quadrilateral is 40. The radius of the quadrilateral is __?__ .

In Exercises 1–8, refer to right triangle ABC shown at the right.

Complete the tables. *(Pages 310–311)*

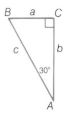

	a	b	c
1.	$9\sqrt{3}$	?	?
3.	$2\sqrt{3}$	?	?
5.	?	4	?
7.	?	9	?

	a	b	c
2.	?	$3\sqrt{3}$	?
4.	?	?	10
6.	?	?	12
8.	?	?	$6\sqrt{3}$

10–5 Area: Regular Polygons

Given the length of one side of a regular polygon and the apothem, you can find the area of the polygon.

EXAMPLE 1   Each side of a regular hexagon is 14 centimeters long and the length of its apothem is $7\sqrt{3}$ centimeters.

   a. Find the area of one triangle formed by consecutive radii of the hexagon.

   b. Find the area of the regular hexagon.

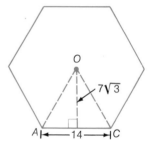

Solutions:

a. Area of triangle $= \frac{1}{2}bh$

$\qquad A = \frac{1}{2} \cdot 14 \cdot 7\sqrt{3} \longleftarrow$ **The apothem is an altitude of $\triangle AOC$.**

$\qquad = 49\sqrt{3}$ cm². $\longleftarrow$ **Area of one triangle is $49\sqrt{3}$ cm².**

b. Area of hexagon $= 6 \cdot 49\sqrt{3} \longleftarrow$ **The consecutive radii form 6 triangles.**

$\qquad = 294\sqrt{3}$ cm². $\longleftarrow$ **Area of hexagon is $294\sqrt{3}$ cm².**

When you know the apothem of a regular polygon, you can use Theorem 10–12 to find the area of the polygon.

Theorem 10–12	The area A of a regular polygon equals one-half the product of its perimeter P and the apothem a. That is, $$A = \frac{1}{2}aP.$$

In Example 2, the term *n-gon* refers to a polygon having n sides.

EXAMPLE 2 Write the *Given*, the *Prove*, and a *Plan of Proof* for Theorem 10–12.

Solution: **Given:** Regular *n*-gon *TWRQP* · · ·; apothem *a*; side *b*; perimeter *P*; area *A*

Prove: $A = \frac{1}{2}aP$

Plan: Draw all the radii of the *n*-gon, forming *n* congruent triangles.

Show that the area of each of these triangles equals $\frac{1}{2}ba$ and that the area of the *n* triangles equals $n(\frac{1}{2}ba)$, or $\frac{1}{2}a(nb)$.

Since $nb = P$, $A = \frac{1}{2}aP$.

A proof of this theorem is asked for in the Written Exercises.

EXAMPLE 3 Find the area of a regular hexagon if its apothem is $8\sqrt{3}$ centimeters.

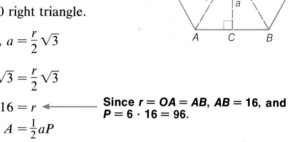

Solution: $m\angle AOB = 60 \longleftarrow \dfrac{360}{n}$, $n = 6$

$\therefore \triangle AOB$ is equilateral. Since $\overline{OC} \perp \overline{AB}$, $\triangle AOC$ is a 30-60 right triangle.

By Theorem 7–7, $a = \dfrac{r}{2}\sqrt{3}$

$$8\sqrt{3} = \frac{r}{2}\sqrt{3}$$

$16 = r \longleftarrow$ **Since $r = OA = AB$, $AB = 16$, and $P = 6 \cdot 16 = 96$.**

$A = \frac{1}{2}aP$

$A = \frac{1}{2}(8\sqrt{3})(96) = 384\sqrt{3}$ **cm²**

CLASSROOM EXERCISES

In Exercises 1–8, the length of one side and the number of sides, *n*, of a regular polygon are given. Find *P*, the perimeter of the polygon.

	AB	n	P
1.	7	4	?
2.	0.75	32	?
3.	$4\sqrt{3}$	6	?
4.	$\frac{9}{2}\sqrt{3}$	6	?

	AB	n	P
5.	$5\frac{1}{2}$	6	?
6.	$\frac{10}{3}$	9	?
7.	$13\sqrt{2}$	8	?
8.	8.3	20	?

WRITTEN EXERCISES

A Complete the table.

Figure	Side	Apothem	Perimeter	Area
1. Regular hexagon	10 cm	$5\sqrt{3}$	?	?
2. Regular polygon	———	12	$48\sqrt{3}$	?
3. Regular polygon	———	$\frac{10}{3}\sqrt{3}$	60	?
4. Regular pentagon	x	y	?	?
5. Square	?	10 dm	?	?
6. Equilateral triangle	12 mm	?	?	?

7. One side of the square at the left below is 12 centimeters long. Find the apothem.

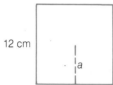
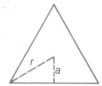

8. The radius of the equilateral triangle at the right above is 12 centimeters. Find the apothem.

In Exercises 9–11, the perimeter P and the apothem a of a regular polygon are given. Find the area.

9. $P = 40;\ a = 5$ **10.** $P = 80\sqrt{3};\ a = 10\sqrt{2}$ **11.** $P = 30\sqrt{3};\ a = 5$

Each side of a square is 16 units long. Find each measure.

12. The apothem   **13.** The perimeter   **14.** The area

Each side of an equilateral triangle is 24 units long. Find each measure.

15. The apothem   **16.** The perimeter   **17.** The area

Each side of a regular hexagon is 6 units long. Find each measure.

18. The apothem   **19.** The perimeter   **20.** The area

21. Each side of a regular pentagon is 13 units long and its apothem is 9 units long. Find its perimeter and its area.

22. Each side of an equilateral triangle is 20 centimeters long. Find its radius, apothem, perimeter, and area.

23. The length of a diagonal of a square is $18\sqrt{2}$ inches. Find the length of a side, the apothem, the perimeter, and the area.

24. Find the apothem of a regular polygon with an area of 625 square yards and a perimeter of 100 yards.

25. Find the apothem of a regular polygon with an area of 144 square meters and a perimeter of 48 meters.

26. Find the perimeter of an equilateral triangle with an apothem of 2 centimeters.

27. Find the perimeter of a regular hexagon with an apothem of 3 meters.

28. Find the apothem of a square with a side of 8 meters.

29. Find the apothem of a regular hexagon with a perimeter of 48 centimeters.

30. Find the area of a regular octagon with apothem of 7 millimeters and a side of 5.8 millimeters.

31. Find the apothem of a square with radius of 10 decimeters.

32. Find the area of a regular hexagon with a side 4 centimeters long.

33. Find the area of an equilateral triangle with a radius of $4\sqrt{3}$ inches.

34. Find the area of a square with an apothem of $4\sqrt{2}$ decimeters.

B

35. An equilateral triangle has an area of $300\sqrt{3}$. Find the apothem.

One side of a square is x units long. Find each of the following in terms of x.

36. The apothem   37. The perimeter   38. The area

39. Prove Theorem 10–12. (HINT: See Example 2, page 459.)

40. The radius of a circle is 6. Find the perimeter of the inscribed equilateral triangle and of the circumscribed equilateral triangle.

41. What is the ratio of the radius of a circle inscribed in an equilateral triangle to an altitude of the triangle?

42. An equilateral triangle is inscribed in a circle whose radius is 14. Find the length of one side of the triangle.

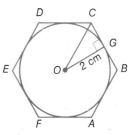

In Exercises 43–45, *ABCDEF* is a regular hexagon circumscribed about circle *O* and radius *OG* = 2 centimeters.

43. Find the apothem of hexagon *ABCDEF*.

44. Find the length of radius *OC*.

45. Find the area of the hexagon. (HINT: First find the area of $\triangle BOC$. Then area of hexagon $ABCDEF = 6$ (area $\triangle BOC$).

46. The radius of regular hexagon *ABCDEF* is 7. Find the area of the hexagon.

47. The radius of regular hexagon *ABCDEF* is *a*. Find the area of the hexagon.

C

48. Find the ratio of the apothem of an equilateral triangle to the radius of its circumscribed circle.

49. For a circle whose radius is x, find the ratio of the area of the inscribed equilateral triangle to the area of the circumscribed equilateral triangle.

10–6 Similarity and Polygons

Recall that two polygons are similar if corresponding angles are congruent and corresponding sides are proportional.

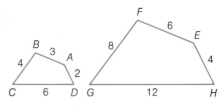

$ABCD \sim EFGH$

EXAMPLE 1 Use the similar polygons at the right to find each ratio.

a. The ratio of the measures of the corresponding sides

b. The ratio of the perimeters

Solutions: a. $\dfrac{6}{12} = \dfrac{4}{8} = \dfrac{3}{6} = \dfrac{2}{4} = \dfrac{1}{2}$ ⟵ — **Ratio of corresponding sides**

b. Perimeter of polygon $ABCD$: $2 + 3 + 4 + 6 = 15$

Perimeter of polygon $EFGH$: $4 + 6 + 8 + 12 = 30$

$\dfrac{15}{30} = \dfrac{1}{2}$ ⟵ — **Ratio of the perimeters**

The results of Example 1 are expressed in general form in Theorem 10–13.

Theorem 10–13

The perimeters of similar polygons have the same ratio as the measures of any two corresponding sides.

Since corresponding angles of any two regular polygons having the same number of sides will be congruent, any two regular polygons having the same number of sides can be proved similar.

Theorem 10–14

Regular polygons of the same number of sides are similar.

It follows from Theorems 10–13 and 10–14 that the perimeters of regular polygons have the same ratios as the measures of any two corresponding sides. Corollary 10–15 extends this equality of ratios to the radii and apothems of regular polygons.

Corollary 10–15

The perimeters of two regular polygons of the same number of sides have the same ratio as their radii or as their apothems.

Other ratio relationships exist between similar polygons. Theorem 10–16 and Corollary 10–17 relate to area.

Theorem 10–16	The areas of two similar polygons have the same ratio as the squares of the measures of any two corresponding sides.
Corollary 10–17	The areas of two regular polygons of the same number of sides have the same ratio as the squares of their radii or as the squares of their apothems.

EXAMPLE 2   Two regular polygons have areas of $54\sqrt{3}$ and $96\sqrt{3}$. The radius of the smaller polygon is 6. Find the radius of the larger.

Solution:

$\dfrac{54\sqrt{3}}{96\sqrt{3}} = \dfrac{9}{16}$ ◄——— **Ratio of the smaller area to the larger area**

$\dfrac{9}{16} = \left(\dfrac{6}{r}\right)^2$ ◄——— **By Corollary 10–17**

$\dfrac{9}{16} = \dfrac{36}{r^2}$

$9r^2 = 576$ ◄——— **Solve for r.**

$r^2 = 64$

$r = 8$ ◄——— **Radius of the larger polygon**

CLASSROOM EXERCISES

1. Find the ratio of the perimeters of two regular pentagons whose sides are 3 centimeters and 7 centimeters.

2. Find the ratio of the areas of two regular octagons whose sides are 4 millimeters and 6 millimeters.

3. The areas of two regular decagons are 64 square units and 81 square units. Find the ratio of their apothems.

4. The areas of two regular hexagons are in the ratio of 4:7. Find the ratio of their radii.

WRITTEN EXERCISES

A   The radii of two regular pentagons are 5 centimeters and 7 centimeters. Write the ratio of each of the following.

1. The sides   2. The apothems   3. The perimeters   4. The areas

The areas of two regular hexagons are 100 and 144. Write the ratio of each of the following.

5. The sides   6. The apothems   7. The radii   8. The perimeters

9. Two similar polygons have apothems of 15 units and 18 units. Find the ratio of their areas.

10. Two regular decagons are inscribed in two circles whose radii are 5 inches and 10 inches. Find the ratio of the areas of the decagons.

11. The areas of two similar polygons are $27\sqrt{2}$ and $48\sqrt{2}$ and the radius of the smaller polygon is 6. Find the radius of the larger polygon.

12. The areas of two similar pentagons are in the ratio of 12:25 and the apothem of the larger pentagon is 5. Find the apothem of the smaller pentagon.

13. Two regular octagons have apothems of 4 centimeters and 6 centimeters and the area of the smaller octagon is 52 square centimeters. Find the area of the larger octagon.

14. The perimeters of two similar polygons are 48 and 72, and the area of the larger is 270. Find the area of the smaller.

B

15. Three regular polygons have apothems in the ratio of 2:3:7. What is the ratio of the areas of these polygons?

16. The measure of each side of a regular polygon is doubled to make another polygon. Find the ratio of the area of the original polygon to the new polygon.

17. The radii of two similar polygons are in the ratio of 2:3 and the sum of their perimeters is 40. Find the perimeters of the two polygons.

18. Given the regular pentagons shown below, explain why they are similar.

19. **Given:** $\triangle ABC \sim \triangle DEF$

    Prove: $\dfrac{\text{Area } \triangle ABC}{\text{Area } \triangle DEF} = \dfrac{b^2}{b_1^2}$

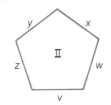

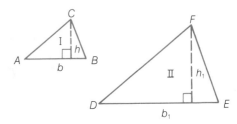

―――― **GEOMETRY REVIEW CAPSULE FOR SECTION 10-7** ――――

In Exercises 1–6, refer to circle O. $\overline{AC}$ is a chord of the circle and $\overleftrightarrow{CD}$ is tangent to the circle at C. *(Pages 348–350, 369–370, 378–379)*

1. If $m\angle AOB = 60$, then $m\overarc{AB} = \underline{\ ?\ }$.

2. If $m\angle ACB = 25$, then $m\overarc{AB} = \underline{\ ?\ }$.

3. If $m\angle DCA = 34$, then $m\overarc{CA} = \underline{\ ?\ }$.

4. If $m\overarc{AB} = 64$, then $m\angle AOB = \underline{\ ?\ }$.

5. If $m\overarc{CA} = 28$, then $m\angle DCA = \underline{\ ?\ }$.

6. If $m\overarc{AB} = 60$ and $m\overarc{CE} = 110$, then $m\angle CFE = \underline{\ ?\ }$.

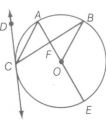

Consumer Applications
Geometry and Wallpapering

Finding the amount of wallpaper needed for a room is an application of area.

To determine how many rolls of wallpaper to purchase, you refer to rules such as these.

Rules	
1	Buy one roll of wallpaper for every 3 square meters of wall area.
2	Subtract one roll of paper for every door and one roll of paper for every two windows.

EXAMPLE   At $5.29 per roll, how much will it cost to wallpaper the four walls of a rectangular room having 2 windows and 1 door and having these dimensions?

Length: 3.2 m   Width: 2.4 m
            Height: 3.1 m

Solution: **1** Find the total area of the four walls.
$$A = 2(3.2 \cdot 3.1) + 2(2.4 \cdot 3.1)$$
$$= 19.84 + 14.88 = \mathbf{34.72 \ m^2}$$

2 Find the number of rolls of wallpaper needed. *Always* round *up* to the next complete roll. $34.72 \div 3 = 11.57$, or **12**

Subtract the allowance for doors and windows. $12 - 2 = \mathbf{10}$

3 Compute the total cost. $5.29 (10) = \mathbf{\$52.90}$

EXERCISES

In Exercises 1–5, complete the table below to find the cost of papering the given room.

	Length	Width	Height	Doors	Windows	Number of Rolls	Cost Per Roll	Total Cost
1.	4.3 m	3.0 m	2.7 m	2	2	?	$5.99	?
2.	4.3 m	3.6 m	2.7 m	1	3	?	$6.25	?
3.	3.0 m	2.4 m	3.0 m	1	4	?	$6.99	?
4.	4.9 m	3.6 m	3.6 m	3	2	?	$7.40	?
5.	3.6 m	3.6 m	2.7 m	2	3	?	$6.49	?

10-7 Circumference and Arc Length

The distance around a polygon is the *perimeter*. The distance around a circle is the **circumference,** C. As the number of sides of a regular polygon is increased, the perimeter approaches the circumference of the circumscribed circle.

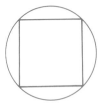  

The ratio of the perimeter, P, to the radius, r, is the same (constant) for all regular polygons that are similar. Since all circles are similar, the ratio of the circumference, C, to the radius, r, is a constant.

Therefore, the ratio of C to $2r$, or d, is also a constant. This suggests the following theorem.

Theorem 10-18	The ratio $\dfrac{C}{d}$ of the circumference C to the measure of the diameter d is the same for all circles.

Number of Sides of the Circumscribed Polygon	Perimeter of Circumscribed Polygon $\div d$
16	3.182597
32	3.151724
64	3.144118
128	3.14223
256	3.141750
512	3.141632
1024	3.141602
2048	3.141595
4096	3.141593

This table shows a method for approximating $\dfrac{C}{d}$, or π (pi).

$$\frac{C}{d} = \pi, \text{ or}$$

$$C = \pi d \text{ or}$$

$$C = 2\pi r$$

EXAMPLE 1 Find the circumference of a circle with $d = 20$.
Express the answer in terms of π.

Solution: $C = \pi d = 20\pi$

The proof of the following corollary is asked for in the Written Exercises.

Corollary 10–19	The circumferences of any two circles have the same ratio as their radii.

Considering a circle as an arc, the degree measure of the arc is 360. Thus, $2\pi r = 360$.

EXAMPLE 2 Find the length of $\overarc{AB}$ (arc AB), where 90 is its degree measure.

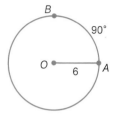

Solution:

$$2\pi r = 360$$

$$12\pi = 360 \longleftarrow \quad r = 6$$

$$\frac{90}{360} = \frac{1}{4} \longleftarrow \quad \frac{\textbf{Degree measure of } \overarc{AB}}{\textbf{Degree measure of a circle}}$$

$$\therefore \frac{1}{4} \cdot 12\pi = 3\pi \longleftarrow \quad \textbf{Length of } \overarc{AB}$$

Corollary 10–20 expresses the results of Example 2 in general terms.

Corollary 10–20	In a circle, the ratio of the length l of an arc to the circumference, $2\pi r$, equals the ratio of the degree measure, m, of the arc to 360. That is, $$\frac{l}{2\pi r} = \frac{m}{360}.$$

EXAMPLE 3 In circle P at the right, $r = 24$ and the length of $\overarc{CD}$ is 16π. Find the degree measure of $\overarc{CD}$.

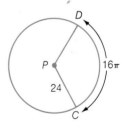

Solution:

$$\frac{l}{2\pi r} = \frac{m}{360} \longleftarrow \quad \begin{array}{l}\textbf{Replace } l \textbf{ with } 16\pi \\ \textbf{and } r \textbf{ with 24.}\end{array}$$

$$\frac{16\pi}{48\pi} = \frac{m}{360}$$

$$\frac{1}{3} = \frac{m}{360} \longleftarrow \quad \textbf{Solve for } m.$$

$$360 = 3m \quad \text{and} \quad 120 = m \quad \text{Thus, } m\overarc{CD} = 120.$$

The proportion in Corollary 10–20 can be solved for l or for m.

$$\frac{l}{2\pi r} = \frac{m}{360}, \text{ or } l = \frac{m}{360}(2\pi r)$$

$$\frac{l}{2\pi r} = \frac{m}{360}, \text{ or } m = \frac{360l}{2\pi r}.$$

CLASSROOM EXERCISES

In Exercises 1–4, express answers in terms of π.

1. Find the circumference of a circle whose radius is 14 centimeters.
2. Find the radius of a circle whose circumference is 34π units.
3. Find the length of an arc whose degree measure is 60 in a circle of radius 4.
4. In circle O, the length of $\overset{\frown}{AB}$ is 4π meters and the length of radius OB is 10 meters. Find the degree measure of $\overset{\frown}{AB}$.

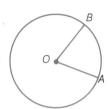

WRITTEN EXERCISES

A   In Exercises 1–6, find the unknown measures. Express answers in terms of π.

	Radius	Diameter	Circumference		Radius	Diameter	Circumference
1.	?	8	8π	2.	6	?	?
3.	?	?	48π	4.	?	6.4	?
5.	?	?	$\frac{15}{8}\pi$	6.	4.7	?	?

7. The circumferences of two circles are 6 units and 12 units. Find the ratio of the radii.
8. The radii of two circles are 2 meters and 8 meters. Find the ratio of the circumferences.
9. The ratio of the circumferences of two circles is 5:8 and the radius of the smaller circle is 10 centimeters. Find the radius of the larger circle.

In Exercises 10–15, the radius, r, and the degree measure, m, of an arc of a circle are given. Find the length of each arc of the circle.

10. $r = 18$; $m = 135$
11. $r = 12$; $m = 45$
12. $r = 24$; $m = 90$
13. $r = 36$; $m = 12$
14. $r = 4$; $m = 60$
15. $r = 8$; $m = 36$

16. In circle O, $\overline{AB}$ is a chord that is 4 centimeters from the center of the circle and radius OA is 8 centimeters. Find the length of $\overset{\frown}{AB}$.

In Exercises 17–22, the arc length, l, and the radius, r, of a circle are given. Find the degree measure of each arc.

17. $r = 6$; $l = 2\pi$
18. $r = 15$; $l = 10\pi$
19. $r = 16$; $l = 4\pi$
20. $r = 35$; $l = 14\pi$
21. $r = 32$; $l = 40\pi$
22. $r = 6$; $l = \frac{8}{3}\pi$

23. An arc of a circle has a measure of 45 and a length of 3π centimeters. Find the radius of the circle.

24. Prove Corollary 10–19. (HINT: Let the radii of the circles equal r and r' respectively. Find the circumference of each circle and compare the ratios.)

25. The radius of a circle is x inches and the circumference is y inches. Find the radius of a circle whose circumference is $2y$ inches in terms of x.

26. Circles O and O' at the left below have equal radii and each circle passes through the center of the other. Find the sum of the lengths of arcs BCD and DAB in terms of a radius r.

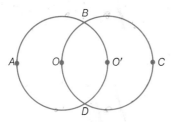 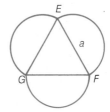

27. In the figure at the right above, $\triangle EFG$ is an equilateral triangle with side of length a. Each side is a diameter of a semicircle. Find the distance around the entire figure.

28. The radius of circle Q is 12. $\triangle ABC$ is inscribed in circle Q with m$\angle A = 58$ and m$\angle B = 63$. Find the length of $\overset{\frown}{BC}$, of $\overset{\frown}{AC}$, and of $\overset{\frown}{AB}$.

29. In circle T at the left below, chord $AB = 14$ and chord $CD = 20$. The radius of the circle is 25. Find the length of $\overset{\frown}{AB}$ and of $\overset{\frown}{CD}$. Express the answers in terms of π.

 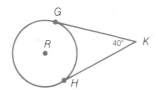

30. In circle R at the right above, $\overline{KG}$ and $\overline{KH}$ are tangent segments, m$\angle K = 40$, and the radius of the circle is 16. Find the length of $\overset{\frown}{GH}$. Express the answer in terms of π.

31. In the figure for Exercise 30, let the radius be r and m$\angle K = x$. Express the length of arc GH in terms of r and x.

32. Triangle ABC is equilateral with side of length s. D, E, and F are the midpoints of the sides. An arc is drawn with each vertex as center and one-half the length of a side as radius. Find, in terms of s, the distance around region DEF.

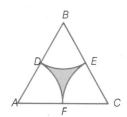

10–8   Area: Circles, Sectors, and Segments

As these figures suggest, the area of a regular polygon approaches the area of a circle as the number of sides increases.

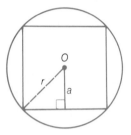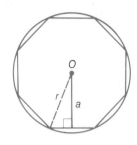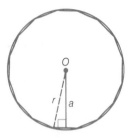

Further, as the number of sides increases, the apothem, a, approaches the radius, r, and the perimeter, P, approaches the circumference, C.

$$A = \tfrac{1}{2}aP \quad\longleftarrow\quad \textbf{Area of a regular polygon}$$

$$A = \tfrac{1}{2}rC \quad\longleftarrow\quad \textbf{The apothem, } \boldsymbol{a,} \textbf{ approaches } \boldsymbol{r} \textbf{ and } \boldsymbol{P} \textbf{ approaches } \boldsymbol{C.}$$

or

$$A = \tfrac{1}{2}r \cdot 2\pi r$$

$$A = \pi r^2$$

Theorem 10–21	The area, A, of a circle with radius, r, is given by this formula. $$A = \pi r^2$$

Corollary 10–22 follows from Theorem 1–21.

Corollary 10–22	The areas of two circles have the same ratio as the squares of their radii.

EXAMPLE 1   a. Find the area of this circle with radius 10.

b. Find the area of the shaded region.

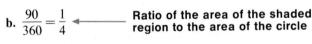

Solutions: a. $A = \pi r^2 \quad\longleftarrow\quad$ **Replace r with 10.**

$A = \pi (10)^2 = 100\pi$ **square units**

b. $\dfrac{90}{360} = \dfrac{1}{4} \quad\longleftarrow\quad$ **Ratio of the area of the shaded region to the area of the circle**

$\therefore \dfrac{1}{4} \cdot \dfrac{100\pi}{1} = 25$

Thus, the area of the shaded region is **25π square units.**

In the figure for Example 1, the shaded region is called a *sector*.

Definition | A **sector of a circle** is a region bounded by an arc of the circle and two radii drawn to the endpoints of the arc.

Corollary 10–23 expresses the results of Example 1 in terms of a sector of a circle.

Corollary 10–23 | In a circle with radius r, the ratio of the area, A, of a sector to the area of the circle (πr^2) equals the ratio of the degree measure m of the arc of the sector to 360.
That is,

$$\frac{A}{\pi r^2} = \frac{m}{360}, \quad \text{or} \quad A = \frac{m}{360}(\pi r^2).$$

EXAMPLE 2   Find the area of the shaded region of circle O where $m\angle AOB = 90$.

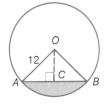

Solution: $\boxed{1}$ Find the area of sector OAB.

Area of sector OAB: $A = \dfrac{m}{360}\pi r^2$

$$= \frac{90}{360}\pi(12)^2$$

$$= \frac{90}{360} \cdot 144\pi = 36\pi \text{ square units}$$

$\boxed{2}$ Find the area of $\triangle OAB$.

Since $\triangle AOC$ is a 45-45 right triangle, $AC = OC$.
By the Isoceles Right-Triangle Theorem, $OC = \frac{12}{2}\sqrt{2} = 6\sqrt{2}$.
Thus, $AB = 12\sqrt{2}$. ←——— **AB = 2AC**

Area of $\triangle AOB$: $A = \frac{1}{2}bh$

$$= \frac{1}{2}(12\sqrt{2})(6\sqrt{2}) \quad \longleftarrow \quad b = AB \text{ and } h = OC$$

$$= 72 \text{ square units}$$

$\boxed{3}$ Area of shaded part = Area of sector OAB − Area of $\triangle OAB$

$$= (36\pi - 72) \text{ square units}$$

In the figure for Example 2, the shaded region is a *segment of the circle*.

Definition | A **segment of a circle** is a region bounded by an arc and its chord.

CLASSROOM EXERCISES

In Exercises 1–4, express answers in terms of π.

1. Find the area of a circle whose diameter is 12 centimeters.

2. Two circles have radii of 2 cm and 3 cm. Find the ratio of their areas.

3. Find the radius of a circle whose area is 25π square units.

4. Find the area of a sector with a 30°-arc and a radius of 6 centimeters.

WRITTEN EXERCISES

A   In Exercises 1–8, find the unknown measures.
Express answers in terms of π.

	Radius	Diameter	Area			Radius	Diameter	Area
1.	?	16	64π		**2.**	30	?	?
3.	?	?	256π		**4.**	$4\frac{3}{4}$	?	?
5.	?	?	$\frac{81}{64}\pi$		**6.**	?	24	?
7.	?	1	?		**8.**	3.2	?	?

9. The radii of two circles are 3 centimeters and 5 centimeters. Find the ratio of their areas.

10. The areas of two circles are 25π and 75π. Find the ratio of their radii.

11. The radius of one circle is twice the radius of a second circle. Find the ratio of their areas.

12. The region bounded between two concentric circles is an **annulus**, or **ring**, as in the figure at the right. Find the area of the annulus bounded by two circles whose radii are 6 and 8.

In Exercises 13–16, the area of each of four circles is given. Find the circumference of each circle.

13. 49π cm²   14. 400π m²   15. $\frac{49}{25}\pi$ m²   16. $\frac{9}{25}\pi$ yd²

In Exercises 17–20, the circumference of each of four circles is given. Find the area.

17. 60π units   18. $\frac{8}{3}\pi$ units

19. 24π units   20. 3.2π units

21. Triangle DEF at the right has sides of 6, 8, and 10. Show that the area of the semicircle on the hypotenuse equals the sum of the areas of the semicircles on the legs.

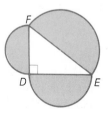

22. Point B is the midpoint of $\overline{AC}$ and $AC = 10$. Find the area bounded by $\overline{AC}$ and the two semicircles.

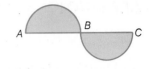

23. In the figure for Exercise 22, what is the ratio of the area bounded by $\overline{AC}$ and the two semicircles to the area of a circle whose radius is AB?

In Exercises 24–26, the radius, r, and the degree measure, m, of an arc of a circle are given. Find the area of the sector that is determined.

24. $r = 2$; $m = 60$ 25. $r = 3$; $m = 90$ 26. $r = 4$; $m = 120$

27. Find the area of each segment in Exercises 24–26.

In Exercises 28–30, the radius, r, and the area, A, of a sector are given. Find the degree measure of the arc.

28. $r = 4$; $A = 4\pi$ 29. $r = 12$; $A = 24\pi$ 30. $r = 20$; $A = 40\pi$

31. Write a formula for the area of a circle in terms of d, the diameter of the circle.

32. A regular hexagon is inscribed in a circle whose radius is 8 centimeters. Find the difference between the areas of the circle and the hexagon.

33. Write a formula for the area of a sector of a circle in terms of the length, l, of its arc and a radius, r.

34. Find the area of a ring bounded by circles with radii of $\frac{1}{2}x$ and x.

35. In Exercise 34, what is the ratio of the area of the ring to the area of the larger circle?

In Exercises 36–38, refer to the figure at the right in which a circle of radius y is inscribed in an equilateral triangle.

36. Express the total area of the shaded regions in terms of y.

37. What is the ratio of the area in Exercise 36 to the area of the circle?

38. What is the ratio of the area in Exercise 36 to the area of the triangle?

39. In the figure at the left below, $DEAR$ is a square inscribed in a circle with radius r. Find the total area of the shaded regions.

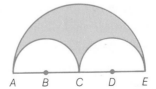

40. In the figure at the right above, three semicircles have their diameters along $\overline{AE}$. C is the center of the large semicircle, and B and D are the centers of the smaller semicircles. If $AE = 2r$, what is the area of the shaded region?

APPLICATIONS

USING AREA, PERIMETER, AND CIRCUMFERENCE

The exercises apply geometric concepts studied in Sections 10–1, 10–7, and 10–8.

A   The 70-story building shown in the photograph is circular in shape. The diameter of the building is 35 meters.

1. What is the area of any floor (cross-section)?

2. To the nearest meter, what is the perimeter of a square having the same area as one floor of the building?

3. What is the circumference of one floor of the building?

4. What is the difference between the perimeter of the square in Exercise 2 and the circumference of one floor in Exercise 3?

5. Refer to your answers to Exercises 1–4 to complete this statement.

If a circle and a square have the same area, then the circumference of the circle will be __?__ (less than or greater than) the perimeter of the square.

B   The diameter of a bull's eye (center circle) of a target is 5 centimeters. The width of each ring is 2.5 centimeters.

6. Find the total area of the target.

7. Find the area of the bull's eye.

Probability is a ratio between 0 and 1 that tells how likely it is that a certain event will happen. Thus, the probability, *p*, of hitting the bull's eye of the target can be expressed as follows:

$$P = \frac{\textbf{Area of Bull's Eye}}{\textbf{Area of Target}}.$$

8. Find the probability of hitting the bull's eye.

9. Find the probability of *not* hitting the bull's eye.

10. Find the total area of the shaded portion of the target.

11. Find the total area of the nonshaded portion of the target.

12. The probability of hitting a shaded portion of the target equals
$\dfrac{\text{area of shaded portion}}{\text{area of target}}$. Compute this probability.

C

13. Find the probability of hitting the outer shaded ring of the target.

BASIC: AREA

Problem: *Given the lengths of the three sides of a triangle, compute the area, x, using Hero's formula (see page 450).*

$$x = \sqrt{s(s - a)(s - b)(s - c)}$$

Program:
```
10 PRINT "ENTER THE LENGTHS OF THE SIDES."
20 INPUT A, B, C
30 LET S = .5 * (A + B + C)
40 LET X = SQR(S * (S - A) * (S - B) * (S - C))
50 PRINT "AREA = "; X
60 PRINT "ANY MORE TRIANGLES (1 = YES, 0 = NO)";
70 INPUT Y
80 IF Y = 1 THEN 10
90 END
```

EXERCISES

A   Run the program above with the following lengths.

1. $A = 15, B = 12, C = 7$
2. $A = 3, B = 4, C = 5$
3. $A = 19, B = 23, C = 14$
4. $A = 62, B = 48, C = 36$
5. $A = 16, B = 21, C = 33$
6. $A = 17, B = 18, C = 19$
7. $A = 24, B = 36, C = 18$
8. $A = 5, B = 12, C = 13$

B   Write a BASIC program for each problem.

9. Given the measures of the base of a triangle and its corresponding altitude, find the area of the triangle.

10. Given the length of one side of an equilateral triangle, find the area of the triangle.

11. Given the area of a rhombus and the length of one of its diagonals, find the length of the other diagonal.

12. Given the measure of the central angle of a regular polygon inscribed in a circle, determine the number of sides of the polygon.

13. Given the length of the radius of a regular hexagon, find the length of the apothem.

14. Given the areas of two similar polygons and the radius of one of them, compute the radius of the other.

15. Given the length of one side of a regular hexagon, compute the area of the hexagon.

In Exercises 1–4, find the area of the given regular polygon. *(Section 10–5)*

1. Apothem: 6; perimeter: $24\sqrt{3}$

2. Apothem: 9; perimeter: 72

3. Triangle; radius: 8

4. Hexagon; perimeter: 54

In Exercises 5–7, two regular hexagons have sides of 3 and 8. Write the ratio of each of the following measures. *(Section 10–6)*

5. The apothems

6. The perimeters

7. The areas

In Exercises 8–10, the radius, *r,* and the degree measure, *m,* of an arc of a circle are given. Find the length of each arc of the circle. *(Section 10–7)*

8. $r = 16$; $m = 120$

9. $r = 12$; $m = 90$

10. $r = 26$; $m = 40$

In Exercises 11–13, the arc length, *l,* and the radius, *r,* of a circle are given. Find the degree measure of each arc. *(Section 10–7)*

11. $r = 4$; $l = 3\pi$

12. $r = 9$; $l = 9\pi$

13. $r = 24$; $l = 4\pi$

In Exercises 14–15, refer to circle *C.* Triangle *RTS* is equilateral and $CD = 12$. *(Sections 10–8)*

14. Find the area of sector *SCR.*

15. Find the area of segment *RDS.*

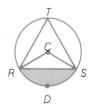

_____ Chapter Summary _____

IMPORTANT TERMS

Altitude (p. 442)
Apothem (p. 452)
Base (p. 442)
Center of a regular polygon (p. 452)
Central angle (p. 453)
Circular region (p. 438)
Circumference (p. 466)

Circumscribed circle (p. 452)
Inscribed circle (p. 452)
N-gon (p. 458)
Polygonal region (p. 438)
Radius of a regular polygon (p. 452)
Sector of a circle (p. 471)
Segment of a circle (p. 471)

IMPORTANT IDEAS

1. Areas of polygonal and circular regions

Rectangle: $A = lw$

Parallelogram: $A = bh$

Triangle: $A = \frac{1}{2}bh$

Equilateral triangle: $A = \frac{s^2\sqrt{3}}{4}$

Rhombus: $A = \frac{1}{2}d_1 d_2$

Trapezoid: $A = \frac{1}{2}h(b + b')$

Regular polygon: $A = \frac{1}{2}aP$

Circle: $A = \pi r^2$

Sector: $A = \frac{m}{360}(\pi r^2)$

Square: $A = s^2$

2. Circles can be circumscribed around, and inscribed within, a polygon. These circles have a common center if and only if the polygon is regular.

3. All regular polygons of the same number of sides are similar.

4. The perimeters of two regular polygons of the same number of sides have the same ratio as their radii, apothems, or corresponding sides.

5. The areas of two regular polygons of the same number of sides have the same ratio as the squares of the measures of their radii, apothems, or corresponding sides.

6. In a circle where r represents the length of a radius, l the length of an arc, and m the degree measure of the arc,

$$\frac{l}{2\pi r} = \frac{m}{360}.$$

Chapter Objectives and Review

Objective: *To find the areas of polygonal regions by using the area Postulates (Section 10–1)*

1. *ABCDE* is a polygonal region in which the area of $\triangle ABE$ is 7, the area of $\triangle EBD$ is 9, and the area of $\triangle DBC$ is 4. Find the area of polygonal region *ABCDE*.

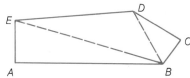

2. A rectangle has a length of 17.4 centimeters and a width of 14.2 centimeters. Find the area of the rectangle.

Objective: *To apply the formulas for the area of a parallelogram and the area of a triangle (Section 10–2)*

3. In parallelogram *GRAM* at the left below, $GR = 8$ centimeters and $MO = 5$ centimeters. Find the area.

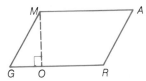

4. In triangle *TEN* at the right above, $\overline{ND} \perp \overline{TE}$, $m\angle T = 60$, $TE = 9$ and $TN = 8$. Find the area.

5. The area of an equilateral triangle is $9\sqrt{3}$ square units. Find the length of a side of the triangle.

6. The legs of a right triangle are 6 centimeters and 9 centimeters. Find the area of the triangle.

Objective: *To apply the formulas for the area of a rhombus and the area of a trapezoid (Section 10–3)*

7. Find the area of a rhombus with diagonals of 5 and 8.

8. The bases of a trapezoid are 10 units and 16 units and the area is 117 square units. Find the altitude.

Objective: *To find the measures of angles and the lengths of segments related to a regular polygon (Section 10–4)*

9. Find the measure of a central angle of a regular polygon with 20 sides.

10. The radius of a regular hexagon is 6 centimeters. Find the length of one side of the hexagon.

11. A regular hexagon is inscribed in a circle whose radius is 8 decimeters. Find the length of the apothem.

Objective: *To apply the formula for the area of a regular polygon (Section 10–5)*

12. Find the area of a regular decagon with an apothem of 4.2 centimeters and a side of 2.73 centimeters.

13. Find the area of an equilateral triangle with a radius of $6\sqrt{3}$.

Objective: *To apply the ratios related to area, perimeter, and segments that are parts of regular polygons (Section 10–6)*

Two similar polygons have apothems of length $2\sqrt{3}$ and $5\sqrt{3}$. Determine each ratio.

14. The corresponding sides   15. The perimeters   16. The areas

Objective: *To apply the formulas for circumference of a circle and length of an arc of a circle (Section 10–7)*

17. Find the radius of a circle whose circumference is 36π.

18. In circle O, $m\angle AOB = 36$ and radius $OA = 8$. Find the length of $\overset{\frown}{AB}$.

19. The circumferences of two circles are 4π units and 8π units. Find the ratio of the radii.

Objective: *To apply the formulas for the area of a circle, area of a sector, and area of a segment (Section 10–8)*

20. Find the area of a circle with circumference of 24π centimeters.

21. The radii of two circles are 4 centimeters and 7 centimeters. Find the ratio of their areas.

22. Find the area of a sector of a circle with a radius of 4 and a degree measure of 120.

23. In circle O, $OB = 6$ and $m\angle AOB = 60$. Find the area of segment ACB.

Objective: *To solve word problems that involve area of polygons (Page 451)*

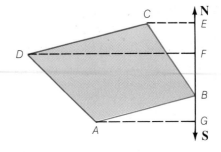

24. In surveying a field, a surveyor laid off north-and-south line *NS* through *B* and then located the east-west lines *CE*, *DF*, and *AG*. He found that *CE* = 5 rods, *DF* = 12 rods, *AG* = 10 rods, *BG* = 6 rods, *BF* = 9 rods, *FE* = 4 rods. Find the area of the field.

Objective: *To solve word problems that involve area, perimeter, and circumference (Page 474)*

25. Find the area of one face of this iron washer if its diameter is 4 centimeters and the diameter of the hole is 2 centimeters.

_____ Chapter Test _____

1. In parallelogram *ABCD*, *DE* = 8 and *AB* = 12. Find the area of the parallelogram.

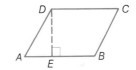

2. In the figure at the right, *ACDE* and *ABFG* are parallelograms with equal altitudes to bases *AC* and *AB*, respectively. If *B* is the midpoint of $\overline{AC}$ and the area of *ABFG* is 124 square units, what is the area of *ACDE*?

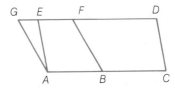

3. In triangle *RST* at the left below, m∠ *R* = 120, *TR* = 8 and *RS* = 9. Find the area of the triangle.

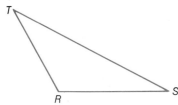

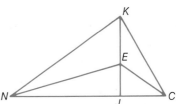

4. In the figure at the right above, *KJ* = 7 centimeters and *EJ* = 3 centimeters. Find the ratio of the area of △*NCE* to the area of △*NCK*.

5. Find the area of an equilateral triangle with a side 3 units long.

6. The length of the hypotenuse of a right triangle is 13 and the length of one leg is 12. Find the area of the triangle.

7. The area of a rhombus is 28 square centimeters and the length of one diagonal is 8 centimeters. Find the length of the other diagonal.

8. In trapezoid *TRAP*, *PA* = 6, *TR* = 10, $\overline{AR} \perp \overline{TR}$, and m∠ *T* = 45. Find the area of the trapezoid.

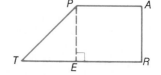

9. Find the measure of each central angle of a regular polygon with 12 sides.

10. The measure of one central angle of a regular polygon is 40. Find the number of sides of the polygon.

11. Find the length of the apothem of a regular hexagon whose radius is 8 centimeters.

12. Find the area of a regular decagon with apothem of 4 millimeters and side of 2.6 millimeters.

13. The perimeters of two regular octagons are 50 and 16. Find the ratio of their radii.

14. The areas of two regular pentagons are in the ratio of 4:49. Find the ratio of their apothems.

15. Find the circumference of a circle whose radius is 7 meters.

16. Find the radius of a circle whose circumference is 24π.

17. In circle *O*, the length of radius *OA* is 7 meters and m∠ *AOB* = 16. Find the length of $\overparen{AB}$.

18. Find the area of a circle whose diameter is 10 centimeters.

19. Find the area of the shaded part of the circle at the right.

20. Find the area of the segment of a circle with radius of 12 centimeters and degree measure of 60.

CHAPTER **11** # Surface Area and Volume

Sections

11-1 **Surface Area: Prisms**

11-2 **Surface Area: Pyramids**

11-3 **Surface Area: Cylinders and Cones**

Applications: Using Surface Area

11-4 **Volume: Prisms and Pyramids**

11-5 **Volume: Cylinders and Cones**

11-6 **Surface Area and Volume: Spheres**

Applications: Using Volume

Features

Consumer Application: Volume and Air Conditioning

Computer Application: Surface Area and Volume

Puzzles

Review and Testing

Geometry Review Capsules

Review: Sections 11–1 through 11–3

Review: Sections 11–4 through 11–6

Chapter Summary

Chapter Objectives and Review

Chapter Test

Cumulative Review: Chapters 1–11

Preparing for College Entrance Tests

11–1   Surface Area: Prisms

The solids shown below are *prisms*. The parts of intersecting planes that determine each prism are its **faces.** Two faces, B and B', are **bases** of each prism. The other faces are **lateral** (side) **faces.** The intersections of the faces are called **edges.**

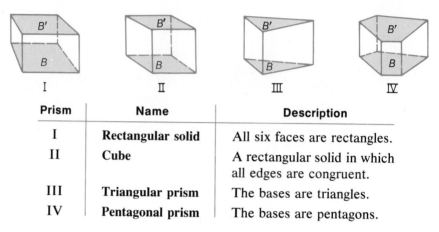

Prism	Name	Description
I	Rectangular solid	All six faces are rectangles.
II	Cube	A rectangular solid in which all edges are congruent.
III	Triangular prism	The bases are triangles.
IV	Pentagonal prism	The bases are pentagons.

The four prisms named in the table are **right prisms** because a lateral edge is perpendicular to the plane of a base. A prism that does not have this property is *oblique*. A **regular prism** is a right prism whose bases are regular congruent polygons.

Oblique Prism

An **altitude of a prism** is a segment that is perpendicular to the planes of the bases and that has an endpoint in each plane. In a right prism, *any lateral edge is an altitude.*

The **lateral surface area** of a prism is the sum of the areas of its lateral faces.

EXAMPLE 1   Find the lateral surface area of this prism.

Solution: The lateral surface has three rectangular faces.

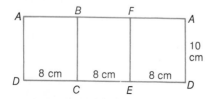

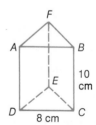

Lateral surface area:

$(8 + 8 + 8) \cdot 10 = 24 \cdot 10$

$= \textbf{240 cm}^2$

The results of Example 1 are stated in general form in Theorem 11–1.

Theorem 11–1	The lateral surface area L of a right prism is the product of the perimeter P of its base and its lateral edge, e. That is, $$L = Pe$$

The **total area** of a prism is the sum of its lateral surface area and the areas of its two bases.

EXAMPLE 2 Find the total area of this regular hexagonal prism.

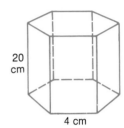

20 cm

4 cm

Solution: **1** Find the lateral area.

$$L = Pe \longleftarrow \quad \textbf{P = 6 · 4; e = 20}$$
$$= (6 \cdot 4)20 = 480 \text{ cm}^2$$

2 Find the area of one base.

$$\text{Area of a base} = \tfrac{1}{2}aP \longleftarrow \quad \textbf{By Theorem 10–12}$$
$$= \tfrac{1}{2} \cdot 2\sqrt{3} \cdot 24$$
$$= 24\sqrt{3} \text{ cm}^2$$

3 Find the total area.

Lateral surface area + Area of bases = Total area

$$480 \quad\quad + \quad 2(24\sqrt{3}) \quad = (480 + 48\sqrt{3}) \text{ cm}^2$$

CLASSROOM EXERCISES

In Exercises 1–4, refer to the figure at the right.

1. Find P, the perimeter of the base.
2. Find L, the lateral surface area.
3. Find the area of one base.
4. Find the total area.

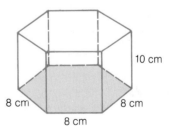

10 cm

8 cm   8 cm

8 cm

A right pentagonal prism has an altitude of 6 meters, and bases with sides of 3 meters, 4 meters, 2 meters, 3.4 meters and 4.6 meters.

5. Find the perimeter of the base.
6. Find the lateral surface area.

WRITTEN EXERCISES

A In Exercises 1–4, refer to the cube at the right.

Find each unknown measure.

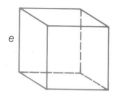

	Lateral Edge e	Perimeter of Base P	Lateral Area L	Area of One Base B	Total Area T
1.	7	?	?	?	?
2.	3	?	?	?	?
3.	?	40	?	?	?
4.	?	?	?	25	?

Refer to this right prism in Exercises 5–9. Each base is a regular polygon. The number of sides and the length of a lateral edge are given.

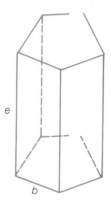

	Sides per Base n	Edge of Base b	Perimeter Base P	Lateral Edge e	Lateral Area L
5.	5	4	?	9	?
6.	6	8	?	12	?
7.	4	7	?	6	?
8.	8	6	?	10	?
9.	10	3	?	7	?

10. The perimeter of the base of a right prism is 37 and a lateral edge is 22. Find the lateral surface area.

11. Find the lateral surface area and the total area of the rectangular solid at the right.

12. The base of a right prism is a rectangle whose width is 6 meters and whose length is 9 meters. The altitude of the prism is 12 meters long. Find the lateral surface area.

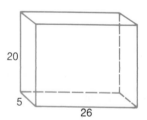

In Exercises 13–17, the measure of an edge of a cube is given. Find the total area.

13. 9 **14.** 3 **15.** $4\frac{1}{2}$ **16.** $4x$ **17.** e

18. Use Exercise 17 to write a formula for the lateral surface area L of a cube in terms of its edge e.

19. Use Exercise 17 to write a formula for the total area T of a cube in terms of its edge e.

The diagonal of one face of a cube is $5\sqrt{2}$ centimeters long.

20. Find the area of one face.   **21.** Find the total area.

In Exercises 22–26, the measure of a diagonal of a face of a cube is given. Find the total area.

22. $6\sqrt{2}$ **23.** $4\sqrt{3}$ **24.** 16   **25.** $x\sqrt{2}$ **26.** d

27. Use Exercise 26 to write a formula for the total area T of a cube in terms of a diagnonal d of one face.

In Exercises 28–34, classify each statement as always true, *A*, sometimes true, *S*, or never true, *N*.

28. The lateral edges of a right prism are perpendicular to both bases.

29. The lateral faces of a prism are rectangles.

30. In any prism the lateral edges are congruent and parallel.

31. The bases of a prism are regular polygons.

32. In an oblique prism, any lateral edge is an altitude of the prism.

33. The bases of any prism are congruent polygons.

34. If two parallel planes intersect a prism, the intersections form two congruent polygons.

B   In Exercises 35–41, refer to the cube at the right. $\overline{BD}$ and $\overline{FH}$ are diagonals of two of the faces and $\overline{DF}$ is a diagonal of the cube. Express any radicals in simplest form.

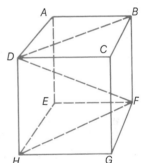

35. What kind of triangle is $\triangle ABD$?

36. What kind of triangle is $\triangle FGH$?

37. Is $\triangle DFH$ a right triangle? Explain.

38. Is $\triangle DFH$ isosceles? Explain.

39. If $CD = 5$, find BD.

40. If $GC = 7$, find BD and FH.

41. If $BD = 6$, find BF. Then use the Pythagorean Theorem to find DF.

42. Find the measure of one edge of a cube if a diagonal of the cube is $4\sqrt{3}$ units long.

C   In the figure at the right, $\overline{AB}$ is perpendicular to the plane of $\triangle BCD$ and $\overline{BD} \perp \overline{CD}$.

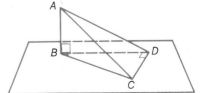

43. Name the right triangles in the figure and the hypotenuse of each.

44. If $AB = 16$, $BD = 10$, and $CD = 4$, find AC.

45. If $AD = 12$, m$\angle DBC = 30$ and m$\angle ADB = 30$, find AC.

Find the area of each polygon. *(Pages 442–444, 458–459)*

1.

2.

3.

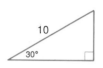

4.

11–2 Surface Area: Pyramids

Pyramid V-ABCDE has its vertex at *V* and pentagon *ABCDE* is its base. The five triangular faces that have *V* as a common point are **lateral faces**. The intersections of the lateral faces, such as $\overline{AV}$, $\overline{BV}$, and $\overline{CV}$, are **edges**. The **altitude** of a pyramid is the segment drawn perpendicular to the base from the vertex of the pyramid.

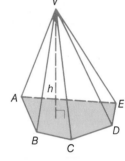

A **regular pyramid** is one whose base is a regular polygon and whose altitude, *VH*, passes through the center of the base. The **slant height,** *s*, of a regular pyramid is the length of the altitude of one of its faces. The lateral faces are congruent triangles.

The **lateral surface area** of a pyramid is the sum of the areas of its lateral faces.

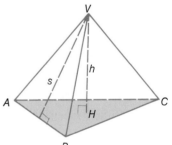

EXAMPLE 1 Find the lateral surface area of regular pyramid *V-WXYZ*.

Solution: The lateral faces are four congruent isosceles triangles.

Lateral surface area:

$4(\text{Area } \triangle VWX) = 4(\frac{1}{2} \cdot b \cdot h)$

$\qquad = 4(\frac{1}{2} \cdot a \cdot s)$

$\qquad = \frac{1}{2}(4a \cdot s) \longleftarrow$ **Perimeter of base: 4a**

$\qquad = \frac{1}{2}Ps$

Theorem 11–2 states the results of Example 1 in general form.

<table>
<tr><td>Theorem 11–2</td><td>The lateral area L of a regular pyramid equals one half the product of its slant height s and the perimeter P of its base. That is,

$$L = \tfrac{1}{2}sP.$$</td></tr>
</table>

Example 2 illustrates how to use this theorem to find the total area of a regular pyramid.

EXAMPLE 2 Find the total area of this regular hexagonal pyramid.

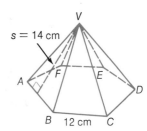

Solution: **1** Find the lateral area.

$L = \tfrac{1}{2}sP \longleftarrow$ **s = 14; P = 6 (12)**

$= \tfrac{1}{2} \cdot 14 \cdot (12 \cdot 6)$

$= 7 \cdot 72 = 504 \text{ cm}^2$

2 Find the area of the base.

$\text{Area} = \tfrac{1}{2}aP \longleftarrow$ **a = 6√3; P = 6 (12)**

$= \tfrac{1}{2} \cdot 6\sqrt{3} \cdot 72$

$= 216\sqrt{3} \text{ cm}^2$

Hexagonal Base

3 Find the total area.

Lateral Surface Area + Area of Base = Total Area

$\quad\quad 504 \quad\quad + \quad 216\sqrt{3} = (504 + 216\sqrt{3}) \text{ cm}^2$

When a pyramid is not regular, you compute the total area by finding the sum of the areas of its faces.

CLASSROOM EXERCISES

A regular pyramid with a triangular base has a slant height of 14 meters. Each side of the base is 12 meters long.

Use this information in Exercises 1–3 to find each measure.

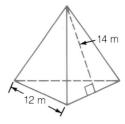

1. Lateral surface area

2. Area of base

3. Total area

WRITTEN EXERCISES

A   Classify each statement as always true, *A*, sometimes true, *S*, or never true, *N*.

1. All lateral faces of a regular pyramid are triangles.

2. The lateral edges of a regular pyramid are congruent segments.

3. The slant height of a regular pyramid is greater than its altitude.

4. A pyramid with a regular polygon for a base is a regular pyramid.

5. A pyramid has two bases which are congruent polygons.

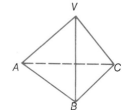

Refer to the triangular pyramid at the right to complete Exercises 6–10. The lateral faces and the base are equilateral triangles.

6. If edge *BC* is 8 centimeters long, then the area of one face is __?__ and the total area is __?__ .

7. If edge *BC* measures 6 centimeters, then the slant height is __?__ , the perimeter of the base is __?__ , and the lateral surface area is __?__ .

8. If the slant height of the regular pyramid is $5\sqrt{3}$, the length of an edge is __?__ , the perimeter is __?__ , and the lateral surface area is __?__ .

9. If an edge of the regular pyramid is *e*, the slant height is __?__ , the perimeter is __?__ , and the lateral surface area is __?__ .

10. If an edge of the regular pyramid is *e*, the area of one face is __?__ , and the total surface area is __?__ .

A regular square pyramid has a slant height of 7 centimeters and a base whose edge is 6 centimeters. Use this information in Exercises 11–13 to find each measure.

11. Lateral surface area   12. Area of the base   13. Total area

A regular hexagonal pyramid has a slant height of 20 and a base whose edge is 6. Use this information in Exercises 14–16 to find each measure.

14. Lateral surface area   15. Area of the base   16. Total area

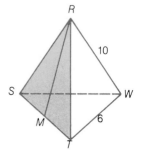

In the regular pyramid *R-STW*, *RW* = 10 and *TW* = 6. Refer to this figure in Exercises 17–20.

17. Find the length of the slant height *RM*.

18. What is the area of one lateral face such as △*RST*? Of three lateral faces?

19. Use Theorem 11-2 to find the lateral area of pyramid *R-STW*.

20. Find the total area of pyramid *R-STW*.

21. The base of a regular pyramid is an octagon with sides of 12 centimeters. The lateral surface area is 768 cm². Find the slant height.

> A pyramid with a square base has a slant height of 8 and a lateral surface area of 144. Find each of the following.

22. Perimeter of the base
23. Area of the base

24. The base of a regular pentagonal pyramid has a perimeter of 45 inches. Find the lateral area if the slant height is 10 inches.

25. The area of the base of a regular quadrangular pyramid is 100 square meters. The altitude of the pyramid is 12 meters. Compute the lateral area and the total area.

26. A regular pyramid has an equilateral triangle for each face. If one edge of the pyramid is 18, find the lateral area and the total area.

B   In Exercises 27–33, refer to pyramid *V-XYZ*. In this figure, $\overline{VX} \perp \overline{YX}$, triangles *VYZ* and *XYZ* are isosceles, *VX* = 6, *ZX* = 8, and *YZ* = 4.

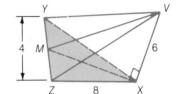

27. Find the areas of triangles *VXZ* and *VXY*.
28. Find *VM*, the altitude of △*VYZ*.
29. What is the area of △*VYZ*?
30. From your answers to Exercises 27 and 29, what is the lateral area *L*?
31. If $\overline{XM}$ is an altitude of △*XYZ*, then *XM* = __?__ .
32. What is the area of △*XYZ*?
33. Use your answers to Exercises 30 and 32 to find *T*, the total area.

> One side of the base of regular pyramid *A-XYZT* is 12 and altitude *AC* of the pyramid is 8. Find each of the following.

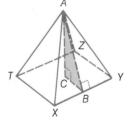

34. *CB*   **35.** *AB*
36. Lateral surface area
37. Total area

> The base of a regular pyramid is a hexagon whose edge is 30 units and whose altitude is 10√3 units. Find each of the following.

38. Slant height   **39.** Lateral surface area

C

40. In the rectangular prism at the right, *T* is the center of the upper face. *T-WXYZ* is a pyramid whose base has the dimensions *a* and *b*. The height of the prism is *c*. Find the lateral area and the total area of the pyramid.

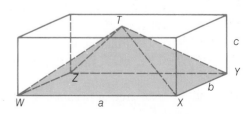

11-3 Cylinders and Cones

The figures below are *cylinders* with circular bases.

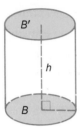

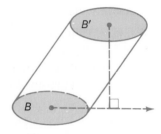

Right Circular Cylinder   **Oblique Circular Cylinder**

In a **right circular cylinder** or in an oblique circular cylinder, the distance between the bases is the **altitude** of the cylinder. The **bases** B and B' are congruent circles.

The **lateral area** of a right circular cylinder is the area of its curved surface. The **total area** is the sum of the lateral area and the area of the two bases.

EXAMPLE 1 Find the total area of this right circular cylinder of radius 3 and altitude 7.

Solution: [1] Find the area of the lateral surface.

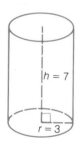

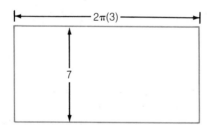

$L = 2\pi(3) \cdot 7 = 42\pi$ ←———— A rectangle with dimensions 7 and $2\pi(3)$ has the same lateral area as the cylinder.

[2] Find the area of the bases.

$A = 2\pi(3)^2$ ←———— Area of circle: πr^2

$\quad = 18\pi$

[3] Find the total area, T.

$T = 42\pi + 18\pi$ ←———— Lateral surface area + Area of bases

$T = 60\pi$

Theorem 11–3 expresses the results of Example 1 as a formula.

Theorem 11–3	For a right circular cylinder with base radius r and altitude h, $$L\text{(lateral area)} = 2\pi rh,$$ and $T\text{(total area)} = 2\pi r(h + r).$$

EXAMPLE 2 Find the lateral area and the total area of this right circular cylinder. Express answers in terms of π.

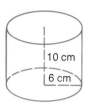

Solution: Use the formulas of Theorem 11–3. Let $h = 10$ and $r = 6$.

$L = 2\pi rh$ $\qquad T = 2\pi r(h + r)$

$L = 2\pi(6)(10)$ $\qquad T = 2\pi(6)(10 + 6)$

$L = 120\pi$ cm^2 $\qquad T = 192\pi$ cm^2

The figures below are *cones* with circular bases.

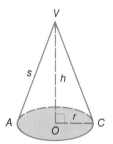

Right Circular Cone

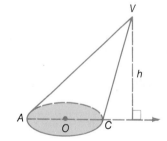

Oblique Circular Cone

The **altitude of a cone** is the length of the segment from the **vertex**, V, perpendicular to the base. In a **right circular cone**, the altitude passes through the center of the base. In the right circular cone above, h is the altitude and s is the slant height.

The **lateral area of a cone** is the area of its curved surface. The **total area** is the sum of the lateral area and the area of the base.

NOTE: Unless otherwise stated, any reference to a cone in this text means right circular cone.

Theorem 11–4	For a right circular cone with slant height s and base circumference $2\pi r$, where r is the radius of the base, $$L\text{(lateral area)} = \pi rs$$ and $T\text{(total area)} = \pi r(s + r).$$

EXAMPLE 3 For a cone with a radius of 5 meters and an altitude of 12 meters, find each of the following.

a. Lateral area   b. Total area

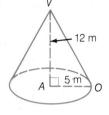

Solutions:

a. Use the Pythagorean Theorem to find the slant height, VO.

In $\triangle VAO$, $(VO)^2 = (VA)^2 + (AO)^2$

$$(VO)^2 = 12^2 + 5^2$$
$$(VO)^2 = 144 + 25$$
$$(VO)^2 = 169$$
$$VO = 13 \text{ m} \longleftarrow \text{ Slant height, } s$$

$L = \pi r s \longleftarrow$ Replace r with 5 and s with 13.

$= \pi \cdot 5 \cdot 13 = 65\pi \text{ m}^2$

b. $T = \pi r (s + r)$

$= \pi \cdot 5 (13 + 5) = 90\pi \text{ m}^2$

CLASSROOM EXERCISES

In Exercises 1–4, find the lateral area and the total area of each figure. Express answers in terms of π.

1.

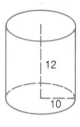

2.

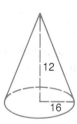

3.

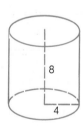

4.

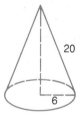

WRITTEN EXERCISES

A   In Exercises 1–4, find the lateral area and the surface area of each figure. Express answers in terms of π.

1.

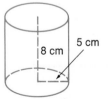

2.

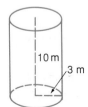

3.

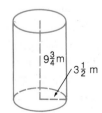

4.

5. Find the lateral area of a right circular cone with a slant height of 12 and base radius of 4.

6. Find the total area of the cone in Exercise 5.

7. Two containers are right circular cylinders. One has a radius of 20 and an altitude of 16. The other has a radius of 10 and an altitude of 32. Find the lateral area of each container.

8. Solve the formula for the lateral area of a right circular cylinder for r.

9. Find the radius of a right circular cylinder with lateral area of 216π and height of 12.

10. What is the height of a right circular cylinder with lateral area of 154π and radius of 7?

11. Solve the formula for the lateral area of a cone for r and for s.

12. Find the radius of a cone with lateral area of 72π and slant height of 9.

13. What is the slant height of a cone with lateral area of $\frac{9\pi}{10}$ and radius of $\frac{3}{5}$?

B

14. A right circular cone has an altitude of 8 centimeters and a base radius of 6 centimeters. Find the lateral area and the total area.

15. Find the height of a right circular cylinder with total area of 528π and with radius of 12.

16. The total area of a cone is 90π and its radius is 5. Find the slant height.

17. Write the formulas $L = 2\pi rh$ and $T = 2\pi r(h + r)$ in terms of h when $r = h$.

18. Write the formulas in Exercise 17 in terms of h when $2r = h$.

19. Rectangle $EFGH$ is revolved about $\overline{EH}$ as an axis generating a right cylinder. Let $HG = x$ and $GF = y$. Find the lateral area of the cylinder in terms of x and y.

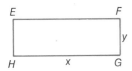

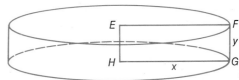

C

20. Right triangle ABC is revolved about $\overline{BC}$ as an axis. Name the figure generated.

21. The radius of the base of a cone of revolution (see Exercise 20) is 3.2 meters and the lateral area is 38.4π m². Find the slant height.

22. The slant height of a cone of revolution (see Exercise 20) is 5 centimeters and the total area is 24π cm². Find the radius of the base.

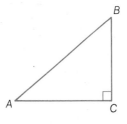

APPLICATIONS

USING SURFACE AREA

These exercises apply geometric concepts studied in Sections 11–1 through 11–3.

A

1. The dimensions of a flower box are shown at the right. Find the number of square centimeters of material needed to build the box. Round your answer to the nearest square centimeter.

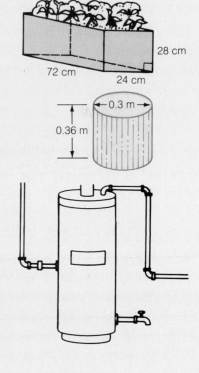

28 cm

72 cm

24 cm

2. A lamp shade has the shape of a right circular cylinder. The diameter of the shade is 0.3 meter and the height is 0.36 meter. To the nearest tenth, how much material is needed for the shade?

0.3 m

0.36 m

3. A hot water tank having the shape of a cylinder is to be insulated by covering the entire outer surface. The diameter of the tank is 2.8 meters and its height is 11.5 meters. To the nearest square meter, how much insulation will be needed? Allow 14 m² of insulation for overlap.

4. A circular box of salt has a radius of $1\frac{1}{2}$ inches and a height of 5 inches. To the nearest square inch, how much heavy cardboard will be needed to make two million such boxes? Allow 5 in² per box for overlap.

B

5. The Great Pyramid of Egypt (also called the pyramid of Khufu) has a height of 148 meters and a square base with a perimeter of 930 meters. Find the lateral surface area of the pyramid.

(HINT: Use a calculator.)

6. The Transamerica Pyramid building in San Francisco has a height of 260 meters and a square base with a perimeter of 140 meters. Find the lateral surface area.

(HINT: Assume that the building is a perfect pyramid. Use a calculator.)

7. Which has the greater lateral surface area, the Great Pyramid of Egypt or the Transamerica Building? How much greater is it?

8. A store sells two types of wrapping paper. Type A contains four rolls per package and sells for $3.99. The dimensions of each roll are 75 cm by 150 cm. Type B contains a single roll with dimensions 88 cm by 500 cm. The package sells for $4.19. For which type will you get more paper for your money?

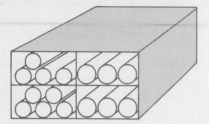

─── Review ─────────────────────────────

In Exercises 1–3, refer to the regular pentagonal prism at the right. *(Section 11–1)*

1. Find the lateral area.

2. Find the total area.

3. The base of a rectangular prism is 7 centimeters wide and 13 centimeters long. The length of a lateral edge is 4 centimeters. Find the lateral area and the total area. *(Section 11–1)*

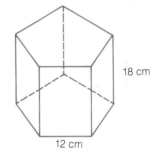

18 cm

12 cm

In Exercises 4–6, refer to regular pyramid *B-DLEN* at the right, The base is a square with a side of 7 units. The slant height is 10 units. *(Section 11–2)*

4. Find the perimeter of the base.

5. Compute the lateral area.

6. Compute the total area.

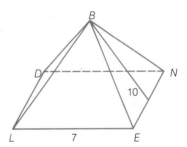

In Exercises 7–10, refer to the right circular cylinder and the cone below. *(Section 11–3)*

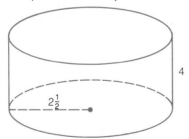

4

$2\frac{1}{2}$

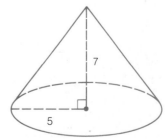

7

5

7. Find the lateral area of the cylinder.

8. Find the total area of the cylinder.

9. Find the lateral area of the cone.

10. Find the total area of the cone.

11-4 Volume: Prisms and Pyramids

The **volume** of a solid is the number of cubic units contained in the solid. If measures are given in centimeters, the volume is stated in terms of cubic centimeters, written cm³. Other measures of volume are cubic meters, m³, cubic feet, ft³, cubic inches, in³, and so on.

	Volume Postulates
Postulate 20	Every geometric solid corresponds to a positive number which is its volume.
Postulate 21	The volume of a solid figure is the sum of the volumes of a finite number of non-overlapping figures of which it is composed.

The rectangular box at the right is made up of 24 congruent cubes. The side of each cube is 1 unit in length. Thus, the volume of each cube is 1 cubic unit, and, by Postulate 21, the volume of the 24 cubes is 24 cubic units.

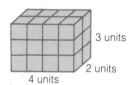

3 units
2 units
4 units

Since the box has three layers, each with 2(4), or 8 cubes,
$$V = (2 \cdot 4) \cdot 3 = 24 \text{ cubic units.}$$

Area of Base ———↑   ↑——— **Height (altitude)**

Postulate 22	The volume V of a rectangular prism is the product of its altitude h, the length of the base l, and the width of the base, w. That is, $$V = lwh.$$

The volume of a prism can be expressed in terms of the area of the base, B.

Theorem 11-5	The volume V of a prism is the product of its altitude h and the area B of the base. That is, $$V = Bh.$$

For a cube, this formula can be stated in terms of an edge, e.

REMEMBER: In a cube, the length, width, and height are the same.

Theorem 11-6	The volume V of a cube with edge e is the cube of e. That is, $$V = e^3.$$

EXAMPLE 1 Find the volume of each solid.

a.

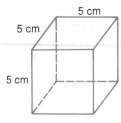

5 cm

5 cm

5 cm

5 cm

Cube

b.

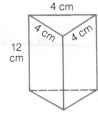

4 cm

4 cm   4 cm

12 cm

Right Triangular Prism

Solutions: **a.** $V = e^3$ ⟵ **By Theorem 11–6**

$V = 5 \cdot 5 \cdot 5$

$V = 125$ **cm³**

b. $V = B \cdot h$ ⟵ **By Theorem 11–5**

$V = \left(\dfrac{s^2}{4}\sqrt{3}\right) \cdot h$

$V = \dfrac{4^2}{4}\sqrt{3} \cdot 12$

$V = 48\sqrt{3}$ **cm³**

If a prism and a pyramid have equal altitudes and their bases have equal areas, the volume of the prism is three times the volume of the pyramid.

h

h

Corollary 11–7

The volume V of a pyramid is one third the product of its altitude h and the area B of its base. That is,

$$V = \tfrac{1}{3}Bh.$$

EXAMPLE 2 Find the volume of each pyramid.

a.

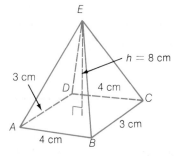

E

$h = 8$ cm

3 cm

D 4 cm

A C

4 cm B 3 cm

b.

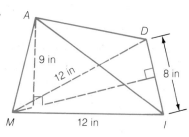

A

D

9 in

12 in

8 in

M 12 in I

Solutions: **a.** $B = (4 \cdot 3) = 12$ **cm²** ⟵ **Area of rectangle ABCD**

$V = \tfrac{1}{3}Bh$ ⟵ **By Theorem 11–7**

$V = \tfrac{1}{3}(12)(8)$

$V = 32$ **cm³**

b. $B = \frac{1}{2}(8)(8\sqrt{2})$ ←――― **Area of isosceles** $\triangle$ **MDI**

$B = 32\sqrt{2}$ in²

$V = \frac{1}{3}Bh$ ←――― **By Theorem 11–7**

$V = \frac{1}{3}(32\sqrt{2})(9)$

$V = 96\sqrt{2}$ in³

CLASSROOM EXERCISES

Find the volume of each solid.

1.

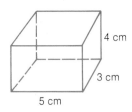

Rectangular Solid

2.

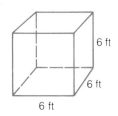

Cube

3.

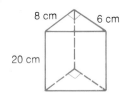

Right Triangular Prism

4.

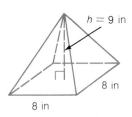

Square Pyramid

5.

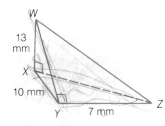

Right Triangular Prism

6.

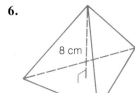

Regular Pyramid

WRITTEN EXERCISES

A   In these exercises, express answers in simplified radical form.

In Exercises 1–4, find the volume of the rectangular solid with the given dimensions.

1. $7 \times 9 \times 5$

2. $3.24 \times 2.64 \times 1.34$

3. $2\frac{1}{3} \times 1\frac{3}{4} \times 5\frac{1}{2}$

4. $8\sqrt{3} \times 5\sqrt{6} \times 7\sqrt{2}$

5. Find the volume of a prism whose base area is 24 square meters and whose altitude is 8 meters.

6. Find the volume of a right triangular prism whose base is an equilateral triangle 10 centimeters on a side and whose altitude is 6 centimeters.

7. The altitude of a right triangular prism is 6 and its base is an isosceles right triangle whose congruent sides are each 8. Find the volume of the prism.

8. The base of a right prism is an equilateral triangle 16 millimeters on a side. The altitude of the prism is 10 millimeters long. Find the volume.

9. Find the volume of a cube that has an edge of 10 meters.

10. Find the volume of a pyramid whose base area is 12 cm² and whose altitude is 5 centimeters.

11. Find the volume of a pyramid whose altitude is $3\frac{1}{2}$ and whose base has an area of 6 square units.

12. Find the volume of a triangular pyramid whose base is a right triangle with legs of 3 and $4\frac{1}{2}$ and whose altitude is 9.

13. Pyramid *V-RST* has an altitude of 5. Its base is an equilateral triangle of side 3. Find its volume.

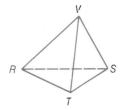

14. Find the volume of a quadrangular pyramid whose altitude is 8 and whose base is a square each of whose sides is 4.

Find the altitude of each rectangular solid having the given volume and area of the base.

15. 64 yd³; 15 yd²   16. 25.75 m³; 5.5 m²

B

17. The base of a regular triangular pyramid is an equilateral triangle. The volume of the pyramid is $960\sqrt{3}$ cm³ and the altitude of the pyramid is 15 cm. What is the length of one side of the base?

18. What is the effect upon the volume of a rectangular solid when one dimension is doubled and the two other dimensions remain the same? When two dimensions are doubled and the third remains the same? When all three are doubled?

19. In pyramid *V-RST*, $\overline{VR}$, $\overline{VT}$, and $\overline{VS}$ each have a length of 4 centimeters. The base is an equilateral triangle each of whose sides is 2 centimeters long. Find the volume.

C

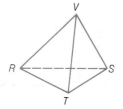

20. Find the volume of a triangular prism whose base is an equilateral triangle *a* units on a side and whose altitude is *b* units.

21. Find the volume of a triangular prism whose base is an isosceles right triangle whose congrument sides are each *a* units in length and whose altitude is *b* units.

Puzzle

The number of cubic centimeters in the volume of a cube is the same as the number of square centimeters in its surface area.

Find the length of an edge of the cube.

11–5   Volume: Cylinders and Cones

A twenty-five cent coin is 1.75 millimeters thick and has a radius of 12 millimeters. When four of these coins are stacked vertically, the stack is 7 millimeters high. When ten of these coins are stacked, the stack is 17.5 millimeters high.

The volume of the stack increases as more coins are added. The total volume depends on the area of each coin and on its thickness or height.

Theorem 11–8

> The volume V of a circular cylinder is the product of the altitude h and the area B of the base. That is,
>
> $$V = Bh \qquad \text{or} \qquad V = \pi r^2 h.$$

EXAMPLE 1   Find the volume of each circular cylinder. Express answers in terms of π.

a.

8 cm

5 cm

Right Cylinder

b.

20 mm

32 mm

Oblique Cylinder

Solutions: a. $V = \pi r^2 h$ ⟵ $r = 5; h = 8$ b. $V = \pi r^2 h$ ⟵ $r = 20; h = 32$

$V = \pi \cdot 5^2 \cdot 8$ $V = \pi \cdot 20^2 \cdot 32$

$V = 200\pi$ cm³ $V = 12{,}800\pi$ cm³

Since the area of the base of a pyramid approximates the area of a circle as the number of sides of the base of the pyramid increases, the formula for the volume of a cone resembles the formula for the volume of a pyramid.

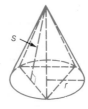
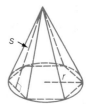

<table>
<tr><td>Theorem
11–9</td><td>The volume V of a circular cone is one third the product of the altitude h and the area B of the base. That is,
$$V = \tfrac{1}{3}Bh \qquad \text{or} \qquad V = \tfrac{1}{3}\pi r^2 h.$$</td></tr>
</table>

EXAMPLE 2 Find the volume of each circular cone. Express answers in terms of π.

a.

24 mm

9 mm

b.

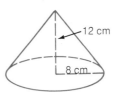

12 cm

8 cm

Solutions:

a. $V = \tfrac{1}{3}\pi r^2 h$ ← $r = 9; h = 24$

$V = \tfrac{1}{3}\pi \cdot 9^2 \cdot 24$

$V = 648\pi$ mm³

b. $V = \tfrac{1}{3}\pi r^2 h$ ← $r = 8; h = 12$

$V = \tfrac{1}{3}\pi \cdot 8^2 \cdot 12$

$V = 256\pi$ cm³

CLASSROOM EXERCISES

Find the volume of each cylinder or cone. Express answers in terms of π.

1.

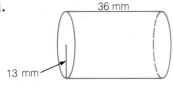

36 mm

13 mm

Cylinder

2.

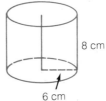

8 cm

6 cm

Cylinder

3.

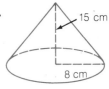

15 cm

8 cm

Cone

WRITTEN EXERCISES

A

In these exercises, express radicals in simplest form. Also, express answers in terms of π, where π occurs.

In Exercises 1–6, find the volume of each right circular cylinder.

1. $r = 6; h = 10$
2. $r = 5; h = 10$
3. $r = 3; h = 15$
4. $r = 2\sqrt{3}; h = 6$
5. $r = 1.25; h = 18$
6. $r = \sqrt{20}; h = \sqrt{8}$

In Exercises 7–12, find the volume of each right circular cone.

7. $r = 5; h = 12$
8. $r = 3.4; h = 8.9$
9. $4 = 3.5; h = 7$
10. $r = 2\sqrt{10}; h = 3.5$
11. $r = 3\sqrt{5}; h = 6$
12. $r = \sqrt{6}; h = 16.8$

The area of the base of a regular pyramid inscribed in a right circular cylinder is $48\sqrt{3}$ square centimeters. The radius of the cylinder is 8 centimeters and its height is 10 centimeters.

Refer to this information in Exercises 13–15.

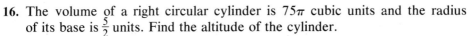

13. What is the volume of the cylinder?

14. Find the volume of the pyramid.

15. What is the ratio of the volume of the pyramid to the volume of the cylinder?

16. The volume of a right circular cylinder is 75π cubic units and the radius of its base is $\frac{5}{2}$ units. Find the altitude of the cylinder.

17. The volume of a right circular cone is 48π cubic units and its altitude is 4 units. Find the radius of the base.

[B]

18. How is the volume of a cone affected by doubling the radius of its base and leaving the altitude unchanged?

19. How does doubling the altitude of a cone while leaving the radius of the base unchanged affect the volume?

20. How is the volume of a cone affected by doubling the altitude *and* doubling the radius of the base?

In the figure at the right, a regular quadrangular prism is circumscribed about a circular cylinder. The altitude of the prism is 5. The radius of the base of the cylinder is 2.

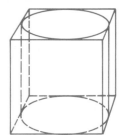

21. Find the volume of the cylinder.

22. Find the volume of the prism.

23. Find the ratio of the volume of the cylinder to the volume of the prism.

24. Find the volume of a right circular cone whose altitude is h units and whose slant height is s units.

25. Find the slant height of the cone at the left below whose volume is 30π cubic inches and whose altitude is 10 inches.

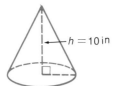

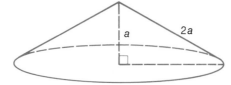

26. Find the volume of the right circular cone at the right above whose altitude is a units and whose slant height is $2a$ units.

27. If $V = \pi r^2 h$ and $T = 2\pi rh + \pi r^2$, find T in terms of r and V.

28. A regular quadrangular pyramid has as its base a square with sides of 3 inches. The altitude of the pyramid is 4 inches. Find its volume.

29. Find the volume of the cone that circumscribes the pyramid in Exercise 28.

30. Find the ratio of the volumes in Exercises 28 and 29.

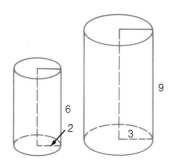

In Exercises 31–38, refer to these similar right circular cylinders.

31. Find the ratio of the radius of the smaller cylinder to the radius of the larger.

32. Find the ratio of the altitude of the smaller cylinder to the altitude of the larger.

33. Find the total area of each cylinder.

34. Find the ratio of the total area of the smaller cylinder to the total area of the larger.

35. Compare the ratios in Exercises 31, 32, and 34.

36. Find the volume of each cylinder.

37. What is the ratio of the volume of the smaller cylinder to that of the larger?

38. Compare the ratios in Exercises 31, 34, and 37.

In Exercises 39–46, refer to these similar right circular cones.

39. What is the ratio of the radius of the smaller cone to that of the larger?

40. What is the ratio of the slant height of the smaller cone to that of the larger?

41. Find the total area of each cone.

42. What is the ratio of the total area of the smaller cone to that of the larger?

43. Compare the ratios in Exercises 39, 40, and 42.

44. Find the volume of each cone.

45. What is the ratio of the volume of the smaller cone to that of the larger?

46. Compare the ratios in Exercises 39, 42, and 45.

Use your answers to Exercises 39–46 to complete these statements.

47. In similar solids, the lengths of corresponding segments have the same __?__ .

48. In similar solids, the total areas have the same ratio as the __?__ of the lengths of any two corresponding segments.

49. In similar solids, the volumes have the same ratio as the __?__ of the lengths of any two corresponding segments.

Ⓒ

50. A cone has a radius of 9 centimeters and a height of 12 centimeters. What is the radius of a circular cylinder of the same height with volume equal to the volume of the cone?

Consumer Applications
Volume and Air Conditioning

Choosing the right size air conditioner for a room is an application of the geometric concept of volume studied in this chapter.

The cooling capacity of an air conditioner is measured in **Btu's (British Thermal Units)**. To find cooling capacity, use this formula.

$$V \times I \times E \div 60 = \text{Btu per hour}$$

V: volume of room
I: insulation factor

E: exposure factor
(direction faced by longest wall)

Insulation Factor	
Well-insulated	10
Poorly-insulated	18

Exposure Factor			
North	East	South	West
16	17	18	20

EXAMPLE How many Btu's per hour are needed to cool a room that is 15 feet wide, 8 feet high, and 20 feet long? The room is well-insulated and the 20-foot wall faces north.

Solution: 1 Find the volume.

$$V = lwh$$
$$V = 20(15)(8) = \textbf{2400 ft}^3$$

2 Apply the formula.

$V \times I \times E \div 60$

$2400(10)(16) \div 60 = \textbf{6400}$ ◄—— **A cooling capacity of 6400 Btu's is needed.**

EXERCISES

Complete the table.

	Dimensions of Room in Feet			Good Insulation?	Exposure	Cooling Capacity
	Length	Width	Height			
1.	12	10	8	No	West	_?_
2.	13	12	10	Yes	South	_?_
3.	20	15	10	No	East	_?_
4.	35	12	8	Yes	North	_?_

The sphere at the right has center *T*.
Refer to this figure in Exercises 1–5.
(Pages 389–393)

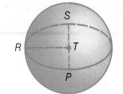

1. Name a radius of the sphere.
2. Name a diameter of the sphere.
3. Name a great circle of the sphere.
4. Name two central angles of the sphere.
5. Name a chord of the sphere.

11-6 Surface Area and Volume: Spheres

The formula for the surface area of a sphere is given in Theorem 11–10.

Theorem 11–10	For a sphere with radius *r*, $$A(\text{surface area}) = 4\pi r^2.$$

Theorem 11–11 gives the formula for the volume of a sphere.

Theorem 11–11	For a sphere with radius *r*, $$V(\text{volume}) = \tfrac{4}{3}\pi r^3.$$

The Example shows how to apply these theorems.

EXAMPLE Find the surface area and the volume of a sphere with
a radius of 12 centimeters.

12 cm

Solutions:

$A = 4\pi r^2$ ⟵ **Replace *r* with 12.** ⟶ $A = \frac{4}{3}\pi r^3$

$\quad = 4\pi \cdot 12^2 \qquad\qquad\qquad\qquad\qquad = \frac{4}{3}\pi \cdot 12^3$

$\quad = 4\pi \cdot 144 \qquad\qquad\qquad\qquad\qquad = \frac{4}{3}\pi \cdot 1728$

$\quad = 576\pi \text{ cm}^2 \qquad\qquad\qquad\qquad\;\; = 2304\pi \text{ cm}^3$

CLASSROOM EXERCISES

1. Find the surface area of a sphere with a radius of 5 centimeters.
2. Find the radius of a sphere with surface area of 36π sq. units.
3. Find the volume of a sphere with a radius of 6 centimeters.
4. Find the surface area of a sphere with a radius of 2.4 centimeters.
5. Find the volume of a sphere with a radius of $4\frac{1}{4}$ inches.

WRITTEN EXERCISES

A In these exercises, express your answers in terms of π when finding area and volume. Simplify any radicals.

In Exercises 1–5, find the surface area of a sphere with the given radius.

1. 5   **2.** 8.2   **3.** $4\frac{1}{2}$ **4.** $9\sqrt{2}$ **5.** $\frac{5}{2}\sqrt{30}$

In Exercises 6–10, find the volume of a sphere with the given radius.

6. 6   **7.** 5.5   **8.** $6\frac{7}{8}$ **9.** $\frac{3}{4}$ **10.** $\frac{1}{2}\sqrt{3}$

In Exercises 11–13, find the radius of a sphere for each given surface area.

11. $\frac{36}{25}\pi$ cm²   **12.** $\frac{49}{16}\pi$ m²   **13.** 1764π yd²

14. Find the volume of a sphere whose diameter is $\frac{3}{4}$.

15. Find the radius of a sphere whose volume is 288π.

16. Find the volume of a sphere if the circumference of a great circle of the sphere is 3π units.

17. Solve $V = \frac{4}{3}\pi r^3$ for r.

18. The volume of a sphere is $\frac{32}{3}\pi$. Find its radius.

A cube whose edge is 20 is circumscribed about a sphere.

19. Find the total surface area of the cube.

20. Find the surface area of the sphere.

21. Find the ratio of the area of the sphere to the area of the cube.

In Exercises 22–24, find the volume of a sphere inscribed in a cube with the given dimensions.

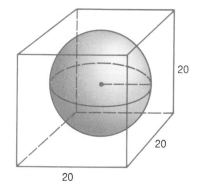

22. One edge of the cube is 20.

23. One edge of the cube is e.   **24.** A diagonal of one face is 4.

25. A diagonal of one face of a cube is 20. What is the volume of the inscribed sphere?

B

26. What is the radius of a sphere in which the number of square units of surface area equals the number of cubic units of volume?

27. Determine the ratio of the volumes of two spheres whose radii are 1 centimeter and 2 centimeters.

28. The ratio of the volumes of two spheres is 125 to 64. What is the ratio of their diameters?

29. The ratio of the radii of two spheres is 3 to 7. The volume of the smaller sphere is 288π cubic units. Find the volume of the larger sphere.

30. In the figure at the left below, the altitude of the right circular cylinder inscribed in the sphere is equal to its diameter. If the radius of the cylinder is 8, What is the ratio of the volume of the cylinder to the volume of the sphere?

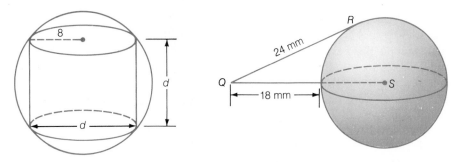

31. In the figure at the right above, the distance from Q to sphere S is 18 millimeters and the length of the tangent segment from Q to the sphere is 24 millimeters. What is the volume of the sphere?

32. A sphere is inscribed in a right circular cylinder. What is the ratio of the volume of the sphere to the volume of the cylinder?

33. Two cones are inscribed in a cylinder, as shown. The diameter and altitude of the cylinder are equal. Find the volume of the cones.

34. What is the volume of the cylinder?

35. Compute the volume of the figure that is inside the cylinder and outside the cones.

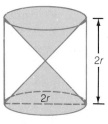

C

36. A small circle of a sphere has 24π as its circumference. The center of the circle is 5 units from the center of the sphere. Compute the volume of the sphere.

37. Express the volume of a cube in terms of the radius r of the circumscribed sphere.

38. A 30-60 right triangle is rotated about its longer leg to generate a right circular cone that is inscribed in a sphere. If the hypotenuse of the right triangle is 12 centimeters, find the volume of the sphere.

A cube is circumscribed about a given sphere and a cube is inscribed in the same sphere. Find each ratio.

39. The volume of the circumscribed cube to the volume of the sphere.

40. The volume of the sphere to the volume of the inscribed cube.

41. The volume of the circumscribed cube to the volume of the inscribed cube.

APPLICATIONS

USING VOLUME

These exercises apply geometric concepts studied in Sections 11–4 through 11–6.

A

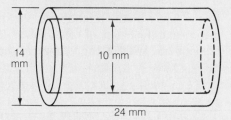

1. The sides of a gardener's cart have the shape of a trapezoid. The parallel bases are 1.2 and 1 meter long respectively, the width is 0.8 meter, and the height is 0.4 meter. About how many cubic meters of soil will the cart hold when completely filled level with the top of the sides?

2. A cylindrical tube has an inside diameter of 10 millimeters and an outside diameter of 14 millimeters. It is 24 millimeters long. How much material is needed to make the tube?

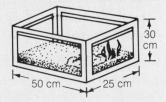

3. A spool holds 10 meters of copper wire. The wire has a diameter of 1 millimeter. How many cubic millimeters of wire are on the spool?

> The number of fish that can be housed in an aquarium depends on the amount of water, the size of the fish, and the capacity of the pump and filter system.

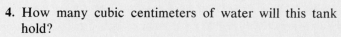

4. How many cubic centimeters of water will this tank hold?

5. If 1000 cm³ = 1 liter, how many liters of water will the tank in Exercise 4 hold?

6. The recommended number of tropical fish for this tank is 50. How many cubic centimeters per fish is this?

7. A goldfish with a length of 5 centimeters requires about 3000 cm³ of water. How many goldfish of this size could live in this tank?

B

8. A pile of crude salt from a refinery has the shape of a cone. The height of the cone is 12 meters and the diameter is 32 meters. The salt is loaded on railroad cars, each having a capacity of 80 m³. How many cars will the pile of salt fill?

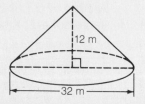

9. A potter shapes a bowl by removing a hemisphere of diameter 16 centimeters from a cylinder of height 9 centimeters. How many cubic centimeters of clay will there be in the bowl?

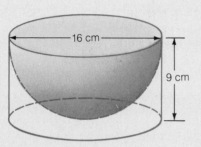

10. How much will it cost to resurface this roof having the shape of a hemisphere if the diameter of the hemisphere is 8 meters and the roofing materials cost $15.80 per square meter?

11. Two right cylinders are packed in a rectangular box for shipping. The dimensions of the box are 4 inches by 8 inches by 16 inches. How many cubic inches of the interior of the box remain for protective packing?

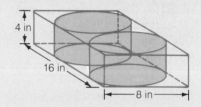

Ⓒ

12. In a chemical plant, a circular cylinder discharges into a cone having the same diameter. The height of the cone is 4 meters and the diameter of the cylinder is 10 meters. If the volume of the cylinder is to be 180% of the volume of the cone, what should be the height of the cylinder?

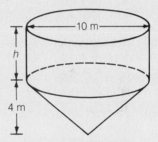

Suppose that a drop of unvaporized gasoline is a sphere having a diameter of 4 millimeters.

13. Suppose that this drop is divided into 8 smaller drops. Each smaller drop has a diameter of 2 millimeters. As compared with the surface area of the original drop, how many times greater is the total surface area of the 8 drops?

14. Suppose that each drop with a diameter of 2 millimeters is divided into 8 smaller drops, each with a diameter of 1 millimeter. As compared with the surface area of the original drop, how many times greater is the total surface area of the 64 drops?

15. Suppose that the vaporizing mechanism in a car's engine continues this splitting for a total of 20 times. As compared with the surface area of the original drop, how many times greater is the total surface area of the divided drops?

In Exercises 1–3, find the volume of the rectangular solid with the given dimensions. *(Section 11–4)*

1. $4 \times 4 \times 4$

2. $3.2 \times 2.8 \times 1.6$

3. $2\sqrt{3} \times 3\sqrt{2} \times 4\sqrt{6}$

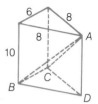

In the figure, the bases of the right prism are isosceles triangles whose equal sides are each 8 and whose bases are 6. The altitude of the prism is 10. *(Section 11–4)*

4. Find the volume of the prism.

5. Find the volume of the pyramid A–BCD.

6. The two storage boxes shown below have equal volume. Compute the height of the taller box. *(Section 11–4)*

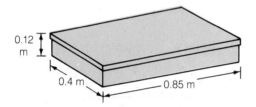
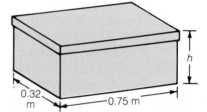

In Exercises 7–10, use the given information to find the volume of the indicated cylinder or cone. *(Section 11–5)*

7. Right circular cylinder:
  $r = 16$; $h = 32$

8. Right circular cylinder:
  $r = \frac{1}{2}$; $h = 8$

9. Right circular cone:
  $r = 7$; $h = 14$

10. Right circular cone:
  $r = \sqrt{6}$; $h = 12$

In Exercises 11–15, find the surface area of a sphere with the given radius. *(Section 11–6)*

11. 6

12. 3.4

13. 5.8

14. $6\sqrt{3}$

15. $4\sqrt{7}$

In Exercises 16–20, find the volume of a sphere with the given radius. *(Section 11–6)*

16. 4

17. 2.2

18. 3.6

19. $2\sqrt{2}$

20. $\frac{3}{8}\sqrt{3}$

Puzzle

A solid ball of string has a diameter of 3 feet. If one cubic inch of string weighs 0.03 pound, how much does the ball of string weigh? (HINT: $1728 \text{ in}^3 = 1 \text{ ft}^3$)

BASIC: SURFACE AREA AND VOLUME

Problem: *Given the measures of the radius and the altitude of a cone, compute its lateral area and its total area.*

Program:

```
10   PRINT "ENTER MEASURES OF RADIUS AND
       ALTITUDE."
20   INPUT R, A
30   LET S = SQR (R↑2 + A↑2)◄──────── S = slant height
40   LET L = 3.14159*R*S
50   LET T = 3.14159*R* (R + S)
60   PRINT "THE LATERAL AREA IS "; L
70   PRINT "THE TOTAL AREA IS "; T
80   PRINT "ANY MORE CONES (1 = YES, 0 = NO)";
90   INPUT X
100  IF X = 1 THEN 10
110  END
```

Analysis:

Statement 30: Statement 30 uses the Pythagorean Theorem to find S.

Statements 40 and 50: In Statements 40 and 50, 3.14159 is used as an approximation for π. The program can also be run using $22/7$ for π.

EXERCISES

A   Run the program above with the following measures for the radius and the altitude.

1. $R = 5, A = 10$
2. $R = 6, A = 8$
3. $R = 23, A = 49$
4. $R = 16.4, A = 10.5$
5. $R = 2.5, A = 3.6$
6. $R = 19.1, A = 25.6$

B   Write a BASIC program for each problem. Use 3.14159 for π.

7. Given the measures of the radius and the altitude of a cone, compute its volume.

8. Given the length of a side of the base of a regular square pyramid and the length of a lateral edge, compute its slant height.

9. Using the information in Exercise 8, compute the total area of the pyramid.

10. Given the volume, the height, and the radius of a right circular geometric solid, determine if it is a cone or a cylinder, or neither.

11. Given the radius of a sphere, compute its volume.

12. Given the surface area of a sphere, compute its radius.

Chapter Summary

IMPORTANT TERMS

Cube (p. 482)
Prism (p. 482)
   Altitude (p. 482)
   Bases (p. 482)
   Edges (p. 482)
   Faces (p. 482)
   Lateral faces (p. 482)
   Lateral surface area (p. 482)
   Oblique (p. 482)
   Regular (p. 482)
   Right (p. 482)
   Total area (p. 483)
Pyramid (p. 486)
   Altitude (p. 486)
   Edges (p. 486)

Pyramid (cont.)
   Lateral faces (p. 486)
   Lateral surface area (p. 486)
   Regular (p. 486)
   Slant height (p. 486)
Right circular cone (p. 491)
   Altitude (p. 491)
   Lateral area (p. 491)
   Total area (p. 491)
   Vertex (p. 491)
Right circular cylinder (p. 490)
   Altitude (p. 490)
   Lateral area (p. 490)
   Total area (p. 490)
Volume (p. 496)

IMPORTANT IDEAS

Surface Area and Volume

Solid	Lateral Surface Area	Total Area	Volume
Right Prism	$L = Pe$	Lateral Surface Area $+$ Area of Bases	Rectangular Solid: $V = Bh$ Cube: $V = e^3$
Pyramid	$L = \frac{1}{2}sP$	Lateral Surface Area $+$ Area of Bases	$V = \frac{1}{3}Bh$
Right Circular Cylinder	$L = 2\pi rh$	$T = 2\pi r(h + r)$	$V = \pi r^2 h$
Right Circular Cone	$L = \pi rs$	$T = \pi r(s + r)$	$V = \frac{1}{3}\pi r^2 h$
Sphere	$A = 4\pi r^2$	$A = 4\pi r^2$	$V = \frac{4}{3}\pi r^3$

Chapter Objectives and Review

Objective: *To calculate the lateral surface area and total area of a right prism (Section 11-1)*

1. Find the lateral surface area and the total area of a right rectangular prism of length 3 centimeters, width 5 centimeters, and height 8 centimeters.

2. Find the lateral surface area and the total area of a cube with an edge of 5 meters.

Objective: *To calculate the lateral surface area and the total area of a pyramid (Section 11–2)*

3. Find the lateral surface area and the total area of a regular pyramid whose base is an equilateral triangle with a side of 6 centimeters and whose slant height is 4 centimeters.

4. The lateral surface area of a regular pyramid is 160 square units and the perimeter of its base is 40 units. Find the slant height.

Objective: *To calculate the lateral area and the total area of a right circular cylinder and a right circular cone (Section 11–3)*

5. Find the lateral area and the total area of a right circular cylinder with a radius of 7 centimeters and an altitude of 10 centimeters.

6. Find the lateral area and the total area of a right circular cone with radius 2 millimeters and height 5 millimeters.

Objective: *To calculate the volume of a right prism and a pyramid (Section 11–4)*

7. Find the volume of a right triangular prism whose base is a right triangle with legs of 3 centimeters and 4 centimeters and whose height is 9 centimeters.

8. Find the volume of a regular pyramid with a square base 5 meters on a side and with an altitude of 9 meters.

Objective: *To calculate the volume of a right circular cylinder and a right circular cone (Section 11–5)*

9. The radius of the base of a right circular cylinder is 6 centimeters and its altitude is 9 centimeters. Find the volume.

10. The base of a cone has an area of 49π square meters and its altitude is 12 meters. Find the volume.

Objective: *To calculate the surface area and volume of a sphere (Section 11–6)*

11. Find the surface area of a sphere with a radius of 3 meters.

12. Find the volume of a sphere with a radius of 6 millimeters.

Objective: *To solve word problems that involve surface area (Pages 494–495)*

13. The dimensions of a packing crate are shown at the right. Find the number of square centimeters of material needed to build the box.

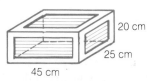

20 cm

25 cm

45 cm

14. A parking lot has pyramid-shaped markers with rectangular bases. The markers are 0.3 meters wide, 0.4 meters long, and 0.8 meters high. How many cubic meters of concrete will be needed to make 20 of these markers?

_____ **Chapter Test** _____

Classify each statement as true, *T*, or false, *F*. If a statement is false, tell why it is false.

1. The lateral faces of a pyramid are triangles.
2. The bases of a prism are congruent polygons.
3. The altitude of a pyramid is the same as the slant height.
4. The total area of a cone equals the lateral area.
5. In a right circular cone, the altitude passes through the center of the base.

Find the total area of each of the following.

6. A cube with an edge of 4.5 centimeters
7. A rectangular prism whose base is a square with a side of 7 and whose lateral edge is 9
8. A pyramid with a slant height of 10 meters and whose base is an equilateral triangle with a side of 6 meters
9. A right circular cylinder with radius 4 and altitude 7
10. A right circular cone whose base has a radius of 4 and whose slant height is 8

Find the volume of each of the following.

11. A triangular prism whose base is an equilateral triangle with a side of 8 centimeters and whose altitude is 10 centimeters long
12. A regular pyramid with a square base of side 12 meters and a slant height of $6\sqrt{5}$ meters
13. A right circular cylinder whose base has a radius of 11 centimeters and whose height is 13 centimeters
14. A right circular cone whose base has a radius of 5 centimeters and whose altitude is 8 centimeters
15. A sphere with a diameter of 30 meters

Cumulative Review: Chapters 1–11

Choose the best answer. Choose *a*, *b*, *c*, or *d*.

1. The adjacent sides of a rectangle are 3 and 5 units long. How long is a diagonal?

   a. 4   b. $\sqrt{34}$

   c. 6   d. 8

2. Triangle *ABC* is isosceles with base *BC*. Find *x*.

   a. 40   b. 70

   c. 110   d. 140

3. In the figure at the right, $m\widehat{AC} = 50$, and $m\angle DEB = 70$. Find $m\widehat{DB}$.

   a. 20   b. 90

   c. 60   d. 120

4. Find the length of a side of a square whose area is 100 square centimeters.

   a. 10   b. 25   c. 50   d. 1000

5. Find the radius of a circle whose circumference is 12π units.

   a. $\sqrt{12}$ b. 6   c. 12   d. 144

6. In parallelogram *ABCD*, *AB* = 14, *AD* = 10, and $m\angle A = 60$. Find the area of the parallelogram.

   a. 35   b. $70\sqrt{3}$

   c. 70   d. 140

7. The areas of two similar polygons are in the ratio of 16:25 and the apothem of the smaller polygon is 8. Find the apothem of the larger polygon.

   a. 6.4   b. 10   c. 12.5   d. 25

8. Find the area of an equilateral triangle with a side 8 units long.

   a. $2\sqrt{3}$ b. $4\sqrt{3}$ c. $16\sqrt{2}$ d. $16\sqrt{3}$

9. The area of a rhombus is 48 and the length of one diagonal is 8. Find the length of the other diagonal.

   a. 6   b. 12   c. 96   d. 192

10. In trapezoid $HBJA$, $HB = 6$, $AJ = 10$, $BJ = 12$, and $m\angle J = 45$. Find the area of the trapezoid.

   a. 48

   b. $48\sqrt{2}$

   c. 96

   d. $96\sqrt{2}$

11. Find the measure of each central angle of a regular octagon.

   a. 36
   b. 45
   c. 60
   d. 72

12. Find the length of the apothem of a regular decagon with a side of 3.4 meters and with an area of 119 square meters.

   a. 0.7
   b. 3.5
   c. 7
   d. 70

13. In circle Q at the right, if $m\angle AQB = 45$ and $QB = 4$, find the area of sector QAB.

   a. 2π

   b. 16π

   c. 4π

   d. 3π

14. Two sides of a triangle measure 4 and 6. What can be the length of the third side?

   a. 2
   b. 5
   c. 10
   d. 13

15. A rectangle with width of 5 is inscribed in a circle with diameter of 13. Find the area of the rectangle.

   a. 12
   b. 30
   c. 60
   d. 65

16. Parallel lines t and m are 6 units apart. If point P is on line t, find the number of points equidistant from t and m and 2 units from P.

   a. 0
   b. 1
   c. 2
   d. 3

17. Find the lateral surface area of the pentagonal prism at the right.

   a. 64
   b. 320
   c. 400
   d. 500

18. Two pyramids have congruent bases, and the altitude of one pyramid is twice the altitude of the other. Find the ratio of their volumes.

   a. 2:1
   b. 3:2
   c. 4:1
   d. 8:1

19. Find the volume of a right circular cylinder with base of radius 3 and a height of 7.

   a. 42π
   b. 49π
   c. $\frac{63}{4}\pi$
   d. 63π

20. Find the volume of a sphere of radius $\frac{1}{2}$.

   a. $\frac{\pi}{6}$
   b. $\frac{\pi}{3}$
   c. $\frac{\pi}{2}$
   d. $\frac{2\pi}{9}$

Preparing for College Entrance Tests

Problems involving ratios occur on many College Entrance tests. In such problems, it is important to express the answer in lowest terms.

REMEMBER: A ratio can be expressed as a fraction, such as $\frac{2}{5}$, or as 2:5.

EXAMPLE: Side QP of rectangle $NQPO$ is a diameter of circle R. If $QR = t$, find
$$\frac{\text{circumference of circle } R}{\text{perimeter of rectangle } MNOP}.$$

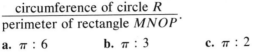

a. $\pi : 6$ b. $\pi : 3$ c. $\pi : 2$

d. $3 : \pi$ e. $2 : \pi$

Solution: $C(\text{circle}) = 2\pi t$ ⟵ radius = **QR = t**

$P(\text{rectangle}) = 6t$ ⟵ **QN = QR = t; QP = NO = 2t**

Thus, $\dfrac{2\pi t}{6t} = \dfrac{\pi}{3}$ ⟵ $\dfrac{\pi}{3}$ can be written $\pi : 3$ **Answer: b**

Choose the best answer. Choose *a, b, c, d,* or *e.*

1. In the figure at the right, circles A, B, and C are tangent to each other. Find
$$\frac{\text{perimeter of } \triangle ABC}{\text{circumference of (circle } A + \text{circle } B + \text{circle } C)}.$$

a. $1 : 2$ b. $1 : 3$ c. $1 : \pi$ d. $1 : \pi$ e. $\pi : 1$

2. If arc $DE = \frac{1}{6}$ of the circumference of circle A and if the length of chord $DE = y$, find
$$\frac{\text{length of chord } DE}{\text{diameter of circle } A}.$$

a. $\pi : 2$ b. π c. $2 : 1$ d. $2\sqrt{2} : 1$ e. $1 : 2$

3. In the figure at the right, a coin with diameter XY is rolled one complete revolution along a plane from position I to position II. Find the ratio
$$\frac{XY}{L}.$$

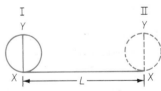

a. $1 : 3$ b. $1 : 2$ c. $\pi : 1$ d. $2 : 1$ e. $1 : \pi$

4. In the figure at the right, if circle Q has a radius r and circle P has a diameter of r, find
$$\frac{\text{circumference of circle } P}{\text{circumference of circle } Q}.$$

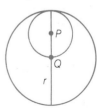

a. $1 : 4$ b. $4 : 1$ c. $1 : 2$

d. $2 : 1$ e. $3 : 1$

Preparing for College Entrance Tests

Applying the basic area formulas (rectangle, square, parallelogram, triangle, trapezoid, circle) is an important technique in finding the area of a shaded region such as in the Example.

REMEMBER: Areas are measures. These measures can be added and subtracted.

EXAMPLE The area of square $ABCD$ is 1.
Find the area of the shaded region.

a. $1 + \frac{\pi}{2}$ b. $1 - \frac{\pi}{2}$ c. $1 - \frac{\pi}{3}$

d. $1 - \frac{\pi}{6}$ e. $1 - \frac{\pi}{4}$

Solution: Since the area of the square is 1, and $BC = CD$, the diameter of the circle is 1 and the radius is $\frac{1}{2}$. Thus, the area of the circle is $\pi(\frac{1}{2})^2$, or $\frac{\pi}{4}$.

Area of shaded region: $1 - \frac{\pi}{4}$ ◀——— **Area of Square -- Area of Circle**

Answer: e

Choose the best answer. Choose *a, b, c, d,* or *e.*

1. Find the area of the shaded region in terms of π.

   a. π b. 2π c. 4π

   d. 3π e. $\frac{5}{2}\pi$

2. In this figure, right triangle ADE overlaps rectangle $ABCF$, $AB = \sqrt{3}$, $BC = 1$, and $\overline{AC} \cong \overline{CD}$.
Find the area of the shaded region.

   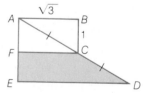

   a. $\sqrt{3}$ b. $\frac{3}{2}\sqrt{3}$ c. $2\sqrt{3}$

   d. $\frac{5}{2}\sqrt{3}$ e. $\frac{\sqrt{3}}{2}$

3. Find the area of the shaded region in rectangle $ABCD$.

   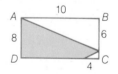

   a. 12   b. 52   c. 54

   d. 46   e. 32

4. Each of these congruent circles is tangent to the sides of the square and to two other circles. The radius of each circle is r. Find the area of the shaded region.

   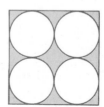

   a. $4r^2(2 - \pi)$ b. $4r^2(2 + \pi)$ c. $4r^2(4 - \pi)$

   d. $4r^2(r + \pi)$ e. $4r^2(\pi - 4)$

CHAPTER **12** **Coordinate Geometry**

Sections

12-1 The Coordinate Plane

12-2 Midpoint Formula

12-3 Slope of a Line

12-4 Slope and Linear Equations

12-5 Parallel and Perpendicular Lines

12-6 Distance Formula

12-7 Equations of Circles

12-8 Coordinate Proofs

Features

Calculator Application: Distance Formula

Puzzle

Review and Testing

Algebra Review Capsules

Geometry Review Capsule

Review: Sections 12–1 through 12–4

Review: Sections 12–5 through 12–8

Chapter Summary

Chapter Objectives and Review

Chapter Test

12-1 The Coordinate Plane

To locate points on a plane, you use two number lines that are perpendicular to each other. The horizontal number line is the *x* **axis**; the vertical number line is the *y* **axis.** The axes separate the plane into four **quadrants.** Points on an axis are not considered to be in any quadrant. The point where the axes meet is called the **origin.**

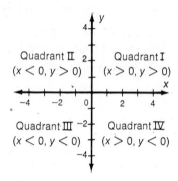

To locate a point in the plane, you use an **ordered pair** of real numbers called the **coordinates** of the point.

$$(x, y)$$

Number of units from the **y** axis   Number of units from the **x** axis

As the figure above shows, *x* is negative in Quadrants II and III; *y* is negative in Quadrants III and IV.

EXAMPLE 1   Name the coordinates of points *A*, *B*, *C*, *D*, and *E*.

Point	Description	Coordinates
A	4 units to the *right* of the *y* axis and 4 units *above* the *x* axis	**(4, 4)**
B	2 units to the *left* of the *y* axis and 5 units *above* the *x* axis	**(−2, 5)**
C	5 units to the *left* of the *y* axis and 4 units *below* the *x* axis	**(−5, −4)**
D	3 units to the *right* of the *y* axis and 2 units *below* the *x* axis	**(3, −2)**
E	At the **origin,** the point where the axes intersect.	**(0, 0)**

Example 2 shows how to determine the equation of a vertical line and of a horizontal line.

EXAMPLE 2 Graph these coordinates. Draw a line through each set of points. Describe each line.

a. $A(4, 4)$; $B(4, 2)$; $C(4, 0)$; $D(4, -1)$
b. $E(-3, -3)$; $F(0, -3)$; $G(2, -3)$; $H(5, -3)$

Solutions:

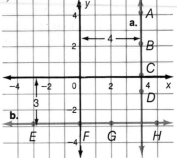

a. The line is vertical. Since *each* point on the line is 4 units to the right of the y axis, the x coordinate of each point is 4.

Thus, the equation for the line is $x = 4$.

b. The line is horizontal. Since *each* point on the line is 3 units below the x axis, the y coordinate for each point is -3.

The equation for the line is $y = -3$.

The equations in Example 2 are expressed in general form in this summary. In the equations, a and b represent real numbers.

Summary

> **Equation of a vertical line:** $x = a$
>
> **Equation of a horizontal line:** $y = b$

Because there is a one-to-one correspondence between the points in the plane and ordered pairs of real numbers, the plane is called the **coordinate plane.**

CLASSROOM EXERCISES

In Exercises 1–5, state the quadrant in which each point is located.

1. $(-2, -5)$ **2.** $(3, -6)$ **3.** $(-8, 4)$ **4.** $(1, 7)$ **5.** $(1, -1)$

In Exercises 6–8, complete each statement. Insert *parallel* or *perpendicular*.

6. The graph of $x = 4$ is ___?___ to the y axis and ___?___ to the x axis.
7. The graph of $y = 6$ is ___?___ to the graph of $y = 4$.
8. The graph of $x = 5$ is ___?___ to the graph of $y = -2$.
9. Point D has coordinates $(-3, 4)$ and point E has coordinates $(-3, -1)$. Graph these points in the coordinate plane. Find the length of $\overline{DE}$.

WRITTEN EXERCISES

Ⓐ   In Exercises 1–5, state the quadrant in which each point is located.

1. $A(5, 7)$ **2.** $B(8, -2)$ **3.** $C(-2, 9)$ **4.** $D(-1, -4)$ **5.** $E(-7, 3)$

In Exercises 6–10, state whether the given point lies on the x axis, the y axis, or is at the origin.

6. $G(-4, 0)$ **7.** $H(0, 9)$ **8.** $J(0, -\frac{1}{2})$ **9.** $K(0, 0)$ **10.** $P(5\frac{1}{2}, 0)$

11. On the same coordinate plane, graph and label each point in Exercises 6–10.

In Exercises 12–24, refer to the coordinate plane at the right.

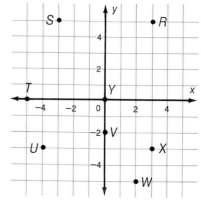

In Exercises 12–15, state the quadrant or axis on which each point lies.

12. W **13.** S **14.** U **15.** T

16. Give the coordinates of each labeled point in the given coordinate plane.

17. Find the length of $\overline{SR}$.

18. Find the length of $\overline{RX}$.

19. Find the length of $\overline{UX}$.

In Exercises 20–24, write the equation for each line.

20. $\overleftrightarrow{SR}$ **21.** $\overleftrightarrow{XU}$ **22.** $\overleftrightarrow{RX}$ **23.** $\overleftrightarrow{TY}$ **24.** $\overleftrightarrow{YV}$

25. Graph these points on the same coordinate plane.

$$A(2, -1); \quad B(2, 2); \quad C(-3, 2); \quad D(-3, -1)$$

In Exercises 26–31, refer to Exercise 25.

26. Write the equation of $\overleftrightarrow{BC}$.   **27.** Write the equation of $\overleftrightarrow{CD}$.

28. Find the lengths of $\overline{AB}$ and $\overline{BC}$.   **29.** Find the lengths of $\overline{CD}$ and $\overline{DA}$.

30. In quadrilateral $ABCD$, name two pairs of parallel segments.

31. Name two perpendicular lines determined by quadrilateral $ABCD$.

B   In Exercises 32–36, write the equation of the line parallel to the y axis and passing through the given point.

32. $A(3, 5)$ **33.** $B(-2, 4)$ **34.** $C(6, -5)$ **35.** $F(0, 7)$ **36.** $Q(-1, -1)$

In Exercises 37–41, write the equation of the line parallel to the x axis and passing through the given point.

37. $A(-2, 4)$ **38.** $B(9, -5)$ **39.** $C(0, 2)$ **40.** $D(-1, -8)$ **41.** $E(0, -8)$

C

42. Rectangle $RSTQ$ has coordinates $R(3, 5)$, $S(3, -3)$, and $T(-2, -3)$. Find the coordinates of point Q.

43. Square $EFGH$ has coordinates $E(2, 3)$, $F(2, 6)$, and $G(5, 3)$. Find the coordinates of point H.

44. Rectangle $ABCD$ has coordinates $A(3, 2)$, $B(-4, 2)$, and $C(-4, -3)$. Find the coordinates of point D and compute the area of the rectangle.

12-2 The Midpoint Formula

Example 1 shows how to apply the methods of coordinate geometry to finding the midpoint of a horizontal line segment.

EXAMPLE 1 Find the coordinates of the midpoint $M(x_m, y_m)$ of $\overline{RQ}$.

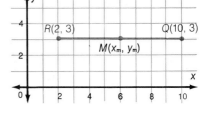

Solution: Since $\overline{RQ}$ is horizontal, the y coordinate of any point on $\overline{RQ}$ is 3. Thus, the y coordinate of M is 3.

Since $2 < x_m < 10$, $RM = x_m - 2$ and $QM = 10 - x_m$.

Since M is the midpoint of $\overline{RQ}$, $RM = QM$.

Thus, $x_m - 2 = 10 - x_m$

$2x_m = 10 + 2$

$$x_m = \frac{10 + 2}{2} \longleftarrow \frac{\textbf{Sum of x coordinates of endpoints}}{\textbf{2}}$$

$x_m = \dfrac{12}{2} = 6 \qquad \therefore M(x_m, y_m) = M(\mathbf{6, 3})$

The results of Example 1 can be expressed in general form. That is, the x coordinate of the midpoint of a horizontal segment with endpoints $P_1(x_1, y_1)$ and $P_2(x_2, y_2)$ is:

$$x_m = \frac{x_1 + x_2}{2} \longleftarrow \frac{\textbf{Sum of x coordinates of endpoints}}{\textbf{2}}$$

It can also be shown that the y coordinate of the midpoint of a vertical segment with endpoints $P_1(x_1, y_1)$ and $P_2(x_2, y_2)$ is:

$$y_m = \frac{y_1 + y_2}{2} \longleftarrow \frac{\textbf{Sum of y coordinates of endpoints}}{\textbf{2}}$$

The Midpoint Formula states the formulas for x_m and y_m as applied to any line — horizontal, vertical, or oblique.

Theorem 12-1

> **The Midpoint Formula**
>
> The coordinates (x_m, y_m) of the midpoint M of the segment whose endpoints are $P_1(x_1, y_1)$ and $P_2(x_2, y_2)$ are
>
> $$x_m = \frac{x_1 + x_2}{2} \quad \text{and} \quad y_m = \frac{y_1 + y_2}{2}.$$

The proof of Theorem 12–1 is asked for in the Written Exercises.

EXAMPLE 2 One endpoint of $\overline{QR}$ is $Q(-2, 1)$. The coordinates of the midpoint are $M(0, \frac{5}{2})$. Find the coordinates of R.

Solution: ① Graph the given points. Draw ray QR.

② Use the Midpoint Formula.

$$x_m = \frac{x_1 + x_2}{2} \quad \longleftarrow \quad x_m = 0;\ x_1 = -2$$

$$0 = \frac{-2 + x_2}{2} \quad \longleftarrow \quad \text{Solve for } x_2.$$

$$0 = -2 + x_2$$

$$2 = x_2$$

$$y_m = \frac{y_1 + y_2}{2} \quad \longleftarrow \quad y_m = \frac{5}{2};\ y_1 = 1$$

$$\frac{5}{2} = \frac{1 + y_2}{2} \quad \longleftarrow \quad \text{Solve for } y_2.$$

$$5 = 1 + y_2$$

$$4 = y_2 \qquad \textbf{Coordinates of endpoint: } R(2, 4)$$

CLASSROOM EXERCISES

Find the coordinates of the midpoint of a segment whose endpoints have the following coordinates.

1. $(2, 5)$ and $(6, 11)$ **2.** $(3, 7)$ and $(-4, 1)$ **3.** $(-1, -8)$ and $(2, 5)$

4. One endpoint of $\overline{AB}$ is $A(-3, 2)$, and the midpoint of $\overline{AB}$ is $M(-1, 5)$. Find the coordinates of point B.

WRITTEN EXERCISES

A In Exercises 1–6, the coordinates of the endpoints of a segment are given. Find the coordinates of each midpoint, M.

1. $P(6, 1)$; $R(4, 2)$ **2.** $A(3, -2)$; $B(7, 8)$ **3.** $R(4, -1)$; $T(-3, 7)$

4. $T(-1, -8)$; $A(-5, -2)$ **5.** $F(a, 0)$; $C(0, b)$ **6.** $S(sa, sb)$; $L(sc, sd)$

In Exercises 7–12, the coordinates of endpoint Q of segment QR are given. The coordinates of M, the midpoint of $\overline{QR}$, are also given. Find the coordinates of R, the other endpoint.

7. $Q(-1, 4)$; $M(1, 3)$ **8.** $Q(1, 1)$; $M(-2, 0)$ **9.** $Q(1, 4)$; $M(\frac{3}{2}; \frac{3}{2})$

10. $Q(4, 1)$; $M(1, 2)$ **11.** $Q(-1, -2)$; $M(-2, 1)$ **12.** $Q(a, b)$; $M(\frac{a}{2}, \frac{b}{2})$

13. The midpoint of $\overline{EF}$ is $M(2, 3)$ and point E is at the origin. Find the coordinates of point F.

Quadrilateral *ABCD* has coordinates *A*(0, 0), *B*(5, 1), *C*(7, 4) and *D*(2, 3). Use this information for Exercises 14–20.

14. Graph quadrilateral *ABCD*.

Find each midpoint.

15. Side *AB*
16. Side *BC*
17. Side *CD*
18. Side *AD*
19. Diagonal *AC*
20. Diagonal *BD*

B

21. Prove Theorem 12–1.

Given: $\overline{P_1P_2}$ with endpoints (x_1, y_1) and (x_2, y_2);
Point $M(x_m, y_m)$ is the midpoint of $\overline{P_1P_2}$;
$x_1 < x_m < x_2$

Prove: $x_m = \dfrac{x_1 + x_2}{2}$ and $y_m = \dfrac{y_1 + y_2}{2}$

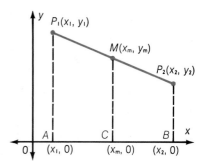

Plan: Draw $\overline{P_1A}$, $\overline{MC}$, and $\overline{P_2B}$ perpendicular to the *x* axis.

Then $\overline{P_1A} \parallel \overline{MC} \parallel \overline{P_2B}$. The coordinates of *A*, *C*, and *B* are $(x_1, 0)$, $(x_m, 0)$, and $(x_2, 0)$ respectively. Since *M* is the mid-point of $\overline{P_1P_2}$, $P_1M = MP_2$. $\therefore AC = BC$.

Complete the proof for x_m. The proof for y_m is similar.

22. The endpoints of $\overline{XY}$ are $X(-5, 8)$ and $Y(r, 1)$. The midpoint of $\overline{XY}$ is $M(2, s)$. Find the values of *r* and *s*.

23. The endpoints of $\overline{AB}$ are $A(-5, 3)$ and $B(b, -1)$. The midpoint of $\overline{AB}$ is $M(-1, m)$. Find *m* and *b*.

C

In Exercises 24–25, graph *A*(−2, 2), *B*(4, 1), *C*(2, 5) and *D*(−1, −2). Then find the coordinates of point *T* as described.

24. *T* is $\frac{2}{3}$ the distance from *A* to *B*.
25. *T* is $\frac{3}{4}$ the distance from *C* to *D*.

26. In the figure for Exercise 21, let *P*(*x*, *y*) be a point between P_1 and P_2 such that $P_1P = \frac{1}{3}P_1P_2$. Determine formulas for the coordinates of *P* in terms of the coordinates of P_1 and P_2.

———— **ALGEBRA REVIEW CAPSULE FOR SECTION 12–3** ————

Simplify each expression. *(Pages 16, 17–19)*

1. $0 - 10$
2. $0 - (-6)$
3. $4 - (-17)$
4. $-5 - (-12)$
5. $\dfrac{(-3) - 2}{7 - 5}$
6. $\dfrac{2 - (-3)}{5 - 7}$
7. $\dfrac{6 - (-4)}{9 - 2}$
8. $\dfrac{(-4) - 10}{2 - 9}$
9. $\dfrac{9 - 3}{7 - 2}$
10. $\dfrac{3 - 9}{2 - 7}$
11. $\dfrac{(-15) - 3}{(-2) - (-8)}$
12. $\dfrac{3 - (-15)}{(-8) - (-2)}$

12-3 Slope of a Line

The steepness of a line is the ratio called *slope*.

Definition

For any two points $P(x_1, y_1)$ and $Q(x_2, y_2)$ on $\overleftrightarrow{PQ}$,

$$\text{slope} = m = \frac{\text{vertical change}}{\text{horizontal change}} = \frac{y_2 - y_1}{x_2 - x_1}, \quad (x_2 \ne x_1).$$

EXAMPLE 1 Find the slope of the line containing the points $P(2, 3)$ and $Q(6, 5)$.

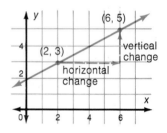

Solution:

$m = \dfrac{y_2 - y_1}{x_2 - x_1}$ ◄—— **Replace y_2 with 5 and y_1 with 3.**
◄—— **Replace x_2 with 6 and x_1 with 2.**

$m = \dfrac{5 - 3}{6 - 2} = \dfrac{2}{4}$, or $\dfrac{1}{2}$ ◄—— **Lowest terms**

NOTE: If you used $(x_1, y_1) = (6, 5)$ and $(x_2, y_2) = (2, 3)$, you would also find that $m = \frac{1}{2}$.

EXAMPLE 2 Find the slope of $\overleftrightarrow{AB}$ passing through $A(-3, 5)$ and $B(4, -2)$.

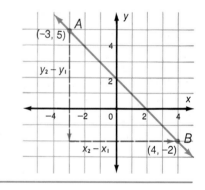

Solution:

$m = \dfrac{y_2 - y_1}{x_2 - x_1}$ ◄—— **Replace y_2 with -2 and y_1 with 5.**
◄—— **Replace x_2 with 4 and x_1 with -3.**

$m = \dfrac{-2 - 5}{4 - (-3)}$

$m = \dfrac{-7}{4 + 3} = \dfrac{-7}{7}$, or -1

EXAMPLE 3 Find the slope of the line containing each pair of points.

    a. $(-1, 4); (4, 4)$ **b.** $(2, -1); (2, 3)$

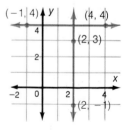

Solutions:

a. Let $(x_1, y_1) = (-1, 4)$ and $(x_2, y_2) = (4, 4)$.

$m = \dfrac{4 - 4}{4 - (-1)} = \dfrac{0}{4 + 1} = 0$ ◄—— **Zero divided by any nonzero number is zero.**

b. Let $(x_1, y_1) = (2, -1)$ and $(x_2, y_2) = (2, 3)$.

$m = \dfrac{3 - (-1)}{2 - 2} = \dfrac{4}{0}$ ◄—— **The slope is *undefined*, since division by zero is undefined.**

Lines with positive slope slant upward to the right; lines with negative slope slant downward to the right. The slope of a horizontal line is 0. The slope of a vertical line is undefined. This is why the slope formula states that $x_2 \neq x_1$.

CLASSROOM EXERCISES

Find the slope of the line passing through the given points.

1. $A(3, 1)$; $B(4, 5)$ **2.** $C(5, -6)$; $D(-2, -4)$ **3.** $E(2, 5)$; $F(7, 9)$

4. $X(5, 2)$; $Y(-1, 2)$ **5.** $Q(5, -1)$; $P(5, 5)$ **6.** $T(9, -2)$; $W(-2, -2)$

WRITTEN EXERCISES

A

State whether the slope of each line is *positive, negative, zero,* or *undefined.*

1.    **2.**    **3.**   **4.**

Find the slope of a line containing the two given points. If the line is vertical, write *undefined.*

5. $P_1(6, 3)$; $P_2(4, 1)$ **6.** $P_1(-4, -6)$; $P_2(2, -3)$ **7.** $P_1(-2, 6)$; $P_2(-1, 9)$

8. $P_1(4, 6)$; $P_2(4, -5)$ **9.** $P_1(\frac{3}{4}, -2)$; $P_2(\frac{1}{4}, 4)$ **10.** $P_1(a, b)$; $P_2(c, d)$

11. Find the slope of each side of $\triangle ABC$ with vertices $A(-3, 3)$, $B(2, 4)$, and $C(1, -2)$.

12. Find the slope of each side of quadrilateral $ABCD$ with vertices $A(3, 2)$, $B(-3, 1)$, $C(-4, -2)$, and $D(2, -1)$.

B

13. A line passing through $A(4, 3)$ and $B(x, 8)$ has a slope of -4. Find x.

14. A line passing through $A(-2, -7)$ and $B(2, y)$ has a slope of $\frac{3}{2}$. Find y.

15. A line passes through the points $P_1(2a, 3b)$ and $P_2(a, -b)$. Find the slope.

16. Triangle ABC has vertices $A(2, 4)$, $B(6, -4)$, and $C(-4, -2)$. Find the slope of $\overline{AB}$, $\overline{BC}$, and $\overline{CA}$.

17. In the triangle for Exercise 16, let D, E, and F be the midpoints of $\overline{AB}$, $\overline{BC}$, and $\overline{CA}$, respectively. Find the coordinates of D, E, and F.

18. Use your answers to Exercises 16 and 17 to compare the slopes of $\overline{AB}$ and $\overline{EF}$, of $\overline{BC}$ and $\overline{FD}$, and of $\overline{CA}$ and $\overline{DE}$.

C

In which of Exercises 19–22 are points *A, B,* and *C* collinear?

19. $A(-4, -2)$; $B(0, -4)$; $C(2, -5)$ **20.** $A(0, 0)$; $B(\frac{1}{2}, 3)$; $C(1, 5)$

21. $A(-1, 5)$; $B(2, 6)$; $C(4, 7)$ **22.** $A(8b, 8a)$; $B(2b, -a)$; $C(4b, 2a)$

Solve each equation for *y* in terms of *x*. The first one is done for you.

1. $2x + 3y = 4$

$3y = 4 - 2x$

$y = \dfrac{4 - 2x}{3}$

2. $2x + y = 4$

4. $2y = 6x - 2$

6. $3x + 7y = 21$

8. $9 - 3y = 4x$

3. $y - 2x = -4$

5. $3x = y + 6$

7. $2y + 4x + 6 = 0$

9. $1 - 5y = 3x$

Simplify each expression. *(Page 224)*

10. $3(x - 4)$

14. $\frac{1}{9}(x - 9)$

11. $-2(x - 6)$

15. $-\frac{5}{7}(q + 7)$

12. $-1(t + 8)$

16. $-\frac{3}{15}(11 - 5d)$

13. $-1(16 - 5r)$

17. $\frac{10}{3}(9r - 10)$

12–4 Slope and Linear Equations

You can draw the graph of a line if you know its slope and the coordinates of a point on the line.

EXAMPLE 1 Draw the graph of a line that contains the point $P(3, -2)$ and has a slope of $\frac{2}{3}$.

Solution: ① Graph $P(3 - 2)$.

② Since the slope is $\frac{2}{3}$, another point is 2 units up from (vertical change), and 3 units to the right of (horizontal change), $P(3, -2)$.

Plot this point, and draw the line.

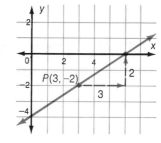

The algebraic model of a line is a **linear equation**. If you know the slope of a line and a point on the line, the equation can be written in the **point-slope form,** where *m* is the slope and (x_1, y_1) is a point on the line.

$$y - y_1 = m(x - x_1) \quad \longleftarrow \quad \text{Point-slope form}$$

EXAMPLE 2 Write an equation of the line graphed in Example 1. Use the point-slope form.

Solution: $y - y_1 = m(x - x_1) \quad \longleftarrow$ **Replace y_1 with -2 and x_1 with 3.**

$y - (-2) = \frac{2}{3}(x - 3)$

$y + 2 = \frac{2}{3}(x - 3) \quad \longleftarrow$ **Point-slope form**

The equation in Example 2 can be solved for y in terms of x.

$$y + 2 = \tfrac{2}{3}(x - 3)$$
$$y + 2 = \tfrac{2}{3}x - 2 \quad\longleftarrow\quad \textbf{Add } -2 \textbf{ to each side.}$$
$$y = \tfrac{2}{3}x - 4$$

The equation $y = \tfrac{2}{3}x - 4$ is in the **slope-intercept form**,

$$y = mx + b,$$

where m is the slope and b is the **y intercept**, where $(0, b)$ is the point at which the line crosses the y axis.

EXAMPLE 3 Write these equations in slope-intercept form. Then read the slope and y intercept from this form.

  a. $3y - 2x = 7$ **b.** $x = \tfrac{2}{3}y - 1$

Solutions: **a.** $3y - 2x = 7$ **b.** $x = \tfrac{2}{3}y - 1$

$$3y = 2x + 7 \qquad\qquad x + 1 = \tfrac{2}{3}y, \text{ or } \tfrac{2}{3}y = x + 1$$
$$y = \tfrac{1}{3}(2x + 7) \qquad\qquad y = \tfrac{3}{2}(x + 1)$$
$$y = \tfrac{2}{3}x + \tfrac{7}{3} \;\longleftarrow\; y = mx + b \;\longrightarrow\; y = \tfrac{3}{2}x + \tfrac{3}{2}$$
$$m: \tfrac{2}{3} \quad y \text{ intercept: } \tfrac{7}{3} \qquad\qquad m: \tfrac{3}{2} \quad y \text{ intercept: } \tfrac{3}{2}$$

CLASSROOM EXERCISES

1. Graph the line that contains the point $(-3, 2)$ and has a slope of $\tfrac{1}{2}$.

Use the given point, P, and slope, m, to write an equation of the line in point-slope form.

2. $P(0, 5)$; $m = -3$ 3. $P(-3, 2)$; $m = \tfrac{3}{5}$ 4. $P(1, -1)$; $m = 2$

Write each equation in slope-intercept form. Then identify m and b.

5. $x + 2y = 5$ 6. $2x - 6y = 2$ 7. $3x - y - 5 = 0$

WRITTEN EXERCISES

A   In Exercises 1–6:

  a. Graph the line with the given slope and containing the given point.
  b. Write an equation in point-slope form for each line.

1. $m = 3$; $P(0, 0)$ 2. $m = \tfrac{1}{5}$; $P(-2, -6)$ 3. $m = \tfrac{2}{3}$; $P(-2, 4)$
4. $m = \tfrac{1}{4}$; $P(2, 3)$ 5. $m = \tfrac{1}{2}$; $P(-1, 0)$ 6. $m = -1$; $P(0, 4)$

Use the given point, P, and the given slope, m, to write an equation of the line in slope-intercept form.

7. $P(5, 2)$; $m = 3$ **8.** $P(3, -5)$; $m = -2$ **9.** $P(0, 3)$; $m = \frac{2}{3}$

10. $P(3, 4)$; $m = 0$ **11.** $P(-1, -5)$; $m = \frac{3}{4}$ **12.** $P(-2, 4)$; $m = -\frac{4}{3}$

Write each equation in slope-intercept form. Identify m and b.

13. $2x + y = 4$ **14.** $x = \frac{3}{2}y + 2$ **15.** $3x + 4y = 12$

16. $3x = y + 8$ **17.** $2x + 3y = 6$ **18.** $x - 2y = 0$

In Exercises 19–24, use the given slope and y intercept to write an equation of the line in slope-intercept form.

19. $m = 1$; $b = 2$ **20.** $m = 2$; $b = 5$ **21.** $m = 2$; $b = -3$

22. $m = -1$; $b = 3$ **23.** $m = \frac{1}{3}$; $b = 4$ **24.** $m = -\frac{1}{2}$; $b = 3$

B   Write an equation in slope-intercept form of a line passing through the given points.

25. $A(3, 1)$; $B(5, 6)$ **26.** $R(-5, -2)$; $S(7, 5)$ **27.** $X(0, 0)$; $Y(-5, 1)$

Graph each equation. Use the slope and y intercept.

28. $y = 3x + 1$ **29.** $y - 2x = -7$ **30.** $5y + 2x = 10$

31. In the figure at the right, line k passes through $Q(x_1, y_1)$ and has a slope of m. Use this information to derive the point-slope form for the equation of a line. Begin by selecting P as another point on k such that its coordinates are (x, y).

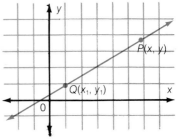

C   The vertices of $\triangle ABC$ are $A(3, -1)$, $B(-5, 5)$, and $C(2, 6)$.

32. Write equations for $\overline{AB}$, $\overline{BC}$, $\overline{AC}$ in slope-intercept form.

33. Write an equation of the median from C to side AB in slope-intercept form.

34. Show that the equation of a line with x intercept, a, and y intercept, b, is

$$\frac{x}{a} + \frac{y}{b} = 1, \ a \neq 0, \ b \neq 0.$$

_____ **Review** _____

Classify each statement as true, T, or false, F. *(Section 12–1)*

1. $P(-2, 5)$ is in Quadrant III.   **2.** $Q(3, -4)$ is in Quadrant IV.

3. For $A(-2, 3)$ and $B(-2, -2)$, $AB = 5$.   **4.** For $C(6, -7)$ and $D(-1, -7)$, $CD = 7$.

5. The line $y = 3$ is perpendicular to the x axis.

6. The line $x = -4$ is parallel to the y axis.

7. An equation of the line passing through points $(3, -4)$ and $(3, 5)$ is $y = 3$.

8. An equation of the line passing through points $(-5, 6)$ and $(4, 6)$ is $y = 6$.

In Exercises 9–11, the coordinates of the endpoints of a segment are given. Find the coordinates of the midpoint, M. *(Section 12–2)*

9. $R(5, -2); S(7, 4)$ **10.** $T(-4, 3); V(3, -4)$ **11.** $P(-6, -3); Q(8, -2)$

12. One endpoint of $\overline{RS}$ is $R(-3, 7)$, and the midpoint of $\overline{RS}$ is $(3, 5)$. Find the coordinates of point S.

Find the slope of the line passing through the given points. *(Section 12–3)*

13. $A(-4, 6); B(-1, 0)$ **14.** $D(-3, -1); E(3, 3)$ **15.** $G(-4, 5); H(2, 5)$

16. Find the slope of each side of $\triangle ABC$ with vertices $A(-2, 1)$, $B(2, 3)$, and $C(3, -2)$. *(Section 12–3)*

Write each equation in slope-intercept form. *(Section 12–4)*

17. $2y + 3x - 6 = 0$ **18.** $4x = 7 - 3y$ **19.** $3x + 4 = 2y$

Use the given information to write an equation of the line in slope-intercept form. *(Section 12–4)*

20. $m = -3; b = \frac{5}{2}$ **21.** $m = \frac{3}{2}; b = 6$

22. The line passes through $P(-3, -2)$ and has a slope of $\frac{3}{4}$.

23. The line passes through $M(0, -7)$ and has a slope of $-\frac{2}{5}$.

———— **ALGEBRA REVIEW CAPSULE FOR SECTION 12–5** ————

Write the negative reciprocal of each number. The first one is done for you.

1. $\frac{1}{2}$ Answer: $-\frac{2}{1}$, or -2 **2.** 2 **3.** -8 **4.** -17 **5.** -1

6. $\frac{2}{3}$ **7.** $-\frac{2}{b}$ **8.** $-\frac{3}{2t}$ **9.** $\frac{1}{5}$ **10.** $-4\frac{2}{3}$ **11.** $-1\frac{1}{8}c$

Complete. The first one is done for you.

12. $\frac{3}{4} \cdot \underline{\ ?\ } = 1$ Answer: $\frac{4}{3}$ **13.** $\frac{3}{4} \cdot \underline{\ ?\ } = -1$ **14.** $-\frac{3}{4} \cdot \underline{\ ?\ } = 1$

15. $-\frac{3}{4} \cdot \underline{\ ?\ } = -1$ **16.** $\frac{1}{8} \cdot \underline{\ ?\ } = -1$ **17.** $-\frac{5}{3} \cdot \underline{\ ?\ } = 1$

12–5 Parallel and Perpendicular Lines

Example 1 illustrates that nonvertical parallel lines have the same slope.

EXAMPLE 1 Line AB is parallel to line CD as shown.

    a. Find the slope of each line.

    b. Compare the slopes.

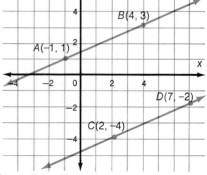

Solutions: **a.** For $\overleftrightarrow{AB}$, let $(-1,\ 1) = (x_1,\ y_1)$ and $(4,\ 3) = (x_2,\ y_2)$.

$$m = \frac{3 - 1}{4 - (-1)} \quad \longleftarrow \quad m = \frac{y_2 - y_1}{x_2 - x_1}$$

$$m = \frac{3 - 1}{4 + 1} = \frac{2}{5} \quad \longleftarrow \quad \textbf{Slope of } \overleftrightarrow{AB}$$

For $\overleftrightarrow{CD}$, let $(2,\ -4) = (x_1,\ y_1)$ and $(7,\ -2) = (x_2,\ y_2)$.

$$m = \frac{-2 - (-4)}{7 - 2}$$

$$m = \frac{-2 + 4}{5} = \frac{2}{5} \quad \longleftarrow \quad \textbf{Slope of } \overleftrightarrow{CD}$$

    b. $\therefore$ slope of $\overleftrightarrow{AB}$ = slope of $\overleftrightarrow{CD}$.

It can also be shown that lines having the same slope are parallel.

Theorem 12–2

> Two nonvertical lines are parallel if and only if they have the same slope.

Recall that the slope of vertical lines is not defined. However, *any two vertical lines are parallel to each other.*

In Example 2, the slopes of two perpendicular lines are considered.

EXAMPLE 2 Line EF is perpendicular to line GF as shown.

    a. Find the slope of each line.

    b. Find the product of the slopes.

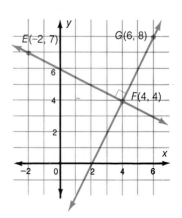

Solutions: **a.** For $\overleftrightarrow{EF}$, let $(-2,\ 7) = (x_1,\ y_1)$ and let $(4,\ 4) = (x_2,\ y_2)$.

$$m = \frac{4 - 7}{4 - (-2)} \quad \longleftarrow \quad m = \frac{y_2 - y_1}{x_2 - x_1}$$

$$m = \frac{4 - 7}{4 + 2} = \frac{-3}{6} = -\frac{1}{2} \quad \longleftarrow \quad \textbf{Slope of } \overleftrightarrow{EF}$$

For $\overleftrightarrow{GF}$, let $(6, 8) = (x_1, y_1)$ and let $(4, 4) = (x_2, y_2)$.

$$m = \frac{4-8}{4-6} = \frac{-4}{-2} = 2 \longleftarrow \quad \textbf{Slope of } \overleftrightarrow{GF}$$

b. Product of slopes: $-\frac{1}{2} \cdot 2 = -1$

The slopes, 2 and $-\frac{1}{2}$, are negative reciprocals of each other, since their product is -1.

Theorem 12-3	Two nonvertical lines are perpendicular if and only if their slopes are negative reciprocals.

To determine whether two lines are parallel, perpendicular, or neither parallel nor perpendicular, first write the equations of the lines in slope-intercept form.

EXAMPLE 3 Determine whether the graphs of the equations listed below are *parallel, perpendicular,* or *neither parallel nor perpendicular,* to the graph of $3y - 2x = 7$.

a. $4x - 6y = 9$ **b.** $3x - 2y = 11$ **c.** $4y + 6x = 12$

Solutions: $\boxed{1}$ Solve each equation for y. Read the slope from this equation.

$$3y - 2x = 7$$
$$3y = 7 + 2x$$
$$y = \frac{7}{3} + \frac{2}{3}x \qquad \text{Slope: } \frac{2}{3}$$

a. $4x - 6y = 9$	**b.** $3x - 2y = 11$	**c.** $4y + 6x = 12$
$-6y = -4x + 9$	$-2y = -3x + 11$	$4y = 12 - 6x$
$y = \frac{-4x}{-6} + \frac{9}{-6}$	$y = \frac{-3x}{-2} + \frac{11}{-2}$	$y = \frac{12}{4} - \frac{6x}{4}$
$y = \frac{2}{3}x - \frac{3}{2}$	$y = \frac{3}{2}x - \frac{11}{2}$	$y = 3 - \frac{3}{2}x$
$m = \frac{2}{3}$	$m = \frac{3}{2}$	$m = -\frac{3}{2}$

$\boxed{2}$ Compare each slope with $\frac{2}{3}$, the slope of $3y - 2x = 7$.

a. Same slope

The lines are **parallel.**

b. $\frac{2}{3} \cdot \frac{3}{2} = 1$

The lines are **neither parallel nor perpendicular.**

c. $\frac{2}{3} \cdot \left(-\frac{3}{2}\right) = -1$

The lines are **perpendicular.**

CLASSROOM EXERCISES

In Exercises 1–4, complete each statement.

1. Line k has a slope of $-\frac{2}{3}$. The slope of a line parallel to k is __?__. The slope of a line perpendicular to k is __?__.
2. Line q contains the points $(7, -3)$ and $(4, 2)$. The slope of a line parallel to q is __?__. The slope of a line perpendicular to q is __?__.
3. Find the slope of a line parallel to the graph of $y = 3x + 4$.
4. Find the slope of a line perpendicular to the graph of $3x + 6y = 7$.
5. Write Theorem 12–2 as a conditional and its converse.
6. Write Theorem 12–3 as a conditional and its converse.

WRITTEN EXERCISES

A   In Exercises 1–4, find the slope of $\overleftrightarrow{AB}$ and $\overleftrightarrow{CD}$. State whether the two lines are *parallel, perpendicular,* or *neither parallel nor perpendicular.*

1. $A(-2, 7), B(3, 6);\quad C(4, 2), D(9, 1)$
2. $A(0, 0), B(-5, 3);\quad C(5, 2), D(0, 5)$
3. $A(2, 5), B(8, 7);\quad C(-3, 1), D(-2, -2)$
4. $A(5, 3), B(-5, -2);\quad C(6, -2), D(4, 5)$

Classify the graphs of each pair of equations as *parallel, perpendicular,* or *neither parallel nor perpendicular.*

5. $4x - y = 3;\ 12x - 3y = 3$
6. $3x - 10y = 7;\ 5x + 4y = 0$
7. $x = \frac{2}{3}y;\ 3y + 2x = 0$
8. $4y + x = 17;\ 2x + 4y = 1$
9. $y = 2x + 8;\ y - 2x = 5$
10. $3x + y = 4;\ x - 3y = 4$

11. Which of the following have graphs parallel to the graph of $5y - 3x = 17$?
   a. $y = -\frac{3}{5}x + 4$
   b. $10y = 6x + 7$
   c. $y = \frac{5}{3}x - 6$

12. Which of the following have graphs perpendicular to the graph of $x + y = 7$?
   a. $y = x - 4$
   b. $x + y = 6$
   c. $2x + 2y = -12$

In any of the following exercises that ask for the equation of a line, write the equation in the form $y = mx + b$.

In Exercises 13–15, write an equation of the line that passes through $(6, -3)$ and meets the given condition.

13. The line is parallel to the graph of $y = -5x - 3$.
14. The line is parallel to the graph of $y + 2x = 7$.
15. The line is parallel to the x axis.

In Exercises 16–18, write an equation of the line that passes through $(-4, -3)$ and meets the given condition.

16. The line is perpendicular to the graph of $y = 4x - 3$.

17. The line is perpendicular to the y axis.

18. The line is perpendicular to the graph of $4 + 3y = -2x$.

19. Write an equation of the line that contains the point $(0, -3)$ and is parallel to the graph of $4x - y = -7$.

20. Write an equation of the line that contains the point $(-4, -7)$ and is perpendicular to the graph of $2x - 3y = 6$.

21. The line that contains $E(a, 3)$ and $F(2, 0)$ is parallel to the line that contains $D(2, 8)$ and $C(-3, -4)$. Find a.

22. The line through $R(5, -3)$ and $S(0, k)$ is perpendicular to the line through $T(-3, 2)$ and $V(-2, -5)$. Find k.

23. Show that a triangle with vertices $A(2, 5)$, $B(8, 1)$ and $C(-2, -1)$ is a right triangle. (HINT: Show that two of its sides are perpendicular.)

24. Prove the first part of Theorem 12–2.

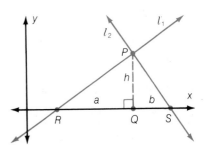

Given: $k \parallel v$; m_1 is the slope of k;
m_2 is the slope of v.

Prove: $m_1 = m_2$

Plan: From a point P on k and a point S on v, drop perpendicular segments PQ and ST to the x axis. Then $\dfrac{PQ}{QR} = \dfrac{ST}{TU}$. But $m_1 = \dfrac{PQ}{QR}$ and $m_2 = \dfrac{ST}{TU}$. $\therefore m_1 = m_2$.

Also consider the case where k and v are both parallel to the x axis.

25. Prove the first part of Theorem 12–3.

Given: $l_1 \perp l_2$; m_1 is the slope of l_1;
m_2 is the slope of l_2.

Prove: $m_1 m_2 = -1$

Plan: Let l_1 and l_2 intersect at P and meet the x axis at R and S respectively. Drop perpendicular $\overline{PQ}$ to the x axis. Let $PQ = h$, $QR = a$, and $QS = b$.

In right triangle PRS, $\overline{PQ}$ is the altitude to the hypotenuse. Thus, $\dfrac{a}{h} = \dfrac{h}{b}$.

But $m_1 = \dfrac{h}{a}$ and $m_2 = -\dfrac{h}{b}$. If $m_2 = -\dfrac{h}{b}$, then $-m_2 = \dfrac{h}{b}$.

If $m_1 = \dfrac{h}{a}$, $\dfrac{1}{m_1} = \dfrac{a}{h}$. Since $\dfrac{a}{h} = \dfrac{h}{b}$, $\dfrac{1}{m_1} = -m_2$. $\therefore m_1 m_2 = -1$.

In Exercises 1–6, use the Pythagorean Theorem to compute the unknown measures. *(Pages 310–311)*

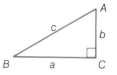

1. $a = 5; b = 12; c = $ ___?___
2. $a = 8; b = 15; c = $ ___?___
3. $a = 3; b = 4; c = $ ___?___
4. $a = 20; b = 21; c = $ ___?___
5. $a = 13; b = 15; c = $ ___?___
6. $a = 17; b = 20; c = $ ___?___

12-6 The Distance Formula

Example 1 shows how to find the distance between two points in a plane when the points do not lie on either a horizontal or a vertical line.

EXAMPLE 1 Find AB.

Solution:

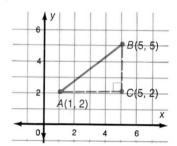

$\boxed{1}$ Form a right triangle by drawing the horizontal segment, $\overline{AC}$, and the vertical segment, $\overline{BC}$. Thus, $\overline{AB}$ is the hypotenuse of a right triangle.

$\boxed{2}$ Apply the Pythagorean Theorem.

$$(AB)^2 = (AC)^2 + (BC)^2$$
$$= |5 - 1|^2 + |5 - 2|^2$$
$$= 4^2 + 3^2 = 25 \quad \text{Thus, } AB = 5.$$

The procedure of Example 1 is expressed as the Distance Formula.

Theorem 12-4

Distance Formula
The distance d between two points $P_1(x_1, y_1)$ and $P_2(x_2, y_2)$ is
$$d = \sqrt{(x_2 - x_1)^2 + (y_2 - y_1)^2}.$$

You are asked to prove this theorem in the Written Exercises.

EXAMPLE 2 Show that a triangle with vertices $A(3, -1)$, $B(8, 4)$ *and* $C(4, 6)$ is isosceles. (HINT: Show that the lengths of two sides are equal.)

Solution:

$$AB = \sqrt{(8-3)^2 + (4-(-1))^2} \qquad BC = \sqrt{(4-8)^2 + (6-4)^2}$$
$$= \sqrt{5^2 + 5^2} \qquad\qquad\qquad = \sqrt{(-4)^2 + 2^2}$$
$$= \sqrt{50}, \text{ or } 5\sqrt{2} \qquad\qquad = \sqrt{20}, \text{ or } 2\sqrt{5}$$
$$CA = \sqrt{(3-4)^2 + (-1-6)^2}$$
$$= \sqrt{(-1)^2 + (-7)^2}$$
$$= \sqrt{50}, \text{ or } 5\sqrt{2} \qquad \text{Since } AB = CA, \triangle ABC \text{ is isosceles.}$$

CLASSROOM EXERCISES

Find the distance between points *A* and *B*.

1. $A(-2, 5)$; $B(-2, 0)$
2. $A(7, -1)$; $B(-3, -1)$
3. $A(-7, 6)$; $B(3, -4)$
4. $A(7, -1)$; $B(-3, -11)$
5. $A(a, b)$; $B(3, 3)$
6. $A(c, d)$; $B(-4, 4)$

WRITTEN EXERCISES

A　　Find the distance between each pair of points.

1. $A(4, 3)$; $B(1, 2)$
2. $A(-4, 1)$; $B(-5, 4)$
3. $R(7, -5)$; $S(2, -6)$
4. $R(-1, -2)$; $S(3, 6)$
5. $C(4, -3)$; $D(-4, 3)$
6. $E(-3, 3)$; $F(0, -4)$
7. $A(7, 1)$; $B(6, 2)$
8. $C(2, 2)$; $D(5, 2)$
9. $P(-2, 4)$; $Q(-2, -5)$
10. $M(-1, -3)$; $N(4, -3)$
11. $R(a, b)$; $S(c, d)$
12. $T(a, b)$; $U(c, b)$

13. Find the perimeter of triangle ABC with vertices $A(-1, -2)$, $B(2, -2)$ and $C(-1, -6)$.

14. Use the distance formula to show that $A(-4, 1)$, $B(5, 4)$ and $C(2, -2)$ are vertices of an isosceles triangle.

15. Use the distance formula and the Pythagorean Theorem to show that $D(2, -2)$, $E(5, 4)$ and $F(-4, 1)$ are the vertices of a right triangle.

16. Describe another method that could be used in Exercise 15 to show that $\triangle DEF$ is a right triangle.

17. Determine whether the triangle with vertices $R(-3, 2)$, $S(6, 5)$ and $T(3, -1)$ is isosceles, equilateral or scalene.

18. Show that the triangle with vertices $A(1, -1)$, $B(7, 1)$ and $C(5, -3)$ is an isosceles right triangle.

19. Find the length of the radius of a circle that has its center at $O(-3, 4)$ and passes through the point $P(2, -5)$.

20. Find the lengths of the diagonals of a rectangle with vertices $R(-6, -8)$, $S(5, -8)$, $T(5, -5)$ and $Q(-6, -5)$.

B

21. Prove Theorem 12–4.

Given: $P_1(x_1, y_1)$ and $P_2(x_2, y_2)$

Prove: $P_1P_2 = \sqrt{(x_2 - x_1)^2 + (y_2 - y_1)^2}$

Plan: Form a right triangle by drawing the horizontal segment P_1Z and the vertical segment, P_2Z. By the Pythagorean Theorem, $(P_1P_2)^2 = (P_1Z)^2 + (P_2Z)^2$ and $(P_1P_2)^2 = |x_2 - x_1|^2 + |y_2 - y_1|^2$.

Thus, $P_1P_2 = \sqrt{|x_2 - x_1|^2 + |y_2 - y_1|^2}$.

Since $|x_2 - x_1|^2 = (x_2 - x_1)^2$ and $|y_2 - y_1|^2 = (y_2 - y_1)^2$, it is not necessary to use absolute value in the formula.

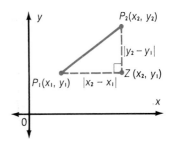

22. Use the distance formula to show that $A(0, 2)$, $B(7, 1)$, $C(12, 4)$ and $D(5, 5)$ are the vertices of a parallelogram.

23. Use the distance formula to show that the points $A(-5, 7)$, $B(-3, 4)$ and $C(-1, 1)$ are collinear. (HINT: Show that the longest distance is the sum of the two shorter distances.)

C

24. The vertices of isosceles trapezoid $ABCD$ are $A(0, 0)$, $B(a, 0)$, $C(a - c, b)$, and $D(c, b)$. Show that $\overline{AB}$ is parallel to $\overline{CD}$ and that $\overline{AD}$ is *not* parallel to $\overline{BC}$.

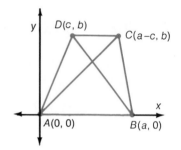

25. Show that diagonals AC and BD are congruent.

26. Show that sides AD and BC are equal in length.

The vertices of $\triangle ABC$ are $A(0, 0)$, $B(a, 0)$ and $C(b, c)$.

27. Prove that the line segment joining the midpoints of any two sides of the triangle is parallel to the third side.

28. Prove that the line segment joining the midpoints of any two sides of the triangle is one-half as long as the third side.

CALCULATOR APPLICATIONS

Distance Formula

You can use a scientific calculator with parentheses keys to find the distance between two points in a plane.

EXAMPLE Find the distance between $A(-2, 5)$ and $B(3, 6)$.

Use the Distance Formula to find AB.

SOLUTION $AB = \sqrt{(x_2 - x_1)^2 + (y_2 - y_1)^2} = \sqrt{(3 - (-2))^2 + (6 - 5)^2}$

$$(\quad 3 \quad - \quad 2 \quad +/- \quad) \quad x^2 \quad +$$

$$(\quad 6 \quad - \quad 5 \quad) \quad x^2 \quad = \quad \sqrt{x}$$

$$5.0990195$$

EXERCISES

Use a scientific calculator to find the distance between each pair of points.

1. $C(2, 3)$; $D(5, -9)$
2. $P(-2, 1)$; $Q(-4, -5)$
3. $Y(-9, 4)$; $Z(-1, 3)$
4. $R(0, 12)$; $S(-9, 0)$
5. $G(4, 7)$; $H(-3, -12)$
6. $J(2, 8)$; $K(-15, 20)$
7. $N(3, -6)$; $O(15, 24)$
8. $W(3, -15)$; $X(-6, 25)$
9. $E(21, -5)$; $F(-13, 10)$

12-7 Equations of Circles

You can use the distance formula to determine an equation of a circle.

EXAMPLE 1 Write an equation of the circle with center at the origin and with radius 3.

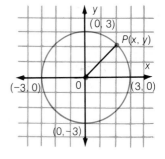

Solution: Let $P(x, y)$ be any point on the circle.

Since the distance from the origin to $P(x, y)$ is 3,

$$\sqrt{(x-0)^2 + (y-0)^2} = 3$$

$$\sqrt{x^2 + y^2} = 3 \longleftarrow \text{Square both sides.}$$

$$x^2 + y^2 = 9 \longleftarrow \text{Equation of the circle}$$

Using the distance formula and a similar procedure, you can determine the equation of a circle with center at (h, k) and radius r.

Theorem 12-5

> The circle with center (h, k) and radius r has the equation
> $$(x - h)^2 + (y - k)^2 = r^2.$$

Example 2 shows how to apply this theorem.

EXAMPLE 2 Write an equation in standard form of a circle with center at $(5, -2)$ and radius 4.

Solution: Use Theorem 12-5 with $(h, k) = (5, -2)$ and $r = 4$.

$$(x - h)^2 + (y - k)^2 = r^2 \longleftarrow \begin{array}{l}\textbf{Replace } h \textbf{ with 5, } k \textbf{ with } -2, \\ \textbf{and } r \textbf{ with 4.}\end{array}$$

$$(x - 5)^2 + (y - (-2))^2 = 4^2$$

$$(x - 5)^2 + (y + 2)^2 = 16 \longleftarrow \text{Standard form}$$

Given the equation of a circle, you can compare it with the standard form in Theorem 12-5 to determine the center and radius of the circle.

EXAMPLE 3 Find the center and radius of the circle with equation

$$(x + 2)^2 + (y - 5)^2 = 49.$$

Solution: Write the equation in the form $(x - h)^2 + (y - k)^2 = r^2$.

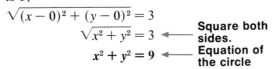

$$(x - (\underline{-2}))^2 + (y - 5)^2 = 7^2$$

Center: $(-2, 5)$ Radius: 7

CLASSROOM EXERCISES

Write an equation of each circle with the given center, C, and radius, r.

1. $C(0, 0)$; $r = 5$ **2.** $C(0, 0)$; $r = 9$ **3.** $C(0, 0)$; $r = 6$

4. $C(1, 1)$; $r = 3$ **5.** $C(5, -2)$; $r = 7$ **6.** $C(-3, 4)$; $r = 2$

Find the center and the radius of each circle.

7. $(x - 0)^2 + (y - 0)^2 = 3^2$ **8.** $x^2 + y^2 = 8^2$ **9.** $(x - 4)^2 + (y + 3)^2 = 10^2$

WRITTEN EXERCISES

A   In Exercises 1–5, write an equation of the circle with center at the origin and with the given radius.

1. $r = 11$ **2.** $r = 4$ **3.** $r = \frac{1}{3}$ **4.** $r = 0.2$ **5.** $r = \frac{3}{4}$

In Exercises 6–11, write an equation of the circle having the given center, C, and radius, r.

6. $C(-5, 2)$; $r = 6$ **7.** $C(6, 3)$; $r = 13$ **8.** $C(4, -\frac{1}{2})$; $r = 15$

9. $C(-4, -5)$; $r = 5$ **10.** $C(\frac{1}{3}, -2)$; $r = 9$ **11.** $C(\frac{2}{3}, 2)$; $r = \frac{2}{5}$

Find the center and radius of each circle.

12. $x^2 + (y + 2)^2 = 16$ **13.** $(x - \frac{1}{2})^2 + (y + 3)^2 = 4$ **14.** $(x - 3)^2 + (y + 3)^2 = 25$

15. $(x - 7)^2 + (y + 8)^2 = (3)^2$ **16.** $(x + 6)^2 + (y + 1)^2 = \frac{1}{4}$ **17.** $(x - a)^2 + (y + t)^2 = p^2$

B   In Exercises 18–21, write an equation of the circle with center at the origin and tangent to the line whose equation is given.

18. $x = 3$ **19.** $y = 7$ **20.** $x = -6$ **21.** $y = -2$

In Exercises 22–24, write an equation of the circle with the given center, C, and passing through the given point, P.

22. $C(-2, 3)$; $P(2, 3)$ **23.** $C(2, 5)$; $P(2, 3)$ **24.** $C(-1, 3)$; $P(1, 4)$

Write an equation of the circle whose diameter has the given endpoints.

25. $P(0, 1)$; $Q(18, 1)$ **26.** $P(-2, -5)$; $Q(-2, -11)$ **27.** $P(3, 1)$; $Q(3, -6)$

C

28. Find an equation of the circle that passes through $P(4, 3)$, $Q(-3, 4)$, and $R(-5, 0)$.

29. Find the area of the ring formed by the circles whose equations are $(x + 4)^2 + (y - 3)^2 = 25$ and $(x + 4)^2 + (y - 3)^2 = 100$.

30. Find an equation of the circle tangent to the line whose equation is $y = -\frac{3}{2}x + 3$ if the origin is the center of the circle.

12–8　Coordinate Proofs

You can use the methods of coordinate geometry to prove theorems.

EXAMPLE 1　Prove that the midpoint of the hypotenuse of a right triangle is equidistant from the vertices.

Proof:　$\boxed{1}$ Draw the right triangle so that its right angle, $\angle C$, is at the origin, and its legs lie on the x and y axes.

Let the coordinates of A be $(2a, 0)$ and of B be $(0, 2b)$, where a and b are positive numbers. (The coefficient 2 is used to avoid fractions.)

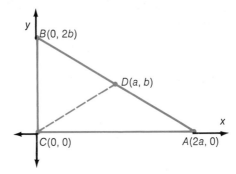

$\boxed{2}$ Find the coordinates of D, the midpoint of $\overline{AB}$.

x coordinate: $\dfrac{2a + 0}{2} = a$ $\qquad\qquad$ y coordinate: $\dfrac{0 + 2b}{2} = b$

Thus, D has coordinates (a, b).

$\boxed{3}$ Show that $DB = DA = DC$.

$DB = \sqrt{(a - 0)^2 + (b - 2b)^2} = \sqrt{a^2 + b^2}$

$DA = \sqrt{(2a - a)^2 + (0 - b)^2} = \sqrt{a^2 + b^2}$

$DC = \sqrt{(a - 0)^2 + (b - 0)^2} \;\; = \sqrt{a^2 + b^2}$

$\therefore D(a, b)$ is equidistant from the vertices.

Example 2 also uses coordinate methods to prove a theorem.

EXAMPLE 2　Prove that the length of the median of a trapezoid is equal to one-half the sum of the bases.

Proof:　$\boxed{1}$ Place the trapezoid in the coordinate plane so that one vertex is at the origin. Choose convenient values for the coordinates of the other vertices.

2 Find the coordinates of mid-points E and F.

Midpoint E: $\left(\dfrac{2a + 0}{2}, \dfrac{2d + 0}{2}\right)$
$= (a, d)$

Midpoint F: $\left(\dfrac{2b + 2c}{2}, \dfrac{2d + 0}{2}\right)$
$= (b + c, d)$

3 Find the length of median EF.

$$EF = \sqrt{(b + c - a)^2 + (d - d)^2} = \sqrt{(b + c - a)^2} = b + c - a$$

4 Find one-half the sum of the bases.

$$BC = \sqrt{(2b - 2a)^2 + (2d - 2d)^2} = \sqrt{(2b - 2a)^2} = 2b - 2a$$
$$AD = \sqrt{(2c - 0)^2 + (0 - 0)^2} = \sqrt{(2c)^2} = 2c$$
$$BC + AD = 2b + 2c - 2a$$
$$\tfrac{1}{2}(BC + AD) = \tfrac{1}{2} \cdot 2(b + c - a) = b + c - a$$
$$\therefore EF = \tfrac{1}{2}(BC + AD).$$

An important step in writing a coordinate proof is the selection of correct, convenient coordinates for the vertices of the figure. When possible, use the origin as one vertex with at least one side on a coordinate axis.

CLASSROOM EXERCISES

Without introducing any new letters, name the missing coordinates for the vertices of each figure.

1. **Square**

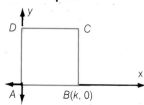

2. **Rectangle**

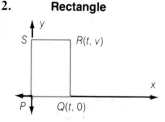

3. **Isosceles Right Triangle**

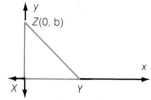

4. **Isosceles Triangle**

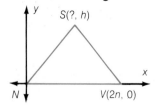

5. **Trapezoid**

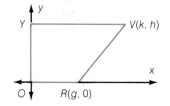

6. **Parallelogram**

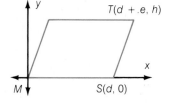

WRITTEN EXERCISES

A Without introducing any new letters, name the missing coordinates for the vertices of each figure.

1. Square

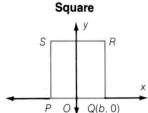

2. Equilateral Triangle

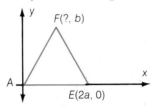

3. Isosceles Trapezoid

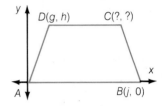

4. Parallelogram

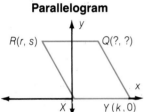

5. Square

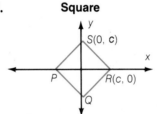

6. Rectangle

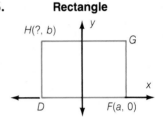

In each isosceles triangle in Exercises 7 and 8, use coordinate methods to determine each of the following.

a. The coordinates of midpoints D and E

b. The lengths of medians BD and AE

7.

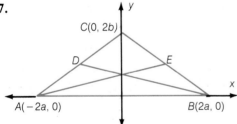

8.

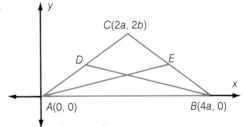

9. Use the figure to prove the theorem of Example 1.

Plan: First find the coordinates of midpoint D. Then find DB, DA, and DC.

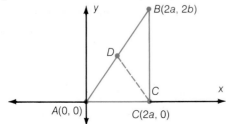

10. In the figure below, $\triangle ABC$ is a 30-60 right triangle and $m\angle B = 30$. Use the distance formula to find AB.

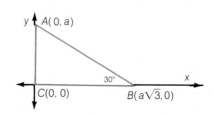

Coordinate Geometry **543**

11. Refer to the figure at the right.

Show that the segments joining the mid–points of the opposite sides of a quadri–lateral bisect each other.

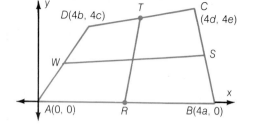

B Use the methods of coordinate geometry to prove each statement.

12. The diagonals of any rectangle are congruent.

13. The diagonals of a square are perpendicular to each other.

14. If a trapezoid is isosceles, then the diagonals are congruent.

15. The diagonals of a parallelogram bisect each other.

16. The opposite sides of a parallelogram are congruent.

17. The diagonals of a rhombus are perpendicular to each other. (HINT: Let the vertices be $(0, 0)$, (b, c), $(a, 0)$, $(b + a, c)$.)

18. If two sides of a quadrilateral are parallel and congruent, then the figure is a parallelogram.

19. If the diagonals of a parallelogram are perpendicular to each other, then the parallelogram is a rhombus.

C

20. The altitudes of a triangle are *concurrent*. (Three or more lines are **concurrent** if they have a point in common.)

21. The medians of a triangle are concurrent in a point that is two-thirds of the distance from each vertex to the midpoint of the opposite side.

22. Show that an equation of the perpendicular bisector of the segment with endpoints (a, b) and (c, d) is

$$2(c - a)x + 2(d - b)y + a^2 + b^2 - c^2 - d^2 = 0.$$

23. Given that a line k has the equation $ax + by + c = 0$ and that a given point has coordinates (x_1, y_1). Find an equation of a line containing the given point and perpendicular to k. Write an expression for the distance, d, of the given point from k.

Puzzle

The lanes on the running track shown at the right are one meter wide and are numbered from smallest to largest.

How many meters headstart should a runner in Lane 2 have over a runner in Lane 1 so that each will cover 800 meters at the finish line?

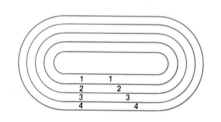

Review

Classify the graphs of each pair of equations as *parallel, perpendicular,* or *neither parallel nor perpendicular.* *(Section 12–5)*

1. $y = \frac{1}{2}x + 2;\ -2x - y = 3$

2. $y = 5 - x;\ -5y = 5x - 2$

3. $3y + 4x = 8;\ 4y - 3x = 9$

4. $2y = \frac{3}{4}x;\ 2y = -\frac{3}{4}x$

5. Write an equation in slope-intercept form of the line that passes through the point $T(-4,\ 7)$ and is parallel to the line through $A(6,\ 7)$ and $B(-2,\ 5)$.

6. Write an equation in slope-intercept form of the line that passes through the point $V(3,\ -6)$ and perpendicular to the graph of $4x + 2y = 7$.

In Exercises 7–9, find the distance between each pair of points. *(Section 12–6)*

7. $A(0,\ -3),\ B(5,\ -4)$ **8.** $M(-7,\ 3),\ N(6,\ -2)$ **9.** $P(-3,\ -4),\ Q(2,\ -8)$

10. Find the perimeter of the triangle whose vertices are $A(-1,\ -1)$, $B(1,\ 2)$, and $C(4,\ 0)$. *(Section 12–6)*

11. Rhombus $ABCD$ has vertices $A(1,\ 2)$, $B(4,\ 3)$, $C(3,\ 0)$, and $D(0,\ -1)$. Find the lengths of diagonals AC and BD. *(Section 12–6)*

Give the coordinates of the center and the length of the radius of each circle whose equation is given. *(Section 12–7)*

12. $x^2 + y^2 - 49 = 0$ **13.** $x^2 + y^2 = 144$ **14.** $(x - 3)^2 + (y + 2)^2 = 16$

15. Write the equation of a circle with a radius of 6 and center at $C(-8,\ 5)$. *(Section 12–7)*

16. Use the methods of coordinate geometry to prove that the sum of the squares of the sides of a parallelogram equals the sum of the squares of the diagonals. *(Section 12–8)*

Chapter Summary

IMPORTANT TERMS

Coordinate plane (p. 521)
Coordinates of a point (p. 520)
Linear equation (p. 528)
Ordered pair (p. 520)
Point-slope form (p. 528)
Quadrants (p. 520)

Slope-intercept form (p. 529)
Slope of a line (p. 526)
x axis (p. 520)
y axis (p. 520)
y intercept (p. 529)

IMPORTANT IDEAS

1. The Midpoint Formula: The coordinates $(x_m,\ y_m)$ of the midpoint M of the segment whose endpoints are $P_1(x_1,\ y_1)$ and $P_2(x_2,\ y_2)$ are

$$x_m = \frac{x_1 + x_2}{2} \quad \text{and} \quad y_m = \frac{y_1 + y_2}{2}.$$

2. For any two lines whose slopes are m_1 and m_2:

    a. The lines are parallel if and only if $m_1 = m_2$.

    b. The lines are perpendicular if and only if $m_1 \cdot m_2 = -1$.

3. The Distance Formula: The distance d between two points $P_1(x_1, y_1)$ and $P_2(x_2, y_2)$ is given by this formula.

$$d = \sqrt{(x_2 - x_1)^2 + (y_2 - y_1)^2}$$

4. Equation of a circle: The circle with center (h, k) and radius r has the equation

$$(x - h)^2 + (y - k)^2 = r^2.$$

——— Chapter Objectives and Review ———

Objective: *To name and graph the coordinates of a point in the coordinate plane (Section 12–1)*

Graph on the same set of axes.

1. $R(-5, 3)$ **2.** $S(-2, 4)$ **3.** $T(-3, -4)$ **4.** $Q(2\frac{1}{2}, 4)$

Objective: *To find the coordinates of the midpoint of a segment (Section 12–2)*

Find the midpoint of each segment having the given endpoints.

5. $A(4, 7); B(-2, 5)$ **6.** $F(-1, -2); G(0, -3)$ **7.** $P(-3, 2); Q(-3, 5)$

8. One endpoint of $\overline{AB}$ is $A(-1, 5)$ and the midpoint of $\overline{AB}$ is $(1, 3)$. Find the coordinates of point B.

Objective: *To find the slope of a line given two points on the line (Section 12–3)*

Find the slope of a line passing through the given points.

9. $A(3, 2); B(-7, 2)$ **10.** $C(5, -7); D(-3, 2)$

Objective: *To write the equation of a line (Section 12–4)*

Write an equation of line k in slope-intercept form.

11. Line k contains the point $P(2, -3)$ and has a slope of $\frac{3}{2}$.

12. Line k contains the points $A(4, 2)$ and $B(6, 7)$.

Objective: *To graph a line using its slope and y intercept (Section 12–4)*

Write each equation in slope-intercept form. Then graph the equation.

13. $2x + y = 7$ **14.** $3x + 2y = 6$ **15.** $3x - y = 9$

Write an equation of the line passing through the given points.

16. $A(6, 1); B(-4, 3)$ **17.** $E(-4, 1); F(8, 0)$

Objective: *To use slope to identify parallel and perpendicular lines (Section 12–5)*

Classify the graphs of each pair of equations as *parallel, perpendicular,* or *neither parallel nor perpendicular.*

18. $2y = 4x + 8$; $y - 2x = 5$ **19.** $x + 2y = 12$; $2x + 2y = 3$

Objective: *To find the distance between two points in the coordinate plane (Section 12–6)*

Find the distance between each pair of points.

20. $A(1, 2)$; $B(4, 6)$ **21.** $C(-1, -3)$; $D(7, 3)$

22. Use the distance formula to show that $A(5, 5)$, $B(-1, 7)$ and $C(-2, -6)$ are the vertices of an isosceles triangle.

Objective: *To write the equation of a circle (Section 12–7)*

In Exercises 23–25, write an equation of the circle having the given center, C, and radius, r.

23. $C(0, 0)$; $r = 3$ **24.** $C(1, 2)$; $r = 5$ **25.** $C(-2, 4)$; $r = \frac{1}{2}$

Objective: *To determine the center and radius of a circle from its equation (Section 12–7)*

Determine the center and radius of each circle.

26. $x^2 + y^2 = 16$ **27.** $(x - 1)^2 + y^2 = 25$ **28.** $(x + 2)^2 + (y - 3)^2 = 49$

Objective: *To use coordinate geometry to prove theorems (Section 12–8)*

Use the methods of coordinate geometry to prove each statement.

29. The median of a trapezoid is parallel to the bases of the trapezoid.

30. The median of a trapezoid is equal in length to one-half the sum of the bases of the trapezoid.

In Exercises 1–4, complete each statement.

1. The point $A(2, -3)$ is in Quadrant __?__.

2. The graph of $y = 4$ is __?__ (perpendicular, parallel) to the x axis.

3. The slope of a line defined by $y = -4x + 7$ is __?__, and the coordinates of the y intercept are (__?__, __?__).

4. The slope of a line that contains the points $A(2, -3)$ and $B(-6, 5)$ is __?__.

5. The endpoints of $\overline{AB}$ are $A(-5, 2)$ and $B(3, 6)$. Find the midpoint of $\overline{AB}$.

6. Find the distance between the points $C(-3, 2)$ and $D(5, -2)$.

7. Find the slope of a line that is parallel to the graph of $2x - y + 5 = 0$.

8. Find the slope of a line that is perpendicular to the graph of $3x + 2y = 9$.

9. Write, in point-slope form, an equation of the line that passes through the point $(2, -3)$ and has a slope of $\frac{1}{2}$.

10. Write, in slope-intercept form, an equation of a line that passes through the points $A(4, 10)$ and $B(2, 6)$.

11. Are the graphs of the lines whose equations are $x = \frac{3}{2}y$ and $3y + 2x = 7$ parallel, perpendicular, or neither parallel nor perpendicular?

12. Use the distance formula to show that $A(-4, 1)$, $B(5, 4)$ and $C(2, -2)$ are the vertices of an isosceles triangle.

13. Write an equation of the circle with center $C(-2, 3)$ and radius 4.

14. Use the formula for slope to show that $D(2, -2)$, $E(11, 3)$ and $F(-3, 7)$ are the vertices of a right triangle.

15. Use the methods of coordinate geometry to prove that the diagonals of an isosceles trapezoid are congruent.

CHAPTER **13** Introduction to Transformations

Sections   13-1   Reflections

            13-2   Special Reflections

            13-3   Rotations

            13-4   Dilations

Review
and   Chapter Summary
Testing
            Chapter Objectives and Review

            Chapter Test

            Cumulative Review: Chapters 12-13

13-1 Reflections

A **transformation** is a relation in which a point P is paired with *exactly one* point P' (P prime), called its **image**. One such transformation is a **reflection**.

EXAMPLE 1 Find the image of points A, B, C, and D where k is the reflecting line, or **line of reflection**. Note that D is on line k.

Solution:

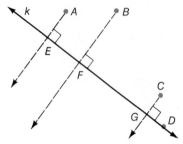   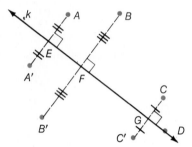

Draw perpendiculars from A, B, and C to line k. Since D is on line k, this cannot be done for point D.

Measure $\overline{AE}$. Locate A' such that $AE = A'E$. Repeat this to find B' and C'. Since D is on line k, D is **its own image.**

Thus, the reflection of a point P over a line k *maps* P, called the **preimage**, onto its image, P'. If P is on k, then P is its own image. Note that line k is the perpendicular bisector of $\overline{AA'}$, $\overline{BB'}$, and $\overline{CC'}$.

Since two points determine a line, you can find the image of a line by reflecting any two of its points. Two points also determine a ray provided one of the points is the endpoint of the ray. Thus, to find the image of a ray, you must find the image of its endpoint and the image of one other point of the ray.

EXAMPLE 2 Reflect $\overleftrightarrow{MP}$ over line k and reflect $\angle ABC$ over line n.

Solution:

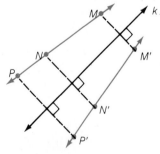   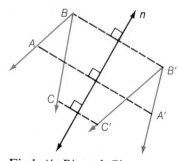

Find M' and P'.
Then draw $\overleftrightarrow{M'P'}$.

Find A', B', and C'.
Then draw $\overrightarrow{B'A'}$ and $\overrightarrow{B'C'}$.

By measuring $\overline{MP}$ and $\overline{M'P'}$ you will find that $MP = M'P'$. Similarly, $m\angle ABC = m\angle A'B'C'$. Thus, as a result of reflections over a line, segments map onto congruent segments and angles map onto congruent angles. Since polygons are composed of segments and angles, it follows that a line reflection of a polygon will result in a congruent polygon.

Thus, *a reflection is a congruence mapping.*

In the figure at the right, points A and P are given. A is to be reflected over P. To find the image of A, draw $\overleftrightarrow{AP}$ as shown. Locate point A' such that P is the midpoint of $\overline{AA'}$. This is a *point reflection*.

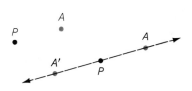

CLASSROOM EXERCISES

In Exercises 1–8:

a. Name the least number of points needed to reflect each figure.

b. Which points of each figure should be reflected?

1. Line
2. Ray
3. Segment
4. Angle

5. Triangle
6. Rectangle
7. Hexagon
8. Pentagon

9. Will the answers to Exercises 1–8 differ for a reflection over a line and a reflection over a point?

WRITTEN EXERCISES

A   In Exercises 1–6:

a. Copy each figure.

b. Find the reflection over line k for the figure.

1.

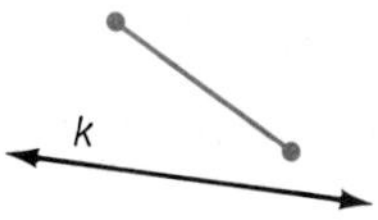

2.

3.
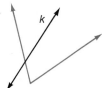

4.
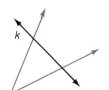

5.

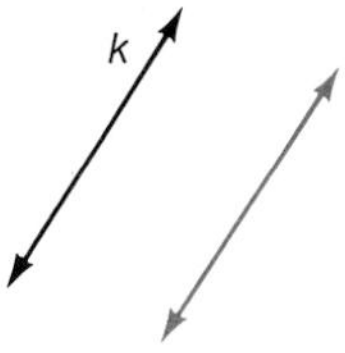

6.

7. Given lines *r* and *s* at the left below such that *r* is the image of *s* over a line *k* (not shown). Copy the figure and find *k*.

8. Copy the figure at the right above in which *A'* is the image of *A*. Find the image of ∠*A*.

9. Copy the figure at the right. Reflect the midpoints of each side of △*ABC* over line *m*. Then use the midpoints to find the image of △*ABC*.

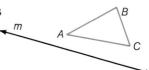

10. A surveyor wishes to find a point *C* on line *m* such that the distance from *A* to *C* to *B* is a minimum. Where on *m* should the surveyor place *C*?

11. Copy the figure at the left below. Reflect points *A*, *B*, and *C* over *P*. Draw △*ABC* and its image △*A'B'C'*. Compare the corresponding sides and angles.

12. Copy the figure at the right above. Reflect $\overline{AB}$ through *P*. Then reflect that image through *Q*. Label the image *A'B'*. What kind of figure does quadrilateral *AA'B'B* appear to be?

13. In trapezoid *ABCD* below, *S* and *T* are the midpoints of the nonparallel sides. Copy the trapezoid. Then show by a point reflection over point *S* that the area of the trapezoid equals the area of the rectangle whose height equals the height of the trapezoid, and whose base has length *ST*.

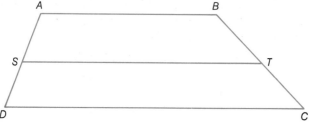

13-2 Special Reflections

If a line can be drawn through a geometric figure such that the figure on one side of the line is the reflection of the figure on the opposite side, the line is a **line of symmetry**, or *axis of symmetry*. The geometric figure is *symmetrical with respect to the line*. Some geometric figures, such as a square, are symmetrical with respect to more than one line.

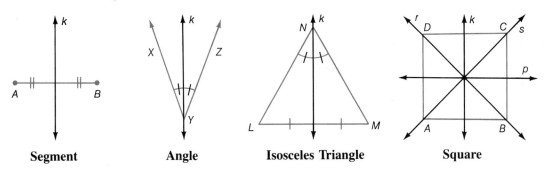

| Segment | Angle | Isosceles Triangle | Square |

A reflection over a line produces a "mirror" effect. The image is the opposite of the geometric figure being reflected.

EXAMPLE 1 Find the image of $\triangle EFG$ over k. Then find the image when $\triangle E'F'G'$ is reflected over line m, where $k \parallel m$.

Solution:

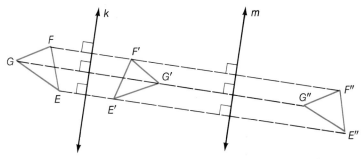

NOTE: E'' is read "E double prime."

Example 1 illustrates a *composition of two reflections* over two parallel lines. This type of mapping of points is a **translation.** In Example 1, $\triangle E''F''G''$ is the image of $\triangle EFG$ under the translation. Since the image under a reflection is a congruence mapping, a composition of reflections is also a congruence mapping. Thus,

$$\triangle EFG \cong \triangle E''F''G''$$

It can be shown that a segment and its image are parallel under a translation. Thus, in Example 1,

$$\overline{FG} \parallel \overline{F''G''}, \overline{FE} \parallel \overline{F''E''}, \text{ and } \overline{EG} \parallel \overline{E''G''}.$$

EXAMPLE 2 Find the image of $\triangle EFG$ by reflecting $\triangle E''F''G''$ (the image of $\triangle EFG$ under the translation in Example 1) over line r, where $r \perp m$. Draw $\overline{FF'''}$ and label the intersection of $\overline{FF'''}$ and r as O. Compare FO with FF'''.

Solution:

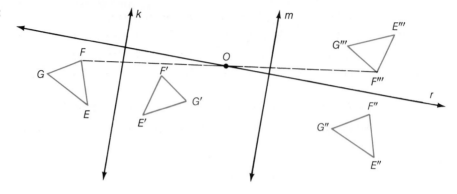

$$FF''' = 8 \text{ cm} \qquad FO = 4 \text{ cm} \qquad \therefore FO = \tfrac{1}{2}FF'''$$

Example 2 illustrates a composition of reflections called a *glide reflection*. A **glide reflection** maps every point P of a given geometric figure onto its image P''' by a translation followed by a reflection over a line that is perpendicular to the lines of translation.

It can be shown that the line of reflection bisects every such segment PP''' as is suggested by Example 2.

CLASSROOM EXERCISES

In Exercises 1–8, state the number of lines of symmetry for each figure. Make a sketch to help you.

1. Scalene triangle

2. Right (not isosceles) triangle

3. Equiangular triangle

4. Isosceles triangle

5. Rhombus

6. Isosceles trapezoid

7. Kite

8. Rectangle

For Exercises 9–10, state whether the indicated composition of reflections is a translation.

9.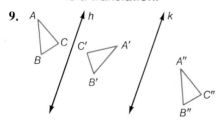

10.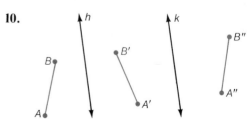

WRITTEN EXERCISES

A

1. State the number of lines of symmetry for each letter.

A B C D E H I J

In Exercises 2–7, give the number of lines of symmetry for each figure.

2. **Rectangle**   **3.** **Right Triangle**   **4.** **Isosceles Trapezoid**

5. **Square**   **6.** **Circle**   **7.** **Equilateral Triangle**

Copy each figure below. In each case, $h \parallel k$. Translate $\overline{PQ}$ by reflecting it first over line h and then by reflecting the image over k.

8.   **9.**

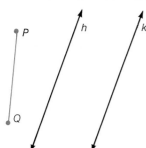 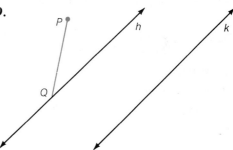

In Exercises 10–11, copy the figure. Then find an image under a glide reflection over k.

10.   **11.**

In Exercises 12–15, P', P'', P''' are all images of P under glide reflections over line k.

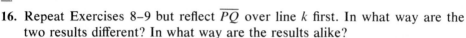

12. If $PL = 3$, find $P'L$.

13. If $PM = 4\frac{1}{2}$, find PP''.

14. If $PP''' = 5$, find NP'''.

15. If $PM = a$, find PP''.

16. Repeat Exercises 8–9 but reflect $\overline{PQ}$ over line k first. In what way are the two results different? In what way are the results alike?

17. Point P is mapped onto P' under a glide reflection. P is two centimeters from the reflecting line. The translation portion of the glide is a distance of three centimeters. Find PP'.

In Exercises 18–19, $\overline{AB}$ is translated to its image of $\overline{A'B'}$. Find the coordinates of the missing endpoint.

18. $A(-1, 5)$, $B(4, 3)$; $A'(1, 2)$, $B'(?, ?)$ 19. $A(1, -3)$, $B(4, -2)$; $B'(-2, 2)$, $A'(?, ?)$

20. In the figure at the right, $m \parallel k$. Copy the figure. Draw the image of $\triangle ABC$ over k. Then reflect the image, $\triangle A'B'C'$, over m. Measure $\overline{AA''}$, $\overline{BB''}$, and $\overline{CC''}$. Compare each of these measures with the distance between m and k.

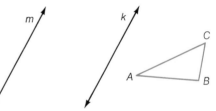

21. The image of $A(-3, 2)$ under a glide reflection is $A'(5, -2)$ and the line of reflection is the x axis. Find the coordinates of the intersection of $\overline{AA'}$ with the line of reflection.

22. The line of reflection for a glide reflection is the graph of $y = x$. Point B is the image of point $A(2, 5)$ under this glide reflection and $\overline{AB}$ intersects the graph of $y = x$ in $(6, 6)$. Find the coordinates of B.

23. Points P and P' at the left below are two centimeters apart and P' is the image of P under a translation. Copy the figure and find two parallel lines for the translation.

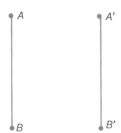

24. In the figure at the right above, $\overline{A'B'}$ is the image of $\overline{AB}$ under a translation. Copy the figure and find two parallel lines for the translation.

13-3 Rotations

A composition of two reflections over two intersecting lines is a **rotation**.

EXAMPLE 1 **a.** Find the image of $\triangle ABC$ by reflecting it over line s and then over line r, where s and r intersect in Q and m$\angle Q = 45$.

b. Find m$\angle BQB''$ and m$\angle CQC''$. Compare them with m$\angle Q$.

Solution: **a.**

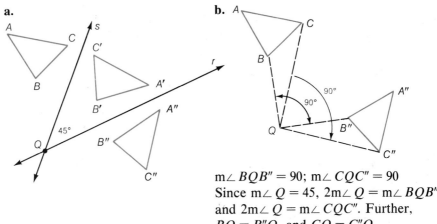

m$\angle BQB'' = 90$; m$\angle CQC'' = 90$
Since m$\angle Q = 45$, 2m$\angle Q = $ m$\angle BQB''$
and 2m$\angle Q = $ m$\angle CQC''$. Further,
$BQ = B''Q$, and $CQ = C''Q$.

In Example 1, Q is the *center of rotation*. The angle determined by a preimage point, the center of rotation, and the image is twice the measure of the angle formed by the intersection of the reflecting lines. Further, the segment determined by the preimage and the center of rotation is congruent to the segment determined by the image and the center of rotation.

EXAMPLE 2   Find the image of $\triangle EFG$ under a rotation for m$\angle Q = 43$ and m$\angle Q = 90$.

Solutions: **a.**

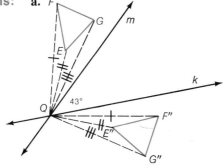

b.

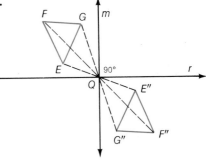

Draw $\angle EQE''$, $\angle FQF''$, and $\angle GQG''$, where each equals 2m$\angle Q$, or 86. Since $EQ = QE''$, $FQ = QF''$, and $GQ = QG''$, locate E'', F'', and G''.

Draw $\angle EQE''$, $\angle FQF''$, and $\angle GQG''$, where each equals 2m$\angle Q$, or 180. Since $EQ = QE''$, $FQ = QF''$, and $GQ = QG''$, locate E'', F'', and G''.

Example 2 indicates that a rotation can be performed by using an **angle of rotation.** For example, m∠ *GQG″* = 2(43), where 43 is the measure of the angle formed by *m* and *k*.

Example 2b illustrates a special rotation called a **half-turn,** since the measure of the angle of rotation is 180.

WRITTEN EXERCISES

A   In Exercises 1–3, first reflect the figure in red over *h*, then over *k*.

1.

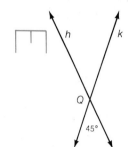

2.

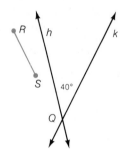

3.

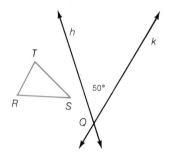

4. Reflect the figure in Exercise 1 first over *k* and then over *h*.

5. Reflect the figure in Exercise 2 first over *k* and then over *h*.

6. Reflect the figure in Exercise 3 first over *k* and then over *h*.

7. In Exercise 2, find the measures of $\overline{RS}$ and $\overline{R'S'}$.

8. Use a protractor to find the measures of ∠ *RQR′* and ∠ *SQS′* in Exercise 2.

9. In the figure at the left below, point *A* is mapped onto point *B* under a rotation through angle *Q*. Find the measure of ∠ *AQB*.

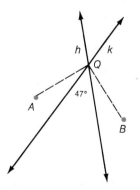

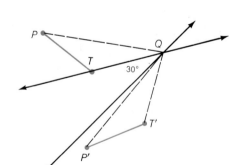

10. In the figure at the right above, $\overline{PT}$ is mapped onto $\overline{P'T'}$ under a rotation through angle *Q*. Find the measure of ∠ *PQP′* and ∠ *TQT′*.

11. Point *X* is mapped onto point *Y* by a rotation whose center is *A* and m∠ *XAY* = 164. Find the measure of the acute angle formed by the reflecting lines of the rotation.

12. In the figure at the left below, Q is the center of rotation.

Find the image of $\overline{ST}$ under a rotation of 72° clockwise.

13. In the figure at the right above, A is mapped onto C by a counterclockwise rotation with center P. By the first reflection of the rotation, A is mapped onto B. Then B is then mapped onto C by a second reflection.

Find the two reflecting lines and find their intersection P.

14. Copy $\triangle ABC$ and point P below and rotate $\triangle ABC$ through 50° using P as the center of rotation.

(HINT: Find B' and A' in a manner similar to that shown for finding C'.)

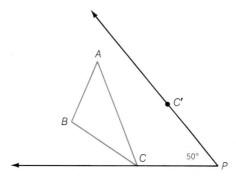

For Exercises 15–16, copy the given figure and the lines of reflection q and r ($q \perp r$). Reflect the figure first over q, then over r.

15.

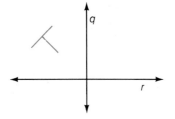

16.

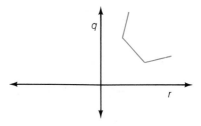

Write the coordinates of the image of each point under a rotation of 90° with the origin as center.

17. (5, 0) **18.** (3, 1) **19.** (−3, 1) **20.** (−2, −3)

13-4 Dilations

Reflections, translations, glide reflections, and rotations are transformations that preserve *distance, betweenness, collinearity,* and *angle measure.* Such transformations are **isometries (congruence mappings)**.

EXAMPLE 1   Transform $\overline{AC}$ such that $OA' = 2\frac{1}{2}OA$, $OB' = 2\frac{1}{2}OB$, and $OC' = 2\frac{1}{2}OC$.

Solution:

Draw rays OA, OB, and OC.
Measure $\overline{OA}$. Multiply by $2\frac{1}{2}$
to find A' on $\overrightarrow{OA}$.
Measure $\overline{OB}$. Multiply by $2\frac{1}{2}$
to find B' on $\overrightarrow{OB}$.
Measure $\overline{OC}$. Multiply by $2\frac{1}{2}$
to find C' on $\overrightarrow{OC}$.
Draw $\overline{A'C'}$.
Note that A', B', and C' are
collinear and that B' is between
A' and C'.

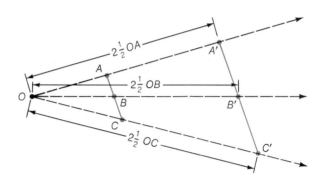

Under this transformation, AC is *not* congruent to $A'C'$. Since distance is *not* preserved, this is *not* an isometry. However, collinearity and betweenness are preserved.

EXAMPLE 2   Transform $\triangle XYZ$ such that $QX' = 2QX$, $QY' = 2QY$, and $QZ' = 2QZ$. Compare the measure of each angle in $\triangle XYZ$ with the measure of its image.

Solution:

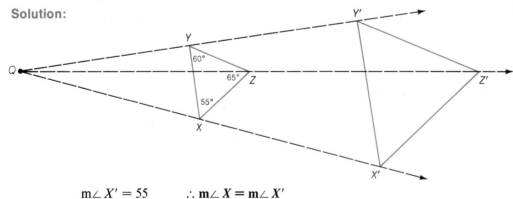

$m\angle X' = 55$ $\therefore m\angle X = m\angle X'$
$m\angle Y' = 60$ $\therefore m\angle Y = m\angle Y'$
$m\angle Z' = 65$ $\therefore m\angle Z = m\angle Z'$

Thus, **angle measure is preserved** under this transformation.

Examples 1 and 2 each illustrate a **dilation** (or **size transformation**), where O and Q are the *centers of the dilations*. The **magnitude**, k, of the dilation in Example 1 is $2\frac{1}{2}$. In Example 2, $k = 2$.

EXAMPLE 3 **a.** Find the image of square $ABCD$ where $k = \frac{1}{2}$.

b. Compare the measure of each side and angle in square $ABCD$ with that of both sides and angles of its image.

Solutions:

a. Since $k = \frac{1}{2}$,

$OA' = \frac{1}{2}OA$,

$OB' = \frac{1}{2}OB$,

$OC' = \frac{1}{2}OC$, and

$OD' = \frac{1}{2}OD$.

b. $A'B' = \frac{1}{2}AB$;

$B'C' = \frac{1}{2}BC$;

$C'D' = \frac{1}{2}CD$;

$D'A' = \frac{1}{2}DA$

$m\angle A = m\angle A'$; $m\angle B = m\angle B'$; $m\angle C = m\angle C'$; $m\angle D = m\angle D'$

∴ Square $ABCD$ and its image are **similar.**

Examples 2 and 3 illustrate that angle measure is preserved in a dilation.

In Example 3, the dilation is a **contraction,** since $0 < k < 1$.

In Examples 1 and 2, the dilation is an **expansion,** since $k > 1$.

If $k = 1$, the dilation is an **identity mapping,** since each image point is its own preimage.

CLASSROOM EXERCISES

In Exercises 1 and 2 use a ruler to find QA', QA, QB', and QB. Then find k, the ratio of QA' to QA and the ratio of QB' to QB.

1.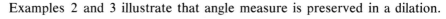

2.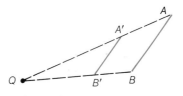

3. In Exercise 1, $A'B' = \underline{}\ AB$.

4. In Exercise 2, $A'B' = \underline{}\ AB$.

WRITTEN EXERCISES

A   In Exercises 1–10, refer to the figure at the right below.

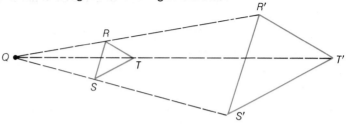

1. If $QS' = 12$ and $QS = 3$,
   then $k = \underline{\ ?\ }$.

2. If $k = 5$ and $QR = 8$,
   then $QR' = \underline{\ ?\ }$.

3. If $QR = 3$ and $RR' = 2$,
   then $k = \underline{\ ?\ }$.

4. If $k = 3$ and $QR = 2$, then $RR' = \underline{\ ?\ }$.   5. If $k = 2$ and $SR = 7$, then $S'R' = \underline{\ ?\ }$.

6. If $k = 4$ and $ST = \frac{3}{4}$, then $S'T' = \underline{\ ?\ }$.   7. If $QS':QS = 5:3$, then $R'T':RT = \underline{\ ?\ }$.

8. If R' is between Q and R, then $k \underline{\ ?\ } 1$. $(>, =, <)$

9. If $m\angle R = 94$, then $m\angle R' = \underline{\ ?\ }$.

10. If $m\angle S = 20$ and $m\angle T = 80$, then $m\angle R' = \underline{\ ?\ }$.

11. If three points of a line are mapped onto their images under a dilation, will their images be collinear?

12. Name a property not preserved under a dilation that is preserved under a reflection.

13. Draw isosceles triangle ABC with base AB of 1 cm and each leg 2 cm in length. Select any point in the exterior of $\triangle ABC$, and call it O. Let O be the center of a dilation in which $k = 2$. Find the image triangle $A'B'C'$. Then find $A'B'$, $A'C'$, and $B'C'$.

14. Draw $\triangle ABC$ with sides of 3, $3\frac{1}{2}$, and 4 centimeters. Select any point in the interior of $\triangle ABC$, and call it O. Let O be the center of a dilation with $k = 3$. Find the image triangle $A'B'C'$. What are the lengths of the sides of $\triangle A'B'C'$?

B

15. If the measure of each side of polygon $ABCD$ is $\frac{2}{3}$ the measure of the corresponding side of a polygon $EFGH$ under a dilation in which $k = \frac{3}{2}$, which polygon is the preimage?

16. Draw two parallel segments AB and CD. Find the images of $\overline{AB}$ and $\overline{CD}$ under a dilation in which $k = 2\frac{1}{2}$. Are the images parallel?

17. Draw two perpendicular segments RS and PQ. Find the images of RS and PQ under a dilation in which $k = \frac{1}{2}$. Are the images perpendicular?

C

18. Square $ABCD$ is mapped onto its image by a dilation in which $k = \frac{1}{2}$. The center O has coordinates $(1, 1)$. The vertices of square $ABCD$ have coordinates $A(-1, -3)$, $B(-1, 3)$, $C(5, 3)$, and $D(5, -3)$. Find the coordinates of the vertices of the image and the area of the image.

19. Given $\triangle ABC$ whose vertices have coordinates $A(-3, 0)$, $B(-1, 3)$, and $C(4, 0)$, what is the area of $\triangle ABC$? Let the origin be the center of a dilation in which $k = 2$, and find the image of $\triangle ABC$. What is the area of the image of $\triangle ABC$?

20. The vertices of $\triangle ABC$ are $A(-1, 4)$, $B(1, 5)$, and $C(2, 1)$. What are the coordinates of its image, $\triangle A'B'C'$, in a reflection over the line $x = 3$?

21. Find the coordinates of the image of $\triangle A'B'C'$ in Exercise 20 under a dilation in which $k = \frac{1}{3}$ and the center is $C(-7, 2)$.

22. A square with an area of 4 square units undergoes two dilations, $k = \frac{1}{2}$ in the first, and $k = 3$ in the second. What is the area of the final image?

23. If the dilations in Exercise 22 are made in reverse order, what is the area of the final image?

_____ Chapter Summary _____

IMPORTANT TERMS

Angle of rotation (p. 558)
Congruence mapping (p. 551)
Contraction (p. 561)
Dilation (p. 561)
Expansion (p. 561)
Glide reflection (p. 554)
Half-turn (p. 558)
Identity mapping (p. 561)
Image (p. 550)

Isometry (p. 560)
Line of reflection (p. 550)
Line of symmetry (p. 553)
Magnitude of dilation (p. 561)
Preimage (p. 550)
Point reflection (p. 551)
Reflection (p. 550)
Rotation (p. 557)
Transformation (p. 550)
Translation (p. 553)

IMPORTANT IDEAS

1. Examples of congruence mappings or isometries are reflections, translations, glide reflections, and rotations.

2. A dilation is a transformation but not necessarily an isometry, since distance may not be preserved.

_____ Chapter Objectives and Review _____

Objective: _To find the reflection of a set of points over a given line. (Section 13–1)_

Copy each figure. Find the reflection over line k for each figure.

1.

2.

3.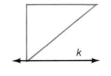

4.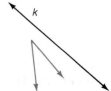

Objective: *To identify lines of symmetry in a plane geometric figure. (Section 13–2)*

In Exercises 5–8 state the number of lines of symmetry for each figure.

5.   6.   7.   8.

Objective: *To translate a given figure (Section 13–2)*

Copy the figure. Translate $\overline{RS}$ by reflecting it first over line *h*, then over line *k*.

9.   10.

Objective: *To transform a given figure in a glide reflection. (Section 13–2)*

Copy the figure. Then find an image under a glide reflection over *k*.

11.    12.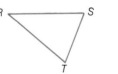

Objective: *To rotate a given figure (Section 13–3)*

13. Copy the figure at the left below. Rotate $\overline{PQ}$ by reflecting it over *h* and then reflecting that image over *k*.

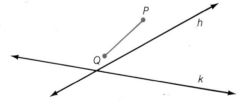

14. Copy the figure at the right above. Find the image of $\overline{AB}$ under a clockwise rotation of 80°. Use *T* as the center of rotation.

Objective: *To apply dilations to geometric figures. (Section 13–4)*

Exercises 15–18 refer to a dilation that maps $\overline{AB}$ onto $\overline{A'B'}$. The center of the transformation is *Q* and the magnitude is *k*.

15. If $k=3$ and $QA=9$, $QA'=$ __?__ . 16. If $k=\frac{1}{2}$ and $QA=7$, $QA'=$ __?__ .

17. If $k=4$ and $AB=8$, $A'B'=$ __?__ . 18. If $QA:QA'=2:3$, $AB:A'B'=$ __?__ .

Chapter Test

In the rhombus at the right, *YQ* is the line of reflection.
Name the image of each of the following.

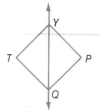

1. *T*
2. *Y*
3. $\overline{TY}$
4. $\overline{YQ}$
5. ∠*P*
6. ∠*YQT*

7. Two parallel lines of reflection are five centimeters apart. Point *P* is one centimeter from one of the given lines. *P* is reflected over that line and then over the second line. Find the distance from *P* to its final image.

8. Under a rotation with center *Q* that maps *P* onto *P'*, the angle *PQP'* has a measure of 154. Find the measure of the acute angle formed by two intersecting lines that reflect *P* onto *P'*.

For Exercises 9–10, copy the given figure and the lines *q* and *r*. Then reflect the given figure over *q* and reflect that image over *r*. State whether the composition of the reflections is a *rotation* or *translation*.

9.

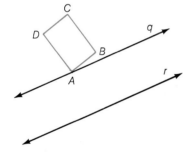

10.

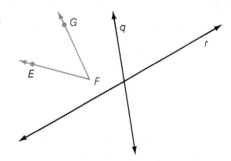

11. How many lines of symmetry does a regular hexagon have?

In Exercises 12–15, point *Q* is the center of a dilation that maps *A*, *B*, and *C* onto *A'*, *B'*, and *C'*.

12. If $QA':QA = 4:1$, then the magnitude $k = \underline{\quad?\quad}$.
13. If $k = \frac{3}{2}$ and $QA = 12$, then $QA' = \underline{\quad?\quad}$.
14. If $k = 3$ and $BC = 1.5$, then $B'C' = \underline{\quad?\quad}$.
15. If $k = \frac{1}{2}$ and $AC = 17$, then $A'C' = \underline{\quad?\quad}$.

Cumulative Review: Chapters 12-13

Choose the best answer. Choose *a, b, c,* or *d.*

1. What is the length of the line segment that joins $P_1(x_1, y_1)$ to $P_2(x_2, y_2)$?

   a. $(x_2 - x_1)^2 + (y_2 - y_1)^2$
   b. $\sqrt{(x_2 - y_2)^2 + (x_1 - y_1)^2}$
   c. $\sqrt{(x_2 - x_1)^2 + (y_2 - y_1)^2}$
   d. $\sqrt{(x_2 - x_1) + (y_2 - y_1)}$

2. Find the midpoint of $\overline{QR}$ for $Q(-3, 7)$ and $R(1, -3)$.

   a. $(-2, 4)$ **b.** $(-1, 2)$ **c.** $(4, 10)$ **d.** $(-1, -2)$

3. Find the measure of the angle between lines k_1 and k_2 if their slopes are $\frac{2}{3}$ and $-\frac{3}{2}$ respectively.

   a. 30   **b.** 45   **c.** 60   **d.** 90

4. What is the relationship between the slopes m_1 and m_2 of lines l_1 and l_2 if l_1 is parallel to l_2?

   a. $m_1 = m_2$ **b.** $m_1 < m_2$ **c.** $m_1 > m_2$ **d.** $m_1 \neq m_2$

5. In which quadrant is the point $R(-3, -4)$ located?

   a. I   **b.** II   **c.** III   **d.** IV

6. Which ordered pair could be the coordinates of equilateral triangle ABC if B has coordinates $(-3, 0)$ and C has coordinates $(3, 0)$?

   a. $(0, 3)$ **b.** $(0, -3)$ **c.** $(0, 3\sqrt{3})$ **d.** $(0, 3\sqrt{2})$

7. Line t has a slope of $\frac{3}{4}$. Which equation represents a line parallel to line t?

   a. $y = \frac{4}{3}x$ **b.** $y = -\frac{4}{3}x$ **c.** $y = -\frac{3}{4}x$ **d.** none of these

8. Which is the equation of a circle with center at the origin and radius of 7 units?

   a. $x^2 + y^2 = 7$
   b. $x^2 + y^2 = 49$
   c. $x^2 - y^2 = 7$
   d. $x^2 - y^2 = 49$

9. If $A(-4, y)$ and $B(-6, -3)$ lie on a line whose slope is $\frac{1}{2}$, find the value of y.

   a. 2   **b.** -2 **c.** 3   **d.** $-2\frac{1}{2}$

10. Which of the following has more than one axis of symmetry?

   a. a line
   b. an isosceles triangle
   c. a circle
   d. an angle

11. Which transformation fails to preserve the measure of a line segment?
    a. a rotation **b.** a dilation
    c. a reflection **d.** a translation

12. Which of the following properties is preserved in a dilation?
    a. angle measure **b.** congruence
    c. distance **d.** none of these

13. Which of the following is not always an isometry?
    a. a reflection **b.** a translation
    c. a rotation **d.** none of these

14. What is the least number of points needed to reflect a triangle?
    a. 1 **b.** 2 **c.** 3 **d.** an infinite number

15. Triangle ABC is reflected over line k forming triangle DEF. Name the pre-image of point B.
    a. D **b.** E **c.** F **d.** none of these

16. How many lines of symmetry has a rhombus?
    a. 1 **b.** 2 **c.** 3 **d.** 4

17. What is the composition of two reflections over two intersecting lines?
    a. a rotation **b.** a translation
    c. a dilation **d.** all of these

18. A glide reflection is a translation followed by a reflection over a line k. What is the relation of line k to the lines of translation?
    a. They meet at a 45°–angle. **b.** They are parallel.
    c. They are perpendicular. **d.** They are oblique.

19. Give the coordinates of the center of the circle with equation
    $$(x - 6)^2 + y^2 = 100$$
    a. $(0, 0)$ **b.** $(6, 0)$ **c.** $(0, -6)$ **d.** $(-6, 0)$

20. Find the distance between $T(2, 3)$ and $S(-4, 7)$.
    a. $\sqrt{10}$ **b.** $6\sqrt{2}$ **c.** $2\sqrt{13}$ **d.** $\sqrt{2}$

21. $A(0, 2)$ and $C(2, 0)$ are opposite vertices of square $ABCD$. If the length of a diagonal is $k\sqrt{2}$, find k.
    a. 1 **b.** 2 **c.** 3 **d.** 4

Table of Squares and Square Roots

No.	Square	Square Root	No.	Square	Square Root	No.	Square	Square Root
1	1	1.000	51	2601	7.141	101	10,201	10.050
2	4	1.414	52	2704	7.211	102	10,404	10.100
3	9	1.732	53	2809	7.280	103	10,609	10.149
4	16	2.000	54	2916	7.348	104	10,816	10.198
5	25	2.236	55	3025	7.416	105	11,025	10.247
6	36	2.449	56	3136	7.483	106	11,236	10.296
7	49	2.646	57	3249	7.550	107	11,449	10.344
8	64	2.828	58	3364	7.616	108	11,664	10.392
9	81	3.000	59	3481	7.681	109	11,881	10.440
10	100	3.162	60	3600	7.746	110	12,100	10.488
11	121	3.317	61	3721	7.810	111	12,321	10.536
12	144	3.464	62	3844	7.874	112	12,544	10.583
13	169	3.606	63	3969	7.937	113	12,769	10.630
14	196	3.742	64	4096	8.000	114	12,996	10.677
15	225	3.873	65	4225	8.062	115	13,225	10.724
16	256	4.000	66	4356	8.124	116	13,456	10.770
17	289	4.123	67	4489	8.185	117	13,689	10.817
18	324	4.243	68	4624	8.246	118	13,924	10.863
19	361	4.359	69	4761	8.307	119	14,161	10.909
20	400	4.472	70	4900	8.367	120	14,400	10.954
21	441	4.583	71	5041	8.426	121	14,641	11.000
22	484	4.690	72	5184	8.485	122	14,884	11.045
23	529	4.796	73	5329	8.544	123	15,129	11.091
24	576	4.899	74	5476	8.602	124	15,376	11.136
25	625	5.000	75	5625	8.660	125	15,625	11.180
26	676	5.099	76	5776	8.718	126	15,876	11.225
27	729	5.196	77	5929	8.775	127	16,129	11.269
28	784	5.292	78	6084	8.832	128	16,384	11.314
29	841	5.385	79	6241	8.888	129	16,641	11.358
30	900	5.477	80	6400	8.944	130	16,900	11.402
31	961	5.568	81	6561	9.000	131	17,161	11.446
32	1024	5.657	82	6724	9.055	132	17,424	11.489
33	1089	5.745	83	6889	9.110	133	17,689	11.533
34	1156	5.831	84	7056	9.165	134	17,956	11.576
35	1225	5.916	85	7225	9.220	135	18,225	11.619
36	1296	6.000	86	7396	9.274	136	18,496	11.662
37	1369	6.083	87	7569	9.327	137	18,769	11.705
38	1444	6.164	88	7744	9.381	138	19,044	11.747
39	1521	6.245	89	7921	9.434	139	19,321	11.790
40	1600	6.325	90	8100	9.487	140	19,600	11.832
41	1681	6.403	91	8281	9.539	141	19,881	11.874
42	1764	6.481	92	8464	9.592	142	20,164	11.916
43	1849	6.557	93	8649	9.644	143	20,449	11.958
44	1936	6.633	94	8836	9.695	144	20,736	12.000
45	2025	6.708	95	9025	9.747	145	21,025	12.042
46	2116	6.782	96	9216	9.798	146	21,316	12.083
47	2209	6.856	97	9409	9.849	147	21,609	12.124
48	2304	6.928	98	9604	9.899	148	21,904	12.166
49	2401	7.000	99	9801	9.950	149	22,201	12.207
50	2500	7.071	100	10,000	10.000	150	22,500	12.247

Table of Sines, Cosines, and Tangents

Angle	Sin	Cos	Tan	Angle	Sin	Cos	Tan
0°	.0000	1.0000	.0000	45°	.7071	.7071	1.0000
1	.0175	.9998	.0175	46	.7193	.6947	1.0355
2	.0349	.9994	.0349	47	.7314	.6820	1.0724
3	.0523	.9986	.0524	48	.7431	.6691	1.1106
4	.0698	.9976	.0699	49	.7547	.6561	1.1504
5	.0872	.9962	.0875	50	.7660	.6428	1.1918
6	.1045	.9945	.1051	51	.7771	.6293	1.2349
7	.1219	.9925	.1228	52	.7880	.6157	1.2799
8	.1392	.9903	.1405	53	.7986	.6018	1.3270
9	.1564	.9877	.1584	54	.8090	.5878	1.3764
10	.1736	.9848	.1763	55	.8192	.5736	1.4281
11	.1908	.9816	.1944	56	.8290	.5592	1.4826
12	.2079	.9781	.2126	57	.8387	.5446	1.5399
13	.2250	.9744	.2309	58	.8480	.5299	1.6003
14	.2419	.9703	.2493	59	.8572	.5150	1.6643
15	.2588	.9659	.2679	60	.8660	.5000	1.7321
16	.2756	.9613	.2867	61	.8746	.4848	1.8040
17	.2924	.9563	.3057	62	.8829	.4695	1.8807
18	.3090	.9511	.3249	63	.8910	.4540	1.9626
19	.3256	.9455	.3443	64	.8988	.4384	2.0503
20	.3420	.9397	.3640	65	.9063	.4226	2.1445
21	.3584	.9336	.3839	66	.9135	.4067	2.2460
22	.3746	.9272	.4040	67	.9205	.3907	2.3559
23	.3907	.9205	.4245	68	.9272	.3746	2.4751
24	.4067	.9135	.4452	69	.9336	.3584	2.6051
25	.4226	.9063	.4663	70	.9397	.3420	2.7475
26	.4384	.8988	.4877	71	.9455	.3256	2.9042
27	.4540	.8910	.5095	72	.9511	.3090	3.0777
28	.4695	.8829	.5317	73	.9563	.2924	3.2709
29	.4848	.8746	.5543	74	.9613	.2756	3.4874
30	.5000	.8660	.5774	75	.9659	.2588	3.7321
31	.5150	.8572	.6009	76	.9703	.2419	4.0108
32	.5299	.8480	.6249	77	.9744	.2250	4.3315
33	.5446	.8387	.6494	78	.9781	.2079	4.7046
34	.5592	.8290	.6745	79	.9816	.1908	5.1446
35	.5736	.8192	.7002	80	.9848	.1736	5.6713
36	.5878	.8090	.7265	81	.9877	.1564	6.3138
37	.6018	.7986	.7536	82	.9903	.1392	7.1154
38	.6157	.7880	.7813	83	.9925	.1219	8.1443
39	.6293	.7771	.8098	84	.9945	.1045	9.5144
40	.6428	.7660	.8391	85	.9962	.0872	11.4301
41	.6561	.7547	.8693	86	.9976	.0698	14.3007
42	.6691	.7431	.9004	87	.9986	.0523	19.0811
43	.6820	.7314	.9325	88	.9994	.0349	28.6363
44	.6947	.7193	.9657	89	.9998	.0175	57.2900
45	.7071	.7071	1.0000	90	1.0000	.0000	

Postulates

Postulate 1	Every line contains at least two distinct (different) points. (p. 10)
Postulate 2	Every plane contains at least three distinct, noncollinear points. (p. 10)
Postulate 3	Space contains at least four noncoplanar points. (p. 10)
Postulate 4	For any two distinct points, there is exactly one line containing them. (p. 10)
Postulate 5	For any three distinct noncollinear points, there is exactly one plane containing them. (p. 10)
Postulate 6	If any two distinct points lie in a plane, the line containing these points lies in the plane. (p. 10)
Postulate 7	If two distinct planes have one point in common, they have at least two points in common. (p. 10)

Postulate 8   **The Ruler Postulate** (p. 17)

a. To every distinct pair of points there corresponds exactly one positive number. This number is the distance between the two points.

b. To every real number there corresponds a point on the number line. To every point on the number line there corresponds a real number.

Postulate 9   **The Protractor Postulate** (p. 23)

a. To every angle there corresponds exactly one real number between 0 and 180. This number is the measure of the angle.

b. Let C be the endpoint of opposite rays CA and CB such that $\overrightarrow{CA}$ is paired with O and CB is paired with 180. If P is a point in the plane where P is not on $\overleftrightarrow{AB}$ and n is a real number such that $0 < n < 180$, then there is exactly one ray CE, with E on the same side of $\overleftrightarrow{AB}$ as P, such that $\overrightarrow{CE}$ is paired with n and m $\angle ACE = n$.

Postulate 10   **Linear Pair Postulate** (p. 30)

If two angles form a linear pair, then they are supplementary.

Postulate 11   *SAS* **Postulate** (p. 95)

If two triangles have two sides and the included angle of one triangle congruent respectively to two sides and the included angle of the other triangle, then the triangles are congruent.

Postulate 12   *ASA* **Postulate** (p. 100)

If two triangles have two angles and the included side of one triangle congruent respectively to two angles and the included side of the other triangle, then the triangles are congruent.

Postulate 13	**SSS Postulate** (p. 100)
	If two triangles have three sides of one triangle congruent respectively to the three sides of the other triangle, then the triangles are congruent.
Postulate 14	**HA Postulate** (p. 132)
	If two right triangles have the hypotenuse and an acute angle of one triangle congruent respectively to the hypotenuse and an acute angle of the other, then the triangles are congruent.
Postulate 15	Through a point not on a given line, there is exactly one line parallel to the given line. (p. 162)

Area Postulates

Postulate 16	To each polygon, there corresponds a positive number which is its area. (p. 438)
Postulate 17	Congruent triangles have the same area. (p. 438)
Postulate 18	The area of a polygon is the sum of the areas of the nonoverlapping triangular regions into which it can be separated. (p. 438)
Postulate 19	The area, A, of a rectangle is the product of its length, l, and its width, w. That is, $A = lw$. (p. 438)

Volume Postulates

Postulate 20	Every geometric solid corresponds to a positive number which is its volume. (p. 496)
Postulate 21	The volume of a solid figure is the sum of the volumes of a finite number of non-overlapping figures of which it is composed. (p. 496)
Postulate 22	The volume V of a rectangular prism is the product of its altitude h, the length, l, of the base, and the width, w, of the base. That is, $V = lwh$. (p. 496)

Theorems

Theorem 1-1   If two distinct planes intersect, then their intersection is a line. (p. 11)

Theorem 1-2   If two distinct lines intersect, then their intersection is a point. (p. 11)

Theorem 1-3   If a line and a plane intersect and the plane does not contain the line, then their intersection is a point. (p. 11)

Theorem 1-4   A segment has exactly one midpoint. (p. 19)

Theorem 1-5   **Midpoint Theorem** (p. 19)

If M is the midpoint of $\overline{AB}$, then $AM = \frac{1}{2} AB$.

Theorem 1-6   An angle has exactly one bisector. (p. 25)

Theorem 1-7   **Angle Bisector Theorem** (p. 25)

If $\overrightarrow{AY}$ is the bisector of $\angle XAZ$, then m $\angle XAY = \frac{1}{2}$ m $\angle XAZ$.

Theorem 1-8   If two intersecting lines form equal adjacent angles, then the lines are perpendicular. (p. 31)

Theorem 1-9   Through a given point on a line in a plane, there is exactly one line in that plane perpendicular to the given line. (p. 32)

Theorem 1-10   In a plane, a segment has exactly one perpendicular bisector. (p. 32)

Theorem 2-1   Congruence is an equivalence relation. (p. 44)

Theorem 2-2   If a point is not on a line, then the point and the line determine exactly one plane. (p. 49)

Theorem 2-3   If two distinct lines intersect, then they determine exactly one plane. (p. 49)

Theorem 2-4   If two angles are supplements of the same angle, then they are congruent. (p. 57)

Theorem 2-5   If two angles are supplements of congruent angles, they they are congruent. (p. 58)

Theorem 2-6   If two angles are complements of the same angle, then they are congruent. (p. 58)

Theorem 2-7   If two angles are complements of congruent angles, then they are congruent. (p. 58)

Theorem 2-8   **Vertical Angle Theorem** (p. 59)

Verticle angles are congruent.

Theorem 2-9   If one angle of a linear pair is a right angle, then the other is also a right angle. (p. 66)

Theorem 2-10   If two intersecting lines form one right angle, then they form four right angles. (p. 66)

Corollary 2-11	Perpendicular lines form four right angles. (p. 67)
Corollary 2-12	All right angles are congruent. (p. 67)
Theorem 2-13	If two lines are perpendicular, then they form congruent adjacent angles. (p. 67)
Theorem 2-14	If two intersecting lines form congruent adjacent angles, then the lines are perpendicular. (p. 67)

Theorem 3-1	**Isosceles Triangle Theorem** (p. 108)
	If two sides of a triangle are congruent, then the angles opposite these sides are congruent.
Corollary 3-2	**Equilateral Triangle Corollary** (p. 108)
	If three sides of a triangle are congruent, then the three angles are also congruent.
Theorem 3-3	**Converse of Isosceles Triangle Theorem** (p. 109)
	If two angles of a triangle are congruent, then the sides opposite these angles are congruent.
Corollary 3-4	**Converse of Equilateral Triangle Corollary** (p. 109)
	If the three angles of a triangle are congruent, then the three sides are congruent.
Theorem 3-5	The bisector of the vertex angle of an isosceles triangle is the perpendicular bisector of the base. (p. 114)
Theorem 3-6	The median from the vertex angle of an isosceles triangle is pependicular to the base and bisects the vertex angle. (p. 114)
Theorem 3-7	If a point lies on the perpendicular bisector of a segment, then the point is equidistant from the endpoints of the segment. (p. 115)
Theorem 3-8	If a point is equidistant from the endpoints of a segment, then the point lies on the perpendicular bisector of the segment. (p. 116)
Corollary 3-9	If two points are each equidistant from the endpoints of a segment, they determine its perpendicular bisector. (p. 116)
Theorem 3-10	**Common Segment Theorem** (p. 121)
	If four collinear points, in order, are A, B, C, D or A, C, B, D and $\overline{AB} \cong \overline{CD}$, then $\overline{AC} \cong \overline{BD}$.
Theorem 3-11	**Common Angle Theorem** (p. 122)
	If four coplanar rays are, in order, $\overrightarrow{XA}$, $\overrightarrow{XB}$, $\overrightarrow{XC}$, $\overrightarrow{XD}$ or $\overrightarrow{XA}$, $\overrightarrow{XC}$, $\overrightarrow{XB}$, $\overrightarrow{XD}$ and $\angle AXB \cong \angle CXD$, then $\angle AXC \cong \angle BXD$.
Theorem 3-12	**HL Theorem** (p. 132)
	If two right triangles have the hypotenuse and one leg of one triangle congruent respectively to the hypotenuse and one leg of the other, then the triangles are congruent.
Corollary 3-13	In an isosceles triangle, the altitude to the base bisects the base and bisects the vertex angle. (p. 133)

Theorem 3-14	Through a point not on a line, there is exactly one line perpendicular to the given line. (p. 133)
Theorem 3-15	If a point is on the bisector of an angle, it is equidistant from the sides of the angle. (p. 133)
Theorem 3-16	If a point in the interior of an angle is equidistant from the sides of the angle, then it is on the bisector of the angle. (p. 134)
Theorem 4-1	**Exterior Angle Inequality Theorem** (p. 157) The measure of an exterior angle of a triangle is greater than the measure of either of its remote interior angles.
Theorem 4-2	If two lines are cut by a transversal so that alternate interior angles are congruent, then the lines are parallel. (p. 162)
Theorem 4-3	If two parallel lines are cut by a transversal, then alternate interior angles are congruent. (p. 163)
Theorem 4-4	If two lines are cut by a transversal so that interior angles on the same side of the transversal are supplementary, then the lines are parallel. (p. 168)
Theorem 4-5	If two parallel lines are cut by a transversal, then interior angles on the same side of the transversal are supplementary. (p. 168)
Theorem 4-6	In a plane, if two lines are both perpendicular to a third line, then the lines are parallel. (p. 169)
Theorem 4-7	In a plane, if a line is pependicular to one of two parallel lines, then it is perpendicular to the other line also. (p. 169)
Theorem 4-8	If two lines are cut by a transversal so that corresponding angles are congruent, then the lines are parallel. (p. 174)
Theorem 4-9	If two parallel lines are cut by a transversal, then corresponding angles are congruent. (p. 174)
Theorem 4-10	Two parallel lines determine exactly one plane. (p. 174)
Theorem 4-11	Two distinct lines parallel to the same line are parallel to each other. (p. 174)
Theorem 4-12	**Triangle-Sum Theorem** (p. 182) The sum of the measures of the angles of a triangle is 180.
Corollary 4-13	If two angles of one triangle are congruent to two angles of another triangle, then the third angles are congruent. (p. 183)
Corollary 4-14	A triangle can have no more than one right angle or one obtuse angle. (p. 183)
Corollary 4-15	The acute angles of a right triangle are complementary. (p. 187)
Corollary 4-16	The measure of each angle of an equilateral triangle is 60. (p. 187)
Corollary 4-17	**SAA Corollary** (p. 187) If two triangles have a side and two angles of one congruent respectively to a side and two angles of the other, then the triangles are congruent.

| **Corollary 4-18** | **Exterior Angle-Sum Corollary for Triangles** (p. 188) |
| | The measure of one exterior angle of a triangle equals the sum of the measures of its remote interior angles. |

| **Theorem 4-19** | **Angle-Sum Theorem for Polygons** (p. 193) |
| | The formula for the sum, S, of the measures of the angles of a polygon of n sides is $S = (n - 2)180$. |

| **Corollary 4-20** | If a polygon has n sides and if all of its angles are congruent, then the formula for the measure, a, of one of its angles is |
| | $a = \dfrac{(n - 2)180}{n}$. (p. 194) |

| **Corollary 4-21** | **Exterior Angle-Sum Corollary for Polygons** (p. 197) |
| | The sum E of the measures of the exterior angles of a polygon made by extending each of its sides in succession is 360. |

| **Corollary 4-22** | If a polygon of n sides is equiangular, then the measure e of one of its exterior angles is $e = \dfrac{360}{n}$. (p. 197) |

| **Theorem 5-1** | A diagonal of a parallelogram forms two congruent triangles. (p. 209) |

| **Corollary 5-2** | The opposite sides of a parallelogram are congruent. (p. 209) |

| **Corollary 5-3** | The opposite angles of a parallelogram are congruent. (p. 209) |

| **Corollary 5-4** | Two parallel lines are equidistant at all points. (p. 210) |

| **Theorem 5-5** | The diagonals of a parallelogram bisect each other. (p. 210) |

| **Theorem 5-6** | Any two consecutive angles of a parallelogram are supplementary. (p. 210) |

| **Theorem 5-7** | If both pairs of opposite sides of a quadrilateral are congruent, then the quadrilateral is a parallelogram. (p. 213) |

| **Theorem 5-8** | If two sides of a quadrilateral are parallel and congruent, then the quadrilateral is a parallelogram. (p. 213) |

| **Theorem 5-9** | If the diagonals of a quadrilateral bisect each other, the quadrilateral is a parallelogram. (p. 214) |

| **Theorem 5-10** | The diagonals of a rectangle are congruent. (p. 220) |

| **Theorem 5-11** | The diagonals of a rhombus are perpendicular to each other. (p. 220) |

| **Theorem 5-12** | Each diagonal of a rhombus bisects a pair of opposite angles. (p. 220) |

| **Theorem 5-13** | If a segment joins the midpoints of two sides of a triangle, then it is parallel to the third side and its length is one–half the length of the third side. (p. 225) |

| **Theorem 5-14** | The median of a trapezoid is parallel to the bases and its length is one–half the sum of the lengths of the bases. (p. 228) |

| **Theorem 5-15** | If three or more parallel lines cut off congruent segments on one transversal, they cut off congruent segments on any transversal. (p. 229) |

Corollary 5-16	If a line is parallel to one side of a triangle and bisects a second side, then it bisects the third side also. (p. 229)
Corollary 5-17	If a line is parallel to the bases of a trapezoid and bisects one of the nonparallel sides, then it bisects the other side also. (p. 229)
Theorem 5-18	If two sides of a triangle are not congruent, then the angles opposite these sides are not congruent, and the smaller angle is opposite the smaller side. (p. 236)
Theorem 5-19	If two angles of a triangle are not congruent, then the sides opposite these angles are not congruent, and the smaller side is opposite the smaller angle. (p. 236)
Theorem 5-20	The perpendicular segment from a point to a line is the shortest distance from the point to the line. (p. 237)
Theorem 5-21	**Triangle Inequality Theorem** (p. 243) The sum of the lengths of two sides of a triangle is greater than the length of the third side.
Theorem 5-22	**The Hinge Theorem** (p.244) If two sides of one triangle are congruent to two sides of another triangle and if the included angles are not congruent, then the remaining sides are also not congruent, and the smaller side is opposite the smaller angle.
Theorem 5-23	**Converse of the Hinge Theorem** (p. 244) If two sides of one triangle are congruent to two sides of another triangle and if the third sides are not congruent, then the angles opposite the third sides are also not congruent, and the smaller angle is opposite the smaller side.
Theorem 5-24	All plane angles of the same dihedral angle are congruent. (p. 249)
Theorem 6-1	$\frac{a}{b} = \frac{c}{d}$ if and only if $ad = bc$ ($b \neq 0, d \neq 0$). (p. 260)
Theorem 6-2	If $\frac{a}{b} = \frac{c}{d}$, then $\frac{a+b}{b} = \frac{c+d}{d}$ and $\frac{a-b}{b} = \frac{c-d}{c}$. (p. 265)
Theorem 6-3	If three parallel lines intersect two transversals, then the lines divide the transversals proportionally. (p. 271)
Corollary 6-4	If a line intersecting the interior of a triangle is parallel to one side, then **the line divides the other two sides** proportionally. (p. 272)
Corollary 6-5	If a line intersecting the interior of a triangle is parallel to one side, then either side intersected by the line is to one of its segments as the other side is to its corresponding segment. (p. 272)
Corollary 6-6	If a line divides two sides of a triangle proportionally, then the line is parallel to the third side. (p. 274)
Corollary 6-7	The bisector of an angle of a triangle divides the opposite side into segments that are proportional to the adjacent sides of the triangle. (p. 274)
Corollary 6-8	If two lines are cut by three parallel planes, the corresponding segments are proportional. (p. 275)

Theorem 6-9	***AAA* Similarity Theorem** (p. 283)
	If the angles of one triangle are congruent to the angles of another triangle, then the triangles are similar.
Corollary 6-10	***AA* Similarity Corollary** (p. 284)
	If two angles of one triangle are congruent to two angles of a second triangle, then the triangles are similar.
Corollary 6-11	**Right-Triangle Similarity Corollary** (p. 284)
	If two right triangles have an acute angle of one congruent to an acute angle of the other, then the triangles are similar.
Corollary 6-12	If a line parallel to one side of a triangle determines a second triangle, then the second triangle will be similar to the original triangle. (p. 284)
Theorem 6-13	***SAS* Similarity Theorem** (p. 288)
	If an angle of one triangle is congruent to an angle of another, and the sides including these angles are proportional, then the triangles are similar.
Theorem 6-14	***SSS* Similarity Theorem** (p. 288)
	If the corresponding sides of two triangles are proportional, then the triangles are similar.
Corollary 6-15	The perimeters of two similar triangles are proportional to any pair of corresponding sides. (p. 289)
Corollary 6-16	The altitudes of similar triangles are proportional to any pair of corresponding sides. (p. 289)
Corollary 6-17	The medians of similar triangles are proportional to any pair of corresponding sides. (p. 289)
Theorem 7-1	The altitude to the hypotenuse of a right triangle forms two triangles that are similar to each other and to the original triangle. (p. 306)
Corollary 7-2	The altitude to the hypotenuse of a right triangle is the geometric mean between the segments of the hypotenuse. (p. 306)
Corollary 7-3	If the altitude to the hypotenuse of a right triangle is drawn, either leg is the geometric mean between the hypotenuse and the segment of the hypotenuse adjacent to the leg. (p. 307)
Theorem 7-4	**Pythagorean Theorem** (p. 310)
	In any right triangle, the square of the length of the hypotenuse equals the sum of the squares of the lengths of the other two sides.
Theorem 7-5	**Pythagorean Theorem Converse** (p. 311)
	If the square of the length of one side of a triangle equals the sum of the squares of the lengths of the other two sides, then the triangle is a right triangle.
Theorem 7-6	**Isosceles Right Triangle Theorem** (p. 316)
	In an isosceles right triangle with legs of length a and hypotenuse of length c, $a = \frac{c}{2}\sqrt{2}$ and $c = a\sqrt{2}$.

Theorem 7-7	**30-60 Right Triangle Theorem** (p. 317)
	In any right triangle with acute angle measures of 30 and 60 and with hypotenuse of length s, the length of the leg opposite the angle with measure 30 (shorter leg) is $\frac{s}{2}$ and the length of the leg opposite the angle with measure 60 (longer leg) is $\frac{s}{2}\sqrt{3}$.
Theorem 8-1	In the same circle or in congruent circles, two arcs are congruent if and only if their central angles are congruent. (p. 349)
Theorem 8-2	**Common Arc Theorem** (p. 350)
	If four points on a circle are, in order, A, B, C, D, or A, C, B, D, and $\overset{\frown}{AB} \cong \overset{\frown}{CD}$, then $\overset{\frown}{AC} \cong \overset{\frown}{BD}$.
Theorem 8-3	In the same or in congruent circles, if two arcs are congruent, then their chords are congruent. (p. 354)
Theorem 8-4	In the same or in congruent circles, if two chords are congruent, then their arcs are congruent. (p. 354)
Theorem 8-5	If a diameter of a circle is perpendicular to a chord, then the diameter bisects the chord and its arc. (p. 355)
Theorem 8-6	If a chord of a circle bisects a second chord and its arc, then the first chord is a diameter and it is perpendicular to the second chord. (p. 355)
Theorem 8-7	If a diameter bisects a chord that is not a diameter, then it is perpendicular to the chord and bisects its arc. (p. 355)
Theorem 8-8	In the same or in congruent circles, two chords are congruent if and only if they are equidistant from the center. (p. 360)
Theorem 8-9	In the same or in congruent circles, if two chords are not congruent, then their distances from the center of the circle are not equal, and the longer chord is closer to the center. (p. 360)
Theorem 8-10	In the same or in congruent circles, if the distances of two chords from the center of the circle are not equal, then the chords are not congruent, and the chord that is closer to the center is the longer chord. (p. 361)
Theorem 8-11	If a line in the plane of a circle is tangent to a circle, then the line is perpendicular to the radius drawn to the point of contact. (p. 364)
Theorem 8-12	If a line in the plane of a circle is perpendicular to a radius at its outer endpoint, then the line is tangent to the circle. (p. 365)
Theorem 8-13	The two tangent segments from the same exterior point of a circle are congruent. (p. 365)
Corollary 8-14	Two tangents to a circle from a given point in the exterior of the circle determine an angle that is bisected by the segment joining the given point to the center of the circle. (p. 365)
Theorem 8-15	The measure of an inscribed angle is one half-the measure of its intercepted arc. (p. 369)

Theorem 8-16	If inscribed angles intercept the same arc or congruent arcs, the angles are congruent. (p. 370)
Corollary 8-17	An inscribed angle is a right angle if and only if it is inscribed in a semicircle. (p. 375)
Corollary 8-18	If two secants of the same circle are parallel, then the arcs between them are congruent. (p. 375)
Corollary 8-19	The opposite angles of an inscribed quadrilateral are supplementary. (p. 375)
Theorem 8-20	If a tangent and a secant (or chord) intersect in a point on a circle, the measure of the angle formed is one half-the measure of the intercepted arc. (p. 378)
Theorem 8-21	If two secants (or chords) intersect in the interior of a circle, the measure of an angle formed is one-half the sum of the measures of the arcs intercepted by the angle and its verticle angle. (p. 378)
Theorem 8-22	If two secants, a tangent and a secant, or two tangents intersect in the exterior of a circle, the measure of the angle formed is one-half the difference of the measures of the intercepted arcs. (p. 379)
Theorem 8-23	If two chords intersect in the interior of a circle, the product of the lengths of the segments of the first chord equals the product of the lengths of the segments of the second chord. (p. 383)
Theorem 8-24	If a tangent and a secant intersect in the exterior of a circle, the square of the tangent segment equals the product of the secant segment and the external secant segment. (p. 384)
Corollary 8-25	If two secants intersect in the exterior of a circle, the product of the lengths of one secant segment and its external segment equals the product of the lengths of the other secant segment and its external segment. (p. 384)
Theorem 8-26	If a plane intersects a sphere, the intersection is either a point or a circle. (p. 389)
Theorem 9-1	The perpendicular bisectors of the sides of a triangle are concurrent in a point that is equidistant from the vertices of the triangle. (p. 425)
Theorem 9-2	The bisectors of the angles of a triangle are concurrent in a point that is equidistant from the sides of a triangle. (p. 426)
Theorem 9-3	The altitudes of a triangle are concurrent. (p. 426)
Theorem 9-4	The medians of a triangle are concurrent. (p. 426)
Theorem 10-1	The area of a parallelogram is the product of its base, b, and the corresponding altitude, h. That is, $A = bh$. (p. 442)
Corollary 10-2	Parallelograms with equal bases and equal altitudes have equal areas. (p. 442)
Theorem 10-3	The area, A, of a triangle is one-half the product of a base, b, and its corresponding altitude, h. That is, $A = \frac{1}{2}bh$. (p. 443)
Corollary 10-4	Triangles with equal bases and equal altitudes have equal areas. (p. 443)

Corollary 10-5	For an equilateral triangle with side of length s, $A(\text{area}) = \frac{s^2\sqrt{3}}{4}$. (p. 443)
Corollary 10-6	The area A of a rhombus is one-half the product of the lengths of its diagonals, d_1 and d_2. That is, $A = \frac{1}{2}d_1d_2$. (p. 447)
Theorem 10-7	The area A of a trapezoid is one-half the product of its altitude and the sum of its bases, b and b' (read: "b prime"). That is, **Area of $ABCD = \frac{1}{2}bh + \frac{1}{2}b'h = \frac{1}{2}bh\,(b + b')$. (p. 448)**
Theorem 10-8	A polygon is regular if and only if a circle can be inscribed in the polygon and a circle with the same center can be circumscribed about the polygon. (p. 452)
Corollary 10-9	The measure, a, of each central angle of a regular polygon of n sides is $\frac{360}{n}$. That is, $a = \frac{360}{n}$. (p. 453)
Corollary 10-10	A radius of a regular polygon bisects an angle of the polygon. (p. 454)
Corollary 10-11	The apothem of a regular polygon is the perpendicular bisector of a side of the polygon. (p. 454)
Theorem 10-12	The area A of a regular polygon equals one-half the product of its perimeter P and the apothem a. That is, $A = \frac{1}{2}aP$. (p. 458)
Theorem 10-13	The perimeters of similar polygons have the same ratio as the measures of any two corresponding sides. (p. 462)
Theorem 10-14	Regular polygons of the same number of sides are similar. (p. 462)
Corollary 10-15	The perimeters of two regular polygons of the same number of sides have the same ratio as their radii or as their apothems. (p. 462)
Theorem 10-16	The areas of two similar polygons have the same ratio as the squares of the measures of any two corresponding sides. (p. 463)
Corollary 10-17	The areas of two regular polygons of the same number of sides have the same ratio as the squares of their radii or as the squares of their apothems. (p. 463)
Theorem 10-18	The ratio $\frac{C}{d}$ of the circumference C to the measure of the diameter d is the same for all circles. (p. 466)
Corollay 10-19	The circumferences of any two circles have the same ratio as their radii. (p. 467)
Corollary 10-20	In a circle, the ratio of the length l of an arc to the circumference, $2\pi r$, equals the ratio of the degree measure, m, of the arc to 360. That is, $$\frac{l}{2\pi r} = \frac{m}{360}. \text{ (p. 467)}$$
Theorem 10-21	The area, A, of a circle with radius r is given by the formula, $A = \pi r^2$. (p. 470)
Corollary 10-22	The areas of two circles have the same ratio as the squares of their radii. (p. 470)

Corollary 10-23   In a circle with radius r the ratio of the area, A, of a sector to the area of the circle (πr^2) equals the ratio of the degree measure m of the arc of the sector to 360. That is,

$$\frac{A}{\pi r^2} = \frac{m}{360}, \quad \text{or} \quad A = \frac{m}{360}\,(\pi r^2).\ \text{(p. 471)}$$

Theorem 11-1   The lateral surface area L of a right prism is the product of the perimeter P of its base and its lateral edge, e. That is,

$$L = Pe.\ \text{(p. 483)}$$

Theorem 11-2   The lateral area L of a regular pyramid equals one-half the product of its slant height s and the perimeter P of its base. That is,

$$L = \tfrac{1}{2}sP.\ \text{(p. 487)}$$

Theorem 11-3   For a right circular cylinder with base radius r and altitude h,

$$L \text{ (lateral area)} = 2\pi rh,$$
$$T \text{ (total area)} = 2\pi r(h + r).\ \text{(p. 491)}$$

Theorem 11-4   For a right circular cone with slant height s and base circumference $2\pi r$, where r is the radius of the base,

$$L \text{ (lateral area)} = \pi rs \quad \text{and}$$
$$T \text{ (total area)} = \pi r(s + r).\ \text{(p. 491)}$$

Theorem 11-5   The volume V of a prism is the product of its altitude h and the area B of the base. That is, $V = Bh.$ (p 496)

Theorem 11-6   The volume V of a cube with edge e is the cube of e. That is, $V = e^3.$ (p. 496)

Corollary 11-7   The volume V of a pyraamid is one third the product of its altitude h and the area B of its base. That is, $V = \tfrac{1}{3}Bh.$ (p. 497)

Theorem 11-8   The volume V of a circular cylinder is the product of the altitude h and the area B of the base. That is,

$$V = Bh \quad \text{or} \quad V = \pi r^2 h.\ \text{(p. 500)}$$

Theorem 11-9   The volume V of a circular cone is one third the productof the altitude h and the area B of the base. That is,

$$V = \tfrac{1}{3}Bh \quad \text{or} \quad V = \tfrac{1}{3}\pi r^2 h.\ \text{(p. 501)}$$

Theorem 11-10   For a sphere with radius r, A (surface area) $= 4\pi r^2.$ (p. 505)

Theorem 11-11   For a sphere with radius r, V (volume) $= \tfrac{4}{3}\pi r^3.$ (p. 505)

Theorem 12-1   **Midpoint Formula**

The coordinates (x_m, y_m) of the midpoint M of the segment whose endpoints are $P_1\,(x_1, y_1)$ and $P_2(x_2, y_2)$ are

$$x_m = \frac{x_1 + x_2}{2} \quad \text{and} \quad y_m = \frac{y_1 + y_2}{2}.\ \text{(p. 523)}$$

Theorem 12-2 Two nonvertical lines are parallel if and only if they have the same slope. (p. 532)

Theorem 12-3 Two nonvertical lines are perpendicular if and only if their slopes are negative reciprocals. (p. 533)

Theorem 12-4 **Distance Formula**

The distance d between two points $P_1(x_1, y_1)$ and $P_2(x_2, y_2)$ is
$$d = \sqrt{(x_2 - x_1)^2 + (y_2 - y_1)^2}.\text{ (p. 536)}$$

Theorem 12-5 The circle with center (h, k) and radius r has the equation
$$(x - h)^2 + (y - k)^2 = r^2.\text{ (p. 539)}$$

Symbols

$\angle, \angle\!\!\!\angle$	angle(s)	mm	millimeter(s)
a	apothem	$\overset{\frown}{BC}$	minor arc determined by B and C
$\approx$	is approximately equal to	$\sim p$	not p
A	area	$\parallel$	parallel, is parallel to
B	area of the base	$\square$	parallelogram
b	length of the base	P	perimeter
C	circumference	$\perp$	perpendicular, is perpendicular to
cm	centimeter(s)	π	pi
$\cong$	congruent, is congruent to	$P(x,y)$	point P with coordinates x and y
cos	cosine	n-gon	polygon with n sides
cm^3	cubic centimeter(s)	$p \rightarrow q$	If p, then q.
m^3	cubic meter(s)	$p \leftrightarrow q$	p if and only if q
$^\circ$	degree(s)	r	radius
d	diameter; length of a diagonal	$\frac{a}{b}$ $a:b$	ratio of a to b
e	lateral edge of a polygon	$\overrightarrow{AB}$	ray with endpoint A and passing through point B
h	height; length of an altitude		
$>$	is greater than	$\overline{AB}$	segment with endpoints A and B
$\geq$	is greater than or equal to	$\sim$	similar, is similar to
$<$	is less than	sin	sine
$\leq$	is less than or equal to	s	slant height
$\not\cong$	is not congruent to	m	slope
km	kilometer	cm^2	square centimeter(s)
l	length of an arc	m^2	square meter(s)
L	lateral area	$\sqrt{x}$	positive square root of x
AB	length of $\overline{AB}$, the distance between points A and B	tan	tangent
		$\therefore$	therefore
$\overleftrightarrow{AB}$	line containing points A and B	T	total area
$\overset{\frown}{BAC}$	major arc determined by B and C	$\triangle, \triangle\!\!\!\triangle$	triangle(s)
$m\overset{\frown}{AB}$	measure of arc AB	V	volume
m	meter(s)		

GLOSSARY

Acute angle   An angle whose measure is greater than 0 and less than 90 (p. 24)

Adjacent angles   Two coplanar angles with the same vertex and a common side but no interior points in common (p. 29)

Alternate interior angles   The angle pairs, $\angle 1$ and $\angle 4$, $\angle 2$ and $\angle 3$, in the figure below (p. 158)

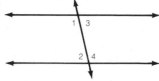

Altitude of a parallelogram   A perpendicular segment whose endpoints lie on opposite sides of the parallelogram (p. 442)

Altitude of a triangle   A segment from one vertex perpendicular to the opposite side, or perpendicular to the line containing the opposite side (p. 72)

Angle   The figure formed by two noncollinear rays having the same endpoint (p. 7)

Angle of elevation (depression)   The angle the line of sight makes with the horizontal (p. 333)

Apothem   The radius of the inscribed circle of a regular polygon (p. 452)

Arc of a chord   The smaller of the two arcs with the same endpoints as the chord (p. 354)

Base angles of an isosceles triangle   The angles opposite the equal sides (p. 4)

Base of an isosceles triangle   The side other than the two equal sides (p. 4)

Bases of a trapezoid   The parallel sides of a trapezoid (p. 208)

Betweenness for points   For three distinct points A, B, and C, A is *between* B and C if (1) A, B, and C are collinear, and (2) $BA + AC = BC$. (p. 18)

Biconditional   A statement in *if and only if* form (p. 67)

Bisect   To separate into two equal parts (p. 19)

Bisector of an angle   Ray AY is the *bisector* of $\angle XAZ$ if $\overrightarrow{AY}$ is between $\overrightarrow{AX}$ and $\overrightarrow{AZ}$ and $m\angle XAY = m\angle YAZ$. (p. 25)

Center of a regular polygon   The common center of its inscribed and circumscribed circles (p. 452)

Central angle of a circle   An angle whose vertex is at the center of the circle (p. 348)

Central angle of a regular polygon   An angle formed by two consecutive radii of the polygon (p. 453)

Chord of a circle   A segment with endpoints on the circle (p. 344)

Circle   The set of all points in a plane at a given distance from a fixed point of the plane
The fixed point is the *center* of the circle and the given distance is the *radius.* (p. 344)

Circumference   The distance around a circle (p. 466)

Collinear points   Points that lie on the same line (p. 7)

Complementary angles Two angles whose measures have a sum of 90 Each angle is a *complement* of the other. (p. 29)

Concentric circles Circles having the same center and radii of different lengths (p. 345)

Concurrent lines Three or more lines having a point in common (p. 425)

Conditional A statement in *if-then* form, *If p, then q,* where *p* and *q* are statements In a conditional, *p* is the *hypothesis* and *q* is the *conclusion.* (p. 49)

Congruent angles *Angles* whose measures are equal (p. 25)

Congruent circles *Circles* whose radii are congruent (p. 349)

Congruent segments *Segments* whose measures are equal (p. 19)

Congruent triangles Two *triangles* whose corresponding angles are congruent and whose corresponding sides are congruent (p. 90)

Contrapositive The statement formed when the *if* and *then* parts of the inverse of a conditional are interchanged (p. 140)

Converse The statement formed when the *if* and *then* parts of a conditional are interchanged (p. 67)

Coordinate plane A plane that associates number pairs or coordinates with points The *x* and *y* axes separate the coordinate plane into four regions or quadrants. (p. 521)

Coordinate(s) of a point On a number line, a number associated with a point on the line (p. 17) In a plane, the *ordered pair* of real numbers associated with a point in the plane (p. 520)

Coplanar points Points that lie in the same plane (p. 7)

Corollary A statement whose proof follows directly from a theorem or a definition (p. 67)

Corresponding angles Two angles in *corresponding* positions relative to two lines and a transversal (p. 173)

Cosine ratio In a right triangle, the *cosine* of an acute angle is the ratio $\frac{\text{length of the adjacent side}}{\text{length of the hypotenuse}}$. (p. 328)

Deductive reasoning In deductive reasoning, conclusions are arrived at from accepted facts. (p. 51)

Degree When using a *protractor* to measure an angle, the unit of measure is the *degree.* (p. 23)

Diagonal A segment, other than a side, joining two vertices of a polygon (p. 72)

Diameter of a circle A chord passing through the center of a circle (p. 344)

Dihedral angle The union of two non-coplanar half-planes whose edges are the same line The line is the *edge* of the dihedral angle and the half-planes are its *faces.* (p. 248)

Dilation A *dilation* is a *size transformation*. It is a *contraction* if $0<k<1$, where *k* is the *magnitude* of the dilation. If $k>1$, it is an *expansion* and if $k=1$, it is an *identity mapping* (p. 561)

Distance from a point to a line The length of the perpendicular segment from the point to the line (p. 133)

Equiangular triangle A triangle with three equal angles (p. 109)

Equidistant   A point P is equidistant from two other points A and B if $PA = PB$. *(p. 115)*

Equilateral triangle   A triangle with three congruent sides (p. 101)

Exterior angle of a triangle   The *angle* formed by extending one side of the triangle (p. 156)

Geometric mean   If a, b, and x are positive numbers and $\frac{a}{x} = \frac{x}{b}$, then x is the geometric mean between a and b. (p. 266)

Glide reflection   A *glide reflection* maps every point of a given geometric figure onto its image by a translation followed by a reflection over a line that is perpendicular to the lines of translation. (p. 554)

Golden Ratio   The ratio $\frac{1 + \sqrt{5}}{2}$ (p. 270)

Great circle   The circle formed by the intersection of a sphere and a plane passing through its center (p. 390)

Half-plane   The part of a plane on one side of a line (p. 248)

Half-turn   A rotation in which the measure of the angle of rotation is 180 (p. 558)

Hypotenuse   In a right triangle, the side opposite the right angle (p. 132)

Image   The reflection of a geometric figure (p. 550)

Indirect proof   In an *indirect proof*, you assume the negation of the conclusion. Then you reason until you reach a contradiction. Finally, you conclude that what you assumed in false and what you wished to prove is true. (p. 127)

Inductive reasoning   In inductive reasoning, conclusions are based on observations. (p. 76)

Inscribed angle   An angle whose vertex lies on the circle and whose sides contain chords of the circle (p. 369)

Inscribed polygon   A polygon all of whose vertices lie on a circle (p. 362)

Intercepted arc   An angle intercepts an arc if (1) the endpoints of the arc are on the angle; (2) all points of the arc, except the endpoints, are in the interior of the angle; and (3) each side of the angle contains an endpoint of the arc. (p. 369)

Inverse   The statement formed when both parts of a conditional are negated (p. 140)

Isometry   A transformation that preserves *distance, betweenness, angle measure,* and *collinearity* (p. 560)

Isosceles triangle   A triangle with two congruent sides (p. 101)

Lateral surface area   The sum of the areas of the lateral faces of a solid (p. 482)

Legs of an isosceles triangle   The two equal sides (p. 4)

Legs of a right triangle   The sides that form the right angle (p. 132)

Linear pair   Adjacent angles such that two of the rays are opposite rays (p. 29)

Line of reflection   The perpendicular bisector of the line segment joining a point with its image (p. 550)

Line of symmetry   If the figure on one side of a line is the reflection of the figure on the opposite side, the line is a *line of symmetry,* or *axis of symmetry.* (p. 553)

Line segment   Any two distinct points on a line and all the points between them (p. 8)

Locus   A set of points determined by certain conditions (p. 418)

Major arc   If ∠ABC is a central angle in circle B, points A and C and all points of the circle in the exterior of ∠ABC form a *major arc*. (p. 348)

Measure of an arc   The *measure of a minor arc* equals the measure of its central angle. The *measure of a semicircle* is 180. The *measure of a major arc* equals $360 - m$, where m is the measure of the central angle of its minor arc. (p. 348)

Median of a trapezoid   The segment joining the midpoints of the nonparallel sides (p. 228)

Median of a triangle   A segment from a vertex to the midpoint of the opposite side (p. 72)

Midpoint of an arc B is the *midpoint* of AC if B is a point on AC and mBA = mBC. (p. 349)

Midpoint of a segment   Point M is the *midpoint* of AB if M is between A and B and if AM = MB. (p. 18)

Minor arc   If ∠ABC is a central angle in circle B, points A and C and all points of the circle in the interior of ∠ABC form a *minor arc*. (p. 348)

Negation   The opposite of the original statement (p. 127)

Noncollinear points   Points that do not lie on the same line (p. 7)

Noncoplanar points   Points that do not lie in the same plane (p. 7).

Obtuse angle   An angle whose measure is greater than 90 and less than 180 (p. 24)

Opposite rays   If Y is between X and Z on $\overleftrightarrow{XZ}$, then $\overrightarrow{YX}$ and $\overrightarrow{YZ}$ are *opposite rays*. (p. 7)

Ordered pair   A pair of real numbers, such as (x, y), one of which is designated as first (x) and the other as second (y) (p. 520)

Origin   In the coordinate plane, the point where the axes meet (p. 520)

Parallel lines   Lines in the same plane that do not intersect (p. 162)

Parallelogram   A quadrilateral with both pairs of opposite sides parallel (p. 208)

Perimeter   The sum of the lengths of the sides of a polygon (p. 72)

Perpendicular bisector   In a plane, the line (segment, ray) that is perpendicular to a segment at its midpoint (p. 32)

Perpendicular lines   Two lines (rays, segments) that intersect to form a right angle (p. 31)

Plane angle   The intersection of the dihedral angle and a plane perpendicular to its edge (p. 248)

Point–slope form   The equation of a line written in the form $y - y_1 = m (x - x_1)$, where m is the slope and (x_1, y_1) is a point on the line (p. 528)

Polygon   A closed plane figure with segments as sides (p. 71)

Polygonal region   A *region* consisting of a polygon and its interior (p. 438)

Postulate   A statement that is accepted without proof (p. 10)

Preimage   A point that is mapped onto its image (p. 550)

Prism   A solid formed by the intersecting planes that are its *faces*   Two faces are *bases* and the others are *lateral* (side) *faces.* The intersections of the faces are called *edges*. An *altitude of a prism* is a segment that is perpendicular to the planes of the bases and that has an endpoint in each plane. (p. 482)

Proportion   An equation that states that two ratios are equal (p. 260)

Pyramid   A solid whose lateral faces are triangles that have one point, the *vertex* of the pyramid, in common   The intersections of the lateral faces are *edges*. The *base* of a pyramid is a polygon. The *altitude* of a pyramid is a segment drawn perpendicular to the base from the vertex of the pyramid. (p. 486)

Quadrant   One of four regions formed by the axes of the xy–plane (p. 520)

Radical   In the expression $\sqrt{50}$, $\sqrt{}$ is the *radical symbol*, 50 is the *radicand*, and $\sqrt{50}$ is the *radical*. (p. 266)

Radius of a regular polygon   The radius of the circumscribed circle of the polygon (p. 452)

Ratio   The comparison of two numbers by division (p. 260)

Ray   *Ray AB ($\overrightarrow{AB}$)* is that part of $\overleftrightarrow{AB}$ which contains point A and extends without end through point B. A is the endpoint of $\overrightarrow{AB}$. (p. 7)

Rectangle   A parallelogram with four right angles (p. 208)

Rectangular solid   A prism in which all six faces are rectangles (p. 482)

Regular polygon   A polygon that is both equiangular and equilateral (p. 194)

Regular pyramid   A pyramid whose base is a regular polygon and whose altitude passes through the center of the base (p. 486)

Remote interior angles   The angles of a triangle that are not adjacent to a given exterior angle (p. 156).

Rhombus   A parallelogram with all four sides congruent (p. 208)

Right angle   An angle whose measure is 90 (p. 24)

Right circular cone   A solid with a circular base and whose altitude passes through the center of the base (p. 491)

Right circular cylinder   A solid with congruent circular bases   The perpendicular distance between the bases is the *altitude* of the cylinder. (p. 490)

Right prism   A prism whose lateral edge is perpendicular to the plane of a base (p. 482)

Rotation   A composition of two reflections over two intersecting lines (p. 557)

Scalene triangle   A triangle with no equal sides (p. 3)

Secant   A line that intersects a circle in two points (p. 344)

Sector of a circle   A region bounded by an arc of the circle and two radii drawn to the endpoints of the arc (p. 471)

Semicircle   The union of the endpoints of a diameter and all points of a circle lying on one side of the diameter (p. 348)

Similar polygons   Two *polygons are similar* if corresponding angles are congruent and corresponding sides are proportional. (p. 280)

Sine ratio   In a right triangle, the *sine of* an acute angle is the ratio $\dfrac{\text{length of the opposite leg}}{\text{length of the hypotenuse}}$. (p. 328)

Skew lines   Lines that do not intersect and are not coplanar (p. 162)

Slant height   The length of the altitude of one of the faces of a regular pyramid (p. 486)

Slope   For any two points $P(x_1,y_1)$ and $Q(x_2,y_2)$ on $\overleftrightarrow{PQ}$, slope $= m = \dfrac{y_2 - y_1}{x_2 - x_1}$, $x_1 \neq x_2$. *(p. 526)*

Slope–intercept form   The equation of a line written in the form $y = mx + b$, where m is the slope and b is the y intercept (p. 529)

Space   The set of all points (p. 2)

Sphere   The set of all points in space at a given distance from a fixed point in space (p. 389)

Square   A rectangle with all four sides congruent (p. 208)

Straight angle   The angle formed by a pair of opposite rays (p. 29)

Supplementary angles   Two angles whose measures have a sum of 180 (p. 29)

Tangent   A line that intersects a circle in exactly one point (p. 344)

Tangent ratio   In a right triangle, the *tangent* of an acute angle is the ratio $\dfrac{\text{length of the opposite leg}}{\text{length of the adjacent leg}}$. (p. 322)

Theorem   A mathematical statement that can be proved (p. 11)

Transformation   A relation in which a point P is paired with exactly one point P', called its image (p. 550)

Translation   A composition of two reflections over two parallel lines (p. 553)

Trapezoid   A quadrilateral with exactly one pair of parallel sides (p. 208)

Triangle   The figure formed by three segments which join three noncollinear points (p. 8)

Vertex of an angle   The common point of the sides of an angle (p. 3)

Vertex angle of an isosceles triangle   The angle opposite the base (p. 4)

Vertical angles   The nonadjacent angles formed when two lines intersect (p. 29)

Volume   The number of cubic units contained in a solid (p. 496)

y intercept   The y coordinate of the point at which a line crosses the y axis (p. 529)

Index

Boldfaced *numerals indicate the pages that contain formal or informal definitions.*

AAA Similarity Theorem, 283
Absolute value, **17**, 37
Acute angle, **24**, 37, 132
Adjacent angles, **29**, 37
Adjacent sides of a polygon, **72**, 83
Alternate angles, **158**, 202
Alternate exterior angles, **158**, 202
Alternate interior angles, **158**, 202
Altitude, **442**, 476
  of cone, **491**
  of parallelogram, **442**
  of prism, **482**, 512
  of pyramid, **486**, 512
  of right circular cylinder, **490**, 512
  of triangle, **72**, 83
Angle, **7**, 37
  acute, **24**, 37, 132
  adjacent, **29**, 37
  alternate, **158**, 202
  alternate exterior, **158**, 202
  alternate interior, **158**, 202
  base, of isosceles triangle, **4**, 37
  bisector of, **25**, 37, 101, 114
  central, in circle, **348**, 395
  central, in sphere, **389**
  central, of a regular polygon, **453**, 476
  complementary, **29**, 37
  congruent, **25**, 37, 70, 102, 138
  consecutive, of a polygon, **72**, 83
  consecutive, of a quadrilateral, **210**, 254
  corresponding, **173**-175, 202
  of depression, **333**, 339
  dihedral, **248**, 249, 254
  of elevation, **333**, 339
  exterior, **158**
  exterior of, **24**, 37
  included, of a triangle, **95**
  inscribed, **369**-372, 375, 395
  interior, **158**, 202
  linear pair, **29**, 37
  measure of, **23**, 37
  obtuse, **24**, 37
  opposite, of quadrilateral, **208**, 254

pairs of, **29**-30
plane, **248**-249, 254
of a polygon, **193**-198, 202
remote interior, **156**-157, 202
right, **24**, 38, 70
of rotation, **558**, 563
sides of, **3**
straight, **29**, 38
supplementary, **29**, 38
tangent of an acute, **322**
of a triangle, **156**-161, 202
vertex of, **3**, 38
vertical, **29**, 38
Applications
  calculator (see Calculator Applications)
  career (see Career Applications)
  computer programming (see Computer Applications)
  consumer (see Consumer Applications)
  using angle pairs, 35
  using angles and arcs of circles, 353
  using angles in polygons, 200
  using area, 451
  using area, perimeter, and circumference, 474
  using chords and arcs of circles, 388
  using constructions and loci, 428
  using dihedral angles, 252
  using inequalities, 252
  using isosceles triangles, 120
  using parallel lines, 179
  using polygons, 75
  using quadrilaterals, 234
  using segments, 22
  using similar polygons, 294
  using the geometric mean, 270
  using the Pythagorean Theorem, 315
  using the sine and cosine ratios, 332
  using surface area, 494
  using triangles, 106
  using volume, 508

Apothem **452**, **458**, 476
Arc **348**-350
  congruent, **349**, 395
  length of, **466**-469
  major, **348**, 395
  midpoint of, **349**, 395
  minor, **348**, 395
Area, 438-480
  of circles, 470-474
  lateral surface, of a prism, **482**, 512
  lateral surface, of a pyramid, **486**, 512
  lateral, of a right circular cone, **491**, 512
  lateral, of a right circular cylinder, **490**, 512
  parallelogram, **442**-446
  regular polygons, **458**
  rhombus, **447**-450
  of sectors of circles, **470**-473
  of segments of circles, **470**-473
  trapezoid, **448**-450
  triangle, **443**-446
ASA Postulate, 100
Axis of symmetry, **553**

Base angles of an isosceles triangle, 4, 37
Base(s), 442, 476
  of circular cylinders, **490**
  of cone, **491**
  of isosceles triangle, **4**, 37, 108
  of parallelogram, **442**
  of prism, **482**, 512
  of triangle, **443**
BASIC Programming (see Computer Applications)
Betweenness of points, **18**, 37
  for circles, **349**
Biconditional, **67**, 83
Bisect, **19**, 37
Bisector
  of an angle, **25**, 37, 101, 114
  perpendicular, **32**, 38, 114, 146
  of a segment, **101**

Calculator Applications
  Checking equations, 28
  Constant ratio formula, 279
  Distance formula, 538
  Evaluating formulas, 196
  Finding the geometric mean, 269
  Hero's formula, 450
  Similar polygons, 282
  Trigonometric functions, 331
Career Applications
  Astronomy, 320
  Chemistry, 219
  Design Engineering, 14
  Geology, 416
  Mathematics, 394
  Optometry, 167
Center
  of a circle, **344**
  of a regular polygon, **452**, 476
  of a sphere, **389**
Center of rotation, 557
Central angles, 348-353
  of a circle, **348**, 395
  of a regular polygon, **453**, 476
  of a sphere, **389**
Centroid of a triangle, 426, 429
Chord(s), 360-363, 395
  of a circle, **344**, 395
  congruent, **354**-359
  of a sphere, **389**
Circle(s), 344-393, 395
  area, **438**, 470-474
  center, **344**
  central angle, **348**, 395
  chord, **344**, 395
  circumference, **466**-469, 476
  concentric, **345**, 395
  congruent, **349**, 395
  diameter, **344**, 395
  equations of, 539-540
  inscribed angle, **369**-372, 375, 395
  major arc, **348**, 395
  minor arc, **348**, 395
  radius, **344**, 395
  secant, **344**
  sectors of, **471**, 476
  segments of, **471**, 476
  semicircle, **348**, 395
  tangent to, **344**, 364-369
Circular region, 438, 476

Circumcenter of a triangle, 425, 429
Circumference of a circle, 466-469, 476
Circumscribed circle, 452, 476
Circumscribed polygons, 452-454
Collinear points, 7, 37
Complementary angles, 29, 37
Computer Applications
  Angles, 36
  Angles in circles, 369
  Angles in triangles and polygons, 201
  Area, 475
  Perimeter, 82
  Right triangles, 338
  Similarity, 296
  Surface area and volume, 511
  Triangles, 253
Concentric circles 345, 395
Conclusion of if-then statement, 49, 83
Concurrent lines, 425, 429
Conditional, 49, 67, 83, 91, 140
Cone(s)
  altitude, **491**
  lateral area, **491**
  right circular, **491**
  total area, **491**
  vertex, **491**
  volume of, **500**-503
Congruence, 90, 91, 146
Congruence mapping, 551, 563
Congruent
  angles, **25**, 37, 70, 102, 138
  arcs, **349**-395
  chords, **354**, 359
  circles, **349**, 395
  segments, **19**, 37, 70, 102, 138
  triangles, **90**, 100-105, 138
Consecutive angles
  of a polygon, **73**, 83
  of a quadrilateral, **210**, 254
Consecutive sides
  of a polygon, **73**
  of a quadrilateral, **210**, 254
Constructions
  angle congruent to a given angle, 402
  bisecting an angle, 403
  circumscribing a circle about a triangle, 410

  dividing a given line segment into congruent parts, 413
  geometric mean, 414
  inscribing a circle in a triangle, 411
  line parallel to a given line, 406
  line perpendicular to a given line at a point on the line, 405
  line perpendicular to a given line from a given point not on the line, 405
  locating the center of a given circle, 410
  perpendicular bisector of a segment, 406
  proportional segments, 413
  segment congruent to a given segment, 402
  tangent to a circle at a given point on the circle, 409
  tangent to a circle from a point outside the circle, 409
Consumer Applications
  Advertising, 144
  Air Conditioning, 504
  Banking, 279
  Driving, 81
  Wallpapering, 465
Contraction, 561, 563
Contradiction, 127, 146
Contrapositive, 140, 146
Converse, 67, 83, 140
Convex polygon, 71, 83
Coordinate(s), 17, 37
  of a point, **520**, 545
Coordinate geometry, 520-544
  proofs, 541-548
Coordinate plane, 521-522, 545
Coplanar points, 7, 37
Corollary, 67, 83
Corresponding angles, 173-175, 202
Cosine ratio, 328-329, 332, 339
Counterexample, 141, 146
Cube, 482, 512
  volume of, **496**-498
Cylinder(s)
  altitude, **490**
  bases, **490**
  lateral area, **490**
  oblique circular, **490**

right circular, 490
total area, **490**
volume of, 500-503

Deductive reasoning, 49-56, 83
Definitions and logic, **7**-9
Degree, **23**, 37
Depression, angle of, **333**, 339
Diagonal(s) of polygon, **72**, 83
Diameter
    of a circle, **344**, 395
    of a sphere, **389**
Dihedral angle(s), **248**-252, 254
    adjacent, **249**
    face(s), **248**
Dilation(s), **561**, 563
    magnitude of, 561
Distance
    between points, **17**, 37
    from point to line, **360**
Distance formula, 536-538

Edge(s)
    of a half-plane, **248**
    of prism, 482, 512
    of pyramid, 486, 512
Elevation, angle of, **333**, 339
Endpoints, 7, 37, 383
Equation(s) of a circle, 539-540
Equation of a line, **528**
    point-slope form, **528**, 545
    slope-intercept form, **529**, 545
Equiangular, **109**, 146
    polygon(s), **194**, 202
    triangle, **101**
Equidistant, **115**, 146
Equilateral
    polygon, **194**, 202
    triangle, **3**, 37, 101, 108
Equivalence relation(s), **44**, 83
Existence proof, 133, 146
Expansion, **561**, 563
Exterior of an angle, **24**, 37
Exterior angle(s), **158**, 202
    alternate, **158**, 202
    of a polygon, **197**-198, 202
    of a triangle, **156**-161, 202
External secant segments, **384**

Face(s)
    of dihedral angle, **248**
    of prism, **482**, 512

Fourth proportional, **267**, 297

Gear ratio, 264, 297
Geometric mean, **266**, 270, 296
Geometry 2
    coordinate, 520-548
Glide reflection, **554**, 563
Graph(s)
    of a linear equation, 528
    of an ordered pair, 520-521
Golden Ratio, **270**, 297
Golden Rectangle, **270**, 297
Great circle of a sphere, **389**-390,
    395

H.A. Postulate, 132
Half-plane, **248**, 254
    edge of, **248**
Half-turn, 558, 563
Hexagon(s), **72**, 83
H.L. Theorem, 132
Hypotenuse, **132**, 146
Hypothesis of if-then statement,
    49, 83

Identity mapping, 561, 563
Identity property, **91**, 146
If- then statement, **140**
    conclusion, **49**, 83
    conditional, **49**, 67, 83, 91, 140
    converse, **67**, 83, 140
    hypothesis, **49**, 83
    negation, **127**, 146
Image, **550**, 563
Incenter of a triangle, **426**, 429
Included angle of a triangle, **95**
Included side of a triangle, **100**
Indirect proof, **127**-128, 146
Inductive reasoning, **76**-79, 83
Inequalities, **157**
Inscribed angle(s), **369**-372, 375,
    395
Inscribed circle, **452**, 476
Inscribed polygon, **361**, 395,
    452-454
Intercepted arc, **369**, 395
Interior
    of an angle, **24**, 37
    of a triangle, **72**
Interior angle(s), **158**, 202
Intersection
    of lines, 96

of loci, 422-424
of planes, 11
Inverse, **140**, 146
Isometry, **560**, 563
Isosceles right triangle, **316**
Isosceles trapezoid, **208**
Isosceles triangle, **3**, 37, 101,
    108-120
    base, **4**, 37
    base angles, **4**, 37
    legs, **4**, 37, 108
    vertex angle, **4**, 37, 108

Kite, 213, 254

Lateral area
    of cone, **491**, 512
    of right circular cylinder, **490**,
    512
Lateral face(s)
    of prism, **482**, 512
    of pyramid, **486**, 512
Lateral surface area
    of prism, **482**, 512
    of pyramid, **486**, 512
Legs
    of isosceles triangle, **4**, 37, 108
    of right triangle, **132**
Length(s)
    of arcs, **466**-469
    of segments, **383**-387
Line(s), 2, 31, 37, 164
    equations of, 528
    in plane of a circle, 344
    parallel, 162-181, 202
    perpendicular, **31**, 38, 70, 139
    of reflection, **550**, 563
    of sight, **333**, 339
    of symmetry, **553**, 563
    skew, **162**, 202
    slope of, **526**, 528, 545
Linear equation, **528**, 545
Linear pair, **29**, 37
Locus, 418-424, 429
    and constructions, 425-428
    drawing and describing, 418-
    419
    intersection of, 422-424
Logic
    biconditional, **67**, 83
    conclusion, **49**, 83
    conditional, **49**, 67, 83, 91, 140

contradiction, **127**, 146
contrapositive, **140**, 146
converse, **67**, 83, 140
counterexample, **141**, 146
hypothesis, **49**, 83
if-then statement, **49**, 140
indirect proof, **127**-128, 146
inductive reasoning, **76**-79, 83
inverse, **140**
negation, **127**, 146

Magnitude of dilation, 561, 563
Major arc, **348**, 395
  measure of, 348
Mean
  geometric, **266**, 270, 297
Measure
  of an angle, **23**, 37
  of segments, **17**
Median, **72**, 83
  of a trapezoid, **228**, 254
  of a triangle, **73**
Midpoint, **18**, 37, 101
  of an arc, **349**, 395
  of a segment, **523**-524
Midpoint formula, 523-525
Minor arc, **348**, 395
  measure of, **348**

Negation, 127, 146
Noncollinear points, **7**, 37
Noncollinear rays, **7**, 37
Noncoplanar points, **7**, 37

Oblique circular cylinder(s), 490
Oblique prism, **482**, 512
Obtuse angle, **24**, 37
Octagon, **71**, 83
Opposite angles of a quadrilateral,
  208, 254
Opposite rays, **7**, 38
Opposite sides of a quadrilateral,
  208, 254
Ordered pair, **520**, 545
Origin, **520**
Orthocenter, **426**, 429
Overlapping triangles and con-
  gruence, 121

Parallel lines, 162-181, 202
Parallelogram(s), **208**-210,
  213-214, 224

altitude of, **442**
area, **442**-446
base, **208**
Pentagon, **72**, 83
Perimeter of a polygon, **73**, 83
Perpendicular bisector, **32**, 38,
  114, 146
  constructing, 406
Perpendicular lines, **31**, 38, 139
  theorems of, 67-71
Plane, **2**, 7, 37
Plane angle, **248**-249, 254
Point(s), **2**, 37
  betweenness of, 18, 37
  collinear, **7**, 37
  coordinates of, 520, 545
  distance between, **17**, 37
  reflection, 551, 563
Point-slope form, 528, 545
Polygon(s), **72**-76, 83
  adjacent sides of, **73**
  angles of, 193-196
  area of regular, 458-461
  central angle of regular, **453**,
    476
  circumscribed about a circle,
    452-456
  consecutive angles of, **72**, 83
  consecutive sides of, **72**
  convex, **71**, 83
  diagonal of, **72**, 83
  equiangular, **194**, 202
  equilateral, **194**, 202
  exterior angles of, **197**
  inscribed in a circle, **361**, 362-
    364, 452-456
  perimeter, **72**
  radius of regular, **452**-454, 476
  regular, **194**, 452
  similar, **280**-282
Polygonal region(s), **438**-441,
  458-461, 476
Postulate(s), **10**-13, 38
Preimage, **550**
Preparing for College Entrance
  Tests, 153, 154, 303, 304, 435,
  436, 517, 518
Prism(s), **482**-485, 512
  altitude of, **482**, 512
  base(s), **482**, 512
  edge(s), **482**, 512
  face(s), **482**, 512

lateral face(s), **482**, 512
lateral surface area of **482**, 512
oblique **482**, 512
pentagonal **482**
regular, **482**, 512
right, **482**, 512
total area, **483**, 512
volume of, **496**-499
Proof, **44**-79
  deductive reasoning, **49**-56, 83
  equivalence relation, **44**, 83
  indirect, **127**-128, 146
  inductive reasoning, **76**, 79, 83
  two-column form, 57-65
Proof, Aids in
  Proving an angle is a right
    angle, 70
  Proving angles congruent, 70,
    102, 138
  Proving lines or segments per-
    pendicular, 70, 139
  Proving lines parallel, 180
  Proving segments congruent,
    70, 102, 138
  Proving a quadrilateral is a
    parallelogram, 214
  Proving triangles congruent,
    102
  Proving triangles similar, 293
Proportion(s), **260**-261, 265, 274,
  297
Protractor, **23**, 38
Protractor postulate, 23
Pyramid(s), **486**-489, 512
  altitude, **486**, 512
  edge(s), **486**, 512
  lateral faces, **486**, 512
  lateral surface area, **486**, 512
  regular, **486**, 512
  slant height, **486**, 512
  volume of, **497**-499
  total area, **487**
Pythagorean Theorem, 310-311

Quadrants, 520, 545
Quadrilateral(s), **71**, 83, 208-218
  parallelograms, **208**-210, 213-
    214, 224
  rectangle, **208**, 224
  rhombus, **208**, 224
  square, **208**, 224
  trapezoid, **208**, 224

Radicals, 266
Radius
   of a circle, **344**, 395
   of a regular polygon, **452**-454,
     476
   of a sphere, **389**
Ratio, **260**-261, 264, 297
Ray, **2**, 38, 114
   betweenness of, 25
   bisector of angle, **25**
   opposite, **7**, 29, 38
Real numbers, 157
Rectangle, **208**, 220, 224
Rectangular solid, **482**
Reflection(s), 550-556, 563
   glide, **554**, 563
   line of, **550**, 563
   point, **551**, 563
Reflexive property, **44**, 83
Region
   circular, **438**, 476
   polygonal, **438**-441, 458-461,
     476
Regular polygon(s), **194**, 202
   apothem of, **452**, 458, 476
   area, **438**
   center of, **452**
   central angle of, **453**, 476
   radius of, **452**-454, 476
Regular prism(s), **482**, 512
Regular pyramid, **486**, 512
Remote interior angles, **156**-157,
   202
Rhombus, **208**, 220-224
   area, 447-450
Right angle, **24**, 38, 70
Right circular cone, **491**-493, 512
   altitude, **491**, 512
   lateral area, **491**, 512
   total area, **491**, 512
   vertex, **491**, 512
Right circular cylinder(s), **490**-
   491, 512
   altitude, **490**, 512
   lateral area, **490**, 512
   total area, **490**, 512
Right prism, **482**, 512
Right triangle, **306**-342
   congruence in, 132
   hypotenuse of, **132**, 146
   isosceles, **316**
   legs of, **132**

Pythagorean Theorem,
   310-311
   similar, **306**-309
   special, 316-319
   tangent ratio, **322**-327
Rotation(s), **557**-559, 563
   angle of, **558**, 563
Ruler Postulate, 17

SAS Postulate, 95
SAS Similarity Theorem, 288
Scalene triangle, **3**, 38
Secant(s), **344**, 395
Sector of a circle, **471**, 476
Segment(s), **8**, 17-22, 38, 164
   congruent, **19**, 37, 70, 102,
     138
   endpoints, **8**, 37
   lengths of, **383**-387
   measure of, **17**
   midpoint of, **523**-524
Segment of a circle, **471**, 476
Semicircle, **348**, 395
   measure of, **348**
Side(s)
   of an angle, **3**
   consecutive of a polygon, **72**
   consecutive of a quadri-
     lateral, **210**, 254
   of a triangle, **3**
Similar polygons, **280**-282, 293,
   297, 462-464
Similar right triangles, **306**-309
Similar triangles, **283**-295
Simplest form of a radical, **266**,
   297
Sine ratio, **328**-329, 332, 339
Skew lines, **162**, 202
Slant height of pyramid, **486**, 512
Slope(s)
   and linear equations, 528-530
   of a line, **526**-530, 545
   of parallel lines, **532**-535
   of perpendicular lines, **532**-535
Slope-intercept form, **529**, 545
Space, **2**, 38
Sphere, **389**-392, 395
   center, **389**
   central angle, **389**
   chord, **389**
   diameter, **389**
   great circle, **389**-390, 395

radius, **389**
surface area, **505**-507, 512
volume, **505**-507, 512
Square, **208**, 220-222, 224
SSS Postulate, 100
SSS Similarity Theorem, 288
Statements (see if-then state-
   ments)
   biconditional, **67**, 83
   conclusion, **49**, 83
   conditional, **49**, 83, 91, 140
   contrapositive, **140**, 146
   converse, **67**, 83, 140
   hypothesis, **49**, 83
   negation, **127**, 146
Straight angle, **29**, 38
Summaries
   Aids in proof (see Proof, Aids
     in)
   Assumptions from a figure, 96
   Finding and describing a locus,
     419
   If-then statements, 50
   Properties of a parallelogram,
     210
   Properties of a quadrilateral,
     222
   Reasons used in proofs, 51
   Surface area and volume form-
     ulas, 512
   Writing an indirect proof, 128
   Writing a two-column proof, 57
Supplementary angles, **29**, 38
Surface area
   of solids, **482**-495
   of spheres, **505**-507, 512
Symmetric property, **44**, 83
   axis of, **553**
   line of, **553**, 563
   with respect to a line, 553

Tangent(s), **344**, 364-368, 395
Tangent ratio, **322**-323, 327, 339
Tangent segment, **365**, 395
Theorem(s), **11**, 38
Total area
   of cone, **491**, 512
   of prism, **483**, 512
   of pyramid, **487**
   of right circular cylinder, **490**,
     512
Transitive property, **44**, 83

Translation, **553**, 563
Transversal, **158**, 202
Trapezoid(s), **208**, 213, 224
  area, **448**-450
  base(s), **208**
  isosceles, **208**
  median of, **228**, 254
Triangle(s), **8**, 38, 71-72
  altitude of, **72**, 83
  angles of, **156**-161, 202
  area, **443**-446
  centroid of, **426**, 429
  circumcenter of, **425**, 429
  congruent, **90**, 100-105, 138
  equiangular, **101**
  equilateral, **3**, 37, 101, 108
  exterior angle of, **156**-161, 202
  incenter of, **426**, 429
  included angle of, **95**
  included side of, **100**
  interior of, **72**
  isosceles, **3**, 37, 101, 108-120
  median of, **72**
  orthocenter of, **426**, 429
  overlapping, 121
  remote interior angle of,
    156-157, 202
  right, **306**-342
  scalene, **3**, 38
  sides of, **3**
Trigonometric ratio, 323, 329,
  339
  cosine, **328**-329, 332, 339
  sine, **328**-329, 332, 339
  tangent, **322**-323, 327, 339
Trigonometry, **323**

Uniqueness proof, 133, 146

Vertex
  of an angle, **3**, 38
  of cone, **491**
Vertex angle of isosceles triangle,
  4, 38, 108
Vertical angles, **29**, 38
Volume, 496-510, 512
  of cone, **501**-503
  of cube, **496**-498
  of circular cylinder, **500**
  of prism, **496**-498
  of pyramid, **496**
  of sphere, **505**

x axis, 520, 545

y axis, 520, 545
y intercept, **529**, 545

ANSWERS TO SELECTED EXERCISES

The answers are provided for all of the problems in the *Reviews* and *Review Capsules*. The answers for the *Computer Applications* and the *Puzzles* appear in the *Solution Key*. For all other types of exercises, the answers to the odd-numbered problems are provided.

CHAPTER 1: INTRODUCTION TO GEOMETRY

Page 4   Classroom Exercises   1. Ray TU   3. Angle WHY   5. $\overrightarrow{HJ}, \overrightarrow{HG}$ 7. $\overrightarrow{GH}$ 9. isosceles
11. vertex angle

Page 5   Written Exercises   1. f, i   3. c   5. d, g, k   7. T   9. T   11. T   13. T   15. $\overline{PA}, \overline{PT}, \overline{AT}$;
$\angle PAT, \angle ATP, \angle TPA$ 17. $\overline{BN}, \overline{NE}, \overline{BE}; \angle BNE, \angle NEB, \angle NBE$ 19. $\overline{BN}, \overline{GN}, \overline{BG}; \angle NGB, \angle GBN, \angle BNG$
21. $\overline{HJ}$ 23. $\angle H, \angle J; \angle KHJ, \angle KJH$ 25. $\triangle MPQ: \overline{MQ}; \angle PMQ, \angle PQM; \overline{PM}, \overline{PQ}; \angle P$ or $\angle MPQ; \triangle MRQ: \overline{MQ};$
$\angle RMQ, \angle RQM; \overline{RM}, \overline{RQ}; \angle R$ or $\angle MRQ$ 27. $\overline{RS}, \overline{RT}, \overline{ST}; \angle R$ or $\angle SRT, \angle S$ or $\angle RST, \angle T$ or $\angle RTS$; Yes; Yes;
Yes   29. four   31. three; six; three   33. $\overrightarrow{AD}, \overrightarrow{AC}, \overrightarrow{AB}$ 35. $\overline{FE}; \overline{EG}; \overline{HE}; \overline{FG}; \overline{HG}; \overline{FH}$ 37. $\overline{AB}, \overline{BC},$
$\overline{CD}, \overline{DE}, \overline{AC}, \overline{AD}, \overline{AE}, \overline{BD}, \overline{BE}, \overline{CE}$

Page 8   Classroom Exercises   1. b, a   3. c, a, b

Page 8   Written Exercises   1. point   3. plane   5. line and point   7. b, a   9. b, a   11. c, b, a
13. Coplanar points are points that lie in the same plane; Points that lie in the same plane are coplanar points.
15. An isosceles triangle is a triangle with two equal sides; A triangle with two equal sides is an isosceles triangle.
17. An equilateral triangle is a triangle with three equal sides; A triangle with three equal sides is an equilateral
triangle.   19. No; A triangle is a geometric figure, but it is not a line.   21. No; Any two rays do not necessarily form an angle.   23. Yes   25. No; The three segments must join three noncollinear points.   27. The
term being defined (angle) is not named.   29. The set to which coplanar points belong is not identified.
31. Polygon is not a previously defined term.   33. Opposite rays are rays that lie on the same line and have
exactly one point in common.

Page 11   Classroom Exercises   1. Postulate 5   3. Postulate 6   5. B

Page 12   Written Exercises   1. T; Theorem 1-2   3. T; Postulate 2   5. F; Postulate 5   7. F; Postulate 5
9. T; Theorem 1-1   11. line   13. 1 point   15. postulate   17. Any three of the points P, X, Z;
Postulate 2   19. Z; Theorem 1-3   21. The plane containing W, Z, and Y; the plane containing W, Y, and X;
the plane containing W, P, and X; the plane containing W, P, and Z; Postulate 2   23. $\overleftrightarrow{WZ}$; Theorem 1-1
25. An infinite number.   27. An infinite number.   29. One   31. One   33. 4

Page 15   Career Applications   For Exercises 1-3, answers will vary. For Exercises 4-6, follow the procedure
of Example 2.

Page 16   Review   1. $\overline{WT}$ and $\overline{WH}$ 2. isosceles triangle   3. $\angle T, \angle H; \angle WTH, \angle WHT$ 4. $\triangle WAT, \triangle WAH$
5. T, A, H   6. W, A, H, or W, A, T   7. ray, angle, triangle   8. segment, triangle   9. ray, endpoint of a ray,
opposite rays   10. segment, triangle, equilateral triangle   11. C; Theorem 1-2   12. D; Theorem 1-3
13. A, D, E; Definition of collinear points   14. G, D, C, E, F; Definition of coplanar points

Page 16   Algebra Review Capsule for Section 1-4   1. 6   2. 6   3. 11   4. 5   5. 13   6. 4   7. 12   8. 20
9. 0   10. 8   11. 16   12. 10   13. 9   14. 64   15. 16   16. 24   17. 20   18. $33\frac{1}{3}$ 19. $21\frac{5}{7}$
20. −48

Page 19 Classroom Exercises   1. 4   3. D   5. 8   7. C   9. C   11. =   13. =

Page 20 Written Exercises   1. 5   3. 7   5. 8   7. 9   9. 20   11. 6   13. 9   15. 24   17. 20
19. 16   21. 12   23. 20   25. 24   27. 32   29. 16   31. C   33. 16   35. $\overline{BT}$ (or $\overline{SD}$)
37. Theorem 1-4   39. GH = 5; HJ = 6; GJ = 11; Yes   41. $|22 - 28| + |28 - 37| = 6 + 9 = 15$; $|37 - 22|$
$= 15$. Therefore, $|22 - 28| + |28 - 37| = |37 - 22|$; 22 refers to H, 28 refers to J, and 37 refers to K. J is
between H and K, because H, J, and K are collinear and HJ + JK = HK.   43. 125   45. 86   47. $\overline{XY}$
49. WX   51. WY; XZ   53. 1. Z 2. V 3. X 4. Z   55. s = -2 57. s = 26, r = 45   59. t = 32
61. K: -3; L: 9   63. $y = \dfrac{5}{42}$ 65. $y = \dfrac{3}{8}$ 67. By the Ruler Postulate, each endpoint of the given segment
is associated with a real number. Between these two numbers there is exactly one midpoint coordinate. Again,
by the Ruler Postulate, the midpoint coordinate is associated with just one point of the segment, the midpoint.
69. x = 10 <u>or</u> x = -4 71. x = 3   73. y = -17 <u>or</u> y = -1

Page 22 Applications   1. 40 yards   3. 60 yards   5. Impossible to tell; not enough information is given.
7. Tilson

Page 25 Classroom Exercises   1. 30   3. 90   5. 20   7. 45   9. 80   11. $\angle$FBC   13. HBE
15. Theorem 1-7   17. $\overrightarrow{BE}$

Page 26 Written Exercises   1. 22   3. 150   5. 130   7. 28   9. 55   11. 30   13. 49   15. 34
17. 39   19. T; Theorem 1-6.   21. T; An acute angle is an angle whose measure is greater than 0 and less
than 90. The measure of the angles formed if an acute angle is bisected is less than 45.   23. T; A right angle
is an angle whose measure is 90. The measure of the angles formed if a right angle is bisected is 45.   25. F;
unless $\overrightarrow{BD}$ bisects $\angle$ABC   27. 70   29. 120   31. 30   33. $\overrightarrow{AC}$ 35. 39   37. 54; Theorem 1-7
39. No; Theorem 1-6   43. 30   45. 40; 71   47. 150; 60   49. 11 or 85   51. By the Protractor
41.   Postulate, each ray of the given angle is associated with a real number. Between
these two numbers there is exactly one number, the coordinate of the bisector.
By the Protractor Postulate, the bisector's coordinate is associated with just one
ray in the interior of the given angle, the bisector.   53. 6, 10, 15   55. r = 140,
t = 68 <u>or</u> r = 68, t = 140

Page 28 Algebra Review Capsule for Section 1-6   1. 70   2. 30   3. 45   4. 20   5. 50   6. 75   7. 43
8. 18   9. $21\frac{1}{2}$ 10. 100   11. 55   12. 55   13. 24   14. 25   15. $16\frac{5}{6}$

Page 28 Calculator Exercises   (See the Review Capsule for Section 1-6.)

Page 32 Classroom Exercises   1. $\angle$DEB and $\angle$AEC   3. 90   5. $\angle$FEB   7. $\angle$AEF   9. 110   11. Yes;
Theorem 1-9

Page 32 Written Exercises   1. 150   3. 48   5. 65   7. 70   9. 40   11. 48   13. m$\angle$A   15. 60; 30
17. 45   19. 72, 108   21. 80, 100, 10   23. 120, 60, 30   25. 90   27. Angles ABD and DBC; angles
ABE and EBC; both   29. Angles 9 and 10; angles 10 and 11; angles 11 and 12; angles 9 and 12   31. Yes
33. 2   35. 3   37. 1   39. 65   41. 145   43. False, by definition of vertical angles.   45. False, because
the sum of the measures of an angle and its complement is 90.   47. False. Two angles do not have to form a
linear pair to be supplementary.   49. True. Two angles whose measures have a sum of 90 are complementary
angles.   51. 100 $-$ y (b)   53. x   55. Let the given measure be a. Its complement is 90 $-$ a and its supplement is 180 $-$ a. a + 2(90 $-$ a) = 180 $-$ a   57. Let the given measure be a. Its complement is 90 $-$ a.
$\frac{1}{2}$(a + (90 $-$ a)) = 45

Page 35   Applications   1. $\angle 3, \angle 4; \angle 1, \angle 2$ 3. $\angle 1, \angle 3; \angle 1, \angle 4; \angle 2, \angle 3; \angle 2, \angle 4$ 5. $m\angle 1 = 40, m\angle 2 = 140$
7. $\angle 2, \angle i; \angle 1, \angle r$ 9. 25   11. 60

Page 37   Review   1. 4   2. 10   3. 2   4. 10   5. 19   6. 33   7. 100   8. 65   9. 130   10. 65
11. 35   12. 5   13. Any two of $\angle 1, \angle 2,$ or $\angle 3$ 14. $\angle DOF,$ or $\angle DOG$ 15. $m\angle 1 = 65, m\angle 2 = 25$ 16. 43
17. $m\angle C = 70, m\angle B = 110$

Page 38   Chapter Objectives and Review   1. F   3. T   5. F   7. T   9. isosceles   11. scalene
13. $\angle AEB, \angle DEA, \angle CED, \angle DEB, \angle CEB$ 15. $\triangle ABC, \triangle CAD$ 17. undefined   19. defined   21. undefined
23. defined   25. NG; not enough information   27. G   29. Postulate 6   31. Theorem 1-3   33. 9
35. 9   37. R   39. PQ   41. $37\frac{1}{2}$ 43. $\cong$ 45. $=$ 47. 75   49. 85   51. 175   53. 90   55. T
57. T   59. acute   61. obtuse   63. 38   65. vertical   67. adjacent   69. supplementary   71. 90
73. supplementary   75. perpendicular bisector   77. 9 yards

Page 42   Chapter Test   1. A, D, C   3. A, B, C   5. $\angle ABC$ 7. endpoint, noncollinear rays, angle   9. line
11. 19   13. 110; $\angle QSN$ and $\angle NSP$ are a linear pair and supplementary angles.   15. 39; An angle has exactly
one bisector.   17. $\angle AFG, \angle GFC$ 19. 10

CHAPTER 2:   INTRODUCTION TO PROOF

Page 46   Classroom Exercises   1. $\overline{EF}$ 3. $\angle A$ 5. $\overline{PQ}$ 7. Distributive Property   9. Transitive Property
11. 2. Addition Property   3. Addition Property   4. Multiplication Property

Page 46   Written Exercises   1. Transitive Property   3. Reflexive Property   5. Transitive Property
7. Symmetric Property   9. Addition Property   11. Addition Property   13. Distributive Property
15. Distributive Property   17. Addition Property   19. Multiplication Property   21. 2. Addition
Property   3. Addition Property   4. Multiplication Property   23. 2. Addition Property   3. Multiplication
Property   4. Symmetric Property   25. Multiplication Property   27. Addition and Substitution Properties
29. Multiplication Property   31. Addition Property   33. Substitution Property   35. No. Let $m\angle A = 60$.
$60 + 60 \neq 180$ 37. Yes. If m is perpendicular to n, then n is perpendicular to m.   39. No. Let $m\angle A = 80$,
$m\angle B = 100$, and $m\angle C = 80$. Then angle A is supplementary to angle B, and angle B is supplementary to angle C,
but angle A is not supplementary to angle C.   41. No   43. Yes   45. 2. Reflexive Property   3. Definition
of congruent segments   47. 2. Definition of congruent segments   3. Transitive Property   4. Definition of
congruent segments

Page 50   Classroom Exercises   1. Two angles each have a measure of 35; The angles are congruent   Given:
$m\angle A = 35, m\angle B = 35$ Prove: $\angle A \cong \angle B$ 3. $\overrightarrow{AB}$ bisects $\angle DAC$; B is in the interior of $\angle DAC$ Given: $\overrightarrow{AB}$ bisects
$\angle DAC$ Prove: B is in the interior of $\angle DAC$

Page 50   Written Exercises   1. If points are coplanar, then they lie in the same plane.   3. If two angles are
vertical angles, then they are congruent.   5. If it is raining, and I don't use my umbrella.   7. If a citizen is
18, but the citizen cannot vote.

Page 52   Classroom Exercises   For Exercises 1-6, answers may vary.   1. $m\angle KJQ = m\angle QJN$; Definition of
angle bisector   3. $m\angle E + m\angle F = 90$; Definition of complementary angles   5. $\angle 1 \cong \angle 3$; Transitive Property

Page 52   Written Exercises   (In Exercises 1-6, answers may vary.)   1. $m\angle 1 + m\angle 2 = 180$; Definition of
supplementary angles   3. $\overline{PR} \cong \overline{MA}$; Congruent segments are segments whose measures are equal.   5. $\angle A$ and
$\angle R$ are supplementary angles; Definition of supplementary angles   7. 1. Given   2. Angle Bisector Theorem

9. 2. Definition of linear pair   3. Linear Pair Postulate   11. 1. Given   2. Addition Property   3. Definition of complementary angles   13. 1. Given   2. Midpoint Theorem   3. Given   4. Substitution Property 15. 2. Addition Property   3. Given   4. Substitution Property   17. 1. Given   2. If two intersecting lines form congruent adjacent angles, then the lines are perpendicular.   19. Statements: 1. AB = CD   4. AC = BD Reasons: 2. Definition of betweenness of points   3. Substitution Property   4. Addition Property 21. Statements: 3. AC − CB = 4CB   4. AC = 5CB   5. $\frac{1}{5}$AC = CB   Reasons: 1. Example, p. 51 2. Given   4. Add. Prop. for Eq.   5. Multiplication Property   23. Statements: 3. AB + BD = AC + CD   4. AB = CD   Reasons: 1. Given   2. Definition of betweenness of points   3. Substitution Property   4. Addition Property   25. 1. ∠M and ∠V are right angles. (Given)   2. m∠M = 90; m∠V = 90 (Def. of right angles)   3. m∠M = m∠V (Substitution Prop.)   4. ∠M ≅ ∠V (Def. of congruent angles)

Page 60   Classroom Exercises   1. Theorem 2-6   3. Theorem 2-5   5. 1. Def. of linear pair   2. If two angles form a linear pair, then they are supplementary   3. Given   4. Th. 2-4

Page 61   Written Exercises   1. 1. Given   2. Def. of complementary angles   3. Substitution Prop. 4. Addition Prop.   5. Angles that have the same measure are congruent.   3. 1. Given   2. Def. of linear pair 3. If two angles form a linear pair, then they are supplementary.   4. Th. 2-4   5. 1. Given   2. Vertical Angle Th.   3. Transitive Prop.   7. Statements: 1. ∠1 ≅ ∠2   2. 3   3. ∠1 ≅ ∠3   Reasons: 2. Vertical Angle Th. 3. Substitution Prop.   9. Statements: 1. ∠1 and ∠2 are supplementary.   2. 1; 2   6. ∠3 and ∠4 are sup- plementary.   Reasons: 2. Def. of supplementary ∠s   3. Vertical Angle Th.   4. Def. of ≈ ∠s   5. Subst. Prop. 6. Def. of supplementary ∠s   11. 1. ∠1 ≅ ∠8 (Given)   2. ∠5 ≅ ∠8 (Vertical Angle Th.)   3. ∠1 ≅ ∠5 ((1), (2). Substitution Prop.)   13. 1. ∠2 ≅ ∠3; ∠5 ≅ ∠8 (Vertical Angle Th.)   2. m∠2 = m∠3; m∠5 = m∠8 ((1). Def. of congruent angles)   3. ∠2 and ∠5 are supplementary. (Given)   4. m∠2 + m∠5 = 180 ((3). Def. of supple- mentary angles)   5. m∠3 + m∠8 = 180   ((2), (4). Substitution Prop.)   6. ∠3 and ∠8 are supplementary. ((5). Def. of supplementary angles)   15. 1. ∠1 and ∠2 are complementary; ∠3 and ∠4 are complementary. (Given)   2. m∠1 + m∠2 = 90; m∠3 + m∠4 = 90 ((1). Def. of complementary angles)   3. m∠1 + m∠2 = m∠3 + m∠4   ((2). Substitution Prop.)   4. ∠1 ≅ ∠4 (Given)   5. m∠1 = m∠4 ((4). Def. of congruent angles) 6. m∠1 + m∠2 = m∠3 + m∠1   ((3), (5). Substitution Prop.)   7. m∠2 = m∠3   ((6). Addition Prop.) 8. ∠2 ≅ ∠3   ((7). Def. of congruent angles)   17. 1. ∠ABC is a right angle. (Given)   2. m∠ABC = 90 ((1). Def. of right angle)   3. m∠1 + m∠2 = m∠ABC (Def. of betweenness of rays)   4. m∠1 + m∠2 = 90 ((2), (3). Substitution Prop.)   5. ∠1 ≅ ∠C; ∠2 ≅ ∠A (Given)   6. m∠1 = m∠C; m∠2 = m∠A   ((5). Def. of congruent angles)   7. m∠C + m∠A = 90   ((4), (6). Substitution Prop.)   8. ∠A and ∠C are complementary. ((7). Def. of complementary angles)   19. 1. ∠1 and ∠2 are vertical angles.   (Def. of vertical angles) 2. ∠1 ≅ ∠2 ((1). Vertical Angle Th.)   3. m∠1 = m∠2 ((2). Def. of congruent angles)   4. m∠B = m∠D; m∠1 = 2 m∠B (Given)   5. m∠2 = 2 m∠D ((3), (4). Substitution Prop.)   21. 1. △ABC is isosceles; △ABD is isosceles. (Given)   2. BA = BC; BA = BD ((1). Def. of isosceles triangle)   3. BC = BD ((2). Substitution Prop.)   4. △BCD is isosceles. ((3). Def. of isosceles triangle)   23. 1. ∠1 and ∠4 are supplementary. (Given)   2. m∠1 + m∠4 = 180   ((1). Def. of supplementary angles)   3. ∠1 and ∠2 are a linear pair; ∠3 and ∠4 are a linear pair. (Def. of linear pair)   4. m∠1 + m∠2 = 180; m∠3 + m∠4 = 180 ((3). Linear Pair Post.) 5. m∠1 + m∠2 + m∠3 + m∠4 = 360 ((4). Addition Prop.)   6. m∠2 + m∠3 = 180 ((2), (5). Addition Prop.) 7. ∠2 and ∠3 are supplementary. ((6). Def. of supplementary angles)

Page 64   Review   1. Symmetric Prop.   2. Multiplication Prop.   3. Substitution Prop.   4. Addition Prop.   5. 2. Distributive Prop.   3. Addition Prop.   4. Addition Prop.   5. Multiplication Prop. 6. 2. Distributive Prop.   3. Addition Prop.   4. Multiplication Prop.   7. a. A triangle is equilateral; The measure of each angle is 60.   b. Given: Equilateral triangle ABC   Prove: m∠A = m∠B = m∠C = 60 8. a. Three points are noncollinear; The three points determine one plane.   b. Given: Points A, B, and C are noncollinear   Prove: Points A, B, and C determine one plane.   9. a. Two lines are perpendicular; The lines form right angles.   b. Given: k ⊥ m   Prove: Angles 1, 2, 3, and 4 are right angles.   10. 1. Given   2. If two

lines are perpendicular, they intersect to form right angles 3. Def. of right angle **11.** Reasons: 1. Given
2. Def. of right angle 3. Substitution Prop. 4. Def. of congruent angles **12.** Statements: 3. linear pair
4 supplementary 7. supplementary Reasons: 2. They have equal measures. 3. Def. of linear pair
4. They are supplementary. 5. Def. of supplementary angles 6. Substitution Prop. 7. Def. of supplementary
angles

Page 68 Classroom Exercises 1. T 3. F 5. F 7. Two angles are complementary if and only if the sum
of their measures is 90; the sum of the measures of two angles is 90 if and only if they are complementary.

Page 68 Written Exercises 1. Th. 2-10 3. Th. 2-14 5. Th. 2-14 7. Angles CDA and CDB are congruent
and adjacent; Th. 2-13. Segments AB and CD form right angles CDA and CDB; Cor. 2-11. 9. Angles KQF,
FQG, and GQH are right angles; Th. 2-10. 11. If two angles are supplementary, then they form a linear pair.
13. If two angles are congruent, then they are complements of congruent angles. 15. If two angles are
congruent, then they are vertical angles. **17.** 1. $\angle 1$ and $\angle 2$ are a linear pair. (Given) 2. $\angle 1$ and $\angle 2$ are
supplementary. ((1). Linear Pair Post.) 3. $m\angle 1 + m\angle 2 = 180$ ((2). Def. of supplementary angles)
4. $\angle 1$ is a right angle. (Given) 5. $m\angle 1 = 90$ ((4). Def. of right angle) 6. $90 + m\angle 2 = 180$ ((3), (5).
Substitution Prop.) 7. $m\angle 2 = 90$ ((6). Addition Prop.) 8. $\angle 2$ is a right angle. ((7). Def. of right angle)
19. Given: Lines k and t intersect at E; Angles 1 and 2 are adjacent; $\angle 1 \cong \angle 2$ Prove: $k \perp t$
1. Lines k and t intersect at E; Angles 1 and 2 are adjacent; $\angle 1 \cong \angle 2$ (Given) 2. $m\angle 1 = m\angle 2$ ((1). Def. of
congruent angles) 3. $k \perp t$ ((2). Th. 1-8) **21.** Given: Lines k and m intersect forming $\angle 1, \angle 2, \angle 3$, and $\angle 4$.
Prove: Four pairs of supplementary angles are formed. 1. Line k and m intersect forming $\angle 1, \angle 2, \angle 3$, and $\angle 4$.
(Given) 2. $\angle 1$ and $\angle 2, \angle 2$ and $\angle 3, \angle 3$ and $\angle 4, \angle 4$ and $\angle 1$ form linear pairs. ((1). Def. of linear pair)
3. $\angle 1$ and $\angle 2, \angle 2$ and $\angle 3, \angle 3$ and $\angle 4, \angle 4$ and $\angle 1$ are supplementary. ((2). Linear Pair Post.)

Page 71 Geometry Review Capsule for Section 2-5 1. Yes 2. Yes 3. Yes 4. No

Page 72 Classroom Exercises 1. pentagon 3. $\angle D$ (or $\angle B$) 5. quadrilateral

Page 73 Written Exercises 1. Segments AB and DC 3. Segments HB, HC, HD, HE, and HF 5. Angles H
and A; angles B and C 7. T 9. F 11. T 13. T 15. Altitude 17. Altitude 19. $\overline{DE}$ is an
altitude. 21. Altitude: $\overline{EC}$; Median: $\overline{EC}$; Angle bisector: ray CE 23. Altitudes: segments AE and EB
25. 43.0 m 27. 22 29. $16y + 3$ 31. 47 cm, 48 cm, 49 cm 33. 47 35. 5 37. 20
39. 1. $\overleftrightarrow{AB} \perp \overleftrightarrow{XY}$ (Given) 2. $\angle AXY \cong \angle BXY$ ((1). Th. 2-13) 3. $m\angle AXY = m\angle BXY$ ((2). Def. of
congruent angles) 4. $m\angle AXY = m\angle 1 + m\angle 2; m\angle BXY = m\angle 3 + m\angle 4$ (Def. of betweenness of rays)
5. $m\angle 1 + m\angle 2 = m\angle 3 + m\angle 4$ ((3), (4). Substitution Prop.) 6. $\angle 1 \cong \angle 4$ (Given) 7. $m\angle 1 = m\angle 4$
((6). Def. of congruent angles) 8. $m\angle 1 + m\angle 2 = m\angle 3 + m\angle 1$ ((5), (7). Substitution Prop.) 9. $m\angle 2 = m\angle 3$
((8). Addition Prop.) 10. Ray XY bisects $\angle WXZ$. ((9). Def. of angle bisector)

Page 75 Applications 1. length: 9 m; width: 5 m 3. 50 ft 5. 3 7. 10 9. For Ex. 5-8, draw an
equilateral triangle, a square, and a regular pentagon and hexagon. Draw lines to connect all the vertices.

Page 77 Classroom Exercises 1. deductive 3. deductive

Page 77 Written Exercises 1. 180 3. acute 5. The conclusion is not always correct. 7. 180 9. 180
11. 3025 13. 7225 15. 2, 4, 8, 16, 32 17. inductive 19. a. 16, 25 b. n^2 21. a. 15, 24
b. $n^2 - 1$ 23. a. 63, 124 b. $n^3 - 1$ 25. prime number

Page 79 Applications 1. inductive 3. deductive

Page 80 Review 1. Th. 2-9 2. Cor. 2-12 3. Th. 2-13 4. ∠BDC is a right angle; Th. 2-9 5. ∠2, ∠3, and ∠4 are right angles; Th. 2-10 6. F; E is not the midpoint of $\overline{AC}$. 7. T; $\overline{BE} \perp \overline{AC}$ (Given) 8. T; m∠CBD and m∠DBE are both 20. 9. F; $\overline{BD}$ is not perpendicular to $\overline{AC}$. 10. 16 11. inductive 12. deductive 13. inductive

Page 81 Consumer Applications 1. b 3. c 5. a 7. b 9. c

Page 84 Chapter Objectives and Review 1. Multiplication Prop. 3. Substitution and Addition Prop. 5. Distributive Prop. 7. 2. Distributive Prop. 3. Addition Prop. 4. Multiplication Prop. 9. a. Two angles are complements of the same angle; The two angles are congruent. b. Given: ∠1 and ∠2 are complementary. ∠3 and ∠2 are complementary. Prove: ∠1 ≅ ∠3 11. △ABC is an isosceles triangle; Def. of isosceles triangle 13. $\overleftrightarrow{AC} \perp \overrightarrow{BD}$; Th. 2-14 15. 1. Given 2. Given 3. (2). Def. of linear pair 4. (1), (3). Th. 2-14 17. Statements: 2. 90; m∠4; 90 7. m∠1 = m∠4 Reasons: 1. Given 2. Def. of complementary angles 3. Substitution Prop. 4. Vertical Angle Th. 5. Def. of congruent angles 6. Substitution Prop. 8. Def. of congruent angles 19. 1. Lines p, q, and r intersect at E. (Given) 2. ∠GEP and ∠1 are vertical angles; ∠GEN and ∠2 are vertical angles. ((1). Def. of vertical angles) 3. ∠GEP ≅ ∠1; ∠GEN ≅ ∠2 ((2). Vertical Angle Th.) 4. ∠2 ≅ ∠1 (Given) 5. ∠GEP ≅ ∠GEN ((3), (4). Substitution Prop.) 6. m∠GEP = m∠GEN ((5). Def. of congruent angles) 7. Ray EG bisects ∠PEN. ((6). Def. of angle bisector) 21. ∠ADC and ∠BDC are right angles, Def. of perpendicular lines; ∠1 and ∠2 are complementary and ∠3 and ∠4 are complementary, Def. of complementary angles; ∠1 ≅ ∠4, Th. 2-7; m∠2 = m∠3, Def. of congruent angles 23. $\overline{TS}$ (or $\overline{RQ}$) 25. diagonal 27. EDC 29. $12\frac{1}{2}$ 31. m∠1 = m∠A 33. 280 m

Page 87 Chapter Test 1. 1. Given 2. Add. Prop. 3. Add. Prop. 4. Mult. Prop. 3. Given: Two lines are perpendicular Prove: The lines form congruent adjacent angles 5. ∠ABD is a right angle; Def. of complementary angles, Def. of right angle 7. 1. ∠1 ≅ ∠3; ∠2 ≅ ∠3 (Given) 2. ∠1 ≅ ∠2 ((1). Substitution Prop.) 3. a ⊥ b ((2). Th. 2-14) 9. pentagon 11. consecutive (or adjacent) 13. inductive 15. deductive

CHAPTER 3 CONGRUENT TRIANGLES

Page 91 Classroom Exercises 1. ∠A ⟷ ∠D, ∠B ⟷ ∠E, ∠C ⟷ ∠F, $\overline{AB}$ ⟷ $\overline{DE}$, $\overline{BC}$ ⟷ $\overline{EF}$, $\overline{AC}$ ⟷ $\overline{DF}$ 3. ∠J 5. K 7. not a congruence 9. S, G 11. T, S, K

Page 92 Written Exercises 1. CB; D 3. D 5. E 7. Segment FE 9. ∠G ≅ ∠J, ∠H ≅ ∠K, ∠R ≅ ∠P, $\overline{GH}$ ≅ $\overline{JK}$, $\overline{HR}$ ≅ $\overline{KP}$, $\overline{GR}$ ≅ $\overline{JP}$ 11. No 13. Yes 15. Yes 17. Yes 19. ZSX 21. SXZ 23. SZX 25. Segment ZS 27. Every line segment is congruent to itself, since its measure equals itself. 29. Every triangle is congruent to itself, since corresponding parts are congruent. 31. ∠B ≅ ∠D, ∠CAB ≅ ∠ACD, ∠ACB ≅ ∠CAD, $\overline{AB}$ ≅ $\overline{CD}$, $\overline{BC}$ ≅ $\overline{DA}$, $\overline{AC}$ ≅ $\overline{CA}$ 33. △ABC ≅ △ABD; $\overline{AD}$ ⟷ $\overline{AC}$, $\overline{BD}$ ⟷ $\overline{BC}$, $\overline{AB}$ ⟷ $\overline{AB}$ 35. FEH 37. Segment FH 39. Segment FE

Page 93 Geometry Review Capsule for Section 3-2 1. F; A line extends without end in two opposite directions. 2. T; A line segment consists of two endpoints and all the points between them. 3. T; The vertex of an angle is the common point of its two sides. 4. F; In a scalene triangle, no two sides are equal in length. 5. F; A line extends in two opposite directions without end. 6. T; Points that are on the same line are collinear. 7. F; Every plane contains at least three distinct, noncollinear points. 8. T; If two distinct lines (or rays) intersect, then their intersection is a point.

Page 96 Classroom Exercises 1. Not congruent 3. △RST ≅ △VWU 5. △HFM ≅ △RMF 7. Yes 9. Yes 11. No 13. Yes

Page 97 Written Exercises 1.-3. Mark any two sides and the included angle. 5. $\triangle$QSP $\cong$ $\triangle$RSP 7. Not congruent 9. Not congruent 11. The congruent angle is not the included angle. 13. Yes 15. 1. Given 2. Given 3. Def. of midpoint of a segment 4. SAS Post. **17.** 1. $\overline{AB} \cong \overline{CD}$; $\angle ABD \cong \angle CDB$ (Given) 2. $\overline{BD} \cong \overline{BD}$ (Identity) 3. $\triangle ABD \cong \triangle CDB$ ((1), (2). SAS Post.) 4. $\overline{AD} \cong \overline{CB}$ ((3). CPCTC) **19.** Add the following step. 5. $\overline{BA} \cong \overline{ED}$ ((4). CPCTC) **21.** 1. S is the midpoint of $\overline{XZ}$; T is the midpoint of $\overline{YZ}$. (Given) 2. SZ = $\frac{1}{2}$XZ; TZ = $\frac{1}{2}$YZ ((1). The Midpoint Th.) 3. $\triangle$XYZ is isosceles. (Given) 4. XZ = YZ ((3). Def. of isosceles triangles 5. TZ = $\frac{1}{2}$XZ ((2), (4). Substitution Prop.) 6. SZ = TZ ((2), (5). Substitution Prop.) 7. $\overline{XZ} \cong \overline{YZ}$; $\overline{SZ} \cong \overline{TZ}$ ((4), (6). Def. of congruent segments) 8. $\angle Z \cong \angle Z$ (Identity) 9. $\triangle$YSZ $\cong$ $\triangle$XTZ ((7), (8). SAS Post.) 10. $\angle$YSZ $\cong$ $\angle$XTZ ((9). CPCTC)

Page 99 Geometry Review Capsule for Section 3-3 1. EDC 2. CAB 3. $\angle$C 4. $\overline{BC}$ 5. $\angle$B 6. $\overline{CD}$ 7. $\angle$A, or $\angle$BAC 8. $\overline{AC}$

Page 102 Classroom Exercises 1. 10, 9, 4 3. SSS 5. ASA

Page 102 Written Exercises 1.-3. Mark any two angles and the included side. 5. $\overline{AB}$ 7. Segment AD 9. $\overline{MT}$; $\overline{TQ}$ 11. $\angle 7$ 13. $\overline{MO}$ 15. $\overline{CD}$; $\overline{DB}$ 17. $\overline{CE}$ 19. $\angle$WXZ; $\angle 2$ 21. $\overline{WX}$ 23. SAS 25. SSS 27. SAS 29. c 31. Yes **33.** 1. $\angle 1 \cong \angle 2$; $\angle 3 \cong \angle 4$ (Given) 2. $\overline{CD} \cong \overline{CD}$ (Identity) 3. $\triangle$ADC $\cong \triangle$BDC ((1), (2). ASA Post.) **35.** 1. $\angle A \cong \angle B$; $\overline{AD} \cong \overline{BD}$; $\angle 3 \cong \angle 4$ (Given) 2. $\triangle$CDA $\cong \triangle$CDB ((1). ASA Post.) 3. $\angle 1 \cong \angle 2$ ((2). CPCTC) **37.** 1. $\angle 1 \cong \angle 2$; $\angle 3 \cong \angle 4$ (Given) 2. $\overline{RO} \cong \overline{RO}$ (Identity) 3. $\triangle$ROM $\cong \triangle$ORP ((1), (2). ASA Post.) 4. $\overline{PR} \cong \overline{MO}$ ((3). CPCTC) **39.** 1. $\overline{RM} \cong \overline{OP}$; $\angle 3 \cong \angle 4$ (Given) 2. $\overline{RO} \cong \overline{RO}$ (Identity) 3. $\triangle$ROM $\cong \triangle$ORP ((1), (2). SAS Post.) 4. $\angle 1 \cong \angle 2$ ((3). CPCTC) **41.** 1. $\overline{MP}$ and $\overline{JQ}$ intersect at 0. (Given) 2. Angle 2 is a right angle. (Given) 3. $\overline{MP} \perp \overline{JQ}$ ((1), (2). Def. of perpendicular lines) 4. $\angle 2 \cong \angle 1$ ((3). Th. 2-13) 5. $\angle 1 \cong \angle J$ (Given) 6. $\angle 2 \cong \angle J$ ((4), (5). Transitive Prop.) 7. $\angle M \cong \angle K$ (Given) 8. $\overline{OM} \cong \overline{JK}$ (Given) 9. $\triangle$MOQ $\cong \triangle$KJL ((6), (7), (8). ASA Post.) 10. $\angle Q \cong \angle 3$ ((9). CPCTC) **43.** 1. $\overline{AB} \cong \overline{CD}$; $\angle ABC \cong \angle CDB$; $\overline{BC} \cong \overline{DB}$ (Given) 2. $\therefore \triangle$CBA $\cong \triangle$BDC ((1). SAS Post.) **45.** 1. $\angle 3 \cong \angle 4$ (Given) 2. $\angle 3$ and $\angle DGC$ form a linear pair; $\angle 4$ and $\angle AHB$ form a linear pair. (Def. of linear pair) 3. $\angle 3$ and $\angle DGC$ are supplementary; $\angle 4$ and $\angle AHB$ are supplementary. ((2). Linear Pair Post.) 4. $\angle DGC \cong \angle AHB$ ((1), (3). Th. 2-5) 5. $\overline{AG} \cong \overline{HC}$ (Given) 6. AG = HC ((5). Def. of congruent angles) 7. AG = AH + HG; HC = GC + HG (Def. of betweenness of points) 8. AH + HG = GC + HG ((6), (7). Substitution Prop.) 9. AH = GC ((8). Addition Prop.) 10. $\overline{AH} \cong \overline{GC}$ ((9). Def. of congruent segments) 11. $\angle 1 \cong \angle 2$ (Given) 12. $\triangle$AHB $\cong \triangle$DGC ((4), (10), (11). ASA Post.) 13. $\overline{DC} \cong \overline{BA}$ ((12). CPCTC) **47.** 1. $\overline{AF} \cong \overline{FH}$; $\overline{MF} \cong \overline{FB}$ (Given) 2. $\angle AFB \cong \angle MFH$ (Vertical Angle Th.) 3. $\triangle$AFB $\cong \triangle$MFH ((1), (2). SAS Post.) 4. $\overline{AB} \cong \overline{MH}$, $\angle A \cong \angle M$ ((3). CPCTC) 5. MR = MF + FB + BR; AT = AF + FH + HT (Def. of betweenness of points) 6. $\overline{MF} \cong \overline{FB} \cong \overline{BR}$; $\overline{AF} \cong \overline{FH} \cong \overline{HT}$ (Given) 7. MF = FB = BR; AF = FH = HT ((6). Def. of congruent segments) 8. MR = FB + FB + FB; AT = AF + AF + AF ((5), (7). Substitution Prop.) 9. AF = FB (Given) 10. MR = AF + AF + AF ((8), (9). Substitution Prop.) 11. MR = AT ((8), (10). Substitution Prop.) 12. $\overline{MR} \cong \overline{AT}$ ((11). Def. of congruent segments) 13. $\triangle$ABT $\cong \triangle$MHR ((4), (12). SAS Post.)

Page 106 Applications 1. For stability, all four legs have the same length, so $\overline{ZA} \cong \overline{TS}$ and $\overline{ZV} \cong \overline{TR}$. By measurement, you can show that the angles between each pair of legs are congruent, so $\angle AZV \cong \angle STR$. Thus, $\triangle$ZAV $\cong \triangle$TSR by the SAS Post. 3. BC = 1.3 km 5. 11.3 km

Page 107 Review 1. RJK 2. QRP 3. $\overline{JR}$ 4. $\angle Q$ 5. $\overline{PQ}$ 6. Yes 7. No 8. No 9. Statements: 2. $\overline{PR} \cong \overline{PR}$ 4. $\overline{BR} \cong \overline{PM}$ Reasons: 1. Given 3. SAS Post. 4. CPCTC 10. $\overline{LO}$ 11. $\overline{KQ}$ 12. $\overline{MO}$ 13. $\overline{MP}$ 14. $\angle$QML 15. $\overline{KM}$

Page 107 Geometry Review Capsule for Section 3-4 1. isosceles 2. vertex 3. scalene 4. legs 5. equilateral

Page 109 Classroom Exercises 1. Cor. 3-2 3. Cor. 3-4 5. The three sides of a triangle are congruent if an only if the three angles are congruent. 7. EF = 4, Th. 3-3

Page 110 Written Exercises 1. $\overline{CA} \cong \overline{CB}$ is given; ∴ $\angle 2 \cong \angle 1$ by Th. 3-1; $\angle 1$ and $\angle 3$, $\angle 2$ and $\angle 4$ are linear pairs; ∴ $\angle 1$ and $\angle 3$ and $\angle 2$ and $\angle 4$ are supplementary; ∴ $\angle 3 \cong \angle 4$ by Th. 2-5 3. $\angle 2 \cong \angle 4$ is given; ∴ $\overline{BE} \cong \overline{CE}$ by Th. 3-3 and △BEC is isosceles by definition 5. Statements: 6. Complementary; complementary 8. $\angle 2 \cong \angle 4$ Reasons: 1. Given 2. Def. of perpendicular lines 3. Def. of right angles 4. Def. of betweenness of rays 5. Substitution Prop. 6. Def. of complementary angles 7. Given 8. Isosceles Triangle Th. 9. Th. 2-7 7. Statements: 3. PR = PQ; PT = PS 7. $\overline{SQ} \cong \overline{TR}$ Reasons: 1. Given 2. Th. 3-3 3. Def. of congruent segments 4. Def. of betweenness of points 5. Substitution Prop. 6. Addition Prop. 7. Def. of congruent segments 9. 1. $\angle 1 \cong \angle 2$ (Given) 2. $\overline{PT} \cong \overline{PS}$ ((1). Th. 3-3) 3. PT = PS ((2). Def. of congruent segments) 4. $\overline{SQ} \cong \overline{TR}$ (Given) 5. SQ = TR ((4). Def. of congruent segments) 6. PQ = PS + SQ; PR = PT + TR (Def. of betweenness of points) 7. PQ = PR ((3), (5), (6). Substitution Prop.) 8. $\overline{PQ} \cong \overline{PR}$ ((7). Def. of congruent segments) 9. $\angle Q \cong \angle R$ ((8). Th. 3-1) 11. 1. $\overline{PS} \cong \overline{SQ}$; $\overline{PT} \cong \overline{TR}$; $\overline{PQ} \cong \overline{PR}$ (Given) 2. PS = SQ; PT = TR; PQ = PR ((1). Def. of congruent segments) 3. PQ = PS + SQ; PR = PT + TR (Def. of betweenness of points) 4. PQ = 2PS; PR = 2PT ((2), (3). Substitution Prop.) 5. 2PT = 2PS ((2), (4). Substitution Prop.) 6. PT = PS ((5). Multiplication Prop.) 7. $\overline{PT} \cong \overline{PS}$ ((6). Def. of congruent segments) 8. $\angle 1 \cong \angle 2$ ((7). Th. 3-1 13. 1. $\angle A \cong \angle B$ (Given) 2. $\overline{BC} \cong \overline{AC}$ ((1). Th. 3-3) 3. $\angle A \cong \angle C$ (Given) 4. $\overline{BC} \cong \overline{AB}$ ((3). Th. 3-3) 5. $\overline{AC} \cong \overline{BC} \cong \overline{AB}$ ((2), (4). Substitution Prop.) 15. 1. $\angle 1 \cong \angle 2$ (Given) 2. $\overline{EA} \cong \overline{AQ}$ ((1). Th. 3-3) 3. $\angle 3 \cong \angle 4$ (Given) 4. A is the midpoint of $\overline{LU}$. (Given) 5. $\overline{AL} \cong \overline{AU}$ ((4). Def. of midpoint) 6. △EAL ≅ △QUA ((2), (3), (5). SAS Post.) 7. $\overline{EL} \cong \overline{QU}$ ((6). CPCTC) 17. 1. $\angle L \cong \angle U$; $\angle 3 \cong \angle 4$ (Given) 2. A is the midpoint of $\overline{LU}$. (Given) 3. $\overline{AL} \cong \overline{AU}$ ((2). Def. of midpoint) 4. △AEL ≅ △AQU ((1), (3). ASA Post.) 5. $\overline{AE} \cong \overline{AQ}$ ((4). CPCTC) 6. $\angle 1 \cong \angle 2$ ((5). Isosceles Triangle Th.) 19. No two sides of triangle ABC are congruent; Th. 3-3 21. The triangle is not equilateral; Th. 3-4 23. 1. △TQW ≅ △TQV (Given) 2. $\overline{QW} \cong \overline{QV}$ ((1). CPCTC) 3. △QVW is isosceles. ((2). Def. of isosceles triangle) 25. 1. △TQW ≅ △TQV (Given) 2. $\overline{TW} \cong \overline{TV}$ ((1). CPCTC) 3. △TVW is isosceles. ((2). Def. of isosceles triangle) 27. 1. $\overline{VS} \cong \overline{VO}$; $\overline{VE} \cong \overline{VL}$ (Given) 2. $\angle LVO \cong \angle EVS$ (Vertical Angle Th.) 3. △LVO ≅ △EVS ((1), (2). SAS Post.) 4. $\angle 2 \cong \angle 5$ ((3). CPCTC) 5. $\angle 3 \cong \angle 4$ ((1). Th. 3-1) 6. m$\angle 2$ = m$\angle 5$; m$\angle 3$ = m$\angle 4$ ((4), (5). Def. of congruent angles) 7. m$\angle 2$ + m$\angle 3$ = m$\angle 5$ + m$\angle 4$ ((6). Addition Prop.) 8. m$\angle 2$ + m$\angle 3$ = m$\angle ESO$; m$\angle 5$ + m$\angle 4$ = m$\angle LOS$ (Def. of betweenness of rays) 9. m$\angle ESO$ = m$\angle LOS$ ((7), (8). Substitution Prop.) 10. $\angle ESO \cong \angle LOS$ ((9). Def. of congruent angles) 11. $\angle 1$ and $\angle ESO$ form a linear pair; $\angle 6$ and $\angle LOS$ form a linear pair. (Def. of linear pair) 12. $\angle 1$ and $\angle ESO$ are supplementary; $\angle 6$ and $\angle LOS$ are supplementary. ((11). Linear Pair Post.) 13. $\angle 1 \cong \angle 6$ ((10), (12). Th. 2-5 29. 1. Let $\overrightarrow{AD}$ and $\overrightarrow{BE}$ bisect $\angle A$ and $\angle B$ respectively. (Th. 1-6) 2. $\angle A \cong \angle B$ (Given) 3. $\angle 2 \cong \angle 4$ ((1), (2). Def. of angle bisector) 4. $\overline{AB} \cong \overline{AB}$ (Identity) 5. △ABD ≅ △ABE ((2), (3), (4). ASA Post.) 6. $\angle 5 \cong \angle 7$ ((5). CPCTC) 7. $\angle 5$ and $\angle 6$ form a linear pair; $\angle 7$ and $\angle 8$ form a linear pair. (Def. of linear pair) 8. $\angle 5$ and $\angle 6$ are supplementary; $\angle 7$ and $\angle 8$ are supplementary. ((7). Linear Pair Post.) 9. $\angle 6 \cong \angle 8$ ((6), (8). Th. 2-5 10. $\angle 1 \cong \angle 3$ ((1), (2). Def. of angle bisector) 11. $\overline{AD} \cong \overline{BE}$ ((5). CPCTC) 12. △ADC ≅ △BEC ((9), (10), (11). ASA Post.) 13. $\overline{CA} \cong \overline{CB}$ ((12). CPCTC)

Page 113 Geometry Review Capsule for Section 3-5 1. Yes 2. No 3. Yes 4. No 5. Yes 6. Yes 7. Yes 8. No 9. No 10. Yes

Page 116 Classroom Exercises 1. No 3. Yes 5. No 7. Yes 9. No 11. Yes

Page 116 Written Exercises 1. DG = 8 cm, DF = 8 cm, DE = EF = 4 cm 3. m∠1 = 24, m∠4 = 72, m∠HQK = 96, m∠HJK = 96, QM = 9 cm; MJ = 9 cm 5. Triangles PQR, QRS, PSR, PSQ 7. $\overline{AB} \perp \overline{CD}$ (Given); ∠ADC ≅ ∠BDC (Th. 2-13); $\overline{CD} \cong \overline{CD}$ (Identity); $\overline{AD} \cong \overline{DB}$ (Def. of segment bisector); △ADC ≅ △BDC (SAS Post.); $\overline{AC} \cong \overline{CB}$ (CPCTC); △ABC is isosceles. (Def. of isosceles triangle) 9. 1. $\overline{AC} \cong \overline{CB}$ (Given) 2. $\overline{CD} \cong \overline{CD}$ (Identity) 3. Ray CD bisects angle C. (Given) 4. m∠ACD = m∠BCD ((3). Def. of angle bisector) 5. ∠ACD ≅ ∠BCD ((4). Def. of congruent angles) 6. △ACD ≅ △BCD ((1), (2), (5). SAS Post.) 7. ∠CDB ≅ ∠CDA ((6). CPCTC) 8. Angles CDB and CDA are adjacent. (Def. of adjacent angles) 9. $\overline{CD} \perp \overline{AB}$ ((7), (8). Th. 2-14) 10. $\overline{AD} \cong \overline{DB}$ ((6). CPCTC) 11. AD = DB ((10). Def. of congruent segments) 12. $\overline{CD}$ is the perpendicular bisector of $\overline{AB}$. ((9), (11). Def. of perpendicular bisector) 11 Statements: 1. △SQZ and △SEZ are isosceles 2. $\overline{SQ} \cong \overline{QZ}$; $\overline{SE} \cong \overline{EZ}$ Reasons: 3. Cor. 3-9 13. Statements: 1. Q is equidistant from X and Y 7. $\overline{QP} \cong \overline{QP}$ 9. ∠YPQ Reasons: 2. equidistant 3. congruent segments 8. SSS 9. CPCTC 10. perpendicular 11. perpendicular bisector 15. All of the points lie in the plane that is the perpendicular bisector of the segment joining the given points. 17. 1. Segement AC is the perpendicular bisector of segment BD. (Given) 2. AB = AD ((1). Def. of segment bisector) 3. $\overline{AB} \cong \overline{AD}$ ((2). Def. of congruent segments) 4. $\overline{AC} \cong \overline{AC}$ (Identity) 5. ∠BAC ≅ ∠DAC ((1). Th. 2-13) 6. △BAC ≅ △DAC ((3), (4), (5). SAS Post.) 7. ∠B ≅ ∠D ((6). CPCTC) 8. △BCD is isosceles. ((7). Def. of isos. triangle) 19. 1. $\overline{DA} \cong \overline{DC}$; $\overline{BA} \cong \overline{BC}$ (Given) 2. ∠2 ≅ ∠1; ∠ACB ≅ ∠CAB ((1). Th. 3-1) 3. m∠2 = m∠1; m∠ACB = m∠CAB ((2). Def. of congruent angles) 4. m∠DAB = m∠CAB + m∠1; m∠DCB = m∠ACB + m∠2 (Def. of betweenness of rays) 5. m∠DAB = m∠ACB + m∠2 ((3), (4). Substitution Prop.) 6. m∠DAB = m∠DCB ((4), (5). Substitution Prop.) 7. ∠DAB ≅ ∠DCB ((6). Def. of congruent angles) 21. Given: ∠ADE ≅ ∠BED Prove: $\overline{DC} \cong \overline{EC}$ 1. ∠ADE and ∠1 form a linear pair; ∠BED and ∠2 form a linear pair. (Def. of linear pair) 2. ∠ADE and ∠1 are supplementary; ∠BED and ∠2 are supplementary. ((1). Linear Pair Post.) 3. ∠ADE ≅ ∠BED (Given) 4. ∠1 ≅ ∠2 ((2), (3). Th. 2-5) 5. $\overline{DC} \cong \overline{EC}$ ((4). Th. 3-3) 23. 1. $\overline{AB} \cong \overline{DE}$; $\overline{BC} \cong \overline{EF}$; $\overline{AC} \cong \overline{DF}$ (Given) 2. △ABC ≅ △DEF ((1). SSS Post.) 3. ∠A ≅ ∠D ((2). CPCTC) 4. ∠1 ≅ ∠2 (Given) 5. △ACG ≅ △DFH ((1), (3), (4). ASA Post.) 6. $\overline{CG} \cong \overline{FH}$ ((5). CPCTC) 25. 1. $\overline{MS} \cong \overline{RS}$; $\overline{MT} \cong \overline{RT}$ (Given) 2. MS = RS; MT = RT ((1). Def. of congruent segments) 3. S is equidistant from M and R; T is equidistant from M and R. ((2). Def. of equidistant) 4. $\overline{ST}$ is the perpendicular bisector of $\overline{MR}$. ((3). Cor. 3-9) 5. MO = RO ((4). Def. of segment bisector) 6. $\overline{MO} \cong \overline{RO}$ ((5). Def. of congruent segments) 27. Call the points A, B, and C. Segment AB has a plane that is its perpendicular bisector; this is also true of $\overline{AC}$. These two planes intersect in one line.

Page 120 Applications 1. Since it is given that P is directly above M, P lies on the perpendicular bisector of AB. Thus, P is equally distant from A and B, so △APB is isosceles by definition. 3. Since the cables meet at a point equidistant from P and T, the workers should mark off the perpendicular bisector of $\overline{PT}$. The point on the bisector that is 5 meters from the wall is where the cables meet. 5. ASA Postulate 7. ASA Postulate

Page 121 Geometry Review Capsule for Section 3-6 1. Def. of betweenness of points 2. Def. of betweenness of points 3. Addition Prop. 4. Def. of midpoint 5. Def. of betweenness of rays 6. Def. of coplanar points 7. Def. of betweenness of rays 8. Addition Prop.

Page 123 Classroom Exercises 1. $\overline{SP}$ 3. $\overline{TS}$ 5. BCD 7. CDB 9. $\overline{HG}$ 11. F

Page 123 Written Exercises 1. Triangles FGQ and GFH, triangles HJF and QJG, triangles HFQ and QGH; Triangles KNR and KOM, triangles RMN and MRO, triangles ROP and MNP 3. Angle RKN, angle RNK, segment NR; angle MKO, angle KMO, angle MOK, segment MK 5. Segment MN, segment NR, angle MNR, angle NRM, segment NR, segment MN; segment RO, segment OM, angle ROM, angle OMR, segment OM, segment RO 7. 1. $\overline{BC} \cong \overline{CD}$; $\overline{AB} \cong \overline{ED}$ (Given) 2. BC = CD; AB = ED ((1). Def. of congruent segments) 3. BC + AB = CA; CD + ED = CE (Def. of betweenness of points) 4. CD + ED = CA ((2), (3). Substitution Prop.) 5. CA = CE ((3), (4). Substitution Prop.) 6. $\overline{CA} \cong \overline{CE}$ ((5). Def. of congruent segments) 7. ∠C ≅ ∠C (Identity) 8. △ACD ≅ △ECB ((1), (6), (7). SAS Post.) 9. Impossible, unless Q is equidistant from R and S.   **11.** Always possible, since a line can be constructed perpendicular to a given line through a given point not on the line.   **13. 1.** $\overline{XZ} \cong \overline{YZ}$; $\overline{XW} \cong \overline{YU}$ (Given)   **2.** XZ = YZ; XW = YU ((1). Def. of congruent segments)   **3.** XZ = XW + WZ; YZ = YU + UZ (Def. of betweenness of points)   **4.** XW + WZ = YU + UZ ((2), (3). Substitution Prop.)   **5.** YU + WZ = YU + UZ ((2), (4). Substitution Prop.)   **6.** WZ = UZ ((5). Addition Prop.)   **7.** $\overline{WZ} \cong \overline{UZ}$ ((6). Def. of congruent segments)   **8.** $\angle Z \cong \angle Z$ (Identity)   **9.** $\triangle XUZ \cong \triangle YWZ$ ((1), (7), (8). SAS Post.)   **10.** $\therefore \angle 7 \cong \angle 8$ ((9). CPCTC)   **15. 1.** Draw segment XA. (Two points determine a line.)   **2.** $\overline{XY} \cong \overline{XZ}$; $\overline{AY} \cong \overline{AZ}$ (Given)   **3.** $\overline{AX} \cong \overline{AX}$ (Identity)   **4.** $\triangle XAY \cong \triangle XAZ$ ((2), (3). SSS Post.)   **5.** $\angle Y \cong \angle Z$ ((4). CPCTC)   **17. 1.** $\overline{PA} \cong \overline{ST}$ (Given)   **2.** $\overline{PT} \cong \overline{SA}$ ((1). Common Segment Th.)   **3.** $\angle 1 \cong \angle 2$; $\overline{TQ} \cong \overline{AR}$ (Given)   **4.** $\triangle PQT \cong \triangle SRA$ ((2), (3). SAS Post.)   **5.** $\angle Q \cong \angle R$ ((4). CPCTC)   **19. 1.** $\angle UJT \cong \angle STJ$; $\angle SJT \cong \angle UTJ$ (Given)   **2.** $\overline{JT} \cong \overline{JT}$ (Identity)   **3.** $\triangle UJT \cong \triangle STJ$ ((1), (2). ASA Post.)   **4.** $\overline{UJ} \cong \overline{ST}$ ((3). CPCTC)   **21. 1.** $\angle A \cong \angle T$ (Given)   **2.** $\overline{CA} \cong \overline{CT}$ ((1). Th. 3-3)   **3.** $\overline{AO} \cong \overline{TR}$ (Given)   **4.** $\triangle CAO \cong \triangle CTR$ ((1), (2), (3). SAS Post.)   **5.** $\angle 4 \cong \angle 5$ ((4). CPCTC)   **23. 1.** $\overline{AB} \cong \overline{AD}$; $\angle BAE \cong \angle DAE$ (Given)   **2.** $\overline{AE} \cong \overline{AE}$ (Identity)   **3.** $\triangle ABE \cong \triangle ADE$ ((1), (2). SAS Post.)   **4.** $\overline{AC} \cong \overline{AC}$ (Identity)   **5.** $\triangle ABC \cong \triangle ADC$ ((1), (4). SAS Post.)   **6.** $\overline{BE} \cong \overline{DE}$ ((3). CPCTC)   **7.** $\overline{BC} \cong \overline{DC}$ ((5). CPCTC)   **8.** $\overline{EC} \cong \overline{EC}$ (Identity)   **9.** $\triangle EBC \cong \triangle EDC$ ((6), (7), (8). SSS Post.)   **10.** $\angle EBC \cong \angle EDC$ ((9). CPCTC)   **25.** Given: $\triangle ABC \cong \triangle DEF$; $\overline{AG}$ is a median of $\triangle ABC$; $\overline{DH}$ is a median of $\triangle DEF$. Prove: $\overline{AG} \cong \overline{DH}$ **1.** $\triangle ABC \cong \triangle DEF$ (Given)   **2.** $\overline{AC} \cong \overline{DF}$; $\angle C \cong \angle F$ ((1). CPCTC)   **3.** $\overline{BC} \cong \overline{EF}$ ((1). CPCTC)   **4.** BC = EF ((3). Def. of congruent segments)   **5.** AG is a median of $\triangle ABC$; $\overline{DH}$ is a median of $\triangle DEF$. (Given)   **6.** G is the midpoint of $\overline{BC}$; H is the midpoint of $\overline{EF}$ ((5). Def. of median)   **7.** GC = $\frac{1}{2}$ BC; HG = $\frac{1}{2}$ EF ((6). Midpoint Th.)   **8.** GC = $\frac{1}{2}$ EF ((4), (7). Substitution Prop.)   **9.** GC = HF ((7), (8). Substitution Prop.)   **10.** $\overline{GC} \cong \overline{HF}$ ((9). Def. of congruent segments)   **11.** $\triangle ACG \cong \triangle DFH$ ((2), (10). SAS Post.)   **12.** $\overline{AG} \cong \overline{DH}$ ((11). CPCTC)   **27. 1.** $\overline{CA} \cong \overline{CE}$; $\overline{CF}$ bisects $\angle ACE$ (Given)   **2.** $\angle ACF \cong \angle FCE$ ((1). Def. of angle bisector)   **3.** $\overline{CF} \cong \overline{CF}$ (Identity)   **4.** $\triangle ACF \cong \triangle ECF$ ((1), (2), (3). SAS Post.)   **5.** $\angle CAF \cong \angle CEF$ ((4). CPCTC)   **6.** $\angle ACE \cong \angle ACE$ (Identity)   **7.** $\triangle ACD \cong \triangle ECB$ ((1), (5), (6). ASA Post.)   **8.** $\angle 1 \cong \angle 2$ ((7). CPCTC)

Page 126   Review   1. a. if three angles of a triangle are congruent, then the three sides are congruent. **b.** if two angles of a triangle are congruent, then the sides opposite these angles are congruent. **c.** of the Substitution Property.   **2.** T; Cor. 2-12   **3.** T; Linear Pair Post.   **4.** F; Th. 3-8   **5.** F; you cannot add angles, only the measures of angles   **6.** F; Th. 3-6   **7.** T; Th. 3-1   **8.** Yes; Th. 3-1   **9.** Yes; SAS Post.   **10.** No; Def. of betweenness of points   **11.** Yes; CPCTC   **12.** Yes; CPCTC and def. of betweenness of rays   **13.** No; by CPCTC, $\overline{FH} \cong \overline{HR}$, and by def. of congruent segments, FH = HR   **14.** Yes; Addition Prop.   **15.** Yes; Def. of betweenness of points and Substitution Prop.

Page 128   Classroom Exercises   1. $\angle 1 \not\cong \angle 2$ **3.** $m\angle C = m\angle D$ **5.** Angles A and B are not supplementary.   **7.** a, c   **9.** a, b

Page 129   Written Exercises   1. Given: $\angle A \not\cong \angle B$ Prove: $\angle A$ and $\angle B$ are not vertical angles Proof: **a.** vertical **b.** $\cong$ **c.** $\not\cong$ **d.** contradiction **e.** $\angle A$ and $\angle B$ are not vertical angles.   **3.** Given: $m\angle T = 48$; $m\angle B = 32$ Prove: $\angle T$ and $\angle B$ are not complementary. Proof: Assume that $\angle T$ and $\angle B$ are complementary. Then $m\angle T + m\angle B = 90$ by the def. of complementary angles. But, by hypothesis, $m\angle T + m\angle B = 48 + 32 = 80$. It is a contradiction that $m\angle T + m\angle B = 90$ and $m\angle T + m\angle B = 80$. Therefore, the assumption that $\angle A$ and $\angle B$ are complementary is false, and $\angle T$ and $\angle B$ are not complementary.   **5.** Assume that $\angle 1 \cong \angle 3$. Since vertical angles are congruent, $\angle 2 \cong \angle 3$. By the Substitution Prop., $\angle 1 \cong \angle 2$. But by hypothesis, $\angle 1 \not\cong \angle 2$. Therefore, the assumption that $\angle 1 \cong \angle 3$ is false, and angle 1 is not congruent to angle 3.   **7.** Assume that $\angle 2 \cong \angle 4$. Since they are vertical angles, $\angle 1 \cong \angle 2$ and $\angle 4 \cong \angle 3$. Therefore, by the Substitution Prop., $\angle 1 \cong \angle 3$. But, by hypothesis, $\angle 1 \not\cong \angle 3$. Therefore, the assumption that $\angle 2 \cong \angle 4$ is false, and $\angle 2 \not\cong \angle 4$.   **9.** Assume that $\overline{MS} \cong \overline{MH}$. Then triangle MSH is an isosceles triangle by definition, and segment MT, the bisector of the vertex angle, is the perpendicular bisector of the base. But, by hypothesis, segment MT is not a median. Therefore, the assumption that $\overline{MS} \cong \overline{MH}$ is false, and $\overline{MS} \not\cong \overline{MH}$. **11.** Assume that $\overline{ZQ} \cong \overline{ZP}$. Then $\angle Q \cong \angle P$ by Th. 3-1. Since segment GZ is a median, QG = GP or $\overline{QG} \cong \overline{GP}$. Therefore, by the SAS Post., $\triangle QZG \cong \triangle PZG$ and $\angle 1 \cong \angle 2$ by CPCTC. But, by hypothesis, $\angle 1 \not\cong \angle 2$. Therefore, the assumption that $\overline{ZQ} \cong \overline{ZP}$ is false, and $\overline{ZQ} \not\cong \overline{ZP}$. **13.** Assume $\overline{BC}$ and $\overline{KT}$ bisect each other. Then $\overline{BW} \cong \overline{CW}$ and $\overline{KW} \cong \overline{TW}$ by the definition of bisector. By the Vertical Angle Th., $\angle KWB \cong \angle TWC$, and $\triangle KWB \cong \triangle TWC$ by the SAS Post. It follows by CPCTC that $\overline{CT} \cong \overline{BK}$. But, by hypothesis, $\overline{CT} \not\cong \overline{BK}$. Therefore, the assumption that $\overline{BC}$ and $\overline{KT}$ bisect each other is false, and $\overline{BC}$ and $\overline{KT}$ do not bisect each other. **15.** Assume that $\overline{RM} \cong \overline{RT}$. Then, by definition, $\triangle RMT$ is isosceles. It is given that $\overline{RS}$ bisects $\angle MRT$. By Th. 3-5, $\overline{RS}$ is the perpendicular bisector of $\overline{MT}$. But, by hypothesis, $\overline{RS}$ is not perpendicular to $\overline{MT}$. Therefore, the assumption that $\overline{RM} \cong \overline{RT}$ is false, and $\overline{RM} \not\cong \overline{RT}$. **17.** Assume that $\angle X \cong \angle H$. It is given that $\overline{RX} \cong \overline{RH}$, and $\angle R \cong \angle R$ by Identity. $\triangle RMX \cong \triangle RSH$ by the ASA Post., and $\overline{RS} \cong \overline{RM}$ by CPCTC. But, by hypothesis, $\overline{RS} \cong \overline{RM}$. Therefore, the assumption that $\angle X \cong \angle H$ is false, and $\angle X \not\cong \angle H$. **19.** Assume that $\triangle VRC \cong \triangle TSC$. Then $\overline{CR} \cong \overline{CS}$ by CPCTC. By the Isosceles Triangle Th., $\angle CRS \cong \angle CSR$. But, by hypothesis, $\angle CRS \not\cong \angle CSR$. Therefore, the assumption that $\triangle VRC \cong \triangle TSC$ is false, and $\triangle VRC \not\cong \triangle TSC$. **21.** Assume that BX = AW. Since TA = TB, $\angle A \cong \angle B$. $\therefore \triangle TAW \cong \triangle TBX$ by the SAS Post. and TW = TX by CPCTC. But $\overline{TW} \not\cong \overline{TX}$ by hypothesis. Therefore, the original assumption is false, and BX ≠ AW. **23.** Given: $\triangle ABC$; AB ≠ BC; BC ≠ CA; AB ≠ CA; $\overline{BD}$ is a median. Prove: $\overline{BD}$ is not perpendicular to $\overline{AC}$. Proof: Assume $\overline{BD} \perp \overline{AC}$. By Th. 2-13, $\angle BDA \cong \angle BDC$. $\overline{BD} \cong \overline{BD}$ by Identity. $\overline{DA} \cong \overline{DC}$ by the def. of median, and $\triangle BDA \cong \triangle BDC$ by the SAS Post. Then $\overline{AB} \cong \overline{BC}$ by CPCTC, and AB = BC by the def. of congruent segments. But, by hypothesis, AB ≠ BC. $\therefore$ the original assumption is false and $\overline{BD}$ is not perpendicular to $\overline{AC}$. **25.** Given: Line k intersects plane I in point P; plane I does not contain line k. Prove: P is the only point of intersection. Proof: Assume that P is <u>not</u> the only point of intersection. Call the second point of intersection Q. By Postulate 6, if any two distinct points lie in a plane, then the line containing these points lies in the plane. So line k lies in plane I. But, by hypothesis, plane I does not contain line k. $\therefore$ the assumption that P is <u>not</u> the only point of intersection is false, and P <u>is</u> the only point of intersection.

Page 132 Geometry Review Capsule for Section 3-8 Statements: **2.** $\overline{FG} \cong \overline{CP}$ **3.** $\overline{MP} \cong \overline{CP}$ **6.** $\angle G \cong \angle P$ Reasons: **1.** Given **4.** Transitive Prop. **5.** Def. of right triangle **7.** SAS Post.

Page 134 Classroom Exercises **1.** Yes, by the HL Th. **3.** Yes, by the HA Post.

Page 134 Written Exercises **1.** Statements: **6.** $\overline{PS} \cong \overline{RQ}$ Reasons: **1.** Given **2.** Def. of right triangle **3.** Given **4.** Identity **5.** HA Post. **6.** CPCTC **3.** Statements: **2.** right angles **3.** right triangles **7.** FEG **8.** F **9.** $\overline{FA}$ **10.** $\triangle ACF$ is isosceles. Reasons: **1.** Given **2.** Def. of perpendicular lines **3.** Def. of right triangle **4.** Given **5.** Common Segment Th. **6.** Given **7.** HL Th. **8.** CPCTC **9.** Th. 3-3 **10.** Def. of isosceles triangle **5.** **1.** Ray BD bisects angle ABC. (Given) **2.** $m\angle FBG = m\angle EBG$ ((1). Def. of angle bisector) **3.** $\angle FBG \cong \angle EBG$ ((2). Def. of congruent angles) **4.** $\overrightarrow{GF} \perp \overrightarrow{BC}$; $\overrightarrow{GE} \perp \overrightarrow{BA}$ (Given) **5.** Angles GFB and GEB are right angles. ((4). Def. of perpendicular lines) **6.** $\overline{BG} \cong \overline{BG}$ (Identity) **7.** $\triangle BGF \cong \triangle BGE$ ((3), (5), (6). HA Post.) **8.** $\overline{GF} \cong \overline{GE}$ ((7). CPCTC) **9.** GF = GE ((8). Def. of congruent segments) **7.** **1.** Segment AD is the altitude to base BC. (Given) **2.** $\overline{AD} \perp \overline{BC}$ ((1). Def. of altitude) **3.** Angles ADB and ADC are right angles. ((2). Def. of perpendicular lines) **4.** $\overline{AB} \cong \overline{AC}$ (Def. of isosceles triangle) **5.** $\overline{AD} \cong \overline{AD}$ (Identity) **6.** $\triangle ADB \cong \triangle ADC$ ((3), (4), (5). HL Th.) **7.** $\angle 1 \cong \angle 2$ ((6). CPCTC) **9.** **1.** $\angle RTU \cong \angle RUT$ (Given) **2.** $\overline{RT} \cong \overline{RU}$ ((1). Th. 3-3) **3.** Angles S and V are right angles; $\overline{ST} \cong \overline{UV}$ (Given) **4.** $\triangle STR \cong \triangle VUR$ ((2), (3). HL Th.) **5.** $\overline{VR} \cong \overline{SR}$ ((4). CPCTC) **11.** **1.** $\triangle EAD \cong \triangle ECD$ (Proved in Exercise 10.) **2.** $\overline{AE} \cong \overline{EC}$ ((1). CPCTC) **3.** $\overline{BE} \cong \overline{BE}$ (Identity) **4.** $\overline{AB} \cong \overline{BC}$ (Given) **5.** $\triangle BAE \cong \triangle BCE$ ((2), (3), (4). SSS Post.) **13.** **1.** $\overline{XY} \perp \overline{YA}$, $\overline{XY} \perp \overline{YB}$ (Given) **2.** $\angle XYA$ and $\angle XYB$ are right angles. ((1). Def. of perpendicular lines) **3.** $\angle XAB \cong \angle XBA$ (Given) **4.** In $\triangle XAB$, $\overline{XA} \cong \overline{XB}$. ((3). Th. 3-3) **5.** $\overline{XY} \cong \overline{XY}$ (Identity) **6.** $\triangle XYA \cong \triangle XYB$ ((2), (4), (5). HL Th.) **7.** $\overline{YA} \cong \overline{YB}$ ((6). CPCTC) **8.** In $\triangle YAB$, $\angle YAB \cong \angle YBA$. ((7). Th. 3-1)

15. 1. $\overline{PA} \cong \overline{PD}$; $\overline{AT} \cong \overline{DO}$ (Given) 2. $\overline{UP} \perp \overline{AD}$ (Given) 3. $\angle PMA$ and $\angle PMD$ are right angles. ((2). Def. of perpendicular lines) 4. $\overline{PM} \cong \overline{PM}$ (Identity) 5. $\triangle PMA \cong \triangle PMD$ ((1), (4). HL Th.) 6. $\angle APM \cong \angle DPM$ ((5). CPCTC) 7. $\overline{PU} \cong \overline{PU}$ (Identity) 8. PA = PD, AT = DO ((1). Def. of congruent segments) 9. TP = AT + PA; OP = DO + PD (Def. of betweenness of points) 10. TP = DO + PD ((8), (9). Substitution Prop.) 11. TP = OP ((9), (10). Substitution Prop.) 12. $\overline{TP} \cong \overline{OP}$ ((1). Def. of congruent segments) 13. $\triangle PUT \cong \triangle PUO$ ((6), (7), (12). SAS Post.) **17.** 1. $\angle 1 \cong \angle 2$ (Given) 2. $\overline{MQ} \cong \overline{PQ}$ ((1). Th. 3-3) 3. $\angle 5 \cong \angle 6$ (Vertical Angle Th.) 4. $\angle D$ and $\angle E$ are right angles. (Given) 5. $\triangle DQM \cong \triangle EQP$ ((2), (3), (4). HA Post.) 6. $\overline{DQ} \cong \overline{EQ}$ ((5). CPCTC) **19.** 1. $\overline{AB} \perp \overline{BE}$; $\overline{CB} \perp \overline{BD}$ (Given) 2. $\angle ABE$ and $\angle CBD$ are right angles. ((1). Def. of perpendicular lines) 3. $\triangle ABE$ and $\triangle CBD$ are right triangles. ((2). Def. of right triangles) 4. $\overline{BD} \cong \overline{BE}$ (Given) 5. $\overline{AD} \cong \overline{CE}$ (Given) 6. $\overline{AE} \cong \overline{CD}$ ((5). Common Segment Th.) 7. $\triangle ABE \cong \triangle CBD$ ((3), (4), (6). HL Th.) 8. $\overline{BA} \cong \overline{BC}$ ((7). CPCTC)

Page 139 Geometry Review Capsule for Section 3-9 1. If two angles form a linear pair, then the two angles are supplementary; Two angles form a linear pair; Two angles are supplementary. **2.** If an angle has a measure of 125, then the angle is obtuse; An angle has a measure of 125; The angle is obtuse. **3.** If an angle is acute, then it has a measure less than 90; An angle is acute; The angle has a measure less than 90. **4.** If two legs of a triangle measure 4 centimeters, then the triangle is isosceles; Two legs of a triangle measure 4 centimeters; The triangle is isosceles. **5.** If AM = 3 and MB = 4, then AB = 7; AM = 3, MB = 4; AB = 7

Page 141 Classroom Exercises 1. If two segments have equal measures, then they are congruent; If two segments are not congruent, then they do not have equal measures; If two segments do not have equal measures, then they are not congruent. **3.** If a triangle is equiangular, then it is equilateral (True); If a triangle is not equilateral, then it is not equiangular (True); If a triangle is not equiangular, then it is not equilateral (True). **5. a.** If the measure of an angle is 90, then it is a right angle. **b.** If an angle is a right angle, then it has a measure of 90. **c.** An angle is a right angle if and only if it has a measure of 90.

Page 141 Written Exercises 1. If two angles are congruent, then they are supplements of the same angle; If two angles are not supplements of the same angle, then they are not congruent; If two angles are not congruent, then they are not supplements of the same angle. **3.** If two lines form four right angles, then they are perpendicular; If two lines are not perpendicular, then they do not form four right angles; If two lines do not form four right angles, then they are not perpendicular. **5.** If a point is equidistant from the sides of an angle, then it is on the bisector of the angle; If a point is not on the bisector of an angle, then it is not equidistant from the sides of an angle; If a point is not equidistant from the sides of an angle, then it is not on the bisector of the angle. **7.** The converses in Ex. 2-5. **9.** All **11.** The acute angles can have measures of 35 and 55. **13.** Each of two vertical angles can have a measure of 95; neither vertical angle is a right angle. **15.** D **17.** B **19.** C **21.** A kap is a dren if and only if a lep is a frim. **23.** If c = d, then c − d = 0. If c − d = 0, then c = d. **25.** If an angle is an obtuse angle, then its measure is greater than 90 and less than 180. If the measure of an angle is greater than 90 and less than 180, then it is an obtuse angle. **27.** contrapositive **29.** contrapositive **31.** T; T; F; T **33.** ~p: F; F; T; T ~q: F; T; F; T ~q → ~p: T; F; T; T

Page 143 Review 1. Given: $\angle F \not\cong \angle H$ Prove: $\overline{FG} \neq \overline{HG}$ Proof: **a.** = **b.** $\cong$ **c.** $\cong$, of the Isosceles Triangle Th. **d.** $\neq$ **e.** $\overline{FG} \neq \overline{HG}$ **2.** Yes; ASA Post. **3.** Yes; HA Post. **4.** Yes; HL Th. **5.** If corresponding parts of triangles are congruent, then the triangles are congruent; If triangles are not congruent, then corresponding parts of the triangles are not congruent; If corresponding parts of triangles are not congruent, then the triangles are not congruent. **6.** Yes, because both the conditional and its converse are true.

Page 145 Consumer Applications 1. If you buy a Simka watch before December 24, you will save $\frac{1}{3}$. **3.** No **5.** Contrapositive **7.** If a person runs in Soft Shoes, that person cares about his or her ankles. **9.** No **11.** If a person cares about his or her ankles, that person runs in Soft Shoes. **13.** No, not necessarily **15.** Not necessarily **17.** Not necessarily

Page 146 Chapter Objectives and Review 1. GDR, H 3. $\overline{HC}$ 5. Yes 7. Yes 9. ASA Post.
11. ASA Post., SAS Post. **13.** 1. $\angle 1 \cong \angle 2$ (Given) 2. $\angle 1 \cong \angle 3; \angle 2 \cong \angle 4$ (Vertical Angle Th.)
3. $\angle 3 \cong \angle 4$ ((1), (2). Substitution Prop.) 4. $\overline{ST} \cong \overline{SK}$ ((3). Th. 3-3) 5. Triangle TKS is isosceles.
((4). Def. of isosceles triangle) **15.** Given: O is the midpoint of $\overline{PQ}$; $\overline{OQ} \cong \overline{OR}$. Prove: $\angle 1 \cong \angle 2$
1. O is the midpoint of segment PQ. (Given) 2. OP = OQ ((1). Def. of midpoint) 3. $\overline{OP} \cong \overline{OQ}$
((2). Def. of congruent segments) 4. $\overline{OQ} \cong \overline{OR}$ (Given) 5. $\overline{OP} \cong \overline{OR}$ ((3), (4). Transitive Prop.)
6. $\angle 1 \cong \angle 2$ ((5). Th. 3-1) **17.** Conclusion: Segment HE is perpendicular to segment AR and ray HE
bisects angle AHR. The median from the vertex angle of an isosceles triangle is perpendicular to the base and
bisects the vertex angle. **19.** F; ST = 3 and SE = 3.5, $\therefore$ ST $\neq$ SE **21.** T; Cor. 3-9 **23.** T; SAS Post.
25. F; Common Angle Th., $\angle ECG \cong \angle DCE$ **27.** $\triangle RTS$ is not an isosceles triangle. **29.** Assume that
$\overline{DC} \cong \overline{DA}$. Since $\overline{BD} \perp \overline{CA}$, $\angle BDC \cong \angle BDA$ by the def. of perpendicular lines. $\overline{BD} \cong \overline{BD}$ by Identity. Thus,
$\triangle BDC \cong \triangle BDA$ by the SAS Post. Therefore, $\overline{BC} \cong \overline{BA}$ by CPCTC. But, by hypothesis, $\overline{BC} \not\cong \overline{BA}$. Therefore,
the original assumption is false, and $\overline{DC} \not\cong \overline{DA}$. **31.** Yes; HL Th. **33.** If the three sides of a triangle are
congruent, then the three angles are congruent. (True) **35.** If the three sides of a triangle are not congruent,
then the three angles are not congruent. (True) **37.** Given: In $\triangle ABP$, $\overline{MP} \perp \overline{AB}$; AM = 2; MB = 2 Prove:
AP = PB Proof: 1. $\overline{MP} \perp \overline{AB}$ (Given) 2. $\angle PMA \cong \angle PMB$ ((1). Th. 2-13) 3. AM = 2; MB = 2 (Given)
4. AM = MB ((3). Substitution Prop.) 5. $\overline{AM} \cong \overline{MB}$ ((4). Def. of congruent segments) 6. $\overline{PM} \cong \overline{PM}$
(Identity) 7. $\triangle PMA \cong \triangle PMB$ ((2), (5), (6). SAS Post.) 8. $\overline{AP} \cong \overline{PB}$ ((7). CPCTC) 9. AP = PB
((8). Def. of congruent segments)

Page 150 Chapter Test 1. TS 3. $\overline{TN}$ 5. $\angle STN$ 7. T; Th. 3-3 9. T; SSS Post. and CPCTC 11. F;
Common Angle Th. 13. $\triangle ACF \cong \triangle DBE$; SAS Post. 15. Statements: 2. $\overline{AD} \cong \overline{BD}$ 4. $\triangle ADE, \triangle BDC$
6. $\overline{ED} \cong \overline{CD}$ Reasons: 1. Given 3. Given 5. HL Th. 6. CPCTC

Page 151 Cumulative Review: Chapters 1-3 1. c 3. c 5. b 7. d 9. c 11. d 13. Common
Segment Th. 15. c 17. b 19. d 21. a 23. c

Page 153 Preparing for College Entrance Tests 1. c 3. e 5. c

Page 154 Preparing for College Entrance Tests 1. c 3. a

CHAPTER 4: PARALLEL LINES

Page 158 Classroom Exercises 1. ABD 3. $>$ 5. Comparison Prop. 7. Addition Prop. 9. Multiplication Prop. 11. c 13. b 15. a

Page 159 Written Exercises 1. PMT (or MTP) 3. $>$ 5. EFH 7. Angles 2 and F 9. $>$ 11. $<$
13. 105, 125, 130 15. 70, 30, $>$ 17. Interior angles: 3, 4, 5, 6; Exterior angles: 1, 2, 7, 8; Alternate
interior angles: 4 and 6; 3 and 5; Alternate exterior angles: 1 and 7; 2 and 8 19. Interior angles: 2, 3, 9, 12;
Exterior angles: 1, 4, 10, 11; Alternate interior angles: 2 and 12; 3 and 9; Alternate exterior angles: 1 and 11;
4 and 10 21. 3, 6 23. R, 1 25. 4, Z **27.** 1. Angle 1 is an exterior angle of $\triangle ABD$, angle 2 is a remote
interior angle of angle 1. Angle 2 is an exterior angle of $\triangle BCD$, angle 3 is a remote interior angle of angle 2.
(Def. of exterior angle and remote interior angle) 2. $m\angle 1 > m\angle 2$; $m\angle 2 > m\angle 3$ ((1). Th. 4-1)
3. $m\angle 1 > m\angle 3$ (Transitive Prop. of Inequality) **29.** Given: a = b; c $<$ d Prove: a + c $<$ b + d
1. c $<$ d (Given) 2. a + c $<$ a + d ((1). Addition Prop.) 3. a = b (Given) 4. a + c $<$ b + d ((2), (3).
Substitution Prop.) **31.** 1. AB $<$ CD (Given) 2. AB + BD = AD; AC + CD = AD (Def. of betweenness of
points) 3. AB + BD = AC + CD ((2). Substitution Prop.) 4. BD $>$ AC ((1), (3). If a = b and c $<$ d, then
a $-$ c $>$ b $-$ d.) **33.** Given: $m\angle ACB > 90$ Prove: $m\angle A < 90$; $m\angle B < 90$ 1. Extend $\overrightarrow{AC}$ to D. (Postulate
4) 2. $\angle ACB$ and $\angle BCD$ form a linear pair. (Def. of linear pair) 3. $m\angle ACB + m\angle BCD = 180$ ((2). Linear
Pair Post.) 4. $m\angle ACB = 180 - m\angle BCD$ ((3). Addition Prop.) 5. $m\angle ACB > 90$ (Given)

6. $180 - m\angle BCD > 90$ ((4), (5). Substitution Prop.)   7. $90 > m\angle BCD$ ((6). Addition Prop.)
8. $m\angle BCD > m\angle A; m\angle BCD > m\angle B$ (Th. 4-1)   9. $90 > m\angle A$, or $m\angle A < 90; 90 > m\angle B$, or $m\angle B < 90$
((7), (8). Transitive Prop.)

Page 161   Geometry Review Capsule for Section 4-2   1. F; the statement is a contradiction.   2. F; def. of
converse   3. T   4. F; the first step is to assume the negation of what you wish to prove.

Page 164   Classroom Exercises   1. $p \parallel t$ 3. $\overleftrightarrow{BC} \parallel k$ 5. $\angle 1$ and $\angle 4$ 7. Two lines cut by a transversal
are parallel if and only if the alternate interior angles are congruent; The alternate interior angles of two lines
cut by a transversal are congruent if and only if the lines are parallel.

Page 164   Written Exercises   1. $p \parallel q$ 3. $p \parallel q$ 5. angles 14 and 12; angles 11 and 13; angles 4 and 6;
angles 3 and 5   7. $\overline{XS} \parallel \overline{YT}$ 9. $\angle 1 \cong \angle 2$ 11. $\overleftrightarrow{WX} \parallel \overleftrightarrow{TV}$ 13. $m\angle 5 = 100; m\angle 6 = 80; m\angle 7 = 100$
15. 1. $\overline{TZ} \cong \overline{SY}; \overline{XY} \cong \overline{ZW}; \angle 1 \cong \angle 2$ (Given)   2. $XY = ZW$ ((1). Def. of congruent segments)
3. $XZ = XY + YZ; YW = YZ + ZW$ (Def. of betweenness of points)   4. $XZ = YZ + ZW$ ((2), (3). Substitu-
tion Prop.)   5. $XZ = YW$ ((3), (4). Substitution Prop.)   6. $\overline{XZ} \cong \overline{YW}$ (Def. of congruent segments)
7. $\triangle TZX \cong \triangle SYW$ ((1), (6). SAS Post.)   8. $\angle X \cong \angle W$ ((7). CPCTC)   9. $\overline{XT} \parallel \overline{WS}$ ((8). Th. 4-2)
17. Given: Lines a and b are cut by transversal c; $\angle 1 \cong \angle 2$ Prove: $a \parallel b$
1. Lines a and b cut by transversal c, such that $\angle 1 \cong \angle 2$ (Given)
2. $\angle 1 \cong \angle 3; \angle 2 \cong \angle 4$ ((1). Vertical Angle Th.)   3. $\angle 3 \cong \angle 4$
((1), (2). Transitive Prop.)   4. $a \parallel b$ ((3). Th. 4-2)
19. Given: Quadrilateral ABCD; $\overline{AB} \cong \overline{CD}; \overline{BC} \cong \overline{DA}$
Prove: $\overline{AB} \parallel \overline{CD}; \overline{BC} \parallel \overline{DA}$ 1. Quadrilateral ABCD; $\overline{AB} \cong \overline{CD}; \overline{BC} \cong \overline{DA}$
(Given)   2. Draw segment BD. ((1). Post. 4)   3. $\overline{BD} \cong \overline{BD}$ (Identity)   4. $\triangle CDB \cong \triangle ABD$ ((1), (3). SSS
Post.)   5. $\angle BDC \cong \angle DBA; \angle CBD \cong \angle ADB$ ((4). CPCTC)   6. $\overline{AB} \parallel \overline{CD}; \overline{BC} \parallel \overline{DA}$ ((5). Th. 4-2)
21. Given: $a \parallel b; c \parallel d$ Prove: $\angle 1 \cong \angle 2$ 1. $a \parallel b; c \parallel d$; a and b intersect
c and d.   (Given)   2. $\angle 2 \cong \angle 4; \angle 3 \cong \angle 1$ ((1). Vertical Angle Th.)
3. $\angle 3 \cong \angle 5; \angle 4 \cong \angle 6$ ((1). Th. 4-3)   4. $\angle 5 \cong \angle 6$ ((1). Vertical Angle
Th.)   5. $\angle 1 \cong \angle 2$ ((2), (3), (4). Transitive Prop.)
23. 1. C is the midpoint of $\overline{AE}$. (Given)   2. $\overline{AC} \cong \overline{CE}$ ((1). Def. of
midpoint)   3. Extend $\overrightarrow{BC}$ to X; Extend $\overrightarrow{DC}$ to Y. (Two points determine
a ray.)   4. $\overline{AB} \parallel \overline{CD}; \overline{ED} \parallel \overline{CB}$ (Given)   5. $\angle A \cong \angle ACY; \angle E \cong \angle ECX$ ((4). Th. 4-3)   6. $\angle ACY \cong \angle DCE$;
$\angle ECX \cong \angle BCA$ (Vertical Angle Th.)   7. $\angle A \cong \angle DCE; \angle E \cong \angle BCA$ ((5), (6). Transitive Prop.)
8. $\triangle ABC \cong \triangle CDE$ ((2), (7). ASA Post.)   9. $\overline{ED} \cong \overline{CB}$ ((8). CPCTC)

Page 166   Geometry Review Capsule for Section 4-3   (For Exercises 1-3, answers may vary.)   1. $\angle 1$ and $\angle 2$
are supplementary; Linear Pair Post.   2. $\angle 1, \angle 2, \angle 3,$ and $\angle 4$ are right angles; Cor. 2-11   3. $m\angle A < 110$;
Th. 4-1

Page 167   Career Applications   1. 200 cm   3. 67 cm   5. 40 cm

Page 170   Classroom Exercises   1. 117   3. 135, 45   5. Th. 4-6   7. Two lines that are cut by a transversal
are parallel if and only if interior angles on the same side of the transversal are supplementary.

Page 170   Written Exercises   1. $s \parallel y$; Th. 4-4   3. $\overleftrightarrow{DE} \parallel \overline{AB}$; Th. 4-4   5. a. $\angle SZY$; by def. of alternate
interior angles b. $\angle TZY$; by definition c. $\angle RXZ$; by Th. 4-5   7. $\angle ECA$; by Th. 4-5   9. Parallel, by Th. 4-6
11. 122; 58   13. Reasons: 1. Given   2. Th. 4-3   3. Def. of linear pair   4. Linear Pair Post.   5. Def. of
congruent angles   6. Substitution Prop.   7. Def. of supplementary angles   **15.** 1. $\overline{AB} \parallel \overline{DE}; \angle B$ is a right
angle.   (Given)   2. $\overline{AB} \perp \overline{BC}$ ((1). Def. of perpendicular lines)   3. $\overline{DE} \perp \overline{BC}$ ((1), (2). Th. 4-7)

4. Angle DEC is a right angle. ((3). Def. of perpendicular lines)   5. Triangle DEC is a right triangle.
((4). Def. of a right triangle)   **17.** (Use the figure for Example 3 on page 169.)   Given: n ∥ p; n ⊥ q
Prove: q ⊥ p   1. n ∥ p; n ⊥ q   (Given)   2. ∠1 ≅ ∠2   ((1). Th. 4-3)   3. m∠1 = m∠2   ((2). Def. of congruent
angles)   4. Angle 1 is a right angle.   ((1). Cor. 2-11)   5. m∠1 = 90   ((4). Def. of right angle)   6. m∠2 = 90
((3), (5). Substitution Prop.)   7. Angle 2 is a right angle.   ((6). Def. of right angle)   8. q ⊥ p   ((7.) Def. of
perpendicular lines)

19. This biconditional is proved by the indirect method in two parts. Conditional:
If two lines are cut by a transversal and if two alternate exterior angles are not
congruent, then the two lines are not parallel. Proof: Assume that lines m and p
are parallel and are cut by transversal s. Then alternate interior angles, ∠1 and ∠2,
are congruent. Since vertical angles are congruent, ∠1 ≅ ∠3 and ∠2 ≅ ∠4. By the
Substitution Prop., ∠3 ≅ ∠4. But this contradicts the hypothesis that alternate

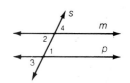

exterior angles are not congruent. Therefore, the assumption is false and the two lines are not parallel.
Converse: If two lines are not parallel then the alternate exterior angles formed when they are cut by a transversal are not congruent. Proof: Assume that the alternate exterior angles are congruent. Then since these are
vertical angles associated with the alternate interior angles, the alternate interior angles are also congruent. By
Th. 4-3, the lines are parallel. This contradicts the hypothesis. Therefore, the assumption is false and the angles
are not congruent.   **21.** 1. H̱T̄ bisects ∠JHP; P̱T̄ bisects ∠HPR   (Given)   2. m∠JHT = m∠THP; m∠TPH
= m∠TPR   ((1). Def. of angle bisector)   3. ∠THP and ∠TPH are complementary   (Given)   4. m∠THP
+ m∠TPH = 90   ((3). Def. of complementary angles)   5. m∠JHT + m∠TPR = 90   ((2), (4). Substitution
Prop.)   6. m∠THP + m∠JHT + m∠TPH + m∠TPR = 180   ((4), (5). Addition Prop.)   7. m∠JHP = m∠JHT
+ m∠THP; m∠HPR = m∠TPH + m∠TPR   (Def. of betweenness of rays)   8. m∠JHP + m∠HPR = m∠JHT
+ m∠THP + m∠TPH + m∠TPR   ((7). Addition Prop.)   9. m∠JHP + m∠HPR = 180   ((6), (8). Substitution
Prop.)   10. ∠JHP and ∠HPR are supplementary   ((9). Def. of supplementary angles)   11. H̱J̄ ∥ P̱R̄
((10). Th. 4-4)

Page 173 Geometry Review Capsule for Section 4-4   1. Alternate interior   2. Alternate interior
3. Interior on the same side of a transversal   4. Alternate exterior   5. Alternate interior   6. Alternate
interior   7. m∠2 = 28, m∠3 = 28, m∠4 = 28, m∠5 = 28, m∠6 = 152, m∠7 = 28, m∠8 = 28, m∠9 = 28

Page 175 Classroom Exercises   1. 5 and 10, 6 and 9; 1 and 9, 5 and 13, 2 and 10, 6 and 14   3. 3 and 6, 2
and 7; 4 and 2, 3 and 1, 8 and 6, 7 and 5   5. Two lines are cut by a transversal so that two corresponding
angles are congruent, if and only if the lines are parallel. or Two lines cut by a transversal are parallel if and
only if corresponding angles are congruent.

Page 175 Written Exercises   1. Angles 3 and W; angles 4 and 6; angles 4 and 2, angles 5 and 1; angles 7 and W
3. Angles 1 and C   5. W̱X̄ ∥ ẔȲ; Th. 4-8   7. A̱C̄ ∥ ḆĒ; Th. 4-2   9. Angle RMQ; by Th. 4-9; angle V; by
Th. 4-9; angle 4 by Th. 4-3   11. A̱B̄ ∥ C̱D̄; Th. 4-11 13. Statements: 3. ∠2 ≅ ∠3   6. ẔW̄ ≅ ẔX̄
Reasons: 2. Th. 4-3   3. Transitive Prop.   4. (1). Th. 4-9   5. (3), (4). Transitive Prop.   6. (5). Th. 3-3
15. 35   **17.** 1. m∠B = m∠x; ∠E and ∠B are supplementary.   (Given)   2. m∠E + m∠B = 180   ((1). Def. of
supplementary angles)   3. m∠E + m∠X = 180   ((1), (2). Substitution Prop.)   4. ∠E and ∠x are supplementary.
((3). Def. of supplementary angles)   5. E̱F̄ ∥ ḆC̄   ((4). Th. 4-4)   **19.** 1. a ∥ c; b ∥ c   (Given)   2. ∠1 ≅ ∠3;
∠3 ≅ ∠2   ((1). Th. 4-9)   3. ∠1 ≅ ∠2   ((2). Transitive Prop.)   4. a ∥ b   ((3). Th. 4-8)   **21.** 1. F̱D̄ ∥ A̱C̄
(Given)   2. Angles EFD and CEF are supplementary.   ((1). Th. 4-5)   3. Angles FDC and C are supplementary.
((1). Th. 4-5)   4. E̱F̄ ∥ C̱B̄   (Given)   5. Angles EFD and FDC are supplementary.   ((4). Th. 4-5
6. ∠C ≅ ∠EFD   ((3), (5). Th. 2-4)   7. ∠CEF ≅ ∠FDC   ((2), (5). Th. 2-4)   **23.** 1. ḆD̄ ∥ E̱G̱; A̱C̄ ∥ E̱F̄
(Given)   2. Extend the ray opposite E̱F̄ to intersect line BD at H.   (Th. 1-2)   3. ∠1 ≅ ∠BHF; ∠BHF ≅ ∠2
((1), (2). Th. 4-9)   4. ∠1 ≅ ∠2   ((3). Transitive Prop.)   **25.** Given: ḆD̄ ⊥ E̱G; A̱C̄ ⊥ E̱F̄; ḆD̄ ∥ E̱F̄; all points

are coplanar. Prove: $\angle 1 \cong \angle 2$ 1. $\overleftrightarrow{BD} \perp \overrightarrow{EG}$; $\overrightarrow{AC} \perp \overrightarrow{EF}$; $\overleftrightarrow{BD} \parallel \overrightarrow{EF}$; all points are coplanar. (Given)   2. Let $\overrightarrow{EF}$ intersect $\overrightarrow{AC}$ at X; Let $\overrightarrow{EG}$ intersect $\overleftrightarrow{BD}$ at Y. ((1). Th. 1-2)   3. $\angle AXF$ is a right angle; $\angle GYA$ is a right angle. ((1), (2). Def. of perpendicular lines)   4. $m\angle AXF = 90$; $m\angle GYA = 90$ ((3). Def. of right angle)
5. $\angle 1 \cong \angle AXF$ ((1). Th. 4-3)   6. $\angle 1$ is a right angle. ((4), (5). Def. of congruent angles and of right angle)
7. $\angle 2$ and $\angle GYA$ are supplementary. ((1), (2). Th. 4-5)   8. $m\angle 2 + m\angle GYA = 180$ ((7). Def. of supplementary angles)   9. $m\angle 2 + 90 = 180$ ((4), (8). Substitution Prop.)   10. $m\angle 2 = 90$ ((9). Addition Prop.)
11. $\angle 2$ is a right angle. ((10). Def. of right angle)   12. $\angle 1 \cong \angle 2$ ((6), (11). Cor. 2-12)   27. Given: In quadrilateral ABCD, $\overline{AD} \parallel \overline{BC}$ and $\overline{AD} \cong \overline{BC}$; diagonals BD and AC intersect at E. Prove: $\overline{AC}$ bisects $\overline{BD}$; $\overline{BD}$ bisects $\overline{AC}$.   1. $\overline{AD} \parallel \overline{BC}$ (Given)   2. $\angle BDA \cong \angle DBC$; $\angle CAD \cong \angle ACB$ ((1). Th. 4-3)   3. $\overline{AD} \cong \overline{BC}$ (Given)
4. $\triangle EDA \cong \triangle EBC$ ((2), (3). ASA Post.)   5. $\overline{ED} \cong \overline{EB}$; $\overline{EA} \cong \overline{EC}$ ((4). CPCTC)   6. $\overline{AC}$ bisects $\overline{BD}$; $\overline{BD}$ bisects $\overline{AC}$ ((5). Def. of bisector)   29. This biconditional is the contrapositive of the biconditional formed by Th. 4-8 and 4-9 (See Classroom Ex. 5). If a conditional is true, then its contrapositive is true.
31. Given: $\overleftrightarrow{AX} \parallel \overleftrightarrow{CY}$ Prove: $m\angle B = m\angle XAB + m\angle YCB$ 1. Introduce $\overleftrightarrow{BD} \parallel \overleftrightarrow{AX}$, with D on the same side of $\overleftrightarrow{BC}$ as A. (Post. 15)   2. $\overleftrightarrow{AX} \parallel \overleftrightarrow{CY}$ (Given)   3. $\overleftrightarrow{BD} \parallel \overleftrightarrow{CY}$ ((1), (2). Th. 4-11)   4. $\angle DBA \cong \angle XAB$ ((1). Th. 4-3)   5. $\angle DBC \cong \angle YCB$ ((3). Th. 4-3)   6. $m\angle DBA = m\angle XAB$; $m\angle DBC = m\angle YCB$ ((4), (5). Def. of congruent angles)   7. $m\angle DBA + m\angle DBC = m\angle B$ (Def. of betweenness of rays)   8. $m\angle XAB + m\angle YCB = m\angle B$ ((6), (7). Substitution Prop.)

Page 179 Applications   1. It is given that each line segment makes an angle of equal measure with the curb so each angle is also congruent. By Th. 4-8, $\ell \parallel m \parallel n \parallel p \parallel q \parallel r$.   3. From the figure, the flight paths of planes A and B both make an angle of $85°$ with the east-west line, so the angles are congruent. By Th. 4-8, the two courses are parallel.   5. $m\angle CEF = m\angle EGH = 65$ 7. $m\angle BDC = 65$

Page 180 Review   1. ABD   2. ABD   3. A, 3   4. 8, 9, 15, 16; 6, 7, 10, 11; 9 and 15, 8 and 16; 6 and 10, 7 and 11   5. 2, 3, 13, 14; 1, 4, 5, 12; 2 and 14, 3 and 13; 1 and 5, 4 and 12   6. 11, 12, 13, 16; 1, 2, 9, 10; 11 and 13, 12 and 16; 1 and 9, 2 and 10   7. 5, 6, 14, 15; 3, 4, 7, 8; 6 and 14, 5 and 15; 3 and 7, 4 and 8   8. $\overrightarrow{LE}, \overrightarrow{AN}$ 9. $\overrightarrow{EA}, \overrightarrow{NL}$ 10. $\overrightarrow{EA}, \overrightarrow{NL}$ 11. p, q; Th. 4-4   12. 111; Th. 4-5   13. $\perp$; Th. 4-7   14. $\parallel$; Def. of perpendicular lines and Th. 4-6   15. 20   16. 3 and 11, 6 and 14, 8 and 16, 7 and 15, 6 and 8, 9 and 11, 16 and 14   17. Statements: 4. 3   5. $\angle 1 \cong \angle 2$ Reasons: 1. Given   2. Th. 4-9   3. Given   4. Th. 4-3   5. Transitive Prop.

Page 181 Algebra Review Capsule for Section 4-5   1. x = 40   2. x = 35   3. $x = 16\frac{2}{3}$ 4. x = 35   5. x = 20   6. x = 23   7. x = 37   8. x = 23   9. x = 10   10. x = 21

Page 183 Classroom Exercises   1. 50   3. 60   5. 90   7. Cor. 4-13

Page 184 Written Exercises   1. 80   3. 60; 60   5. 40; 60; 40; 60; 120   7. 60; 90; 90; 60; 30   9. 90   11. $21\frac{1}{3}$; 76; $82\frac{2}{3}$ 13. $22\frac{1}{2}$, $67\frac{1}{2}$ 15. 108; 36, 36   17. 360   19. 1. Angle A of triangle ABC is congruent to angle A of triangle AED. (Identity)   2. $\angle 1 \cong \angle 2$ (Given)   3. $\angle B \cong \angle E$ ((1), (2). Cor. 4-13   21. 1. Altitude KQ from K to $\overline{JR}$; altitude JP from J to $\overline{RK}$. (Given)   2. $\overline{KQ} \perp \overline{JR}$; $\overline{JP} \perp \overline{RK}$ ((1). Def. of altitude)   3. Angle RQK of triangle RQK and angle RPJ of triangle RPJ are right angles. ((2). Def. of perpendicular lines)   4. $\angle RQK \cong \angle RPJ$ ((3). All right angles are congruent)   5. $\angle R \cong \angle R$ (Ident.)   6. $\angle RKQ \cong \angle RJP$ ((4), (5). Cor. 4-13)   23. 1. $\overline{BD} \perp \overline{AC}$ (Given)   2. $\angle 3$ and $\angle 4$ are right angles. ((1). Def. of perpendicular lines)   3. $\angle 1 \cong \angle C$ (Ex. 22)   4. $\angle 2 \cong \angle A$ ((2), (3). Cor. 4-13)   25. Given: D is any point on $\overline{AB}$; $\overline{DE} \parallel \overline{BC}$; $\overline{DF} \parallel \overline{AC}$ Prove: $m\angle A + m\angle B + m\angle C = 180$ 1. $\overline{DE} \parallel \overline{BC}$, $\overline{DF} \parallel \overline{AC}$ (Given)   2. $\angle A \cong \angle FDB$; $\angle B \cong \angle EDA$; $\angle C \cong \angle BFD$ ((1). Th. 4-9)   3. $\angle BFD \cong \angle EDF$ ((1). Th. 4-3)   4. $\angle EDF \cong \angle C$ ((2), (3). Transitive Prop.)   5. $m\angle EDF + m\angle FDB = m\angle EDB$ (Def. of betweenness of rays)   6. $\angle EDA$ and $\angle EDB$ form a linear pair. (Def. of linear pair)   7. $m\angle EDA + m\angle EDB = 180$ ((6). Linear Pair Post.)

8. m∠EDA + m∠EDF + m∠FDB = 180 ((5), (7). Substitution Prop.)   9. m∠A = m∠FDB; m∠B = m∠EDA; m∠C = m∠EDF ((2), (4). Def. of congruent angles)   10. m∠A + m∠B + m∠C = 180 ((8), (9). Substitution Prop.)   27. Assume that triangle ABC has more than one right angle and that angles A and C are right angles. m∠A + m∠B + m∠C = 180, by Th. 4-12; 90 + m∠B + 90 = 180; m∠B = 0. This is impossible. Therefore, the assumption is false, and a triangle can have no more than one right angle. Assume that a triangle has more than one obtuse angle and that m∠A = 90 + a and m∠C = 90 + c, where a and c are positive real numbers. m∠A + m∠B + m∠C = 180; 90 + a + m∠B + 90 + c = 180; m∠B = −a − c. This is impossible since −a − c is a negative number. Therefore, the assumption is false and a triangle can have no more than one obtuse angle.

29. x = 90 − $\frac{y}{2}$ 31. Given: △ABC is equilateral; △BDE is equilateral.
Prove: $\overline{AE} \cong \overline{CD}$ 1. △s ABC and BDE are equilateral.
(Given)   2. $\overline{AB} \cong \overline{BC}; \overline{BE} \cong \overline{BD}$ ((1). Def. of equilateral triangle)
3. ∠CAB ≅ ∠ABC ≅ ∠ACB; ∠EBD ≅ ∠BDE ≅ ∠BED ((1). Cor. 3-2)
4. m∠CAB = m∠ABC = m∠ACB; m∠EBD = m∠BDE = m∠BED ((3). Def. of
congruent angles)   5. m∠CAB + m∠ABC + m∠ACB = 180; m∠EBD + m∠BDE
+ m∠BED = 180 (Th. 4-12)   6. m∠ABC + m∠ABC + m∠ABC = 180; m∠EBD + m∠EBD + m∠EBD = 180
((4), (5). Substitution Prop.)   7. 3 m∠ABC = 180; 3 m∠EBD = 180 ((6). Distributive Prop.)   8. m∠ABC
= 60; m∠EBD = 60 ((7). Multiplication Prop.)   9. ∠ABC ≅ ∠EBD ((8). Def. of congruent angles)
10. △ABE ≅ △CBD ((2), (8). SAS Post.)   11. $\overline{AE} \cong \overline{CD}$ ((10). CPCTC)

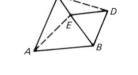

Page 187   Geometry Review Capsule for Section 4-6   1. exterior   2. m∠DBC   3. m∠DBC   4. 180; supplementary angles   5. SAS   6. SAS, SSS   7. ASA

Page 188   Classroom Exercises   1. b   3. b   5. b   7. Cor. 4-18   9. Linear Pair Post.

Page 189   Written Exercises   1. Angles A and D; angles 1 and A   3. Angles m∠1 = 34; m∠2 = 56; m∠3 = 56
5. Always true   7. Sometimes true   9. 155, 155   11. 75, 138   13. 159 − x, 159   15. 56, 62, 62
17. 50   19. 30, 90, 60; right triangle   21. 68, 73, 39   23. 80; 50, 50   25. 120
27. Given: △ABC with right angle at C   Prove: ∠A and ∠B are complementary.   1. △ABC with right angle at
C (Given)   2. m∠C = 90 ((1). Def. of right angle)   3. m∠A + m∠B + m∠C = 180 (Th. 4-12)   4. m∠A
+ m∠B + 90 = 180 ((2), (3). Substitution Prop.)   5. m∠A + m∠B = 90 ((4). Addition Prop.)   6. ∠A and
∠B are complementary. ((5). Def. of complementary angles)
29. Given: $\overline{JK} \cong \overline{MP}; ∠K \cong ∠P; ∠L \cong ∠Q$ Prove: △JKL ≅ △MPQ
1. ∠K ≅ ∠P; ∠L ≅ ∠Q (Given)   2. m∠K = m∠P; m∠L = m∠Q ((1). Def.
of congruent angles)   3. m∠J + m∠K + m∠L = 180; m∠M + m∠P + m∠Q
= 180 (Th. 4-12)   4. m∠J + m∠K + m∠L = m∠M + m∠P + m∠Q
((3). Substitution Prop.)   5. m∠J + m∠P + m∠Q = m∠M + m∠P + m∠Q
((2), (4). Substitution Prop.)   6. m∠J = m∠M ((5). Add. Prop.)   7. ∠J ≅ ∠M ((6). Def. of congruent angles)
8. $\overline{JK} \cong \overline{MP}$ (Given)   9. △JKL ≅ △MPQ ((1), (7), (8). ASA Post.)   31. 2a   33. 40   35. 180 − 4a
37. m∠1 = m∠2 + m∠3 + m∠4   39. 90 + $\frac{a}{2}$ 41. 2 m∠H   43. 3 m∠Z

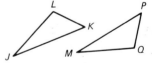

Page 192   Algebra Review Capsule for Section 4-7   2. −2   3. 65   4. 8   5. 8   6. 86   7. 153   8. 12
9. −1$\frac{1}{2}$ 10. 105

Page 195   Classroom Exercises   1. F; Def. of isosceles triangle   3. T; Th. 4-19   5. T; Cor. 4-20

Page 195   Written Exercises   1. 360   3. 1440   5. 1800   7. 108   9. 135   11. 156   13. 154$\frac{2}{7}$
15. 20   17. 45   19. 7   21. 9   23. 29   25. Use the formula S = (n − 2)180, and let S = 1350. Then
n = 9$\frac{1}{2}$, which is not a whole number.   27. Let a = 152; then 152 = $\frac{(n - 2)180}{n}$ and n = 12$\frac{6}{7}$, which is not a

whole number.   29. 16   31. 25   33. 72, 90, 108, 126, 144

Page 196   Calculator Exercises   (See Written Exercise answers above.)

Page 196   Geometry Review Capsule for Section 4-8   1. 141, 141   2. 151, 151   3. 121   4. 78, 150
5. 64, 123

Page 198   Classroom Exercises   1. 180   3. 360   5. 40

Page 198   Written Exercises   1. 20; 18   3. 360   5. 360   7. 360   9. 15   11. 36   13. 24   15. 16
17. 45   19. 11   21. 130   23. No   25. 5 : 3 : 1

Page 199   Review   1. 26   2. 25   3. 76   4. m∠1 = 50, m∠2 = 40, m∠3 = 40   5. m∠1 = 29, m∠2 = 55,
m∠3 = 96, m∠4 = 84, m∠5 = 96, m∠6 = 55   6. 3960   7. 9   8. 60   9. $25\frac{5}{7}$ 10. $12\frac{6}{7}$ 11. 18   12. 40
13. $22\frac{1}{2}$

Page 200   Applications   1. 30   3. △ABC and △DEF   5. From the figure, m∠B = 50 and m∠E = 50.
Therefore, they are congruent by definition. Also, m∠C = 80 and m∠F = 80, so ∠C ≅ ∠F. From the figure,
AB = DE, so $\overline{AB} ≅ \overline{DE}$. ∴ △ABC ≅ △DEF by Cor. 4=17.   7. 1800   9. It is assumed from the figure that the
course of the ship is unchanging, so ∠SRP is an exterior angle of △SRT. Thus, by Th. 4-18, m∠SRP = m∠S
+ m∠T. At point R, m∠SRP = 2 m∠T. By substitution, 2 m∠T = m∠S + m∠T, and m∠S = m∠T. Thus, by
definition, ∠S ≅ ∠T, and $\overline{RS} ≅ \overline{RT}$ by Th. 3-3, so RS = RT.

Page 203   Chapter Objectives and Review   1. ECA   3. CBA, A   5. ∠2, ∠3, ∠5, ∠8   7. ∠3 and ∠5, ∠2 and
∠8   9. ∠4 and ∠8, ∠3 and ∠7, ∠1 and ∠5, ∠2 and ∠6   11. 80   13. $\overline{AD} \parallel \overline{BC}$ 15. $\overline{DC} \parallel \overline{AB}$ 17. ⊥
19. 1. $\overline{EF} \perp \overline{EG}; \overline{HG} \perp \overline{EG}$ (Given)   2. $\overline{EF} \parallel \overline{HG}$ ((1). Th. 4-6)   21. m∠1 = 72, m∠2 = 36   23. m∠1 = 30,
m∠2 = 81   25. 60, 80, 40   27. T   29. T   31. F   33. 162   35. 36   37. From the figure, the angles
shown are corresponding angles. Therefore, the posts are parallel, by Th. 4-8.

Page 206   Chapter Test   1. $\overline{AB} \parallel \overline{DC}$ 3. $\overrightarrow{KH} \parallel \overrightarrow{MP}$ 5. m∠1 = 100, m∠2 = 120   7. 180   9. 140
11. 61   13. 720   15. 24

CHAPTER 5: USING PARALLEL LINES

Page 210   Classroom Exercises   1. $\overline{BC}$ 3. ∠CBA   5. $\overline{QA}$ 7. 40   9. QD (or QB)   11. 180   13. $\overline{SR}$
and $\overline{TQ}$, $\overline{ST}$ and $\overline{RQ}$ 15. ∠S and ∠SRQ, ∠SRQ and ∠Q, ∠Q and ∠STQ, ∠STQ and ∠S   17. m∠2 = 25, m∠3
= 25, m∠4 = 110, m∠S = 45, m∠SRQ = 135, m∠STQ = 135   19. C; Th. 5-5   21. NC

Page 211   Written Exercises   1. T; Cor. 5-2   3. T; Cor. 5-3   5. T; Cor. 5-2 and def. of congruent segments
7. F; △ABC ≅ △ACD by Th. 5-1   9. 72   11. 135, 45   13. 129, 51, 51   15. 8   17. 105   19. 34
21. 39   23. Reasons: 1. Given   2. (1). Th. 5-1   3. (2). CPCTC   25. 1. line k ∥ line m; $\overline{RY} \perp$ line m;
$\overline{SZ} \perp$ line m   (Given)   2. $\overline{RY} \parallel \overline{SZ}$ ((1). Th. 4-7)   3. RYZS is a parallelogram. ((1), (2). Def. of parallelogram)
4. $\overline{RY} ≅ \overline{SZ}$ ((3). Cor. 5-2)   5. RY = SZ ((4). Def. of congruent segments)   27. Given: Parallelogram
ABCD; $\overline{AE} \perp \overline{BD}; \overline{CF} \perp \overline{BD}$ Prove: $\overline{AE} ≅ \overline{CF}; \overline{AE} \parallel \overline{CF}$ 1. $\overline{AE} \perp \overline{BD}; \overline{CF} \perp \overline{BD}$ (Given)   2. $\overline{AE} \parallel \overline{CF}$
((1). Th. 4-6)   3. ∠BEA and ∠DFC are right angles. ((1). Def. of perpendicular lines)   4. △BEA and △DFC
are right triangles. ((3). Def. of right triangle)   5. ABCD is a parallelogram. (Given)   6. $\overline{AB} ≅ \overline{CD}$
((5). Cor. 5-2)   7. $\overline{AB} \parallel \overline{CD}$ ((5). Def. of parallelogram)   8. ∠EBA ≅ ∠FDC ((7). Th. 4-3)
9. △BEA ≅ △DFC ((4), (6), (8). HA Post.)   10. $\overline{AE} ≅ \overline{CF}$ ((9). CPCTC)

29. Given: Parallelogram SQRT   Prove: ∠1 and ∠2 are supplementary; ∠2 and ∠3 are supplementary; ∠3 and ∠4 are supplementary; ∠4 and ∠1 are supplementary. 1. SQRT is a parallelogram. (Given)   2. Extend the sides of SQRT. ((1). Post. 4)   3. $\overleftrightarrow{SQ} \parallel \overleftrightarrow{TR}$, $\overleftrightarrow{ST} \parallel \overleftrightarrow{QR}$ ((2). Def. of parallelogram)   4. ∠1 and ∠2, ∠2 and ∠3, ∠3 and ∠4, ∠4 and ∠1 are pairs of interior angles on the same side of a transversal. ((2), (3). Def. of interior angles on the same side of a transversal) 5. ∠1 and ∠2, ∠2 and ∠3, ∠3 and ∠4, ∠4 and ∠1 are supplementary. ((4). Th. 4-5)   **31.** PR = 8, QS = 20

Page 215 Classroom Exercises 1. P; Th. 5-7   **3.** NP; $\overline{LN}$ is not parallel to $\overline{KJ}$.   **5.** P; Th. 4-2 and Th. 5-8   **7.** Th. 5-9   **9.** Th. 5-8   **11.** Def. of parallelogram   **13.** Th. 5-9 and defs. of midpoint and bisector

Page 215 Written Exercises 1. T; Th. 4-11 and def. of parallelogram   **3.** F; Th. 4-11, Transitive Prop., Th. 5-8   **5.** NP; The figure is not necessarily a parallelogram.   **7.** P; Th. 5-9   **9.** P; Th. 4-2 and def. of parallelogram   **11.** P; Def. of parallelogram   **13.** P; CPCTC and Th. 5-9 (or Th. 5-8)   **15.** P; Defs. of midpoint and bisector; Th. 5-9   **17.** Reasons: 1. Given   2. Def. of midpoint   3. Vertical Angle Th. 4. SAS Post.   5. CPCTC   6. Th. 4-2   7. Def. of midpoint   8. Transitive Prop.   9. Th. 5-8   **19.** Reasons: 1. Given   2. Cor. 5-2   3. Def. of congruent segments   4. Def. of betweenness of points   5. Substitution Prop.   6. Given   7. Addition Prop.   8. Def. of congruent segments   9. Def. of parallelogram   10. Th. 5-8 **21.** T; Contrapositive of Cor. 5-2   **23.** Given: Quadrilateral ABCD; $\overline{AD} \cong \overline{CB}$, $\overline{AB} \cong \overline{CD}$ Prove: Quadrilateral ABCD is a parallelogram.   1. Quadrilateral ABCD; $\overline{AD} \cong \overline{CB}$; $\overline{AB} \cong \overline{CD}$. (Given)   2. Draw diagonal AC. ((1). Post. 4)   3. $\overline{AC} \cong \overline{AC}$ (Identity)   4. △ABC ≅ △CDA ((1), (3). SSS Post.)   5. ∠DCA ≅ ∠BAC; ∠DAC ≅ ∠BCA ((4). CPCTC)   6. $\overline{DC} \parallel \overline{AB}$; $\overline{DA} \parallel \overline{CB}$ ((5). Th. 4-2)   7. ABCD is a parallelogram. ((1), (6). Def. of parallelogram)   **25.** m∠A = 64, m∠B = 116, m∠C = 64, m∠D = 116; Yes **27.** Given: $\overline{PS} \cong \overline{ED}$; ∠3 ≅ ∠4   Prove: PDES is a parallelogram.   1. ∠3 ≅ ∠4 (Given)   2. $\overline{PS} \parallel \overline{ED}$ ((1). Th. 4-2)   3. $\overline{PS} \cong \overline{ED}$ (Given)   4. PDES is a parallelogram. ((2), (3). Th. 5-8) **29.** 1. VKHF is a parallelogram. (Given)   2. $\overline{FH} \parallel \overline{VK}$ ((1). Def. of parallelogram)   3. $\overline{FH} \cong \overline{VK}$ ((1). Th. 5-3)   4. FH = VK ((3). Def. of congruent segments)   5. G is the midpoint of $\overline{FH}$; L is the midpoint of $\overline{VK}$. (Given)   6. FG = $\frac{1}{2}$FH; LK = $\frac{1}{2}$VK ((5). Midpoint Th.)   7. FG = $\frac{1}{2}$VK ((4), (6). Substitution Prop.)   8. FG = LK ((6), (7). Substitution Prop.)   9. $\overline{FG} \cong \overline{LK}$ ((8). Def. of congruent segments) 10. KGFL is a parallelogram. ((2), (9). Th. 5-8)   **31.** Given: Quadrilateral ABCD; ∠A and ∠B are supplementary; ∠B and ∠C are supplementary; ∠C and ∠D are supplementary; ∠A and ∠D are supplementary. Prove: ABCD is a parallelogram.   1. ABCD is a quadrilateral; ∠A and ∠B are supplementary; ∠A and ∠D are supplementary. (Given)   2. ∠A and ∠B are interior angles of $\overline{AD}$ and $\overline{BC}$ and are on the same side of transversal AB; ∠A and ∠D are interior angles of $\overline{AB}$ and $\overline{DC}$ and are on the same side of transversal AD. ((1). Def. of interior angles on the same side of a transversal)   3. $\overline{AD} \parallel \overline{BC}$, $\overline{AB} \parallel \overline{CD}$ ((1), (2). Th. 4-4)   4. ∴ ABCD is a parallelogram. ((3). Def. of parallelogram)   **33.** False; The quadrilateral could be a kite.   **35.** 1. DEFA is a parallelogram. (Given)   2. $\overline{DA} \parallel \overline{EF}$ ((1). Def. of parallelogram)   3. $\overline{DA} \cong \overline{EF}$ ((1). Cor. 5-2) 4. FBCE is a parallelogram. (Given)   5. $\overline{EF} \parallel \overline{CB}$ ((4). Def. of parallelogram)   6. $\overline{EF} \cong \overline{CB}$ ((4). Cor. 5-2) 7. $\overline{DA} \parallel \overline{CB}$ ((2), (5). Th. 4-11)   8. $\overline{DA} \cong \overline{CB}$ ((3), (6). Transitive Prop.)   9. ABCD is a parallelogram. ((7), (8). Th. 5-8)

Page 218 Geometry Review Capsule for Section 5-3 1. rectangle   **2.** rhombus   **3.** square **4.** parallelogram

Page 219 Career Applications 1. a. square   b. square   **3.** a. rectangle   b. hexagon   **5.** a. rectangle b. rectangle   **7.** a. quadrilateral   b. quadrilateral

Page 221 Classroom Exercises 1. parallelogram   **3.** rectangle, rhombus, parallelogram   **5.** rhombus, square   **7.** DS = 5.6, AP = 2.8, PH = 2.8, AH = 5.6

Page 221 Written Exercises 1. $AC = BD = 6$ m; $BE = DE = 3$ m 3. $m\angle ABE = 30$; $m\angle AEB = 120$; $m\angle BEC$ $= 60$; $m\angle EBC = 60$; $m\angle BCE = 60$; $m\angle CDE = 30$; $m\angle EDA = 60$ 5. Yes, by Th. 5-10 7. 45 9. $FH = GP$ $= 28$ cm 11. 90 13. 50 15. They are perpendicular; they bisect each other; they bisect the angles of the rhombus. 17. No 19. All the properties of parallelograms 21. Consecutive sides are congruent; the diagonals are perpendicular to each other; and the diagonals bisect the angles. 23. Square and rhombus; square and rectangle 25. (Refer to the figure in Example 2 on page 220.) 1. LTKE is a rhombus. (Given) 2. LTKE is a parallelogram. ((1). Def. of rhombus) 3. Draw diagonal ET. (Post. 4) 4. $\triangle ELT \cong \triangle EKT$ ((2), (3). Th. 5-1) 5. $\angle 1 \cong \angle 2$; $\angle LTE \cong \angle KTE$ ((4). CPCTC) 6. $\overline{ET}$ bisects $\angle KEL$; $\overline{ET}$ bisects $\angle LTK$. ((5). Def. of angle bisector) 7. Draw diagonal LK. (Post. 4) 8. $\triangle ELK \cong \triangle TLK$ ((2), (7). Th. 5-1) 9. $\angle ELK \cong \angle TLK$; $\angle LKE \cong \angle LKT$. ((8). CPCTC) 10. $\overline{LK}$ bisects $\angle ELT$; $\overline{LK}$ bisects $\angle TKE$. ((9). Def. of angle bisector) 27. 1. DSCK is a parallelogram. (Given) 2. $\overline{DS} \cong \overline{CK}$; $\overline{SC} \cong \overline{DK}$ ((1). Cor. 5-2) 3. $\overline{DS} \parallel \overline{CK}$ ((1). Def. of parallelogram) 4. $\angle 1 \cong \angle 3$ ((3). Th. 4-3) 5. $\angle 1 \cong \angle 2$ (Given) 6. $\angle 2 \cong \angle 3$ ((4), (5). Transitive Prop.) 7. $\overline{SC} \cong \overline{CK}$ ((6). Th. 3-3) 8. $\overline{DS} \cong \overline{SC} \cong \overline{CK} \cong \overline{DK}$ ((2), (7). Transitive Prop.) 9. DSCK is a rhombus. ((8). Def. of rhombus) 29. T; def. of rhombus 31. F; parallelogram whose vertices are not right angles are not rectangles. 33. F; only those rectangles with all four sides congruent are squares. 35. F; by definition, all squares are rectangles. 37. 1. Quadrilateral ABCD is a square. (Given) 2. Quadrilateral ABCD is a parallelogram. ((1). Exercise 36) 3. $\overline{AB} \cong \overline{BC}$; $\overline{BC} \cong \overline{CD}$; $\overline{CD} \cong \overline{AD}$; $\overline{AD} \cong \overline{AB}$ ((1). Def. of square) 4. Quadrilateral ABCD is a rhombus. ((2), (3). Def. of rhombus) 39. Given: Parallelogram ABCD with diagonals AC and BD; $\overline{AC} \cong \overline{BD}$ Prove: ABCD is a rectangle. 1. Parallelogram ABCD with diagonals AC and BD; $\overline{AC} \cong \overline{BD}$ (Given) 2. $\overline{CD} \cong \overline{CD}$ (Identity) 3. $\overline{AD} \cong \overline{BC}$ ((1). Cor. 5-2) 4. $\triangle ADC \cong \triangle BCD$ ((1), (2), (3). SSS Post.) 5. $\angle ADC \cong \angle BCD$ ((4). CPCTC) 6. $\angle ADC$ and $\angle BCD$ are supplementary. ((1). Th. 5-6) 7. $m\angle ADC + m\angle BCD = 180$ ((6). Def. of supplementary angles) 8. $2 m\angle ADC = 180$ ((5), (7). Substitution Prop.) 9. $m\angle ADC = 90$ ((8). Multiplication Prop.) 10. $\angle ADC$ is a right angle. ((9). Def. of right angle) 11. $\angle BCD$, $\angle ABC$, and $\angle DAB$ are right angles. ((1), (10). Exercise 38) 12. Parallelogram ABCD is a rectangle. ((10), (11). Def. of rectangle) 41. Yes 1. In parallelogram ABCD, $\overline{AC} \perp \overline{BD}$; $\overline{AC}$ intersects $\overline{BD}$ at E. (Given) 2. $\angle AEB \cong \angle CEB \cong \angle CED \cong \angle AED$ ((1). Th. 2-13) 3. $\overline{AE} \cong \overline{CE}$; $\overline{BE} \cong \overline{ED}$ ((1). Th. 5-5) 4. $\overline{BE} \cong \overline{BE}$; $\overline{CE} \cong \overline{CE}$; $\overline{DE} \cong \overline{DE}$; $\overline{AE} \cong \overline{AE}$ (Identity) 5. $\triangle AEB \cong \triangle CEB \cong \triangle CED$; $\triangle CED \cong \triangle AED$; $\triangle DEA \cong \triangle BEA$ ((2), (3), (4). SAS Post.) 6. $\overline{AB} \cong \overline{BC} \cong \overline{CD} \cong \overline{AD}$ ((5). CPCTC) 7. ABCD is a rhombus. ((1), (6). Def. of rhombus) 43. 1. Isosceles trapezoid TRAP, $\overline{TP} \cong \overline{RA}$; diagonals TA and RP (Given) 2. $\angle P \cong \angle A$ (The base angles of an isosceles trapezoid are congruent.) 3. $\overline{PA} \cong \overline{PA}$ (Identity) 4. $\triangle PTA \cong \triangle ARP$ ((1), (2), (3). SAS Post.) 5. $\overline{TA} \cong \overline{RP}$ (CPCTC) 45. In quadrilateral KQTE, $\overline{KQ} \cong \overline{KE}$ and $\overline{QT} \cong \overline{ET}$. (Given) 2. $\overline{KT} \cong \overline{KT}$ (Identity) 3. $\triangle KQT \cong \triangle KET$ ((1), (2). SSS Post.) 4. $\angle Q \cong \angle E$ ((3). CPCTC)

Page 224 Algebra Review Capsule for Section 5-4 1. $x = 4$ 2. $p = 3$ 3. $y = 5$ 4. $c = 5$ 5. $n = -2\frac{1}{3}$ 6. $t = 11$ 7. $d = 5$ 8. $w = 3\frac{1}{2}$ 9. $q = 5$

Page 226 Classroom Exercises 1. $4, 3, 2\frac{1}{2}$ 3. $EF = \frac{1}{2} BD$ 5. $EF = GH$

Page 226 Written Exercises 1. 13.6 3. 116 5. $11\frac{1}{2}$ 7. $m\angle 1 = 67$, $m\angle 2 = 113$, $m\angle 3 = 110$, $m\angle 4 = 70$, $m\angle C = 70$ 9. $1\frac{1}{2}$ 11. 10, 20 13. 8 15. 18 m 17. $y = 6\frac{1}{2}$ 19. 1. E, F, G, H are the midpoints of $\overline{AB}$, $\overline{BC}$, $\overline{CD}$, and $\overline{DA}$, respectively. (Given) 2. Draw diagonal AC. (Post. 4) 3. $\overline{HG} \parallel \overline{AC}$; $\overline{EF} \parallel \overline{AC}$ ((1), (2). Th. 5-13) 4. $\overline{HG} \parallel \overline{EF}$ ((3). Th. 4-11) 5. $HG = \frac{1}{2} AC$; $EF = \frac{1}{2} AC$ ((1), (2). Th. 5-13) 6. $HG = EF$ ((5). Substitution Prop.) 7. $\overline{HG} \cong \overline{EF}$ ((6). Def. of congruent segments) 8. EFGH is a parallelogram. ((4), (7). Th. 5-8) 21. 1. Extend $\overline{DE}$ to F so that $\overline{EF} \cong \overline{DE}$. (Ruler Post.) 2. Draw $\overline{BF}$. (Post. 4) 3. D is the midpoint of $\overline{AC}$; E is the midpoint of $\overline{BC}$. (Given) 4. $\overline{BE} \cong \overline{EC}$ ((3). Def. of midpoint) 5. $\angle 3 \cong \angle 4$ (Vertical Angle Th.) 6. $\triangle DEC \cong \triangle FEB$ ((1), (4), (5). SAS Post.) 7. $\angle 1 \cong \angle 2$ ((6). CPCTC) 8. $\overline{AD} \parallel \overline{BF}$ ((7). Th. 4-2) 9. $\overline{DC} \cong \overline{BF}$ ((6). CPCTC) 10. $\overline{AD} \cong \overline{DC}$ ((3). Def. of

midpoint)　11. $\overline{AD} \cong \overline{BF}$　((9), (10). Transitive Prop.)　12. ABFD is a parallelogram.　((8), (11). Th. 5-8)
13. $\overline{DE} \parallel \overline{AB}$　((12). Def. of parallelogram)　14. $\overline{DF} \cong \overline{AB}$　((12). Cor. 5-2)　15. DF = AB　((14). Def. of
congruent segments)　16. E is the midpoint of $\overline{DF}$.　((1). Def. of midpoint)　17. DE = $\frac{1}{2}$ DF　((16). Midpoint Th.)　18. DE = $\frac{1}{2}$ AB　((15), (17). Substitution Prop.)

23. Given: Pentagon PENTA; V, W, X, Y, Z are the midpoints of $\overline{PE}$, $\overline{EN}$, $\overline{NT}$, $\overline{AT}$, and
$\overline{AP}$, respectively.　Prove: VW + WX + XY + YZ + ZV = $\frac{1}{2}$(PN + ET + NA + TP + AE)
1. P = VW + WX + XY + YZ + ZV　(Def. of perimeter)　2. V, W, X, Y, Z are the
midpoints of $\overline{PE}$, $\overline{EN}$, $\overline{NT}$, $\overline{AT}$, and $\overline{AP}$.　(Given)　3. VW = $\frac{1}{2}$ PN; WX = $\frac{1}{2}$ ET;

XY = $\frac{1}{2}$ NA; YZ = $\frac{1}{2}$ TP; ZV = $\frac{1}{2}$ AE　((2). Th. 5-13)　4. VW + WX + XY + YZ + ZV

= $\frac{1}{2}$PN + $\frac{1}{2}$ET + $\frac{1}{2}$NA + $\frac{1}{2}$TP + $\frac{1}{2}$AE　((3). Add. Prop.)　5. VW + WX + XY + YZ + ZV = $\frac{1}{2}$(PN + ET + NA + TP

+ AE)　((4). Distributive Prop.)　6. P = $\frac{1}{2}$(PN + ET + NA + TP + AE)　((1), (5). Substitution Prop.)

Page 228　Algebra Review Capsule for Section 5-5　1. 9n + 1　2. 5p + 3　3. 9y + 6　4. 9r + 6
5. 2w + $\frac{1}{2}$　6. 3z + 3　7. d = 3　8. b = 6　9. h = 2　10. k = $6\frac{1}{3}$

Page 229　Classroom Exercises　1. 10.5 cm　3. 22.5 cm　5. 8, 16　7. AE = EC = 9

Page 229　Written Exercises　1. 20　3. $6\frac{3}{4}$　5. 4t + 1　7. 18　9. $27\frac{1}{2}$　11. $\frac{3}{8}$　13. $\frac{9}{16}$
15. 1. $\overleftrightarrow{AE} \parallel \overleftrightarrow{BF} \parallel \overleftrightarrow{CG} \parallel \overleftrightarrow{DH}$　(Given)　2. Draw $\overline{EX} \parallel \overline{AD}$, $\overline{FY} \parallel \overline{AD}$, and $\overline{GZ} \parallel \overline{AD}$　(Post. 15)　3. AEXB,
BFYC, and CGZD are parallelograms.　((1), (2). Def. of parallelogram)　4. $\overline{AB} \cong \overline{EX}$; $\overline{BC} \cong \overline{FY}$; $\overline{CD} \cong \overline{GZ}$
((3). Cor. 5-2)　5. $\overline{AB} \cong \overline{BC} \cong \overline{CD}$　(Given)　6. $\overline{EX} \cong \overline{FY} \cong \overline{GZ}$　((4), (5). Transitive Prop.)　7. $\overline{EX} \parallel \overline{FY}$
$\parallel \overline{GZ}$　((2). Th. 4-11)　8. $\angle 4 \cong \angle 5 \cong \angle 6$　((7). Th. 4-9)　9. $\angle 1 \cong \angle 2 \cong \angle 3$　((1). Th. 4-9)　10. $\triangle$EXF
$\cong \triangle$FYG $\cong \triangle$GZH　((6), (8), (9). Cor. 4-17)　11. $\overline{EF} \cong \overline{FG} \cong \overline{GH}$　((10). CPCTC)
17. 1. ABCD is an isosceles trapezoid.　(Given)　2. $\overline{AD} \cong \overline{BC}$　((1). Def. of isosceles trapezoid)　3. $\overline{DE} \perp \overline{AB}$;
$\overline{CF} \perp \overline{AB}$　(Given)　4. $\angle$DEA and $\angle$CFB are right angles.　((3). Def. of perpendicular lines)　5. $\triangle$EAD and
$\triangle$FBC are right triangles.　((4). Def. of right triangle)　6. $\overline{DC} \parallel \overline{AB}$　((1). Def. of trapezoid)　7. DE = CF
((6). Cor. 5-4)　8. $\overline{DE} \cong \overline{CF}$　((7). Def. of congruent segments)　9. $\triangle$EAD $\cong \triangle$FBC　((2), (5), (8). HL Th.)
19. Given: ABCD is a trapezoid; $\overleftrightarrow{XY}$ bisects $\overline{AB}$; $\overleftrightarrow{XY} \parallel \overline{AD} \parallel \overline{BC}$　Prove: $\overleftrightarrow{XY}$ bisects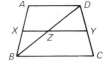
$\overline{CD}$.　1. Draw diagonal BD. Call the intersection of $\overline{BD}$ and $\overline{XY}$ point Z.　(Post. 4)
2. $\overleftrightarrow{XY} \parallel \overline{AD} \parallel \overline{BC}$　(Given)　3. $\overline{XY}$ bisects $\overline{AB}$　(Given)　4. In $\triangle$ABD, $\overline{XY}$ bisects
$\overline{BD}$.　((2), (3). Cor. 5-16)　5. In $\triangle$BCD, $\overline{XY}$ bisects $\overline{CD}$.　((2), (4). Cor. 5-16)
21. Bases: 16, 24; median: 20　**23.** Bases: 34, 62; median: 48　**25.** E　**27.** F
29. I　**31.** m$\angle$ADR = 25, m$\angle$DAB = 25, m$\angle$R = 65, m$\angle$RDB = 65, m$\angle$B = 115,
m$\angle$RAB = 115
33. 1. ABCD is a parallelogram with $\overline{AB}$ extended to E.　(Given)　2. $\angle$ADC and $\angle$BCD are supplementary.
((1). Th. 5-6)　3. $\angle$ADC and $\angle$CEB are supplementary.　(Given)　4. $\angle$BCD $\cong \angle$CEB　((2), (3). Th. 2-4)
5. $\overline{DC} \parallel \overline{AE}$　((1). Def. of parallelogram)　6. $\angle$BCD $\cong \angle$CBE　((5). Th. 4-3)　7. $\angle$CBE $\cong \angle$CEB
((4), (6). Transitive Prop.)　8. $\overline{CB} \cong \overline{CE}$　((7). Th. 3-3)　9. $\overline{CB} \cong \overline{AD}$　((1). Cor. 5-2)　10. $\overline{AD} \cong \overline{CE}$
((8), (9). Transitive Prop.)　11. AECD is an isosceles trapezoid.　((5), (10). Def. of isosceles trapezoid)
35. RS = 11　**37.** Given: ABCD is an isosceles trapezoid; E, F, G, H are the midpoints of $\overline{AB}$, $\overline{BC}$, $\overline{CD}$, and
$\overline{AD}$, respectively.　Prove: EFGH is a rhombus.　1. Draw diagonals AC and BD.　(Post. 4)　2. ABCD is an
isosceles trapezoid.　(Given)　3. $\overline{AD} \cong \overline{BC}$　((2). Def. of isosceles trapezoid)　4. $\angle$A $\cong \angle$B　((2). Ex. 34)
5. $\overline{AB} \cong \overline{AB}$　(Identity)　6. $\triangle$ABD $\cong \triangle$BAC　((3), (4), (5). SAS Post.)　7. $\overline{AC} \cong \overline{BD}$　((6). CPCTC)
8. AC = BD　((7). Def. of congruent segments)　9. E, F, G, H are the midpoints of $\overline{AB}$, $\overline{BC}$, $\overline{CD}$, and $\overline{AD}$.

(Given)   10. $EF = \frac{1}{2}AC$; $FG = \frac{1}{2}BD$; $GH = \frac{1}{2}AC$; $HE = \frac{1}{2}BD$; $\overline{EF} \parallel \overline{AC}$; $\overline{FG} \parallel \overline{BD}$; $\overline{GH} \parallel \overline{AC}$; $\overline{HE} \parallel \overline{BD}$ ((9). Th. 5-13)   11. $EF = \frac{1}{2}BD$; $GH = \frac{1}{2}BD$ ((8), (10). Substitution Prop.)   12. $EF = FG = GH = HE$ ((10), (11). Substitution Prop.)   13. $\overline{EF} \cong \overline{FG} \cong \overline{GH} \cong \overline{HE}$ ((12). Def. of congruent segments)   14. $\overline{EF} \parallel \overline{GH}$; $\overline{FG} \parallel \overline{HE}$ ((10). Th. 4-11)   15. EFGH is a parallelogram.   ((14). Def. of parallelogram)   16. EFGH is a rhombus.   ((14), (15), (13). Def. of rhombus)

Page 233   **Review**   1. $\overline{PA}$ 2. $\overline{AR}$ 3. PWR   4. $\overline{OR}$ 5. ARP   6. WPA   7. m∠WRA = 60
8. m∠PAR = 120   9. PW = 12   10. AO = 8   11. $\overline{TE}$ 12. $\overline{PE}$ 13. $\overline{YE}$, $\overline{TP}$ 14. ∠PET (or ∠PYT)
15. rectangle, square   16. parallelogram, rectangle, rhombus, square   17. rectangle, square   18. rhombus, square   19. 4.6   20. 127   21. 4.4   22. 40   23. 6   24. 12   25. 60   26. 10.95

Page 235   **Applications**   1. m∠B = 55, m∠C = 125, m∠D = 55   3. In triangles BOR, and DAR, ∠1 ≅ ∠2 by the Vertical Angle Th., and m∠1 = m∠2. But m∠1 + m∠3 + m∠5 = 180 and m∠2 + m∠6 + m∠4 = 180 by the Triangle Sum Th. Thus, m∠3 + m∠5 = m∠6 + m∠4 by substitution and the Addition Prop. Since it is given that BR = OR and AR = DR, m∠3 = m∠5 and m∠6 = m∠4 by Th. 3-1. Thus, 2m∠3 = 2m∠4 by substitution and m∠3 = m∠4 by the Multiplication Prop. Therefore BO ∥ AD by Th. 4-2.   5. D and E are given as the midpoints of $\overline{BC}$ and $\overline{AC}$, respectively. Thus, by Th. 5-13, $ED = \frac{1}{2}AB$. If ED = 7 cm, then $7 = \frac{1}{2}AB$, and AB = 14 cm, using the Multiplication Prop.   7. If lines were drawn from B, C, and D perpendicular to each of the first three floors, three right angles would be formed. ∠BAH ≅ ∠CBG ≅ ∠DCF by Th. 4-9. Therefore, by Cor. 4-17, the three right triangles would be congruent, and $\overline{AB} \cong \overline{BC} \cong \overline{CD}$ by CPCTC.
9. 1. $\overline{AE} \parallel \overline{CD}$; AE = CD   (Given)   2. $\overline{AE} \cong \overline{CD}$ ((1). Def. of congruent segments)   3. ACDE is a parallelogram.   ((1), (2). Th. 5-8)   4. $\overline{AC} \cong \overline{ED}$ ((3). Cor. 5-2)   5. AC = ED   ((4). Def. of congruent segments)
6. P is the midpoint of $\overline{AB}$; K is the midpoint of $\overline{BC}$.   (Given)   7. $\overline{PK} \parallel \overline{AC}$; $PK = \frac{1}{2}AC$ ((6). Th. 5-13)
8. $\overline{AC} \parallel \overline{ED}$ ((3). DEf. of parallelogram)   9. $\overline{PK} \parallel \overline{ED}$ ((7), (8). Th. 4-11)   10. ∠KPQ ≅ ∠EMQ; ∠PKQ ≅ ∠MEQ   ((9). Th. 4-3)   11. $EM = \frac{1}{2}ED$ (Given)   12. $EM = \frac{1}{2}AC$ ((5), (11). Substitution Prop.)
13. PK = EM   ((7), (12). Substitution Prop.)   14. $\overline{PK} \cong \overline{EM}$ ((13). Def. of congruent segments)
15. △KPQ ≅ △EMQ   ((10), (14). ASA Post.)   16. $\overline{KQ} \cong \overline{EQ}$ ((15). CPCTC)   17. KQ = EQ   ((16). Def. of congruent segments)

Page 236   **Geometry Review Capsule for Section 5-6**   < 2. < 3. > 4. < 5. >,< (or <,>)

Page 237   **Classroom Exercises**   1. ∠4   3. m∠4 > m∠A   5. m∠A = m∠3   7. m∠A > m∠B

Page 238   **Written Exercises**   1. m∠C < m∠A < m∠B   3. 1. Given   2. Def. of angle bisector   3. Th. 4-1   4. Substitution Prop.   5. By Cor. 4-14, a triangle can have no more than one right or one obtuse angle. In a right triangle, the measure of the right angle is greater than the measure of either acute angle. The hypotenuse is the side of the triangle opposite the right angle. It is the longest side by Th. 5-19.   7. 1. Given   2. Th. 3-1   3. Def. of betweenness of rays   6. Def. of congruent angles   7. Substitution Prop.   8. Th. 5-19
9. 1. m∠X > m∠4   (Given)   2. LK > XL   ((1). Th. 5-19)   3. △KLM is isosceles.   (Given)   4. $\overline{LK} \cong \overline{KM}$ ((3). Def. of isosceles triangle)   5. KM > XL   ((2), (4). Substitution Prop.)   11. 1. WE + EA > WA; NE + EG > GN   (Given)   2. WE + EN = WN; EG + EA = AG   (Def. of betweenness of points)   3. WE + EA + NE + EG > WA + GN   ((1). If a > b and c > d, then a + b > c + d.)   4. WE + NE + EA + EG > WA + GN   ((3). Comm. Prop.)   5. WN + AG > WA + GN   ((2), (4). Subst. Prop.)   13. 1. GHEF is a rectangle.   (Given)
2. ∠HEF and ∠GFE are right angles   ((1). Def. of rectangle)   3. ∠HEF ≅ ∠GFE   ((2). Cor. 2-12)
4. m∠HEF = m∠GFE   ((3). Def. of congruent angles)   5. m∠HEF = m∠1 + m∠3; m∠GFE = m∠2 + m∠4   (Def. of betweenness of rays)   6. m∠1 + m∠3 = m∠2 + m∠4   ((4), (5). Substitution Prop.)   7. m∠1 > m∠2   (Given)   8. m∠3 < m∠4   ((6), (7). For real numbers a, b, c, and d, if a = b and c < d, then a − c > b − d. (Exercise 30, page 161))   15. Hypothesis: m∠B > m∠A and AC = BC or AC < BC. If AC = BC, then ∠B ≅ ∠A by Th. 3-1 and m∠B = m∠A by definition of congruent angles. But ∠B cannot both equal m∠A

and be greater than m∠A. If AC < BC, then m∠B < m∠A by Theorem 5-18. But m∠B cannot be both less than and greater than m∠A. Thus, a contradiction is reached if AC = BC or if AC < BC. Therefore, AC > BC.
17. Given: Parallelogram ABCD with diagonal AC; AB < BC Prove: m∠BAC > m∠DAC 1. Parallelogram ABCD with diagonal AC. (Given) 2. △ABC ≅ △CDA ((1). Th. 5-1) 3. ∠BCA ≅ ∠DAC ((2). CPCTC)
4. m∠BCA = m∠DAC ((3). Def. of congruent angles) 5. AB < BC (Given) 6. m∠BCA < m∠BAC
((5). Th. 5-18) 7. m∠DAC < m∠BAC, or m∠BAC > m∠DAC ((4), (6). Substitution Prop.)
19. 1. AD bisects ∠A; D is on BC. (Given) 2. In △ADB, m∠ADC > m∠DAB. ((1). Th. 4-1) 3. m∠DAB = m∠DAC ((1). Def. of angle bisector) 4. m∠ADC > m∠DAC ((2), (3). Substitution Prop.) 5. AC > CD ((4). Th. 5-19) **21.** In △QRS, 2x + 2y + 2z = 180, or 2x + 2y < 180, and x + y < 90. In △RTS, x + y + w = 180, 180 − w = x + y, 180 − w < 90, 90 − w < 0, w > 90, and m∠T > 90. **23.** Given: △KJL with M on KL; △JML is isosceles with base ML. Prove: KJ > JL 1. m∠LMJ > m∠K (Th. 4-1) 2. △JML is isosceles. (Given) 3. ∠LMJ ≅ ∠L ((2). Th. 3-1) 4. m∠LMJ = m∠L ((3). Def. of congruent angles) 5. m∠L > m∠K ((1), (4). Substitution Prop.) 6. KJ > JL ((5). Th. 5-19) **25.** Let a, b, and c represent the lengths of the sides and h the length of the altitude to the side with length c. 1. h < a; h < b (Th. 5-20) 2. h + h < a + h; a + h < a + b ((1). Addition Prop. of Inequality) 3. 2h < a + b ((2). Transitive Prop. of Inequality) 4. h < ½(a + b) ((3). Multiplication Prop. of Inequality) **27.** Given: Parallelogram ABCD; AB ≠ BC Prove: AC does not bisect ∠DCB. 1. In parallelogram ABCD, draw AC. (Post. 4) 2. AB > BC or AB < BC (Comparison Prop. of Inequality) 3. m∠ACB > m∠BAC or m∠ACB < m∠BAC ((2). Th. 5-18) 4. △DAC ≅ △BCA ((1). Th. 5-1) 5. m∠BAC = m∠DCA ((4). CPCTC) 6. m∠ACB > m∠DCA or m∠ACB < m∠DCA ((3), (5). Substitution Prop.) 7. AC does not bisect ∠DCB. ((6). Def. of angle bisector)
29. Given: Isosceles △RST with base RT. Prove: RT < 2RS 1. △RST is isosceles. (Given) 2. RS ≅ TS ((1). Def. of isosceles triangle) 3. RS = TS ((2). Def. of congruent segments) 4. Draw the altitude from S. Label the altitude SW. (Th. 3-14) 5. SW ⊥ RT ((4). Def. of altitude) 6. RW < RS; WT < TS ((5). Th. 5-20) 7. RW + WT < RS + WT; WT + RS < RS + TS ((6). Addition Prop. of Inequality) 8. RW + WT < RS + TS ((7). Transitive Prop. of Inequality) 9. RW + WT = RT (Def. of betweenness of points) 10. RT < RS + TS ((8), (9). Substitution Prop.) 11. RT < RS + RS ((3), (10). Substitution Prop.) 12. RT < 2RS ((11). Distributive Prop.)

Page 242 Algebra Review Capsule for Section 5-7 1. m > 3 2. x > 6 3. c < 2 4. n > 27 5. z < 2 6. p > 11 7. f > 13 8. x > 1.9 9. q > 8 10. t < 6 11. v < 10 12. y > −5 13. p > −1 14. t > 6 15. r > 4 16. m < −12

Page 244 Classroom Exercises 1. b 3. b 5. c

Page 245 Written Exercises 1. BC + AC > AB, AB + AC > BC 3. Yes 5. Yes 7. Yes 9. Yes 11. Yes 13. Yes 15. > 17. 3 19. 2 21. x > 2 23. 2, 8 25. 6 mm, 30 mm 27. 0.5 cm, 16.1 cm 29. y − x, x + y **31.** 1. In circle O, OA ≅ OC, OB ≅ OD. (Given) 2. DC > AB (Given) 3. m∠COD > m∠AOB ((1), (2). Th. 5-23) **33.** 1. In △XYZ, XZ ≅ YZ. (Given) 2. WZ ≅ WZ (Identity) 3. YW > XW (Given) 4. m∠1 > m∠2 ((1), (2), (3). Th. 5-23) **35.** 1. CD is the perpendicular bisector of AB. (Given) 2. Draw FB. (Post. 4) 3. AD ≅ DB ((1). Def. of segment bisector) 4. FD ≅ FD (Identity) 5. ∠ADF ≅ ∠BDF ((1). Th. 2-13) 6. △AFD ≅ △BFD ((3), (4), (5). SAS Post.) 7. FA ≅ BF ((6). CPCTC) 8. EF + BF > EB (Th. 5-21) 9. EF + FA > EB ((7), (8). Substitution Prop.) 10. EA = EF + FA (Def. of betweenness of points) 11. EA > EB ((9), (10). Substitution Prop.)
37. 1. r + s > d; q + t > d (Th. 5-21) 2. r + s + (q + t) > d + (q + t); q + t + d > d + d ((1). Addition Prop. of Inequality) 3. r + s + q + t > q + t + d ((2). Commutative Prop.) 4. r + s + q + t > 2d ((2), (3). Transitive Prop. of Inequality) **39.** 1. In hexagon ABCDEF, AC, CE, and AE are drawn. (Given) 2. AC < AB + BC; CE < CD + DE; AE < EF + FA ((1). Th. 5-21) 3. AC + CE + AE < AB + BC + CD + DE + EF + FA (For real numbers a, b, c, and d, if a < b and c < d, then a + c < b + d. **41.** Using Th. 5-21, d₁ < a + b and d₁ < c + k. Adding the two inequalities, 2d₁ < a + b + c + k. Again using Th. 5-21, d₂ < b + c and d₂ < a + k.

Adding the two inequalities, $2d_2 < a + b + c + k$. Adding the inequality for $2d_1$ and the inequality for $2d_2$, we have $2(d_1 + d_2) < 2(a + b + c + k)$ or $d_1 + d_2 < a + b + c + k$.

Page 249 Classroom Exercises 1. A-$\overset{\leftrightarrow}{CQ}$-B   3. C-$\overset{\leftrightarrow}{AB}$-Q   5. A-$\overset{\leftrightarrow}{QB}$-C   7. 90

Page 250 Written Exercises 1. Yes; def. of a plane angle of a dihedral angle   3. No; angles KQM and MQO are plane angles of different dihedral angles.   5. d   7. c and d   9. b   11. 12   13. 45   15. 45
17. 45   19. 45   21. Equilateral; 60   23. 90   25. C-$\overset{\leftrightarrow}{XY}$-D, A-$\overset{\leftrightarrow}{XY}$-E   27. A-$\overset{\leftrightarrow}{YX}$-C, B-$\overset{\leftrightarrow}{YX}$-D   29. B-$\overset{\leftrightarrow}{ZW}$-Y, A-$\overset{\leftrightarrow}{XY}$-Z   31. A transversal plane for planes I and II.   33. $\angle 1 \cong \angle 2$ 35. If the plane angles are congruent, they have the same measure by definition. The measure of a dihedral angle is the measure of any of its plane angles. Therefore, the two dihedral angles have the same measure and are congruent.

Page 252 Applications 1. Yes; Th. 3-3   3. No; $m\angle I > m\angle K$ by Th. 5-18   5. Yes; Th. 5-19   7. It is given that BC = EF = 1 m. Thus, $\overline{BC} \cong \overline{EF}$. Also, since the doors are the same size, AC = DF, and $\overline{AC} \cong \overline{DF}$. By the Hinge Th., since $m\angle ACB < m\angle DFE$, AB < DE.   9. $\angle BRC$ and $\angle FVG$, $\angle CRD$ and $\angle GVH$, $\angle DRA$ and $\angle HVE$, $\angle ARB$ and $\angle EVF$ 11. $\overset{\leftrightarrow}{RV}$

Page 254 Review 1. $\angle GLH$ 2. $\angle 1$ 3. $m\angle 1 > m\angle G$ 4. $m\angle K > m\angle 1$ 5. HG > HK   6. Statements: 3. AD = BC   Reasons: 1. Post. 4   2. Th. 5-21   4. Substitution Prop.   7. R-$\overset{\leftrightarrow}{SV}$-T   8. R-$\overset{\leftrightarrow}{SV}$-T   9. $\overline{SV}$
10. V-$\overset{\leftrightarrow}{SR}$-T   11. $\angle VST$

Page 255 Chapter Objectives and Review 1. parallelogram, rectangle   3. trapezoid   5. parallelogram, rectangle, rhombus, square   7. TQR, TSR   9. TR   11. Yes; Th. 5-7   13. Yes; Th. 4-2 and Th. 5-8   15. Yes; H-L Th. and Th. 5-7   17. rhombus   19. rectangle   21. $m\angle C = 83$, $m\angle 1 = 108$, $m\angle 2 = 72$, $m\angle 3 = 25$, $m\angle 4 = 72$, $m\angle 5 = 83$ 23. QR = 5.5   25. 11   27. $\frac{1}{2}(x + y)$ 29. =   31. >   33. False; Th. 5-21
35. True; Th. 5-21   37. True; Th. 5-21   39. B-$\overset{\leftrightarrow}{AT}$-D   41. $\triangle ATB$, $\triangle TBD$ 43. In right triangle KJL, $m\angle L = 55$. Therefore, $m\angle K = 35$ by the Triangle-Sum Th. Thus, KJ > KL by Th. 5-19.   45. $\overline{CF}$

Page 258 Chapter Test 1. parallelogram, rectangle, rhombus, square   3. rhombus, square   5. rectangle, square   7. square   9. is supplementary to   11. $11\frac{1}{2}$ 13. $\overline{PR}$ **15.** 1. In rectangle RSTW, Q is the midpoint of $\overline{RW}$. (Given)   2. RQ = QW ((1). Def. of midpoint)   3. $\overline{RQ} \cong \overline{QW}$ ((2). Def. of congruent segments)   4. $\angle R$ and $\angle W$ are right angles. ((1). Def. of rectangle)   5. $\angle R \cong \angle W$ ((4). Cor. 2-12)
6. RSTW is a parallelogram. ((1). Def. of parallelogram)   7. $\overline{RS} \cong \overline{WT}$ ((6). Cor. 5-2)   8. $\triangle QWT \cong \triangle QRS$ ((3), (5), (7). SAS Post.)

CHAPTER 6: SIMILARITY

Page 261 Classroom Exercises 1. $\frac{3}{4}$ 3. $\frac{4}{5}$ 5. $\frac{1}{3}$ 7. $\frac{5}{1}$ 9. y = 8   11. $\frac{12}{2} = \frac{18}{3}, \frac{3}{18} = \frac{2}{12}, \frac{2}{12} = \frac{3}{18}$
Answers may vary.

Page 262 Written Exercises 1. $\frac{2}{3}$ 3. $\frac{1}{2}$ 5. $\frac{2}{1}$, or 2   7. $\frac{1}{3}$ 9. $\frac{1}{1}$, or 1   11. $\frac{a}{b}$ 13. $\frac{3}{2}$ 15. Yes
17. No   19. No   21. Yes   23. $x = 4\frac{2}{3}$ 25. x = 12   27. x = 2   29. $x = 1\frac{5}{16}$ (For Ex. 31 and 33, answers may vary.)   31. $\frac{7}{3} = \frac{21}{9}, \frac{3}{9} = \frac{7}{21}, \frac{9}{3} = \frac{21}{7}$ 33. $\frac{2}{9} = \frac{50}{225}, \frac{9}{225} = \frac{2}{50}, \frac{225}{9} = \frac{50}{2}$ 35. $\frac{x}{y} = \frac{7}{4}$ 37. $\frac{y}{x} = \frac{10}{15}$
39. $\frac{q}{7} = \frac{w}{4}$ 41. $\frac{b}{a} = \frac{r}{m}, \frac{m}{a} = \frac{r}{b}$ 43. $\frac{b}{r} = \frac{a}{m}, \frac{m}{r} = \frac{a}{b}$ 45. 9, 12   47. 36, 54   49. 30, 60, 120, 150
51. x = 12   53. $x = \frac{1}{2}$ 55. $x = -1\frac{2}{3}$ 57. x = 2

Page 264 **Applications** 1. $\frac{5}{1}$ 3. $\frac{8}{1}$ 5. 6 ft 7. 4.7 cm

Page 265 **Algebra Review Capsule for Section 6-2** 2. 3.87 3. 2.83 4. 7.07 5. 3.46 6. 11.53
7. 6.40 9. x = 9 or −9 10. x = 13 or −13 11. x = 100 or −100 12. x = 15 or −15 13. x = 0.3 or
−0.3 14. x = 0.5 or −0.5 16. x = 3.32 or −3.32 17. x = 4.80 or −4.80 18. x = 6.40 or −6.40 ·
19. x = 9.70 or −9.70 20. x = 8.54 or −8.54 21. x = 9.06 or −9.06

Page 267 **Classroom Exercises** 1. $\frac{5+9}{9}=\frac{10+18}{18}, \frac{5-9}{9}=\frac{10-18}{18}$ 3. $\frac{15+20}{20}=\frac{11+x}{x}, \frac{15-20}{20}=\frac{11-x}{x}$
5. $\frac{20+12}{12}=\frac{50+30}{30}, \frac{20-12}{12}=\frac{50-30}{30}$ 7. $\frac{3+2}{2}=\frac{7+x}{x}, \frac{3-2}{2}=\frac{7-x}{x}$ 9. 6 11. 6a 13. $7\frac{1}{2}$

Page 268 **Written Exercises** 1. T 3. F 5. T 7. T 9. x + 7 11. $\frac{5+13}{13}=\frac{20+52}{52}$ 13. $\frac{2+y}{y}$
$=\frac{8+5}{5}$ 15. $\frac{7-9}{9}=\frac{56-72}{72}$ 17. $\frac{x-3}{3}=\frac{7-2}{2}$ 19. 20 21. 9 23. 10 25. $\sqrt{ab}$ 27. $3\sqrt{5}$
29. $12\sqrt{2}$ 31. $20\sqrt{3}$ 33. $\frac{6\sqrt{5}}{5}$ 35. $\frac{\sqrt{7}}{7}$ 37. $\frac{\sqrt{2}}{6}$ 39. $\frac{\sqrt{6}}{4}$ 41. $\frac{2\sqrt{14}}{7}$ 43. 11.53 45. 13.04
47. $7\frac{1}{2}$ 49. $\frac{21y^2}{x}$ 51. $\frac{bc}{a}$ 53. $\frac{9}{20}$ 55. $\frac{\sqrt{10}}{6}$ 57. $\frac{1}{4}$ 59. $\frac{\sqrt{5}}{10}$ 61. $\frac{\sqrt{6}}{2}$ 63. $10\sqrt{3}$ mm 65. Given: $\frac{a}{b}$
$=\frac{c}{d}$ Prove: $\frac{a \pm b}{b}=\frac{c \pm d}{d}$ 1. $\frac{a}{b}=\frac{c}{d}$ (Given) 2. ad = bc ((1). Th. 6-1) 3. ad ± bd = bc ± bd ((2). Add. Prop.)
4. (a ± b)d = b(c ± d) ((3). Dist. Prop.) 5. $\frac{a \pm b}{b}=\frac{c \pm d}{d}$ ((4). If ad = bc, then $\frac{a}{b}=\frac{c}{d}$. Th. 6-1)

67. 1. $\frac{a}{b}=\frac{c}{d}=\frac{e}{f}=\frac{g}{h}$ (Given) 2. ad = bc; af = be; ah = bg ((1). Th. 6-1) 3. ab = ba (Commutative Prop.)
4. ab + ad + af + ah = ba + bc + be + bg ((2), (3). Add. Prop.) 5. a(b + d + f + h) = b(a + c + e + g)
((4). Dist. Prop.) 6. $\frac{a}{b}=\frac{a+c+e+g}{b+d+f+h}$ ((5). Th. 6-1) 7. $\frac{a+c+e+g}{b+d+f+h}=\frac{a}{b}$ ((6). Symmetric Prop.)

Page 269 **Calculator Exercises** 1. 6.71 3. 20.62 5. 66.27 7. 136.24

Page 270 **Applications** 1. By substituting 1 for w in Equation 2, $\ell^2 = 1(\ell + 1)$, $\ell^2 = \ell + 1$, $\ell^2 - \ell - 1 = 0$.
3. By the Table, $\sqrt{5} \approx 2.236$. Thus, $\ell \approx \frac{1 + 2.236}{2} = 1.618$. 5. Answers will vary. 7. 1.833 − 1.618
= 0.215 9. 5 by 8

Page 271 **Geometry Review Capsule for Section 6-3** 1. $\overline{AB}$ 2. AB 3. 5 4. 18 5. 1 unit long; $1\frac{1}{2}$
units long.

Page 272 **Classroom Exercises** 1. BD 3. $\frac{EA}{AC}$ 5. 32 7. BD 9. AE − CE

Page 273 **Written Exercises** 1. $14\frac{2}{9}$ 3. 9 5. 4 7. $11\frac{1}{4}$ 9. $37\frac{5}{7}$ 11. $11\frac{2}{3}$ 13. $1\frac{1}{2}$ 15. DC = 18;
EC = $13\frac{1}{2}$; BC = $22\frac{1}{2}$ 17. AD = $17\frac{5}{11}$; DC = $30\frac{6}{11}$; BC = 44 **19.** (Refer to the figure for Ex. 10-17 on
page 273) Given: △ABC with $\overline{DE} \parallel \overline{AB}$ Prove: $\frac{CA}{DA}=\frac{CB}{EB}, \frac{CA}{CD}=\frac{CB}{CE}$ 1. In △ABC, $\overline{DE} \parallel \overline{AB}$. (Given)
2. $\frac{CD}{DA}=\frac{CE}{EB}$, or $\frac{DA}{CD}=\frac{EB}{CE}$ ((1). Cor. 6-4) 3. $\frac{CD+DA}{DA}=\frac{CE+EB}{EB}$, or $\frac{DA+CD}{CD}=\frac{EB+CE}{CE}$ ((2). Th. 6-2)
4. CD + DA = CA; CE + EB = CB (Def. of betweenness of points) 5. $\frac{CA}{DA}=\frac{CB}{EB}, \frac{CA}{CD}=\frac{CB}{CE}$ ((3), (4). Substitution Prop.)

Page 275 **Classroom Exercises** 1. F; Cor. 6-6, if $\frac{AS}{SR}=\frac{AT}{TQ}$, then $\overline{ST} \parallel \overline{RQ}$. $\frac{7}{3} \ne \frac{8}{4}$, so $\overline{ST}$ is not parallel to $\overline{RQ}$.
3. 5 5. A line intersecting the interior of a triangle is parallel to one side if and only if it divides the other two
sides proportionally, or A line divides two sides of a triangle proportionally if and only if it is parallel to the
third side.

Page 275 Written Exercises 1. Yes 3. Yes 5. Yes 7. $5\frac{2}{5}$ 9. $10\frac{2}{3}$; $13\frac{1}{3}$ 11. $9\frac{3}{4}$ 13. $7\frac{1}{2}$

15. $13\frac{1}{3}$ 17. $\frac{ak}{b}$ 19. $\frac{bt}{k}$ 21. $\frac{r}{s}=\frac{q}{t}$, $\frac{q}{t}=\frac{y}{z}$, $\frac{r}{s}=\frac{y}{z}$ 23. Assume line QY is not parallel to line RZ. Using

Post. 15, through R draw $\overleftrightarrow{RK} \parallel \overleftrightarrow{QY}$. By Cor. 6-4, $\frac{PQ}{QR}=\frac{PY}{YK}$. If YK ≠ YZ, this contradicts the statement given

that $\frac{PQ}{QR}=\frac{PY}{YZ}$; the assumption is false and $\overleftrightarrow{QY} \parallel \overleftrightarrow{RZ}$. If YK = YZ, lines RZ and RK are the same line and

$\overleftrightarrow{QY} \parallel \overleftrightarrow{RZ}$. 25. a = 4, b = 6, c = 10, d = 15 27. a = 14, b = 19, c = 28, d = 38 29. a = 12, b = 15, c = 16,

d = 20 **31.** 1. In △GHK, $\overline{HB}$ bisects the exterior angle at H. (Given) 2. Through G; draw $\overline{GM} \parallel \overline{BH}$.
(Post. 15) 3. ∠1 ≅ ∠2 ((1). Def. of angle bisector) 4. ∠2 ≅ ∠3 ((2). Th. 4-9) 5. ∠1 ≅ ∠4 ((2). Th.
4-3) 6. ∠3 ≅ ∠4 ((3), (4), (5). Trans. Prop.) 7. $\overline{HG} \cong \overline{HM}$ ((6). Th. 3-3) 8. HG = HM ((7). Def. of

congruent segments) 9. $\frac{KH}{MH}=\frac{KB}{BG}$ ((2). Cor. 6-4) 10. $\frac{KH}{HG}=\frac{KB}{BG}$ ((8), (9). Substitution Prop.) 33. QT

= 20 35. QR = 20, RP = 16, QT = 25, TP = 20 **37.** 1. $\overline{YR}$ bisects ∠Y, $\overline{ZP}$ bisects ∠Z. (Given) 2. $\frac{e}{a+b}$

$=\frac{d}{c}$; $\frac{b}{c}=\frac{a}{d+e}$ ((1). Cor. 6-7) 3. ce = ad + bd; bd + be = ac ((2). Th. 6-1) 4. bd = ce − ad; bd = ac − be

((3). Add. Prop.) 5. ce − ad = ac − be ((4). Substitution Prop.) 6. be + ce = ac + ad ((5). Add. Prop.)
7. e(b + c) = a(c + d) ((6). Dist. Prop.) 8. $\frac{a}{e}=\frac{b+c}{c+d}$ ((7). Th. 6-1)

Page 278 Review 1. No 2. Yes 3. Yes 4. No 5. x = 21 6. $x=7\frac{1}{2}$ 7. $x=6\frac{3}{4}$ 8. $x=3\frac{1}{2}$

9. $\frac{6+11}{11}=\frac{12+22}{22}$, $\frac{6-11}{11}=\frac{12-22}{22}$ 10. $\frac{3+4}{4}=\frac{6+y}{y}$, $\frac{3-4}{4}=\frac{6-y}{y}$ 11. $\frac{x+9}{9}=\frac{14+18}{18}$, $\frac{x-9}{9}$

$=\frac{14-18}{18}$ 12. $\frac{2a+b}{b}=\frac{3+c}{c}$, $\frac{2a-b}{b}=\frac{3-c}{c}$ 13. 7.75 14. 11.22 15. 6.93 16. 6.48 17. $8\frac{2}{3}$

18. 96 19. 2b 20. 30y 21. $4\frac{1}{2}$, $10\frac{1}{2}$ 22. 3, 8 23. 7, 12 24. 9, 12 25. $10\frac{1}{2}$ 26. $23\frac{1}{3}$
27. $14\frac{22}{25}$ mm

Page 279 Consumer Applications 1. 13.7% 3. 14.6% 5. 11.1%

Page 280 Classroom Exercises 1. Yes, corresponding angles are congruent because both triangles are equiangular and corresponding sides have the same ratio because both triangles are equilateral. 3. No. corresponding angles are not congruent. 5. No, because $\frac{32}{36} \neq \frac{16}{20}$, so corresponding sides are not proportional. 7. Yes,

corresponding angles are congruent and $\frac{4}{5.2}=\frac{3}{3.9}$.

Page 281 Written Exercises 1. ∠H ≅ ∠R, ∠K ≅ ∠S, ∠M ≅ ∠T; $\frac{HK}{RS}=\frac{HM}{RT}$, $\frac{HK}{RS}=\frac{KM}{ST}$, $\frac{HM}{RT}=\frac{KM}{ST}$ 3. $\frac{1}{1}$ 5. $\frac{1}{2}$
7. $\frac{2}{1}$ 9. T 11. F; Any rectangle with unequal length and width will not be similar to any square (which is
also a rectangle). 13. T 15. T 17. T 19. $x=13\frac{1}{2}$; y = 18 21. e = 20; f = 54 23. g = 2.4; h = 3.6
25. 85 27. $8\frac{4}{13}$ **29.** Given: TUNA is a parallelogram; $\frac{TP}{AN}=\frac{TE}{AE}$ Prove: △PET ~ △NEA 1. TUNA is a
parallelogram. (Given) 2. TU ∥ AN ((1). Def. of parallelogram) 3. ∠TPE ≅ ∠ANE; ∠PTE ≅ ∠NAE
((2). Th. 4-3 4. ∠PET ≅ ∠NEA (Vertical Angle Th.) 5. Through E, draw a line parallel to $\overline{PU}$. Let S be a
point on this line. (Post. 15) 6. $\overline{ES} \parallel \overline{AN}$ ((2), (5). Th. 4-11) 7. $\frac{TE}{AE}=\frac{PE}{NE}$ ((5), (6). Th. 6-3) 8. $\frac{TE}{AE}$
$=\frac{TP}{AN}$ (Given) 9. $\frac{PE}{NE}=\frac{TP}{AN}$ ((7), (8). Substitution Prop.) 10. △PET ~ △NEA ((3), (4), (7), (8), (9). Def.
of similar polygons)

Page 282 Calculator Exercises See the answers to the Written Exercises above.

Page 283 Geometry Review Capsule for Section 6-6 1. ∠1 and ∠5, ∠2 and ∠6, ∠3 and ∠7, ∠4 and ∠8

2. ∠3 and ∠5, ∠4 and ∠6   3. 180   4. m∠2 = 80, m∠3 = 100, m∠4 = 80, m∠5 = 100, m∠6 = 80, m∠7 = 100, m∠8 = 80   5. m∠A = 55

Page 285 Classroom Exercises   1. Yes Th. 6-9   3. Yes, Cor. 6-11   5. No, because only one pair of angles is congruent.

Page 285 Written Exercises   1. ADE   3. $6\frac{2}{3}$ 5. x = 8; y = 12   **7.** 1. In △RPQ, $\overline{TS} \parallel \overline{PQ}$ (Given)
2. △RTS ~ △RPQ ((1). Cor. 6-12)   **9.** 1. In △MRO, $\overline{TS} \perp \overline{MR}$ and $\overline{OR} \perp \overline{MR}$. (Given) 2. $\overline{OR} \parallel \overline{TS}$
((1). Th. 4-6) 3. △MRO ~ △MST ((2). Cor. 6-12)   **11.** 1. Trapezoid DRTC with diagonals DT and CR
meeting at O; bases DC and RT. (Given) 2. $\overline{DC} \parallel \overline{RT}$ ((1). Def. of trapezoid) 3. △DOC ~ △TOR ((2). Cor.
6-12)   **13.** Reasons: 1. Given 2. Given 3. Th. 4-3 4. Cor. 6-10   **15.** No. Consider, for example, a
square and a rectangle that is not a square.   **17.** 1. $\overline{BD}$ and $\overline{AE}$ are altitudes of △ABC. (Given) 2. $\overline{BD} \perp \overline{AC}$;
$\overline{AE} \perp \overline{CB}$; ∠AEC and ∠BDC are right angles. ((1). Def. of altitude and perpendicular lines) 3. ∠C ≅ ∠C
(Identity) 4. △AEC ~ △BDC ((2), (3). Cor. 6-11   **19.** 1. In △ABC, $\overline{BD}$ and $\overline{AE}$ are altitudes. (Given)
2. $\overline{BD} \perp \overline{AC}$; $\overline{AE} \perp \overline{CB}$; ∠ADF and ∠AEC are right angles. ((1). Def. of altitude and perpendicular lines)
3. ∠DAF ≅ ∠CAE (Identity) 4. △ADF ~ △AEC ((2), (3). Cor. 6-11)   **21.** Given: △ABC is a right triangle
with the right angle at C; $\overline{CD} \perp \overline{AB}$ Prove: AB · AD = AC^2 1. △ABC is a right triangle; $\overline{CD} \perp \overline{AB}$ (Given)
2. ∠CDA is a right angle. ((1). Def. of perpendicular lines) 3. △CDA is a right triangle. ((2). Def. of right
triangle) 4. ∠A ≅ ∠A (Reflexive Prop.) 5. △ABC ~ △ACD ((1), (3), (4). Cor. 6-11) 6. $\frac{AB}{AC} = \frac{AC}{AD}$
((5). Def. of similar polygons) 7. AB · AD = AC · AC, or AB · AD = AC^2 ((6). Th. 6-1)   **23.** By Th. 5-13,
$\overline{AT} \parallel \overline{WE}$, $\overline{AR} \parallel \overline{FE}$, and $\overline{RT} \parallel \overline{WF}$. Since $\overline{AT} \parallel \overline{WE}$, ∠WRA ≅ ∠TAR and ∠TRE ≅ ∠RTA because they are alternate interior angles of parallel lines. ∠E ≅ ∠ATF and ∠W ≅ ∠TAF because they are corresponding angles of ∥
lines. Since $\overline{TR} \parallel \overline{WA}$ and $\overline{AT} \parallel \overline{WR}$, quadrilateral WATR is a parallelogram and ∠W ≅ ∠RTA because they are
opposite angles of the parallelogram. Since $\overline{AR} \parallel \overline{TE}$ and $\overline{AT} \parallel \overline{RE}$, quadrilateral ATER is a parallelogram and
∠E ≅ ∠TAR because they are opposite angles of the parallelogram. Therefore, ∠W ≅ ∠TRE ≅ ∠RTA ≅ ∠TAF
and ∠WRA ≅ ∠E ≅ ∠TAR ≅ ∠ATF. By Cor. 6-10, △WRA ~ △RET ~ △TAR ~ △ATF ~ △WEF.   **25.** This is
possible if three angles and two sides of one triangle are congruent to three angles and two sides of another triangle, but the sides are not corresponding sides.

Page 287 Geometry Review Capsule for Section 6-7   1. 18, 9   2. $\frac{2}{1}$ 3. $\frac{2}{1}$ 4. $\frac{2}{1}$

Page 290 Classroom Exercises   1. 15   3. $4\frac{2}{7}$ 5. MN

Page 290 Written Exercises   1. S; Th. 6-13   3. S; Th. 6-13   5. No   7. Yes, $\frac{1}{5}$ 9. $18\frac{4}{7}$ cm   11. 15 dm
13. Triangles TNG, NAG, ARN, RSA, TAN, TSR, and TRA   **15.** 1. $\frac{ZY}{ZW} = \frac{ZX}{ZU} = \frac{YX}{WU} = \frac{2}{5}$ (Given) 2. △ZYX
~ △ZWU (Th. 6-14) 3. ∠X ≅ ∠U ((2). Def. of similar triangles) 4. $\overline{XY} \parallel \overline{WU}$ ((3). Th. 4-2)   **17.** $\frac{AB}{ED}$
$= \frac{BC}{DC}, \frac{AB}{ED} = \frac{CA}{CE}, \frac{BC}{DC} = \frac{CA}{CE}$ **19.** 1. ∠A ≅ ∠E, ∠B ≅ ∠F (Given) 2. △ABC ~ △EFD ((1). Cor. 6-10) 3. G is the
midpoint of $\overline{AB}$; H is the midpoint of $\overline{EF}$. (Given) 4. $\overline{CG}$ is a median of △ABC; $\overline{DH}$ is a median of △EFD.
((3). Def. of median) 5. $\frac{AC}{ED} = \frac{CG}{DH}$ ((2), (4). Cor. 6-17)   **21.** 7.5   **23.** (Refer to the figure for Ex. 20 on
page 292.) Given: $\frac{BA}{ED} = \frac{AC}{DF} = \frac{BC}{EF}$ Prove: △BCA ~ △EFD   1. On $\overline{AB}$, mark off $\overline{AQ} \cong \overline{DE}$; On $\overline{AC}$, mark off
$\overline{AR} \cong \overline{DF}$. (Post. 8a) 2. Draw $\overline{QR}$. (Post. 4) 3. $\frac{BA}{ED} = \frac{AC}{DF} = \frac{BC}{EF}$ (Given) 4. $\frac{BA}{AQ} = \frac{AC}{AR}$ ((1), (3). Substitution
Prop.) 5. $\overline{QR} \parallel \overline{BC}$ ((4). Cor. 6-6) 6. △AQR ~ △ABC ((5). Cor. 6-12) 7. $\frac{BC}{QR} = \frac{BA}{AQ}$ ((6). Def. of similar
triangles) 8. QR = $\frac{BC(AQ)}{BA}$ ((7). Mult. Prop.) 9. EF = $\frac{BC(ED)}{BA} = \frac{BC(AQ)}{BA}$ ((3), (1). Mult. Prop.
and Substitution Prop.) 10. ∴ QR = EF ((8), (9). Substitution Prop.) 11. △EFD ≅ △QRA ((1), (10). SSS
Post.) 12. △EFD ~ △BCA ((6), (11). Substitution Prop.)   **25.** Given: △ABC ~ △DEF; $\overline{BR}$ is an altitude of
△ABC; $\overline{ES}$ is an altitude of △DEF. Prove: $\frac{BR}{ES} = \frac{AB}{DE} = \frac{BC}{EF} = \frac{AC}{DF}$ 1. △ABC ~ △DEF; $\overline{BR}$ is an altitude of △ABC;

$\overline{ES}$ is an altitude of $\triangle DEF$. (Given)   2. $\overline{BR} \perp \overline{AC}; \overline{EC} \perp \overline{DF}$ ((1). Def. of altitude)   3. $\angle BRC$ is a right angle; $\angle ESF$ is a right angle. ((2). Def. of perpendicular lines)   4. $\angle C \cong \angle F$ ((1). Def. of similar triangles)

5. $\triangle BRC \sim \triangle ESF$ ((3), (4). Cor. 6-11)   6. $\dfrac{BR}{ES} = \dfrac{BC}{EF}$ ((5). Corresponding sides of similar triangles are pro-

portional.)   7. $\dfrac{BC}{EF} = \dfrac{AC}{DF} = \dfrac{AB}{DE}$ ((1). Corresponding sides of similar triangles are proportional.)   8. $\dfrac{BR}{ES} = \dfrac{BC}{EF}$

$= \dfrac{AC}{DF} = \dfrac{AB}{DE}$ ((6), (7). Transitive Prop.)   **27.** Given: $\triangle ABC \sim \triangle DEF$; $\overline{AR}$ and $\overline{DT}$ bisect $\angle A$ and $\angle D$, respective-

ly; $\overline{AS}$ and $\overline{DU}$ are medians to $\overline{BC}$ and $\overline{EF}$, respectively.   Prove: $\dfrac{AR}{DT} = \dfrac{AS}{DU}$.   1. $\triangle ABC \sim \triangle DEF$ (Given)   2. $\angle A$

$\cong \angle D$ ((1). Def. of similar triangles)   3. $m\angle A = m\angle D$ ((2). Def. of cong. angles)   4. $\overline{AR}$ bisects $\angle A$; $\overline{DT}$ bisects

$\angle D$. (Given)   5. $2m\angle RAC = m\angle A; 2m\angle TDF = m\angle D$ ((4). Def. of angle bisector)   6. $2m\angle RAC = 2m\angle TDF$

((3), (5). Subst. Prop.)   7. $m\angle RAC = m\angle TDF$ ((6). Mult. Prop.)   8. $\angle C \cong \angle F$ ((1). Def. of similar triangles)

9. $\triangle RAC \sim \triangle TDF$ ((7), (8). Cor. 6-10)   10. $\dfrac{AR}{DT} = \dfrac{AC}{DF}$ ((9). Corresp. sides of similar triangles are proportional.

11. Median AS to side BC; median DV to side EF (Given)   12. $\dfrac{AS}{DU} = \dfrac{AC}{DF} = \dfrac{BC}{EF} = \dfrac{AB}{DE}$ ((1), (11). Cor. 6-17)

13. $\dfrac{AR}{DT} = \dfrac{AS}{DU}$ ((10), (12). Subst. Prop.)   **29.** 1. $\angle A \cong \angle BDE$; AB $\cdot$ DE = AD $\cdot$ BD (Given)   2. $\dfrac{AB}{AD} = \dfrac{BD}{DE}$ ((1).

Th. 6-1)   3. $\triangle BAD \sim \triangle BDE$ ((1), (2). Th. 6-13)   4. $\angle ABD \cong \angle DBE$ ((3). Def. of similar polygons)   5. In

$\triangle ABC$, $\overline{BD}$ bisects $\angle B$. ((4). Def. of angle bisector)   6. $\dfrac{AB}{AD} = \dfrac{BC}{CD}$ ((5). Cor. 6-7)   7. AB $\cdot$ CD = AD $\cdot$ BC ((6).

Th. 6-1)

Page 293   Review   1. Q   2. D   3. TP   4. ST   **5.** 1. ABCE is a parallelogram. (Given)   2. $\overline{AE} \parallel \overline{BC}$

((1). Def. of parallelogram)   3. $\triangle BCD \sim \triangle FED$ ((2). Cor. 6-12)   **6.** 1. $\overline{AB} \perp \overline{BD}; \overline{ED} \perp \overline{BD}$ (Given)

2. $\angle B$ and $\angle D$ are right angles. ((1). Def. of perpendicular lines)   3. $\triangle ABC$ and $\triangle CDE$ are right triangles.

((2). Def. of right triangle)   4. $\angle BCA \sim \angle ECD$ ((3), (4). Right-Triangle Similarity Cor.)   **7.** By Cor. 6-15,

the ratio of the perimeters of two similar triangles is the same as the ratio of any pair of corresponding sides.

The ratio of the perimeters is $\dfrac{2}{3}$.   **8.** By Cor. 6-17, the medians of a pair of similar triangles are proportional to

any pair of corresponding sides. $\dfrac{\text{Median from } \angle A}{\text{Median from } \angle F} = \dfrac{AB}{FG}$; by substitution, $\dfrac{\text{Median from } \angle A}{\text{Median from } \angle F} = \dfrac{4}{\frac{8}{3}}$, or $\dfrac{3}{2}$.

Page 294   Applications   1. I : $26\frac{2}{3}$ m; II : $53\frac{1}{3}$ m; III : 40 m   3. By the def. of similar polygons, correspond-

ing parts are proportional. Thus, $\dfrac{PQ}{BA} = \dfrac{PT}{BT}$.   5. It is given that PA′ = 2PA and PB′ = 2PB, so $\dfrac{PA}{PA'} = \dfrac{PB}{PB'} = \dfrac{1}{2}$.

Since $\angle APB \cong \angle A'PB'$ by the Reflexive Prop., $\triangle PAB \sim \triangle PA'B'$ by the SAS Similarity Th. By the def. of

similar polygons, $\dfrac{A'B'}{AB} = \dfrac{PA'}{PA}$.   7. Mark off points A″, B″ C″, and D″ along $\overrightarrow{PA}, \overrightarrow{PB}, \overrightarrow{PC}$, and $\overrightarrow{PD}$ so that PA″

$= \frac{1}{2}$PA, PB″ $= \frac{1}{2}$PB, PC″ $= \frac{1}{2}$PC, and PD″ $= \frac{1}{2}$PD. Then draw segments A″B″, B″C″, C″D″, and D″A″.

9. 330 ft   11. Every other rectangle (2nd, 4th, and so on)   13. $29\frac{1}{4}$ ft

Page 297   Chapter Objectives and Review   1. $x = 10\frac{2}{3}$ 3. $x = 8$ 5. $\dfrac{7}{3}$ 7. 16, 32   9. a. $\dfrac{3+5}{5} = \dfrac{12+20}{20}$

b. $\dfrac{3-5}{5} = \dfrac{12-20}{20}$ 11. a. $\dfrac{x+5}{5} = \dfrac{7+35}{35}$ b. $\dfrac{x-5}{5} = \dfrac{7-35}{35}$ 13. 10   15. 63   17. 2   19. 1   21. $5\frac{3}{5}$

23. $a = 21; b = 70; c = 56; d = 63$ **25.** 1. RK = a; TK = b; GR = 2a; HT = 2b (Given)   2. $\dfrac{RK}{GR} = \dfrac{a}{2a}$;

$\dfrac{TK}{HT} = \dfrac{b}{2b}$ ((1). Mult. Prop.)   3. $\dfrac{RK}{GR} = \dfrac{1}{2}; \dfrac{TK}{HT} = \dfrac{1}{2}$ ((2). Multiplicative Ident.)   4. $\overline{RT} \parallel \overline{GH}$ ((3). Cor.

6-6)   5. $\triangle RST \sim \triangle HSG$ ((4). Cor. 6-12)   27. SAS Similarity Th.   29. 9   31. 5 by 7   33. It is assumed

from the figure that both Sarah and the tree are upright, so two right triangles are formed. Also, since

it is known that light reflected from a mirror makes two equal angles, (see page 234) the two right triangles

are similar by the Right-Triangle Similarity Cor. Thus, $\dfrac{\text{Sarah's height}}{\text{distance to mirror}} = \dfrac{\text{tree's height}}{\text{distance to mirror}}$ or $\dfrac{1.3}{1.8} = \dfrac{x}{12.8}$;

$x \approx 9.2$ m.

Page 300 Chapter Test 1. $x = 9\frac{1}{3}$ 3. $x = 12$ 5. 21 7. 21 9. 2 11. F 13. $\triangle ACE, \triangle DCB$
15. 1. ABCD is a parallelogram; $\overline{DE} \perp \overline{AB}$; $\overline{DF} \perp \overline{BC}$ (Given) 2. $\angle AED$ and $\angle CFD$ are right angles. ((1). Def. of perpendicular lines) 3. $\triangle AED$ and $\triangle CFD$ are right triangles ((2). Def. of right triangle) 4. $\angle A \cong \angle C$ ((1). Cor. 5-3) 5. $\triangle AED \sim \triangle CFD$ ((3), (4). Cor. 6-11)

Page 301 Cumulative Review: Chapters 1-6 1. c 3. a 5. c 7. b 9. b 11. b 13. c 15. b 17. b 19. a 21. a

Page 303 Preparing for College Entrance Tests 1. c 3. b 5. e

Page 304 Preparing for College Entrance Tests 1. b 3. b

CHAPTER 7: RIGHT TRIANGLES

Page 307 Classroom Exercises 1. $5\sqrt{2}$ 3. $5\frac{1}{3}$ 5. 6

Page 308 Written Exercises 1. 1. $\frac{x}{m} = \frac{m}{y}$; 2. $\frac{a}{k} = \frac{k}{b}$; 3. $\frac{h}{q} = \frac{q}{k}$ 3. Cor. 7-3 5. Cor. 7-3 7. Cor. 7-2 9. 6 11. 8 13. $19\frac{4}{9}$ 15. 50 17. 6 **19.** 1. In $\triangle DEF$, $\angle D$ is a right angle; $\overline{DR}$ is the altitude to side EF. (Given) 2. $\triangle RDE \sim \triangle RFD$ (Th. 7-1) 3. $\frac{ER}{DR} = \frac{DR}{FR}$ (Def. of similar triangles) 21. 20 23. 3 25. 4 or 1 **27.** 1. $\frac{a}{b} = \frac{b}{c}$ (Given) 2. $ac = b^2$ ((1). Th. 6-1) 3. $ac - 1 = b^2 - 1$ ((2). Add. Prop.) 4. $ac - 1 = (1)(ac - 1)$ (Multiplicative Ident. Prop.) 5. $b^2 - 1 = (b + 1)(b - 1)$ (Factoring) 6. $(1)(ac - 1) = (b + 1)(b - 1)$ ((3), (4), (5). Substitution Prop.) 7. $\frac{ac - 1}{b - 1} = \frac{b + 1}{1}$ ((6). Th. 6-1) **29.** 1. $\frac{a}{b} = \frac{c}{d}$ (Given) 2. $ad = bc$ ((1). Th. 6-1) 3. $ad + d = bc + d$ ((2). Add. Prop.) 4. $ad + d = (a + 1)d$ (Dist. Prop.) 5. $bc + d = (1)(bc + d)$ (Multiplicative Ident. Prop.) 6. $(a + 1)d = (1)(bc + d)$ ((3), (4), (5). Substitution Prop.) 7. $\frac{a + 1}{1} = \frac{bc + d}{d}$ ((6). Th. 6-1) **31.** 1. Right triangle ABC; $\angle A$ is a right angle; $\overline{AD}$ is an altitude; $\frac{AC}{AB} = \frac{1}{2}$ (Given) 2. $\frac{BD}{AB} = \frac{AB}{BC}$, $\frac{CD}{AC} = \frac{AC}{BC}$ ((1). Cor. 7-3) 3. $AB \cdot AB = BD \cdot BC$, or $(AB)^2 = BD \cdot BC$; $CD \cdot BC = AC \cdot AC$ or $(AC)^2 = CD \cdot BC$ ((2). Th. 6-1) 4. $(AB)^2 = (AB)^2(1)$; $(AC)^2 = (AC)^2(1)$ (Mult. Ident. Prop.) 5. $(AB)^2(1) = BD \cdot BC$; $(AC)^2(1) = CD \cdot BC$ ((3), (4). Subst. Prop.) 6. $\frac{(AB)^2}{BD} = \frac{BC}{1}$, $\frac{(AC)^2}{CD} = \frac{BC}{1}$ ((5). Th. 6-1) 7. $\frac{(AC)^2}{CD} = \frac{(AB)^2}{BD}$ ((6). Subst. Prop.) 8. $\frac{(AC)^2}{(AB)^2} = \frac{CD}{BD}$ ((7). Th. 6-1) 9. If $\frac{AC}{AB} = \frac{1}{2}$, then $\frac{CD}{BD} = \frac{1}{4}$ ((1), (8). Given; Substitution Prop.)

Page 309 Algebra Review Capsule for Section 7-2 1. 10 2. a 3. 9b 4. 96 5. $\frac{20}{9}$, or $2\frac{2}{9}$ 6. $\frac{25c}{4}$, or $6\frac{1}{4}c$ 7. $3\sqrt{3}$ 8. $5\sqrt{2}$ 9. $4\sqrt{2}$ 10. $\frac{1}{3}$ 11. $\frac{2\sqrt{5}}{5}$, or $\frac{2}{5}\sqrt{5}$ 12. $\frac{3\sqrt{7}}{7}$, or $\frac{3}{7}\sqrt{7}$

Page 312 Classroom Exercises 1. 20 3. $7\sqrt{2}$ 5. 13 7. Yes 9. Yes

Page 312 Written Exercises 1. 25 3. $\frac{5}{2}$, or $2\frac{1}{2}$ 5. 1 7. $\frac{5}{2}$, or $2\frac{1}{2}$ 9. 11 11. 1 13. $4\sqrt{5}$ 15. No 17. Yes 19. Yes 21. $4\sqrt{2}$ 23. 30 dm 25. $2\sqrt{5}$ cm 27. $8\sqrt{2}$ 29. $h = \frac{\sqrt{3}}{2}s$ 31. $6\sqrt{3}$ 33. $8\sqrt{3}$ **35.** 1. $\angle C$ is a right angle; $\overline{DE} \perp \overline{AB}$ (Given) 2. $\angle A \cong \angle A$ (Ident.) 3. $\triangle AED \sim \triangle ACB$ ((1), (2). Cor. 6-11) 4. $\frac{AE}{AC} = \frac{AD}{AB}$ ((3). Def. of similar triangles) 5. $AE = c - a$; $AC = b$; $AD = b - k$; $AB = c$ (Given) 6. $\frac{c - a}{b} = \frac{b - k}{c}$, ((4), (5). Substitution Prop.) 7. $c^2 - ac = b^2 - bk$, or $ac - bk = c^2 - b^2$ ((6). Th. 6-1;

Add. Prop.)   8. $\dfrac{AE}{AC} = \dfrac{ED}{BC}$ ((3). Def. of similar triangles)   9. ED = k, BC = a (Given)   10. $\dfrac{c-a}{b} = \dfrac{k}{a}$ ((5),
(8), (9). Substitution Prop.)   11. ac − a² = bk; a² = ac − bk ((10). Th. 6-1; Add. Prop.)   12. a² = c² − b²
((7), (11). Trans. Prop.)   13. c² = a² + b² ((12). Add. Prop.)   37. 10√2   39. 12√3   41. 24
43. $\dfrac{4}{3}\sqrt{14}$ dm

Page 315   Applications   1. 127.3 ft   3. 3.5 m   5. 150 ft

Page 316   Algebra Review Capsule for Section 7-3   1. 2√2   2. 2√10   3. 10√2   4. 5√5   5. 7√2
6. 8√2   7. $\dfrac{5\sqrt{2}}{2}$, or $\dfrac{5}{2}\sqrt{2}$ 8. $\dfrac{4\sqrt{3}}{3}$, or $\dfrac{4}{3}\sqrt{3}$ 9. 4√2   10. $\dfrac{7\sqrt{2}}{2}$, or $\dfrac{7}{2}\sqrt{2}$ 11. 5√3   12. 2√5
13. 9   14. 4√6   15. 5√6   16. 6√3   17. 6√15   18. 20   19. 14√6   20. 50   21. 6√2   22. 20
23. 4√5   24. 4√21

Page 318   Classroom Exercises   1. 8√2   3. $\dfrac{3}{4}\sqrt{2}$ 5. 5√2   7. $\dfrac{21}{8}\sqrt{2}$ 9. 2√3, 4   11. 1, 2   13. 7,
14   15. 12, 12√3

Page 318   Written Exercises   1. 12√2   3. 4.63√2   5. 12√2   7. $\dfrac{5}{3}\sqrt{2}$ 9. 9   11. 8√3, 16
13. 15√3, 30   15. 12, 8√3   17. 11, 22   19. 3√3, 6√3   21. 9, 9√3   23. 2.8, 2.8√3   25. $\dfrac{17}{4}$,
$\dfrac{17}{4}\sqrt{3}$ 27. 8√2 cm   29. 15√2 dm   31. 5, 5√3, $\dfrac{10}{3}\sqrt{3}$, $\dfrac{5}{3}\sqrt{3}$, $\dfrac{20}{3}\sqrt{3}$ 33. 2√3, 4√3, 6, 2, 8
35. 6√3, 12√3, 18, 12, 6   37. 10 cm   39. 10√3 cm   41. 6√2 m   **43.** 1. Right △ABC with m∠A = 30
and m∠B = 60 (Given)   2. Extend $\overline{BC}$ to D so that $\overline{CD} \cong \overline{BC}$. (Ruler Post.)   3. Draw $\overline{AD}$. ((2). Post. 4)
4. $\overline{AC} \cong \overline{AC}$ (Ident.)   5. ∠ACB ≅ ∠ACD ((1). Th. 2-13)   6. △ACB ≅ △ACD ((2), (4), (5). SAS Post.)
7. ∠B ≅ ∠D ((6). CPCTC)   8. m∠D = 60 ((1), (7). Subst. Prop.)   9. m∠A + m∠D + m∠BAD = 180 (Triangle-Sum Th.)   10. 60 + 60 + m∠BAD = 180 ((1), (8). Subst. Prop.)   11. m∠BAD = 60 ((10). Add. Prop.)
12. ∠A ≅ ∠D ≅ ∠BAD ((1), (8), (11). Def. of congruent angles)   13. $\overline{AB} \cong \overline{AD} \cong \overline{BD}$ ((12). Th. 3-3)
14. AB = AD = BD ((13). Def. of congruent segments)   15. C is the midpoint of $\overline{BD}$. ((2). Def. of midpoint)
16. BC = $\dfrac{1}{2}$BD ((15). Midpoint Th.)   17. BC = $\dfrac{1}{2}$AB ((14), (16). Subst. Prop.)   18. (AC)² + (BC)² = (AB)²
((1). Pythagorean Th.)   19. (AC)² + ($\dfrac{1}{2}$AB)² = (AB)² ((17), (18). Subst. Prop.)   20. (AC)² = (AB)² − $\dfrac{1}{4}$(AB)²
((19). Add.)   21. (AC)² = $\dfrac{3}{4}$(AB)² ((20). Dist. Prop.)   22. AC = $\sqrt{\dfrac{3}{4}(AB)^2}$, or AC = $\sqrt{3\dfrac{(AB)^2}{4}}$ (Def. of
square root)   23. AC = $\dfrac{AB}{2}\sqrt{3}$ (Same as 22)   45. d = $\dfrac{P}{4}\sqrt{2}$

Page 320   Career Applications   1. $\dfrac{2}{5}$ 3. ∠C ≅ ∠C′ since they are right angles; ∠BAC ≅ ∠B′AC′ since they
are vertical angles. ∴ △ABC ∼ △AB′C′ by the AA Similarity Corollary.   5. Place the object and the lens so that
the image is formed the same distance from the lens as the object is located.

Page 321   Review   1. 2√10   2. 9   3. 3√3   4. 5√2   5. 13   6. c = 2√41   7. b = 16   8. b = √209
9. 7√5   10. 3√7   11. Yes   12. No   13. No   14. Yes   15. 4√2, 4√2, 4, 4   16. 3√2, 6, 3√2,
3√2   17. 10, 10√2, 10√2, 10   18. 13√3, 26   19. 3√3, 6√3   20. $\dfrac{23}{2}$, $\dfrac{23}{2}\sqrt{3}$

Page 322   Algebra Review Capsule for Section 7-4   1. 23   2. 10   3. 6   4. 149   5. 85   6. 49   7. 6
8. 258   9. 27

Page 324   Classroom Exercises   1. I : 3; II : 24; III : a   3. I : tan A = .75, tan B = 1.$\overline{3}$; II : tan A = 2.4,
tan B = .4167; III : tan A = $\dfrac{a}{b}$, tan B = $\dfrac{b}{a}$ 5. x = .1405   7. 49°   9. 171

Page 324   Written Exercises   1. 10; 5.1; 1.9608   3. 15.1; 7.7; 1.9610   5. .5714; 1.7500   7. 1.3333; .75
9. .5543   11. 4.7046   13. .5317   15. 11.4301   17. 30°   19. 78°   21. 44°   23. 1°   25. tan 51°

$= \dfrac{46}{x}$ 27. $\tan 28° = \dfrac{12}{x}$ 29. $\tan x = \dfrac{14}{12}$ 31. 270.1 33. 6.95 35. 1.92 37. 23° 39. 13.56 41. 29°
43. 8.05 45. $x \approx 33.36$ 47. $m\angle X = 54, m\angle Z = 36$ 49. 108.9

Page 327 Applications 1. 18.0 m 3. 494.2 m 5. 67°

Page 329 Classroom Exercises 1. $\dfrac{1}{2}$ 3. $\dfrac{\sqrt{3}}{2}$ 5. $\dfrac{\sqrt{2}}{2}$ 7. 1. .5000, .5000 2. .8660, .8660 3. .8660,
.8660 4. .5000, .5000 5. .7071, .7071 6. .7071, .7071 9. $\sin 55° = \dfrac{BC}{9}$ 11. $\sin 30° = \dfrac{4}{AB}$
13. $\sin 57° = \dfrac{AC}{23}$

Page 330 Written Exercises 1. 349 3. 228 5. 6.6 7. 20.6 9. 194.1 11. 245.8 13. 30 15. 37°
17. 26° 19. $\dfrac{\sqrt{2}}{2}$ 21. 1 23. $\dfrac{\sqrt{3}}{2}$ 25. 1 27. $\sqrt{3}$ 29. $\dfrac{1}{2}$ 31. $a = 6, m\angle A = 37, m\angle B = 53$ 33. $m\angle A$
$= 30, c = 31.2, a = 15.6$ 35. $c = 16.6, m\angle A = 57, m\angle B = 33$ 37. By def. of the trig. ratios, $\tan A = \dfrac{a}{b}$,

$\sin A = \dfrac{a}{c}$, and $\cos A = \dfrac{b}{c}$. Therefore, since $\dfrac{\sin A}{\cos A} = \dfrac{\dfrac{a}{c}}{\dfrac{b}{c}}$, $\dfrac{\sin A}{\cos A} = \dfrac{a}{b}$, and $\dfrac{\sin A}{\cos A} = \tan A$ by substitution.

39. $\sin y = \dfrac{b}{c}; \cos y = \dfrac{a}{c}$ $\therefore \sin^2 y + \cos^2 y = (\dfrac{b}{c})^2 + (\dfrac{a}{c})^2 = \dfrac{b^2 + a^2}{c^2} = \dfrac{c^2}{c^2} = 1$

Page 331 Calculator Exercises See the answers to the Written Exercises for page 324 above.

Page 332 Applications 1. 43.1 m 3. 51 5. 29.7 km

Page 334 Classroom Exercises 1. $\sin 34°$; $x = 56$ 3. $\sin 45°$; $x = 115$ 5. $\cos x$; $x = 20°$

Page 334 Written Exercises 1. 46 m 3. 9° 5. 15 m 7. 2560 m 9. 82 ft 11. 7 m 13. 635 m
15. 832 m 17. 542 m

Page 337 Review 1. $\dfrac{4}{3}, \dfrac{3}{4}$ 2. $\dfrac{12}{5}, \dfrac{5}{12}$ 3. $\dfrac{7}{24}, \dfrac{24}{7}$ 4. $\dfrac{3}{4}, \dfrac{4}{3}$ 5. 11.2 6. 4.2 7. 72° 8. $\dfrac{4}{5}, \dfrac{3}{5}, \dfrac{3}{5}, \dfrac{4}{5}$
9. $\dfrac{12}{13}, \dfrac{5}{13}, \dfrac{5}{13}, \dfrac{12}{13}$ 10. $\dfrac{7}{25}, \dfrac{24}{25}, \dfrac{24}{25}, \dfrac{7}{25}$ 11. $\dfrac{3}{5}, \dfrac{4}{5}, \dfrac{4}{5}, \dfrac{3}{5}$ 12. 7.0 13. 27° 14. 16.1 15. 65° 16. 5.9 m
17. 201 m

Page 339 Chapter Objectives and Review 1. 27 3. $10\dfrac{2}{3}$ 5. 10 7. 5 9. No 11. Yes 13. 16 15. 3
17. $9, 9\sqrt{3}$ 19. .0349 21. 44 23. 55, 35 25. 44 27. $\tan x°$ 29. about 7 31. $CB = 28$ m 33. 43°

Page 342 Chapter Test 1. 5.9 3. 9.2 5. 14.8 7. No 9. 13.9, 16 11. 14.5 13. 57° 15. 48.7 m

CHAPTER 8: CIRCLES

Page 345 Classroom Exercises 1. O 3. $\overline{CD}$ 5. $\overleftrightarrow{BK}$ 7. 2 9. 0 11. 2 13. 32 mm 15. 8 mm

Page 346 Written Exercises 1. $\overline{PE}, \overline{PC}$ 3. diameter; diameter 5. chord 7. tangent 9. chord; chord
11. CE 13. inside 15. 6 17. 7.62 19. $\dfrac{y}{2}$ 21. Any two tangent circles whose interiors do not intersect 23. Any two tangent circles whose interiors intersect 25. T; since a diameter is defined as a chord
27. T; by definition 29. F; any segment between a point on the circle and the center of the circle is a radius.
31. F; only two radii that form a straight angle form a diameter. 33. $4\sqrt{2}$ cm 35. $10\sqrt{3}$ m 37. $m\angle 1$
$= 55; m\angle 2 = 70; m\angle 3 = 70; m\angle 4 = 40; m\angle 5 = 70$

Page 347 Geometry Review Capsule for Section 8-2 **1.** If a triangle is isosceles then it has two congruent angles; If a triangle has two congruent angles then it is isosceles. **2.** If two triangles are similar then two pairs of corresponding angles are congruent; In two triangles, if two pairs of corresponding angles are congruent then the triangles are similar. **3.** If two lines cut by a transversal are parallel then two alternate interior angles are congruent; If two alternate interior angles are congruent then the two lines cut by the transversal are parallel. **4.** If two sides of a triangle are not congruent then the angles opposite these sides are not congruent; If two angles of a triangle are not congruent then the sides opposite these angles are not congruent.

Page 350 Classroom Exercises **1.** ∠APD, ∠DPB, ∠BPC, ∠CPA **3.** $\overparen{AD}$ and $\overparen{CB}$, $\overparen{AC}$ and $\overparen{DB}$ **5.** $\overparen{ADC}$, $\overparen{CAB}$, $\overparen{BAD}$ **7.** 120, 90, 70, 80, 200, 240

Page 350 Written Exercises **1.** 126 **3.** 116 **5.** 256 **7.** 234 **9.** 70 **11.** 110 **13.** 250 **15.** 180 **17.** Draw a central ∠ of two distinct concentric circles. **19.** 109 **21.** 180 **23.** Reasons: 2. Def. of congruent arcs 3. Def. of arc measure 4. Substitution Prop. 5. Def. of congruent angles **25.** 1. Segments AB and CD are diameters of circle O. (Given) 2. ∠DOA ≅ ∠BOC ((1). Vertical Angle Th.) 3. $\overparen{AD} \cong \overparen{BC}$ ((2). Th. 8-1) **27.** 1. $\overparen{TM} \cong \overparen{AE}$ (Given) 2. $\overparen{TA} \cong \overparen{EM}$ ((1). Common Arc Th.) **29.** 51 **31.** 77 **33.** 309 **35.** 283 **37.** 1. Circle O ≅ Circle P, ∠O ≅ ∠P (Given) 2. m∠O = m∠P ((1). Def. of congruent angles) 3. m$\overparen{AB}$ = m∠O; m$\overparen{CD}$ = m∠P ((2). Def. of arc measure) 4. m$\overparen{AB}$ = m$\overparen{CD}$ ((2), (3). Substitution Prop.) 5. $\overparen{AB} \cong \overparen{CD}$ ((4). Def. of congruent arcs) **39.** 60 **41.** m$\overparen{MSR}$ = 120; m$\overparen{SRQ}$ = 120; m$\overparen{SRP}$ = 180; m$\overparen{NRP}$ = 300 **43.** 1. Segment BD is a diameter in circle O. (Given) 2. Draw radii OA and OC in circle O. (Post. 4) 3. $\overline{OB} \cong \overline{OB}$ (Ident.) 4. $\overline{OA} \cong \overline{OC}$ ((2). Def. of circle) 5. $\overline{AB} \cong \overline{BC}$ (Given) 6. △ABO ≅ △CBO ((3), (4), (5). SSS Post.) 7. ∠ABD ≅ ∠CBD ((6). CPCTC) **45.** 1. In circle O, $\overline{AB} \cong \overline{BC} \cong \overline{CA}$ (Given) 2. Draw chords AB, BC, CA, radii OA, OB, and OC in circle O. (Post. 4) 3. ∠AOB ≅ ∠BOC ≅ ∠COA ((1), (2). Th. 8-1) 4. $\overline{OA} \cong \overline{OB} \cong \overline{OC}$ ((2). Def. of circle) 5. △AOB ≅ △BOC ≅ △COA ((3), (4). SAS Post.) 6. $\overparen{AB} \cong \overparen{BC} \cong \overparen{CA}$ ((5). CPCTC) 7. △ABC is equilateral. ((6). Def. of equilateral triangle) **47.** 1. In circle Q, chord AB is parallel to diameter RS. (Given) 2. Draw radii QA and QB. (Post. 4) 3. $\overline{QA} \cong \overline{QB}$ ((2). Def. of circle) 4. In △AQB, ∠A ≅ ∠B. ((3). Isosceles Triangle Th.) 5. ∠RQA ≅ ∠A; ∠SQB ≅ ∠B ((1). Th. 4-3) 6. ∠RQA ≅ ∠SQB ((4), (5). Trans. Prop.) 7. $\overparen{RA} \cong \overparen{SB}$ ((6). Th. 8-1)

Page 353 Applications **1.** 122 cm **3.** 61 cm **5.** 12.2 cm **7.** 90 **9.** 300

Page 354 Geometry Review Capsule for Section 8-3 (For Ex. 1-6, answers may vary.) **1.** Line ℓ ⊥ line m; Th. 2-10 and def. of perpendicular lines **2.** m∠1 = 90; Th. 4-9 **3.** AD = DC; Cor. 3-13 **4.** FH ⊥ EG; Th. 3-6 **5.** $\overline{AC} \cong \overline{BD}$; Th. 5-10 **6.** $\overline{AC} \perp \overline{BD}$; Th. 5-11

Page 356 Classroom Exercises **1.** Def. of congruent segments and Th. 8-4 **3.** Th. 8-1 **5.** Th. 8-5 **7.** Pythagorean Th. **9.** Th. 8-6 and def. of perpendicular lines **11.** In the same or in congruent circles, two chords are congruent if and only if their arcs are congruent; or, In the same or in congruent circles, two arcs are congruent if and only if their chords are congruent.

Page 356 Written Exercises **1.** $\overparen{AB} \cong \overparen{CD}$; Th. 8-4 **3.** Circle A ≅ circle B; def. of congruent circles; $\overline{PQ} \cong \overline{RS}$; Th. 8-3 **5.** $\overline{RS}$ is a diameter and $\overline{RS} \perp \overline{TV}$; Th. 8-6 **7.** $\overline{OB}$ bisects ∠AOB, so m∠1 = m∠BOC and ∠1 ≅ ∠BOC. Since it is given that ∠1 ≅ ∠2, ∠BOC ≅ ∠2 by the Trans. Prop. Thus, by Th. 8-1, $\overparen{BC} \cong \overparen{DE}$, and $\overline{BC} \cong \overline{DE}$ by Th. 8-3. **9.** 1. $\overline{AX} \cong \overline{XB}$; 1. Given 2. Th. 8-4 3. Def. of arc bisector 4. Given 5. Def. of segment bisector 6. Th. 8-6 **11.** Draw AQ, BQ, CQ, and DQ. (Post. 4) 2. $\overline{AQ} \cong \overline{BQ} \cong \overline{CQ} \cong \overline{DQ}$ ((1). Def. of circle) 3. $\overline{AB} \cong \overline{CD}$ (Given) 4. △ABQ ≅ △CDQ ((2), (3). SSS Post.) 5. ∠1 ≅ ∠2 ((4). CPCTC) 6. $\overparen{AB} \cong \overparen{CD}$ ((5). Th. 8-1) **13.** 1. $\overparen{AR} \cong \overparen{CS}$ (Given) 2. $\overparen{AC} \cong \overparen{RS}$ ((1). Common Arc Th.) 3. $\overline{AC} \cong \overline{RS}$

((2). Th. 8-3) **15.** 1. $\overline{GA} \cong \overline{TE}$ (Given) 2. $\overarc{GA} \cong \overarc{TE}$ ((1). Th. 8-4) 3. $\overarc{GT} \cong \overarc{AE}$ ((2). Common Arc Th.) **17.** DY = 6; PD = $3\sqrt{13}$; PO = $3\sqrt{13}$ **19.** 1. $\overline{AD} \perp \overline{AB}$, $\overline{DC} \perp \overline{BC}$; $\overline{BD}$ bisects $\angle ABC$ (Given) 2. $\angle ABD \cong \angle CBD$ ((1). Def. of angle bisector and congruent angles) 3. $\overline{BD} \cong \overline{BD}$ (Ident.) 4. $\triangle ABD \cong \triangle CBD$ ((1), (2). (3). HA Post.) 5. $\overline{AB} \cong \overline{BC}$ ((4). CPCTC) 6. $\overarc{AB} \cong \overarc{BC}$ ((5). Th. 8-4) 7. $m\overarc{AB} = m\overarc{BC}$ ((6). Def. of congruent arcs) **21.** 1. Diameter QR is perpendicular to chord AC (Given) 2. $\overarc{AR} \cong \overarc{CR}$ ((1). Th. 8-5) 3. $\overline{AR} \cong \overline{CR}$ ((2). Th. 8-3) 4. In $\triangle ARC$, $\angle RCA \cong \angle RAC$. ((3). Isosceles Triangle Th.) **23.** 1. Diameter AB $\perp \overline{XW}$ (Given) 2. $m\overarc{AX} = m\overarc{AW}$ ((1). Th. 8-5) 3. $\overarc{AXB} \cong \overarc{AWB}$ ((1). Def. of diameter) 4. $m\overarc{AXB} = m\overarc{AX} + m\overarc{XB}$; $m\overarc{AWB} = m\overarc{AW} + m\overarc{WB}$ (Def. of betweenness of points for circles 5. $m\overarc{AX} + m\overarc{XB} = m\overarc{AW} + m\overarc{WB}$ ((3), (4). Substitution Prop.) 6. $m\overarc{XB} = m\overarc{WB}$ ((2), (5). Substitution Prop.; Add. Prop.) 7. $\overarc{XB} \cong \overarc{WB}$ ((6). Def. of congruent arcs) **25.** 1. In circle O, diameter CE bisects segment AB at D; AD = DB (Given; definition of bisector) 2. Draw radii OA and OB. (Post. 4) 3. OA = OB ((2). Def. of circle) 4. $\overline{CE} \perp \overline{AB}$ ((1), (3). Th. 3-9) 5. Right $\triangle ADO \cong$ Right $\triangle BDO$ ((1), (3), (4). HL Th.) 6. $\angle AOE \cong \angle EOB$ ((5). CPCTC) 7. $\overarc{AE} \cong \overarc{EB}$ ((6). Th. 8-1) 8. Line CE bisects arc AB. ((7). Def. of bisector of an arc) **27.** Draw segments AD and BC. (Post. 4) 2. $\overline{AB} \cong \overline{CD}$ (Given) 3. $\overarc{ADB} \cong \overarc{CBD}$ ((2). Th. 8-4) 4. $m\overarc{ADB} = m\overarc{AD} + m\overarc{DB}$; $m\overarc{CBD} = m\overarc{CB} + m\overarc{BD}$ (Def. of betweenness of points for circles) 5. $m\overarc{AD} + m\overarc{DB} = m\overarc{CB} + m\overarc{BD}$ ((3), (4). Substitution Prop.) 6. $m\overarc{AD} = m\overarc{CB}$ ((5). Add. Prop.) 7. $\overline{AD} \cong \overline{CB}$ ((6). Th. 8-3) 8. $\overline{BD} \cong \overline{BD}$ (Ident.) 9. $\triangle ABD \cong \triangle CDB$ ((2), (7), (8). SSS Post.) 10. $\angle ABD \cong \angle CDB$ ((9). CPCTC) 11. $\overline{DE} \cong \overline{BE}$ ((10). Th. 3-3) 12. $\triangle DBE$ is isosceles with base BD. ((11). Def. of isosceles triangle)

Page 359 Review 1. $\overline{PR}, \overline{PS}$ 2. $\overleftrightarrow{RQ}$ 3. $\overleftrightarrow{TW}$ 4. $\overline{XY}, \overline{RS}, \overline{TW}$ 5. $\overline{RS}$ 6. 86 7. 40 8. 82 9. 159 10. 117 11. 157 12. 117 13. 161 14. 62 15. 84 16. 62 17. 84 18. 214 19. 146 20. 214 21. 298 22. congruent 23. diameter 24. chord, arc 25. arcs, congruent 26. chord, arc

Page 360 Algebra Review Capsule for Section 8-4 1. 6 2. $2\sqrt{2}$ 3. $3\sqrt{3}$ 4. $5\sqrt{2}$ 5. $2\sqrt{3}$ 6. $5\sqrt{3}$ 7. $6\sqrt{2}$ 8. 8 9. 14 10. $10\sqrt{3}$ 11. $3\sqrt{13}$ 12. $11\sqrt{2}$

Page 361 Classroom Exercises 1. a 3. c 5. b

Page 362 Written Exercises 1. 12, 24 3. 8 cm 5. OC = 6, AC = $6\sqrt{3}$; AB = $12\sqrt{3}$ 7. 24 9. $12\sqrt{3}$ cm 11. Isosceles right triangle 13. $4\sqrt{2}$ cm 15. 14 17. 10 **19. Part I** 1. Circle O; $\overline{AB} \cong \overline{CD}$; $\overline{OE} \perp \overline{AB}$; $\overline{OF} \perp \overline{CD}$ (Given) 2. Draw radii OA and OC. ((1). Post. 4) 3. OA = OC; $\overline{OA} \cong \overline{OC}$ ((2). Def. of circle and of cong. segments) 4. AE = $\frac{1}{2}$AB; CF = $\frac{1}{2}$CD ((1). Th. 8-5) 5. AE = CF; $\overline{AE} \cong \overline{CF}$ ((1), (4). Subst. Prop.; def. of congruent segments) 6. $\triangle AEO \cong \triangle CFO$ ((1), (3), (5). HL Th.) 7. $\overline{OE} \cong \overline{OF}$ ((6). CPCTC) **Part II** 1. Circle O; $\overline{OE} \perp \overline{AB}$; $\overline{OF} \perp \overline{CD}$; $\overline{OE} \cong \overline{OF}$ (Given) 2. Draw radii OA and OC. (Post. 4) 3. OA = OC; $\overline{OA} \cong \overline{OC}$ ((2). Def. of circle and congruent segments) 4. $\triangle AEO \cong \triangle CFO$ ((1), (3). HL Th.) 5. $\overline{AE} \cong \overline{CF}$ ((4). CPCTC) 6. AB = 2AE; CD = 2CF ((1). Th. 8-5) 7. AB = CD ((5), (6). Subst. Prop.) 8. $\overline{AB} \cong \overline{CD}$ ((7). Def. of congruent segments) **21.** 1. Circle O; OG < OH; $\overline{OG} \perp \overline{AB}$; $\overline{OH} \perp \overline{CD}$ (Given) 2. Draw $\overline{AE}$ so that AE = CD. (Post. 8a) 3. $\overline{AE} \cong \overline{CD}$ ((2). Def. of congruent segments) 4. Draw $\overline{OF} \perp \overline{AE}$. ((2). Th. 1-9) 5. Draw $\overline{FG}$. (Post. 4) 6. $\overline{OF} \cong \overline{OH}$ ((2). Th. 8-8) 7. OF = OH ((6). Def. of congruent segments) 8. OG < OF ((1), (7). Subst. Prop.) 9. m$\angle 1$ < m$\angle 3$ ((8). Th. 5-8) 10. $\angle OFA$ and $\angle OGA$ are right angles. ((1), (4). Def. of perpendicular lines) 11. m$\angle OFA$ = 90; m$\angle OGA$ = 90 ((10). Def. of right angle) 12. m$\angle 1$ + m$\angle 2$ = 90; m$\angle 3$ + m$\angle 4$ = 90 ((11). Def. of betweenness of rays) 13. m$\angle 1$ = 90 − m$\angle 2$; m$\angle 3$ = 90 − m$\angle 4$ ((12). Add. Prop.) 14. 90 − m$\angle 2$ < 90 − m$\angle 4$ ((9), (13). Subst. Prop.) 15. −m$\angle 2$ < − m$\angle 4$ ((14). Add. Prop. of Inequality) 16. m$\angle 2$ > m$\angle 4$ ((15). Mult. Prop. of Inequality) 17. AG > AF ((16). Th. 5-19) 18. $\overline{OG}$ is the perpendicular bisector of $\overline{AB}$; $\overline{OF}$ is the perpendicular bisector of $\overline{AE}$. ((1), (4). Th. 8-5) 19. AG = $\frac{1}{2}$AB; AF = $\frac{1}{2}$AE ((18). Def. of bisector) 20. $\frac{1}{2}$AB > $\frac{1}{2}$AE ((17), (19). Substitution Prop.) 21. AB > AE

((20). Mult. Prop. of Inequality) 22. AB > CD ((2), (21). Substitution Prop.) 23. $\frac{3}{2}$

Page 364 Geometry Review Capsule for Section 8-5 1. negation 2. contradiction 3. false 4. true

Page 366 Classroom Exercises 1. right triangle 3. isosceles triangle 5. 66

Page 366 Written Exercises 1. 50 3. right scalene 5. isosceles 7. 80 9. 10 11. 80 13. 10
15. 90 − a 17. 90 − a 19. $\overrightarrow{BA}$ and $\overrightarrow{BC}$ are tangents from external point B to circle O, meeting the circle at
points A and C. (Given) 2. Draw $\overline{AC}$. ((1). Post. 4) 3. $\overline{BA} \cong \overline{BC}$ ((1). Th. 8-13) 4. △ABC is isosceles.
((3). Def. of isosceles triangle) **21.** 1. $\overline{PA}$ and $\overline{PB}$ are tangent segments from point P to circle O; radius OB
and $\overline{AB}$ are drawn. (Given) 2. $\overline{OB} \perp \overline{BP}$ ((1). Th. 8-11) 3. m∠ABO + m∠ABP = m∠OBP = 90 ((2). Def. of
betweenness of rays and right angle) 4. $\overline{PA} \cong \overline{PB}$ ((1). Th. 8-13) 5. m∠ABP = m∠A ((4). Isosceles Triangle
Th.) 6. m∠A + m∠ABP + m∠P = 180 (Triangle-Sum Th.) 7. 2m∠ABP + m∠P = 180 ((5), (6). Subst. Prop.)
8. m∠P = 2m∠ABO ((3), (7). Subst. Prop.; Add. Prop.; Mult. Prop.) **23.** 1. $\overline{XY}$ and $\overline{XZ}$ are tangents to circle
T (Given) 2. $\overline{XY} \cong \overline{XZ}$ ((1). Th. 8-13) 3. $\overline{YT}$ and $\overline{ZT}$ are radii. (Given) 4. $\overline{YT} \cong \overline{ZT}$ ((3). Def. of circle)
5. $\overline{XT} \cong \overline{XT}$ (Ident.) 6. △XYT ≅ △XZT ((2), (4), (5). SSS Post.) 7. ∠YXT ≅ ∠ZXT ((6). CPCTC)
8. $\overline{XT}$ bisects ∠YXT ((7). Def. of angle bisector) **25.** 1. Tangent $\overline{MJ}$ and $\overline{MK}$ to circle O. (Given) 2. $\overline{MJ}$
≅ $\overline{MK}$ ((1). Th. 8-13) 3. Tangents $\overline{MK}$ and $\overline{MP}$ to O'. (Given) 4. $\overline{MK} \cong \overline{MP}$ ((3). Th. 8-13) 5. $\overline{MJ} \cong \overline{MP}$
((2), (4). Trans. Prop.) **27.** 1. $\overline{CE}$ and $\overline{NE}$ are tangent segments to circle O; $\overline{OC}$ and $\overline{ON}$ are radii.
(Given) 2. $\overline{CE} \perp \overline{OC}$, $\overline{EN} \perp \overline{ON}$ ((1). Th. 8-11) 3. m∠C = 90; m∠N = 90 ((2). Def. of perpendicular lines
and right angle) 4. Draw $\overline{CN}$. (Post. 4) 5. In △CEN and △CON, m∠CON + m∠C + m∠E + m∠N = 2(180).
(Th. 4-12) 6. m∠CON + m∠E = 180 ((3), (5). Substitution and Add. Prop.) 7. ∠CON and ∠E are supplementary. ((6). Def. of supplementary angles) **29.** Let O be the center of the larger circle, ∠BCA be ∠1,
∠ABC be ∠2, ∠ACO be ∠3, and ∠BCO be ∠4. 1. Through points C and O draw diameter CD of circle O. (Post.
4; def. of diameter) 2. $\overline{OC} \cong \overline{OB}$; $\overline{OC} \cong \overline{OA}$ (Def. of circle and congruent segments) 3. ∠1 ≅ ∠2; ∠3 ≅ ∠4
((2). Isosceles Triangle Th.) 4. m∠DOB = m∠1 + m∠2; m∠AOD = m∠3 + m∠4 (Cor. 4-18) 5. m∠DOB
= 2m∠1; m∠AOD = 2m∠3 ((3), (4). Def. of congruent angles; Substitution Prop.) 6. $\overline{AC}$ is a radius of circle A;
$\overline{AB}$ is a diameter of circle O. (Given) 7. Arc ADB is a semicircle. ((6). Def. of semicircle) 8. m$\overarc{ADB}$ = 180
((7). Def. of measure of a semicircle) 9. m$\overarc{BD}$ + m$\overarc{AD}$ = 180 ((8). Def. of betweenness of points for circles;
Substitution Prop.) 10. m∠DOB + m∠AOD = 180 ((9). Def. of arc measure; Substitution Prop.) 11. 2m∠1
+ 2m∠3 = 180 ((5), (10). Substitution Prop.) 12. m∠1 + m∠3 = 90 ((1). Mult. Prop.) 13. m∠ACB = 90
((12). Def. of betweenness of rays and Subst. Prop.) 14. $\overline{BC} \perp \overline{AC}$ ((13). Def. of perpendicular lines)
15. Line BC is tangent to circle A. ((6), (14). Th. 8-12) **31.** 1. O and O' trisect $\overline{AB}$; radius AO of circle O;
radius BO' of circle O'; O and O' intersect at X and Y. (Given) 2. Draw segments XO, XO', YO and YO'. (Post.
4) 3. AO = OO' = O'B ((1). Def. of segment trisector) 4. Circle O ≅ circle O' ((3). Def. of congruent circles)
5. XO = XO' = OO' = YO = YO' ((4). Def. of circle) 6. △XOO' and △YOO' are equilateral. ((5). Def. of equilateral triangle) 7. m∠XOO' = 60; m∠XO'O = 60 ((6). Cor. 4-16) 8. m∠OAX + m∠AXO = 60 ((7). Cor. 4-18;
Substitution Prop.) 9. $\overline{AO} \cong \overline{OX}$; $\overline{BO'} \cong \overline{O'X}$ (Def. of circle) 10. m∠OAX = m∠AXO ((9). Isosceles Triangle Th.) 11. m∠OAX = 30 ((8), (10). Substitution and Mult. Properties) 12. m∠OAY = 30 ((7)-(11).)
13. m∠XAY = 60 ((11), (12). Def. of betweenness of rays) 14. m∠O'BY = 30 ((7)-(11).) 15. $\overline{AX} \parallel \overline{BY}$
((11), (14). Th. 4-2) 16. Similarly, $\overline{BX} \parallel \overline{AY}$. ((7)-(11), (13)-(15).) 17. AYBX is a parallelogram.
((15), (16). Def. of parallelogram) 18. Angle AOX is supplementary to angle XOO'; Angle BOX is supplementary to angle XO'O. (Def. of linear pair; Linear Pair Post.) 19. ∠AOX ≅ ∠BOX ((7), (18). Def. of congruent angles; Th. 2-5) 20. △AOX ≅ △BOX ((5), (9), (19). SAS Post.) 21. $\overline{AX} \cong \overline{BX}$ ((20). CPCTC)
22. AYBX is a rhombus. ((17), (21). Def. of rhombus)

Page 368 Geometry Review Capsule for Section 8-6 1. $\overarc{AF}$ 2. $\overarc{FE}$ 3. $\overarc{CD}$ 4. $\overarc{DB}$ 5. $\overarc{CA}$ 6. $\overarc{AD}$
7. 27 8. 90 9. 63 10. 90 11. 167 12. 153

Page 370 Classroom Exercises 1. 44 3. ∠CBA (or ∠ABC) 5. 44, 22 7. 2a, a

Page 371 Written Exercises 1. $\overset{\frown}{UV}$ 3. $\overset{\frown}{XW}$ 5. $\overset{\frown}{YZ}$ 7. 40 9. 85 11. 18 13. 62 15. Yes 17. 20 19. $82\frac{1}{2}$ 21. Yes, because they intercept the same arc, arc YZ. 23. Angles EZF and EYF; yes 25. $\overset{\frown}{UAV}$ 27. $\overset{\frown}{XCW}$ 29. $\overset{\frown}{ZEY}$ 31. ∠B and ∠C; ∠D, ∠E and ∠F; ∠DZE and ∠DYE 33. 74 35. 180; 100; 50; 90; 40 37. 66; 44; 70 **39.** 1. $\overline{YU}$, $\overline{YZ}$, $\overline{ZW}$, and $\overline{WU}$ are chords of a circle; From point X outside the circle, $\overline{XZ}$ and $\overline{XU}$ are drawn. (Given) 2. Angles W and Y are inscribed angles. ((1). Def. of inscribed angle) 3. ∠W ≅ ∠Y ((2). Th. 8-16) 4. ∠X ≅ ∠X (Ident.) 5. △XYU ∼ △XWZ ((3), (4). Cor. 6-10)
41. 1. Angle ABC is inscribed in circle O; O is in the exterior of angle ABC. (Given) 2. Through B and O draw diameter BX. (Post. 4; def. of diameter) 3. m∠ABX = $\frac{1}{2}$(m$\overset{\frown}{AX}$); m∠CBX = $\frac{1}{2}$(m$\overset{\frown}{CX}$) ((1), (2). Case I of Th. 8-15) 4. m∠ABX = m∠ABC + m∠CBX (Def. of betweenness of rays) 5. m$\overset{\frown}{AX}$ = m$\overset{\frown}{AC}$ + m$\overset{\frown}{CX}$ (Def. of betweenness of points for circles) 6. m∠ABX − m∠CBX = $\frac{1}{2}$(m$\overset{\frown}{AX}$ − m$\overset{\frown}{CX}$) ((3). Add. and Dist. Prop.) 7. m∠ABC = $\frac{1}{2}$m$\overset{\frown}{AC}$ ((4), (5), (6). Add. and Substitution Prop.)

Page 373 Review 1. 10 2. $4\sqrt{65}$ 3. $8\sqrt{11}$; $8\sqrt{11}$ 4. 12; $12\frac{1}{2}$ 5. $4\sqrt{13}-8$ 6. 68; 22; 68 7. 34; 68 8. 40 9. 20 10. 54 11. 76 12. 38 13. 38

Page 376 Classroom Exercises 1. T; Th. 8-17 3. T; Cor. 8-18 5. F; Cor. 8-19 7. T; Cor. 8-19 9. T; Cor. 4-15 11. If an inscribed angle is a right angle, then it is inscribed in a semicircle; If an angle is inscribed in a semicircle, then it is a right angle.

Page 376 Written Exercises 1. 90 3. 120 5. 60 7. 80 9. 75 11. 130 13. 103 **15.** 1. $\overleftrightarrow{AB} \parallel \overleftrightarrow{CD}$ (Given) 2. m$\overset{\frown}{AC}$ = m$\overset{\frown}{DB}$ ((1). Cor. 8-18) 3. m$\overset{\frown}{CAB}$ = m$\overset{\frown}{AC}$ + m$\overset{\frown}{AB}$; m$\overset{\frown}{DBA}$ = m$\overset{\frown}{DB}$ + m$\overset{\frown}{AB}$ (Def. of betweenness of points for circles) 4. m$\overset{\frown}{CAB}$ = m$\overset{\frown}{DBA}$ ((2), (3). Subst. and Add. Prop.) 5. $\overset{\frown}{CAB}$ ≅ $\overset{\frown}{DBA}$ ((4). Def. of congruent arcs) **17.** 1. △ABC is inscribed in a circle; ∠C is a right angle; $\overline{AB}$ is the hypotenuse. (Given) 2. ∠C is inscribed in semicircle ACB. ((1). Cor. 8-17) 3. $\overline{AB}$ is a diameter. ((2). Def. of semicircle) **19.** 1. Parallel secants AB and RY in circle O. (Given) 2. Draw chord AY. (Post. 4) 3. ∠BAY ≅ AYR ((1), (2). Th. 4-3) 4. m∠BAY = m∠AYR ((3). Def. of congruent angles) 5. m∠BAY = $\frac{1}{2}$m$\overset{\frown}{BY}$; m∠AYR = $\frac{1}{2}$m$\overset{\frown}{AR}$ (Th. 8-15) 6. $\frac{1}{2}$m$\overset{\frown}{BY}$ = $\frac{1}{2}$m$\overset{\frown}{AR}$ ((5). Substitution Prop.) 7. m$\overset{\frown}{BY}$ = m$\overset{\frown}{AR}$ ((6). Mult. Prop.) 8. $\overset{\frown}{BY}$ ≅ $\overset{\frown}{AR}$ ((7). Def. of congruent arcs) **21.** 1. △ABE is inscribed in a circle; $\overline{AB}$ is a diameter; $\overline{DC} \perp \overline{AC}$; $\overline{AC}$ intersects $\overline{ED}$ at B; E, B and D are collinear (Given) 2. ∠E is inscribed in a semicircle. ((1). Def. of semicircle) 3. ∠E is a right angle. ((2). Th. 8-17) 4. ∠C is a right angle. ((1). Def. of perpendicular lines) 5. ∠E ≅ ∠C ((3), (4). Cor. 2-12) 6. ∠ABE ≅ ∠DBC ((1). Def. of vertical angles; Vertical Angle Th.) 7. △AEB ∼ △DCB ((5), (6). Cor. 6-10) **23.** 1. Diameter CD; X is the midpoint of chord EF; Y is the midpoint of chord GH. (Given) 2. $\overline{CD} \perp \overline{EF}$; $\overline{CD} \perp \overline{GH}$ ((1). Th. 8-7) 3. $\overline{GH} \parallel \overline{EF}$ ((2). Th. 4-6) 4. $\overset{\frown}{EG}$ = $\overset{\frown}{FH}$ ((3). Cor. 8-18) **25.** 1. Inscribed △ABC; $\overline{BE}$ bisects ∠B. (Given) 2. ∠A intercepts $\overset{\frown}{BC}$; ∠E intercepts $\overset{\frown}{BC}$. (Def. of inscribed angle) 3. ∠A ≅ ∠E ((2). Th. 8-16) 4. ∠ABD ≅ ∠EBC ((1). Def. of angle bisector) 5. △ABD ∼ △EBC ((3), (4). Cor. 6-10)

Page 378 Geometry Review Capsule for Section 8-8 1. 180 2. its central angle 3. 360 − m, where m is the measure of the central angle of its minor arc 4. 360 5. one-half the measure of its intercepted arc 6. 90

Page 379 Classroom Exercises 1. 118 3. 79 5. 41 7. 67 9. 51

Page 380 Written Exercises 1. Angles CAB, KGY, FGK, FGH, HGY, and TSR 3. $\overset{\frown}{HK}$ 5. $\overset{\frown}{JK}$ 7. 162; 198, 99 9. m∠T = 75, m∠R = 48; m∠S = 57 11. 65 13. 100 15. 60 17. $30\frac{1}{4}$ 19. $18\frac{1}{2}$ 21. 102

23. 282; 102 25. 100 27. $\frac{5}{2}$a **29.** 1. Chords AC and BD intersect at E. (Given) 2. Draw $\overline{BC}$ (Post. 4)
3. $m\angle C = \frac{1}{2}m\overarc{AB}$; $m\angle B = \frac{1}{2}m\overarc{CD}$ (Th. 8-15) 4. $m\angle AEB = m\angle C + m\angle B$ (Cor. 4-18) 5. $m\angle AEB = \frac{1}{2}m\overarc{AB}$
$+ \frac{1}{2}m\overarc{CD}$ ((3), (4). Substitution Prop.) 6. $m\angle AEB = \frac{1}{2}(m\overarc{AB} + m\overarc{CD})$ ((5). Dist. Prop.) **31.** 1. Draw $\overline{PQ}$.
(Post. 4) 2. $m\angle X + m\angle 2 = m\angle 1$ ((1). Cor. 4-18) 3. $m\angle X = m\angle 1 - m\angle 2$ ((2). Add. Prop.) 4. $m\angle 1 = \frac{1}{2}a$;
$m\angle 2 = \frac{1}{2}b$ ((1). Th. 8-15; Th. 8-20) 5. $m\angle X = \frac{1}{2}a - \frac{1}{2}b$ ((3), (4). Substitution Prop.) 6. $m\angle X = \frac{1}{2}(a - b)$
((5). Dist. Prop.) 33. 124 35. 28 37. 72 39. 18 41. 54 43. 90 **45.** 1. $\overline{BE}$ bisects $\angle ABC$.
(Given) 2. $m\angle ABD = m\angle EBC$ ((1). Def. of angle bisector) 3. $\angle ABD \cong \angle EBC$ ((2). Def. of congruent
angles) 4. $m\angle A = \frac{1}{2}m\overarc{BC}$; $m\angle E = \frac{1}{2}m\overarc{BC}$ (Th. 8-15) 5. $m\angle A = m\angle E$ ((4). Substitution Prop.) 6. $\angle A \cong \angle E$
((5). Def. of congruent angles) 7. $\angle ADB \cong \angle ECB$ ((3), (6). Cor. 4-13)

Page 383 Geometry Review Capsule for Section 8-9 1. 9 2. 8 3. 10 4. $2\sqrt{6}$ 5. $\sqrt{ab}$ 6. $4\sqrt{3}a$
7. $\sqrt{6}$ 8. $\sqrt{15}$ 9. D 10. C 11. CD 12. AE

Page 385 Classroom Exercises 1. 8 3. 4, 4, 8 5. $3\frac{1}{2}$ 7. 10 9. 5

Page 385 Written Exercises 1. 6 3. $1\frac{7}{18}$ 5. 18 7. 18 9. 17 11. 6 13. $3\sqrt{3}$ **15.** 1. Chords AB
and CD intersect at E. (Given) 2. Draw $\overline{AC}$ and $\overline{BD}$ ((1). Post. 4) 3. $m\angle A = \frac{1}{2}m\overarc{BC}$; $m\angle D = \frac{1}{2}m\overarc{BC}$; $m\angle C$
$\frac{1}{2}m\overarc{AD}$; $m\angle B = \frac{1}{2}m\overarc{AD}$ (Th. 8-15) 4. $\angle A \cong \angle D$; $\angle C \cong \angle B$ ((3). Def. of congruent angles) 5. $\triangle AEC \sim \triangle DEB$
((4). Cor. 6-10) 6. $\frac{AE}{DE} = \frac{CE}{BE}$ ((5). Def. of similar triangles) 7. $AE \cdot BE = DE \cdot CE$ ((6). Th. 6-1)
17. 12; 4 19. 6; 5 21. 9; 16 23. 3; 27 **25.** 1. Draw $\overline{XT}$ tangent to circle O. (Def. of tangent segment)
2. $\overline{XP}$ is a secant segment with external segment XQ; $\overline{XR}$ is a secant segment with external segment XS. (Given)
3. $(XT)^2 = XP \cdot XQ$; $(XT)^2 = XR \cdot XS$ ((2). Th. 8-24) 4. $XP \cdot XQ = XR \cdot XS$ ((3). Substitution Prop.)
27. 1. D is the midpoint of $\overarc{AB}$; $m\overarc{AD} = m\overarc{DB}$ (Given; Def. of arc midpoint) 2. $\overarc{AD} \cong \overarc{DB}$ ((1). Def. of congruent arcs) 3. $\angle ACD \cong \angle DCB$ ((2). Th. 8-16) 4. $\angle A \cong \angle D$ ((4). Th. 8-16) 5. $\triangle ACE \sim \triangle DCB$ ((3), (4).
Cor. 6-10) 6. $\frac{AC}{CD} = \frac{AE}{BD}$ or AC : CD = AE : BD ((5). Def. of similar triangles) **29.** 1. $\overline{BE}$ is a diameter;

$\overline{BD} \perp \overline{AC}$ (Given) 2. $\overarc{BCE}$ is a semicircle. ((1). Def. of semicircle) 3. $\angle BCE$ is a right angle; $\triangle EBC$ is a right
triangle. ((2). Cor. 8-17; def. of right triangle) 4. $\angle BDA$ is a right angle; $\triangle ABD$ is a right triangle. ((1). Def.
of perpendicular lines and right triangle) 5. $\angle A \cong \angle BEC$ (Th. 8-16) 6. $\triangle ABD \sim \triangle EBC$ ((3), (4), (5). Cor.
6-11) 7. $\frac{AB}{BE} = \frac{BD}{BC}$ ((6). Def. of similar triangles) 8. $AB \cdot BC = BE \cdot BD$ or $AB \cdot BC = DB \cdot BE$ ((7). Th.
6-1) 31. $CR = 8 - \frac{8\sqrt{7}}{3}$; $CS = 8 + \frac{8\sqrt{7}}{3}$ **33.** 1. Parallelogram ABCD; $\angle A$ is acute; altitude BE to $\overline{DC}$,
altitude DF to $\overline{AB}$. (Given) 2. $\overline{AB} \parallel \overline{CD}$ ((1). Def. of parallelogram) 3. $DF = EB$ ((2). Cor. 5-4) 4. $\overline{AB}$
$\cong \overline{CD}$ ((1). Cor. 5-2) 5. $AB = CD$ ((4). Def. of congruent segments) 6. $AB \cdot DF = CD \cdot EB$ ((3), (5). Mult.
Prop.) 7. $\overline{BH}$ is the altitude to $\overline{AD}$. (Given) 8. $\overline{BH} \perp \overline{AD}$, $\overline{DF} \perp \overline{AB}$ ((1), (7). Def. of altitude) 9. $\angle BAH$
$\cong \angle DAF$ (Ident.) 10. Right $\triangle BAH \sim$ right $\triangle DAF$ ((8), (9). Cor. 2-11; def. of perpendicular lines and right
triangle; Cor. 6-11) 11. $\frac{BH}{DF} = \frac{AB}{AD}$ ((10). Def. of similar triangles) 12. $BH \cdot AD = DF \cdot AB$ ((11). Th. 6-1)

Page 388 Applications 1. Since line PT passes through the midpoint of $\overline{RF}$, it bisects the chord and, by
Th. 8-6, $\overleftrightarrow{TP} \perp \overline{RF}$. 3. The Pythagorean Th. 5. 9 7. $r - 9$ 9. 25 in 11. $12\frac{1}{2}$ m

Page 390 Classroom Exercises 1. A, B, P, S, R, N, E, and G 3. Q 5. $\overline{RP}$ 7. $\overleftrightarrow{AB}$ 9. circle Q
11. $\angle RQS$ and $\angle SQP$

Page 390   Written Exercises   1. F, since two spheres with the same center and different radii are not congruent. **3.** T, by def. of a sphere.   **5.** F, since a secant intersects a sphere in two points.   **7.** F, since an infinite number of lines (in one plane) is tangent to a sphere at any given point.   **9.** T, as it is for a circle (Th. 8-8) **11.** One point   **13.** One point   **15.** Empty set   **17.** An infinite number   **19.** When their central angles are congruent.   **21.** Yes   **23.** Yes   **25.** Not always true   **27.** Always true   **29.** Not always true   **31.** Not always true   **33.** 6   **35.** 8 cm   **37.** Two infinite cones facing in opposite directions, with their common vertex being the given point; a circle which is not a great circle.   **39. 1.** If O is not in plane I, let OA be the distance from O to plane I; $\overline{OA} \perp$ plane I (Def. of distance from a point to a plane)   **2.** Draw $\overline{OB}$, $\overline{OC}$, $\overline{AB}$, and $\overline{AC}$, where B and C are any two distinct points in section BCD.   (Post. 4)   **3.** $\overline{OA} \perp \overline{AB}$; $\overline{OA} \perp \overline{AC}$ ((1). If a line is perpendicular to a plane, it is perpendicular to the lines that it intersects in that plane. **4.** $\overline{OB} \cong \overline{OC}$ (Def. of sphere and congruent segments)   **5.** $\overline{OA} \cong \overline{OA}$ (Ident.)   **6.** Right $\triangle OAB \cong$ right $\triangle OAC$ ((3), (4), (5).   Cor. 2-11; def. of right triangle; HL Th.)   **7.** $\overline{AB} \cong \overline{AC}$ ((6). CPCTC)   **8.** Section BCD is a circle with center A. ((7). Def. of circle)   **9.** If O is in plane I, $\overline{OB} \cong \overline{OC}$. (Def. of sphere and congruent segments) **10.** Section BCD is a circle with center O. ((9). Def. of circle)

Page 392   Review   1. 148   **2.** 32; 32   **3.** 200   **4.** 100   **5.** 40   **6.** 80   **7.** 46   **8.** 88   **9.** 66 **10.** 114   **11.** $83\frac{1}{2}$; $96\frac{1}{2}$ **12.** 46   **13.** 28   **14.** 12   **15.** 14; 8   **16.** $13\frac{1}{2}$ **17.** D, E, F, K, L, M, or N **18.** $\overset{\frown}{DE}$ and $\overset{\frown}{EL}$ (Answers may vary.)   **19.** $\overleftrightarrow{MN}$ **20.** Circle C

Page 394   Career Applications   1. Through a point not on a given line, there are infinitely many lines parallel to the given line.   **3.** Through a point not on a given line, there are no lines parallel to the given line.

Page 396   Chapter Objectives and Review   1. $\overleftrightarrow{GH}$ **3.** $\overline{OE}$, $\overline{OF}$, or $\overline{OD}$ **5.** $\overrightarrow{AB}$ **7.** 3   **9.** 4   **11.** 275 **13.** 95   **15.** T   **17.** F   **19.** AB   **21.** 40   **23.** 80; 40   **25.** 50   **27.** 100   **29.** 30   **31.** 33   **33.** 7 **35.** $\overline{PC}$, $\overline{PA}$, or $\overline{PB}$ **37.** $\overline{AF}$ or $\overline{AB}$ **39.** $\overset{\frown}{BF}$, $\overset{\frown}{AF}$, $\overset{\frown}{BC}$, $\overset{\frown}{QC}$, or $\overset{\frown}{AQ}$ **41.** r and t   **43.** $8\frac{1}{3}$

Page 399   Chapter Test   1. 75   **3.** $\overline{ST}$ **5.** $\angle ZYX$ and $\angle ZWX$ **7.** $2\sqrt{14.04}$ **9.** 4, 9   **11.** $15\frac{1}{2}$ **13.** 95; 80   **15.** An infinite number

CHAPTER 9: CONSTRUCTIONS AND LOCI

Page 403   Classroom Exercises   1. Use Construction 1.   **3.** Use Construction 3.

Page 403   Construction Exercises   1. Use Construction 1.   **3.** Use Construction 2.   **5.** Use Construction 3. **7.** Copy $\overline{AB}$, then copy $\overline{CD}$ next to $\overline{AB}$ on the same ray.   **9.** Copy $\overline{AB}$, then $\overline{CD}$ twice.   **11.** (See Ex. 7.) Copy (AB + CD) twice.   **13.** Copy $\overline{CD}$ three times. Then copy $\overline{AB}$ in the opposite direction.   **15.** Use Construction 2 twice.   **17.** Copy $\angle S$. Then copy $\angle K$ twice.   **19.** Copy $\angle S$. Then bisect it twice.   **21.** First copy the base of $\triangle XYZ$. Then at one end point of the base draw an arc corresponding to the length of a leg of $\triangle XYZ$. Draw an arc at the other endpoint of the base corresponding to the length of the third leg of $\triangle XYZ$. Draw segments connecting the endpoints of the base and the point where the two arcs meet.   **23.** First copy the base of $\triangle MVS$. At either end of the base, copy the base angles of $\triangle MVS$. Extend the new ray of each angle until they intersect.   **25.** Use Construction 3 three times.   **27.** Draw a line segment of any length. Mark off two arcs from both ends of the segment corresponding in length to the segment. Draw segments connecting the endpoints of the base and the point where the two arcs meet. This is an equilateral triangle, so each angle has a measure of 60. Use Construction 3 to bisect one of the angles.   **29.** Construct a 60° angle (see Ex. 27). Bisect it twice.   **31.** Construct a linear pair, one of whose angles is 15° (see Ex. 29). The measure of the other angle is 165.   **33.** Draw a ray. Using a point on the ray as the vertex, construct two adjacent angles congruent to the known angles. This produces the third angle of the triangle. Now follow the procedure for Ex. 23.

Page 404   Geometry Review Capsule for Section 9-2   1. T   **2.** F; the triangles are similar, but not necessarily congruent.   **3.** T   **4.** T   **5.** F; by Th. 4-8, the corresponding angles must be congruent.

Page 406   Classroom Exercises   1. Post. 4   **3.** CPCTC   **5.** CPCTC   **7.** Post. 4   **9.** CPCTC   **11.** CPCTC   **13.** CPCTC   **15.** Def. of perpendicular bisector

Page 407   Construction Exercises   1. Use Const. 4.   **3.** Use Const. 6.   **5.** Use Const. 4 to construct $\angle A$. Use Const. 5 to construct the altitude to $\overline{BC}$.   **7.** Use Const. 5 twice.   **9.** Use Const. 7.   **11.** Use Const. 4 and 7.   **13.** Use Const. 6 to find the midpoints of the sides. Then connect the midpoints with the opposite vertices.   **15.** Draw a right angle (see Ex. 5), and then bisect it.   **17.** Bisect a $90°$ angle twice.   **19.** Use Const. 3 to bisect a right angle twice. Subtract the measure of the smallest angle, $22\frac{1}{2}$, from the measure of the right angle, 90, to get a $67\frac{1}{2}°$ angle.   **21.** Draw a line AB. Through a point D not on $\overleftrightarrow{AB}$, draw $\overrightarrow{AD}$. Construct a line DC parallel to $\overleftrightarrow{AB}$ through D. At point C on $\overleftrightarrow{DC}$, construct a line parallel to $\overleftrightarrow{AD}$. The enclosed figure is a parallelogram.   **23.** Draw one of the given sides. At one endpoint, draw a $60°$ angle. The adjacent side has the length of the second given segment. At the endpoint of the second side, construct a line parallel to the first. Construct a line through the remaining endpoint of the first side that is parallel to the second side. Extend the two new rays until they intersect.   **25.** Mark off a length of 4 cm on a ray AY. Label this point B. With A as the center and radius AB, make an arc above $\overline{AB}$. With B as the center and radius AB, make another arc above $\overline{AB}$. Label the intersection of the two arcs D. Draw $\overrightarrow{AD}$. $\overline{AD}$ and $\overline{AB}$ are two sides of an equilateral triangle, $\therefore$ m$\angle A$ = 60. Mark off AC = 3 cm on $\overrightarrow{AD}$. Draw $\overline{CB}$.   **27.** Mark off AB = 2.7 cm on a ray AY. Construct $\angle A$ so that m$\angle A$ = 60. Construct $\angle B$ so that m$\angle B$ = 45. Do this by bisecting an angle with measure of 60 and an angle with measure of 30. Draw $\overline{CB}$. Since the sum of the measures of the angles of a triangle is 180, m$\angle C$ = 45.   **29.** Mark off AB on $\overrightarrow{AY}$. Construct $\angle A$ at A on $\overrightarrow{AY}$. Mark off AD on $\overrightarrow{AX}$. With D as the center and radius CD, make an arc between $\overrightarrow{AX}$ and $\overrightarrow{AY}$. With B as the center and radius BC, make another arc between $\overrightarrow{AX}$ and $\overrightarrow{AY}$. Label the intersection of the two arcs C. Draw $\overline{DC}$ and $\overline{BC}$.   **31.** Given the measures s_1, s_2, b_1, and b_2, where $s_1 < s_2 < b_1 < b_2$. Mark off AB = b_2 on $\overrightarrow{AY}$. Also on $\overrightarrow{AY}$, mark off AE = $b_2 - b_1$ and FB = $b_2 - b_1$. With A and F as centers and radius s_1, draw two arcs above $\overrightarrow{AY}$. With E and B as centers and radius s_2, draw two more arcs above $\overrightarrow{AY}$ intersecting the first two arcs. Label the points of intersection D and C. Draw $\overline{AD}$, $\overline{DC}$, and $\overline{CB}$. Trapezoid ABCD has non-parallel sides of length s_1 and s_2 and bases of length b_1 and b_2. This construction will be impossible if the sum of the lengths of the non-parallel sides is not greater than the difference between the lengths of the bases.   **33.** Draw a segment of length 4 cm, and construct its perpendicular bisector. With the intersection of the lines as center and a radius of $1\frac{1}{2}$ cm, mark off arcs on the perpendicular bisector. Join these 2 points and the endpoints of the first segment. This is a rhombus, since the diagonals of a rhombus are perpendicular and bisect each other, by Th. 5-5 and 5-11.   **35.** $\overline{RS}$ and $\overline{PQ}$ are given as diagonals of a parallelogram. Bisect both diagonals. Through the midpoint M of $\overline{PQ}$, draw $\overleftrightarrow{AB}$.   Mark off OS at N on $\overrightarrow{MB}$ and OR at T on $\overrightarrow{MA}$. Draw $\overline{PN}$, $\overline{NQ}$, $\overline{QT}$, and $\overline{TP}$. The parallelogram is PNQT.   **37.** Draw a line. At a point on the line, construct an angle congruent to the vertex angle, using the point as the vertex. The obtuse angle constructed is equal in measure to the two base angles of the triangle, since the measure of a straight angle is 180. Bisect the obtuse angle to find the measure of each base angle. Draw the base, which is given, and use the measure of the base angles to construct congruent angles at the endpoints of the segment. Extend the lines until they intersect.

Page 408   Geometry Review Capsule for Section 9-3   1. tangent   **2.** center   **3.** semicircle   **4.** $\perp$

Page 411   Classroom Exercises   1. Use Const. 8.   **3.** vertices (see Const. 11)   **5.** Follow the procedure of Ex. 25 on page 408 to construct an equilateral triangle with side of 4 cm. Then use Const. 11 and 12.

Page 412   Construction Exercises   1. Use Const. 8.   **3.** Use Const. 9 to construct two tangents to the circle from A. Extend the radius so that it intersects the circle on the opposite side. At that point, use Const. 8. The three tangents form the sides of an isosceles triangle.   **5.** Use Const. 11.   **7.** Use Const. 12.   **9.** Draw a circle and use Const. 10 to locate the center. Mark off a point on the circle with a compass. Using the same radius, and with center at that point, mark off a point on either side of the first on the circle. Continue until six points are marked. Join the points in order. Since the compass opening did not change, each chord has the same length and is congruent. Thus, ABCDEF is a regular hexagon by definition. 11. Draw a diameter of the circle and its perpendicular bisector. Connect the endpoints of the two diameters to form a quadrilateral. Since the diagonals are perpendicular, it is a rhombus. Since the diagonals are congruent, it is a rectangle. Thus, the figure is a square. 13. Connect the points and draw the perpendicular bisector of the chord. By Th. 8-6, this line is a diameter. With compass opening of 3 cm and center at one of the chord endpoints, mark off a point on the diameter. This is the center of the circle. Use the same compass opening to draw the circle. 15. Construct a line perpendicular to line q passing through the circle's center. At the point where this line intersects the circle, construct a tangent to the circle. 17. Since the given points are endpoints of a chord of the circle, the distance d between them can be no greater than the length of the diameter. Thus, $d \leq 2r$. 19. Follow the procedure for Exercise 14.

Page 414 Classroom Exercises 1. Use Construction 13. 3. Use Construction 15.

Page 414 Construction Exercises 1.-5. Use Const. 13. 7.-9. Use Const. 14. 11. Use Const. 15. 13. Use Construction 14 to find a segment of length x such that $\frac{4.5}{3.5} = \frac{5}{x}$. By definition, x is the fourth proportional. 15. Follow the procedure for Ex. 14. 17. Use Construction 15 to construct a segment with length x such that x is the geometric mean between s and t. Then $\frac{s}{x} = \frac{x}{t}$, and $x^2 = st$, so $x = \sqrt{st}$. 19. Construct a semicircle with diameter $(\frac{1}{3}r + \frac{1}{3}s)$. Then use Construction 15. 21. Construct a semicircle with diameter $(\frac{1}{2}r + r)$. Then use Construction 15. 23. If $4 \cdot 2 = 3x$, then $\frac{3}{4} = \frac{2}{x}$. Use Construction 14. 25. By definition, a segment connecting the given points is a chord of the desired circle. If the chord is extended to intersect the given line, a secant and tangent to the circle are formed. By Th. 8-24, the length of the tangent segment is the geometric mean between the lengths of the secant segment and the external secant segment. Use Construction 15 to find the length of the tangent segment, and mark off an arc of that length on the given line with one endpoint at the intersection point. Construct a perpendicular line at the point of tangency, and construct the perpendicular bisector of the chord. These two lines will meet at the circle's center, since they are both diameters. A circle then drawn through the given points will also be tangent to the given line.

Page 416 Career Applications 1. 70% A, 0% B, 30% C
3. 20% A, 55% B, 25% C 5. 35% A, 10% B, 55% C
7.–11. Refer to the graph at the right.

Page 417 Review 1. Copy segment AB, then copy $\overline{CD}$ next to $\overline{AB}$ on the same ray. 2. Copy $\overline{AB}$, then copy $\overline{CD}$ in the opposite direction. 3. Copy $\overline{CD}$ three times, each time placing the new segment next to the old one. 4. Copy $\overline{AB}$ twice, and then copy $\overline{CD}$ in the opposite direction. 5. Use Construction 2 twice, copying $\angle E$ adjacent to $\angle D$. 6. Use Construction 2 twice, first to copy $\angle D$, then to copy $\angle E$ in the interior. 7. Use Constructions 2 and 3. 8. Use Construction 4. 9. Use Construction 5. 10. Use Construction 6. 11. Use Construction 7. 12. Use Construction 8. 13. Use Construction 9. 14. Use Construction 10. 15. Use Constructions 12 and 11. 16. Use Construction 13. 17. Use Construction 14 18. Use Construction 15.

Page 419 Classroom Exercises 1. T 3. T 5. T

Page 420 Written Exercises (For Exercises 1-19, descriptions only are given.) 1. The locus is the perpendicular bisector of $\overline{RS}$. 3. A circle of radius $2\frac{1}{2}$ cm, concentric with the given circle. 5. A line parallel to the given lines and halfway between them   7. The locus is a circle with the same center as the given circle and radius $\sqrt{5}$.   9. The locus is $\overleftrightarrow{OA}$ excluding points O and A.   11. A line perpendicular to the given line at the given point (excluding the given point)   13. The interior of a circle with center at P and radius r   15. The locus is two lines parallel to the line containing $\overline{AB}$, one on each side of it, and a distance $\frac{1}{2}d$ from it.   17. The locus is P, the point of intersection of the perpendicular bisectors of the 3 segments determined by the given points, A, B, and C.   19. The locus is two lines parallel to $\overleftrightarrow{AB}$, one on either side, each at a distance 2d from $\overleftrightarrow{AB}$. 21. The locus is a cylindrical surface with its axis the line m and its radius d.   23. The locus is a plane parallel to the given planes and halfway between them.   25. The locus is two planes parallel to and on either side of the given plane at a distance of r units from the plane.   27. The locus is a cylindrical surface of length UR and radius RS, with $\overline{TS}$ as its axis.   29. The locus is a right circular cone with radius AC, altitude AB, and slant height BC.   31. The locus is two right circular cones base to base, one with slant height AC and one with slant height AB and both with the same radius.

Page 423   Classroom Exercises   1. 0, 1, 2, 3, or 4   3. 0, 1, 2, 3, or 4   5. 0 or 2

Page 423   Written Exercises   1. For Exercises 1 and 3, a line m that is parallel to and between lines k and r, at a distance of $\frac{1}{2}$ cm from each, is the locus of points equidistant from k and r. The circle with center at V and a radius of $1\frac{3}{4}$ cm is the locus of points $1\frac{3}{4}$ cm from V. The intersection of loci consists of 2 points.   3. The locus consists of 2 points, where line m intersects circle V with radius $1\frac{1}{2}$ cm.   5. The locus consists of 3 points A, B, and C. Points A and C are on a line parallel to line m and on the circle. The radius of the circle is 3 cm with center at X. This line is 1 cm above line m. Point B is on a line parallel to line m and on the circle. This line is 1 cm below line m and is tangent to the circle at 3.   7. The locus consists of 2 points A and B. These points are on a line parallel to line m and on the circle. The radius of the circle is 1.75 cm with center at X. The line is 1 cm above line m.   9. The locus consists of 2 points on the bisector of angle ABC each $\frac{1}{2}$ inch from h.   11. A 90° arc (except endpoints) of a circle with radius 1 cm and center at the vertex of the given angle. 13. The locus of points 3 cm from T is a circle with center at T and radius 3 cm. The locus of points 2 cm from g is two lines, r and s, parallel to and on either side of g and 2 cm from g. The intersection of these lines with the circle is 3 points, since circle T is tangent to one of the lines, s, and intersected by the other, r, in two points.   15. The locus of points equidistant from 2 concentric circles of radii r_1 and r_2 is a third circle, concentric with the others, with radius $\frac{1}{2}(r_1 + r_2)$. The locus of points equidistant from 2 parallel lines is a third line parallel to the others and midway between them. The intersection of these loci, the line and the circle, may be 0, 1, or 2 points, depending upon the distance involved.   17. Case 1 (d < r): The locus of points at distance d from circle O with radius r is 2 circles with centers at O and radii (r + d) and (r − d). These circles may intersect line q in 0, 1, 2, 3, or 4 points. Case 2 (d = r): The locus of points a distance d from the given circle is the point O and a circle with center at O and radius (r + d). This circle and point may intersect line q in 0, 1, 2, or 3 points. Case 3 (d > r): The locus of points a distance d from the given circle is a circle with center O and radius (r + d). The circle may intersect q in 0, 1, or 2 points.   19. The locus consists of two lines perpendicular to each other at the point of intersection of the given lines (that is the bisectors of the angles formed by the given lines).   21. The locus is the intersection of the given line and the plane which is the perpendicular bisector of the segment joining the two given points. This intersection may be no points (if the plane and line are parallel), one point (if they intersect), or the line (if the line lies in the plane).   23. The locus is the plane tangent to the given sphere at the given point.

Page 426   Classroom Exercises   1. F; def. of concurrent and parallel lines   3. T   5. T

Page 426   Written Exercises   1. Construct the perpendicular bisectors of two sides of △ABC. Their point of intersection is the triangle's circumcenter. This point is the center of a circle circumscribed about the triangle. 3. Use Construction 5 three times. 5. Follow the procedures for Ex. 1-4. 7. on a side of: outside 9. inside; at the vertex of the right angle; outside 11. 2 13. $\frac{7}{3}$ 15. Given: In $\triangle ABC$, $\overline{AE}$, $\overline{BF}$, and $\overline{CD}$ are medians. Prove: $\overline{AE}$, $\overline{BF}$, and $\overline{CD}$ are concurrent. 1. Let G be the midpoint of $\overline{AO}$, H be the midpoint of $\overline{BO}$, F be the midpoint of $\overline{AC}$, and E be the midpoint of $\overline{BC}$. (Th. 1-4) 2. $\overline{GH} \parallel \overline{AB}$; GH $= \frac{1}{2}$AB; $\overline{FE} \parallel \overline{AB}$; FE $= \frac{1}{2}$AB ((1). Th. 5-13) 3. $\overline{GH} \parallel \overline{FE}$ ((2). Th. 4-11) 4. GH = FE ((2). Subst. Prop.) 5. $\overline{GH} \cong \overline{FE}$ ((4). Def. of congruent segments) 6. EFGH is a parallelogram. ((4), (5). Th. 5-8) 7. GO = EO; HO = FO ((6). Th. 5-5) 8. AG = GO = EO; HB = HO = FO ((1), (7). Def. of midpoint; Subst. Prop.) 9. AG $= \frac{1}{3}$AE; HB $= \frac{1}{3}$BF ((8). Def. of betweenness of points; Mult. Prop.) 10. AD $= \frac{2}{3}$AE; BO $= \frac{2}{3}$BF ((8), (9). Def. of betweenness of points; Substitution Prop.) 11. Let O' be the point of intersection between $\overline{CD}$ and $\overline{AE}$. (Th. 1-2) 12. Let K be the midpoint of $\overline{CO'}$ and G' be the midpoint of $\overline{AO'}$. ((11). Th. 1-4) 13. $\overline{G'K} \parallel \overline{AC}$; G'K $= \frac{1}{2}$AC; $\overline{DE} \parallel \overline{AC}$; DE $= \frac{1}{2}$AC ((12). Th. 5-13) 14. $\overline{G'K} \parallel \overline{DE}$ ((13). Th. 4-11) 15. G'K = DE ((13). Substitution Prop.) 16. $\overline{G'K} \cong \overline{DE}$ ((15). Def. of congruent segments) 17. DEKG' is a parallelogram. ((14), (16). Th. 5-8) 18. G'O' = O'E; DO' = O'K ((17). Th. 5-5) 19. AG' = G'O' = O'E; DO' = O'K = KC ((12), (18). Def. of midpoint; Substitution Prop.) 20. AG' $= \frac{1}{3}$AE ((19). Def. of betweenness of points; Mult. Prop.) 21. G and G' are the same point. ((9), (20). Ruler Post.) 22. $\overline{AE}$, $\overline{BF}$, and $\overline{CD}$ are concurrent ((21). Def. of concurrent lines)

Page 428 Applications 1. Since the smoke detector should be halfway between the doors and 6-12 in from the ceiling, the position is an intersection of two loci. First find the line which is the perpendicular bisector of a segment between the two doors. The segment of this line 6-12 in from the ceiling is the desired location of the alarm. 3. Draw a triangle by connecting the three trees. Find the point of intersection of the perpendicular bisectors of two of the sides of the triangle. This is where the monument should be erected. 5. Draw a straight line segment between Potsdam and Tolerance. Then construct the perpendicular bisector of the segment. Extend this until it intersects with Route 87.

Page 429 Review 1. The locus is a circle of radius 3.5 cm with the same center as the given circle. 2. The locus is a line parallel to, and halfway between, the given lines. 3. The locus is a circle, centered on the first circle's center, with a radius one-half that of the given circle. 4. For Ex. 4-7, the locus of points 2 cm from line q is 2 parallel lines on either side of q at a distance of 2 cm. The line closer to Y is 1 cm away; the farther line is 5 cm away. Thus, the intersection of the loci is 2 points where the closer line meets the circle of radius 4 cm. 5. The locus is 2 points, where the closer parallel line and a circle of radius 3.5 cm intersect. 6. The locus is 2 points, where the closer parallel line and a circle of radius 4.25 cm intersect. 7. The locus is 3 points, since the closer parallel line and a circle of radius 5 cm intersect in 2 points and the circle is tangent to the farther parallel line. 8. Construct the perpendicular bisectors of two sides of the triangle. Find the point of intersection. 9. Construct the bisectors of two vertices of the triangle. Find the point of intersection. 10. Use Constr. 6 three times to find the midpoints of the sides. Connect each midpoint with its opposite vertex.

Page 430 Chapter Objectives and Review 1. Use Construction 1. 3. Use Construction 2. 5. Use Construction 4. 7. Use Construction 7. 9. Use Construction 8. 11. Use Construction 10. 13. Use Construction 12. 15. Use Construction 14. 17. Points on the perpendicular bisector of the chord are equidistant from the chord's endpoints. Points on the diameter (which is the perpendicular bisector), excluding the endpoints, satisfy the conditions. 19. 2 circles having the same center as the given circle and having radii 1 and 7 21. 3 points located at the intersections of the circle with center P and radius 5 in and the lines k and r parallel to m and 3 in from m on either side of m. 23. perpendicular bisectors of the sides 25. angle bisectors 27. Use Construction 3 twice. Find the point of intersection of the two angle bisectors.

Chapter Test 1. Use Construction 1. 3. Use Construction 3. 5. Use Construction 8. 7. Use Construction 13. 9. Two lines that bisect the two pairs of vertical angles formed by r and s

Page 433 Cumulative Review: Chapters 1-9 1. d 3. b 5. b 7. d 9. a 11. c 13. a 15. d 17. b 19. d

Page 435 Preparing for College Entrance Tests 1. b 3. d 5. c

Page 436 Preparing for College Entrance Tests 1. b 3. c

CHAPTER 10: AREA

Page 439 Classroom Exercises 1. m^2 3. cm^2 5. yd^2 7. ft^2 9. $62\,cm^2$ 11. $7\frac{1}{5}\,m$ 13. $15\,m$

Page 439 Written Exercises 1. 52 sq. units 3. 10 cm 5. 6 7. $900\,m^2$ 9. $25\,yd^2$ 11. 104 sq. units 13. 128 sq. units 15. 16 sq. units 17. $2\frac{1}{2}a^2$ 19. multiplied by six 21. 34 mm 23. $\ell = 14$ units; w = 4 units 25. $\frac{3}{2}\sqrt{3}s^2$ 27. $1800\,m^2$ 29. $312\frac{1}{2}\,in^2$ 31. w = 2 cm; $\ell = 7$ cm 33. $\frac{3}{64}P^2$

Page 444 Classroom Exercises 1. $60\,cm^2$ 3. $45\,cm^2$ 5. $84\,cm^2$

Page 445 Written Exercises 1. $51.84\,cm^2$ 3. 5.2 m 5. $24\sqrt{2}$ 7. 10.0625 cm 9. $2\frac{1}{2}$ cm 11. They have the same base, EA, and the same height, 26 mm. 13. F; In $\triangle ABC$, b = 6, h = 8, A = 24; in $\triangle XYZ$, b = 3, h = 16, A = 24 15. F; see Exercise 13 17. $50\sqrt{3}$ 19. $\frac{q^2}{2}\sqrt{3}$ 21. 64 23. 81 25. $\frac{a^2}{4}$ 27. 16.74 29. 64 31. 180 33. $27\sqrt{3}\,m^2$ **35.** 1. Parallelogram ABCD with altitude EB; EB = h, AB = b (Given) 2. $\overrightarrow{CD} \parallel \overline{AB}$ ((1). Def. of parallelogram) 3. Draw $\overline{AF} \parallel \overline{BE}$ intersecting $\overrightarrow{CD}$ at F. (Post. 15) 4. $\overline{EB} \perp \overline{AB}$; $\overline{EB} \perp \overline{CF}$ ((1). Def. of altitude) 5. $\overline{AF} \perp \overline{AB}$; $\overline{AF} \perp \overline{CF}$ ((3), (4). Th. 4-7) 6. Angles A, B, E, and F of quadrilateral ABEF are right angles. ((4), (5). Def. of perpendicular lines) 7. Quadrilateral ABEF is a rectangle. ((6). Def. of rectangle) 8. Area of ABEF = bh ((7). Post. 19) 9. Draw $\overline{AE}$. (Post. 4) 10. Area ABEF = area $\triangle DAF$ + area $\triangle DAE$ + area $\triangle AEB$ (Post. 18) 11. $\overline{AF} \cong \overline{BE}$ ((2). Cor. 5-4) 12. $\overline{AD} \cong \overline{BC}$ ((1). Cor. 5-2) 13. $\triangle CBE$ and $\triangle DAF$ are right triangles. ((4), (5). Def. of right triangle) 14. $\triangle CBE \cong \triangle DAF$ ((11), (12), (13). HL Th.) 15. Area of $\triangle CBE$ = area of $\triangle DAF$ ((14). Post. 17) 16. Area of ABEF = area of $\triangle CBE$ + area of $\triangle DAE$ + area of $\triangle AEB$ ((10), (14). Substitution Prop.) 17. Area of ABCD = area of $\triangle CBE$ + area of $\triangle DAE$ + area of $\triangle AEB$ (Post. 18) 18. Area of ABCD = bh ((8), (16), (17). Substitution Prop.) **37.** Given: ABCD and EFGH are parallelograms with bases b and b' and altitudes h and h', respectively; b = b'; h = h' Prove: Area of ABCD = area of EFGH 1. Parallelograms ABCD and EFGH have bases b and b' and altitudes h and h', respectively. (Given) 2. Area of ABCD = bh; area of EFGH = b'h' ((1). Th. 10-1) 3. b' = b; h' = h (Given) 4. b'h' = bh ((3). Mult. Prop.) 5. Area of EFGH = bh ((2), (4). Substitution Prop.) 6. Area of ABCD = area of EFGH ((2), (5). Substitution Prop.) **39.** Given: $\triangle ABC$ is equilateral; AB = BC = AC = s Prove: Area of $\triangle ABC = \frac{s^2\sqrt{3}}{4}$ 1. Equilateral triangle ABC has side of length s. (Given) 2. Draw altitude AD. ((1). Th. 1-9) 3. $m\angle B = m\angle A = 60$ ((1). Cor. 4-16) 4. $\overline{AD}$ bisects $\angle A$. ((1). Cor. 3-13; def. of isosceles triangle) 5. $m\angle BAD = 30$ ((3), (4). Def. of angle bisector) 6. AB = s; BC = s (Given) 7. $BD = \frac{1}{2}s$; $AD = \frac{1}{2}s\sqrt{3}$ ((2), (3), (5), (6). 30-60 Right Triangle Th.) 8. Area of $\triangle ABC = \frac{1}{2}(BC)(AD)$ ((2). Th. 10-3) 9. Area of $\triangle ABC = \frac{1}{2}(s)(\frac{1}{2}s\sqrt{3})$ ((6), (7). Substitution Prop.) 10. Area of $\triangle ABC = \frac{1}{4}s^2\sqrt{3}$, or $\frac{s^2\sqrt{3}}{4}$ ((9). Multiplication) 41. $\frac{1}{2}$ 43. 40 45. $\frac{5x}{6}\sqrt{3}$ 47. $18 - 9\sqrt{2}$

NOTE: Answers to Exercises 5, 17, 19, 21, 23, 25, 27, 29, 31, 43, and 45 represent square units.

Page 447 **Geometry Review Capsule for Section 10-3** 1. F; def. of rhombus 2. T 3. F; def. of bases of a trapezoid 4. F; the diagonals of a rhombus are congruent only if the rhombus is a square. 5. T 6. T 7. $\sqrt{85}$ 8. $\sqrt{273}$ 9. $2\sqrt{14}$ 10. 5

Page 448 **Classroom Exercises** 1. 320 cm^2 3. 500 m^2 5. 30 cm^2

Page 449 **Written Exercises** 1. $A = 80$ 3. $5\sqrt{3}$ 5. 9 7. $12\frac{1}{2}$ 9. 3 11. $56\sqrt{2} \text{ cm}^2$ 13. 120 15. $200\sqrt{3}$ 17. $2\sqrt{15}$ 19. (Refer to the figure for Example 1 on page 447.) 1. Rhombus ABCD with diagonals $AC = d_1$ and $DB = d_2$ intersecting at E (Given) 2. $DE = \frac{1}{2}d_2$ ((1). Def. of rhombus; Th. 5-5) 3. Area of $\triangle ADC = \frac{1}{2}d_1 (\frac{1}{2}d_2) = \frac{1}{4}d_1 d_2$ ((1), (2). Th. 10-3) 4. $\triangle ADC \cong \triangle ABC$ ((1). Th. 5-1) 5. Area of $\triangle ADC = $ Area of $\triangle ABC$ ((4). Post. 17) 6. Area of ABCD = Area of $\triangle ABC + $ Area of $\triangle ADC$ ((1). Post. 18) 7. Area of ABCD $= \frac{1}{4}d_1 d_2 + \frac{1}{4}d_1 d_2$ ((3), (5), (6). Substitution and Dist. Prop.) 21. Cor. 10-4 23. From Ex. 21, area of $\triangle AEC = $ area of $\triangle EAL$. By Post. 18, area of $\triangle AEC = $ area of $\triangle CRA + $ area of $\triangle ARE$, and area of $\triangle EAL = $ area of $\triangle LRE + $ area of $\triangle ARE$. By substitution, area of $\triangle CRA + $ area of $\triangle ARE = $ area of $\triangle LRE + $ area of $\triangle ARE$, and area of $\triangle CRA = $ area of $\triangle LRE$ by the Add. Prop. 25. 10 cm, 20 cm 27. 8, 6

Page 450 **Calculator Exercises** 1. 36 3. 60 5. 613

Page 451 **Applications** 1. 20.5 m^2 3. 1600 cm^2 5. $\frac{27}{65}$ 7. $21,168 9. $1312.42 (to the nearest cent)

Page 452 **Geometry Review Capsule for Section 10-4** 1. 180 2. 360 3. 720 4. 1080 5. 1440 6. 1800 7. 60 8. 90 9. 108 10. 135 11. 162 12. 140 13. y cm 14. t

Page 452 **Classroom Exercises** 1. n 3. 8 5. congruent 7. 9 9. If a polygon is regular, then a circle can be inscribed in it and another circle with the same center can be circumscribed about it; If a circle can be inscribed in a polygon and another circle with the same center can be circumscribed about the circle, then the polygon is regular.

Page 454 **Written Exercises** 1. 72 3. 36 5. 18 7. 9 9. 12 11. 160 13. 162 15. 144 17. c $= 10$; $b = 5\sqrt{3}$ 19. $a = 4$; $AD = 4\sqrt{3}$; $AB = 8\sqrt{3}$ 21. $r = 4\sqrt{3}$; $a = 2\sqrt{3}$; $AB = 12$ 23. $c = \frac{2}{3}\sqrt{21}$; b $= \frac{1}{3}\sqrt{21}$ 25. $a = \sqrt{3}$; $AD = 1$; $AB = 2$ 27. $r = 12\sqrt{3}$; $a = 18$; $AB = 12\sqrt{3}$ 29. 7 cm 31. $10\sqrt{3}$ units 33. $24\sqrt{2}$ 35. $\frac{3}{2}\sqrt{3}$ m 37. $3\sqrt{3}$ cm 39. $\frac{y}{2}\sqrt{3}$ m 41. 6 units 43. $\frac{2}{3}$ 45. By Cor. 4-22, the measure e of an exterior angle of a regular polygon of n sides can be represented by the equation $e = \frac{360}{n}$. By Cor. 10-9, the measure a of a central angle of a regular polygon is $a = \frac{360}{n}$. Thus, by substitution, $e = a$. 47. $n = \frac{2\sqrt{3}}{3}r$

Page 457 **Review** 1. 36 cm 2. $64\sqrt{2} \text{ mm}^2$ 3. 10 cm 4. 891 mm^2 5. 37 square units 6. $\sqrt{3} \text{ mm}^2$ 7. 160 sq. units 8. 16 9. 30 sq. units 10. 96 sq. units 11. 18 sq. units 12. 24 13. 81 14. 30 15. 18 16. $5\sqrt{2}$

Page 458 **Geometry Review Capsule for Section 10-5** (For Ex. 1-8, use the 30-60 Right Triangle Th.) 1. $b = 27$; $c = 18\sqrt{3}$ 2. $a = 3$; $c = 6$ 3. $b = 6$; $c = 4\sqrt{3}$ 4. $a = 5$; $b = 5\sqrt{3}$ 5. $a = \frac{4}{3}\sqrt{3}$; $c = \frac{8}{3}\sqrt{3}$ 6. $a = 6$; $b = 6\sqrt{3}$ 7. $a = 3\sqrt{3}$; $c = 6\sqrt{3}$ 8. $a = 3\sqrt{3}$; $b = 9$

Page 459 **Classroom Exercises** 1. 28 3. $24\sqrt{3}$ 5. 33 7. $104\sqrt{2}$

Page 460 **Written Exercises** 1. 60 cm; $150\sqrt{3} \text{ cm}^2$ 3. $100\sqrt{3} \text{ units}^2$ 5. 20 dm; 80 dm; 400 dm^2 7. 6 cm

9. 100 sq. units   11. $75\sqrt{3}$ units^2 13. 64   15. $4\sqrt{3}$ 17. $144\sqrt{3}$ units^2 19. 36   21. 65; $292\frac{1}{2}$ units^2
23. 18 in; 9 in; 72 in; 324 in^2 25. 6 m   27. $12\sqrt{3}$ m   29. $4\sqrt{3}$ cm   31. $5\sqrt{2}$ dm   33. $36\sqrt{3}$ in^2
35. 10   37. 4x   **39.** 1. TWRQP is a regular polygon of n sides with apothem a, side b, perimeter P, and area
A. (Given)   2. Draw all the radii of the polygon. ((1). Post. 4)   3. All the radii are congruent; all the sides
are congruent. ((1). Def. of radius and regular polygon)   4. All the triangles formed by the radii and sides are
congruent. ((3). SSS Post.)   5. The altitude of each triangle is a. ((1), (4). Def. of apothem and altitude)
6. The area of each triangle $= \frac{1}{2}ab$. ((1), (3), (5). Th. 10-3)   7. The area of n triangles $= n(\frac{1}{2}ab)$ ((4), (6).
Mult. Prop.)   8. $n(\frac{1}{2}ab) = \frac{1}{2}a(nb)$ ((7). Associative Prop.)   9. $P = nb$ ((1). Def. of perimeter)   10. The
area of n triangles $= \frac{1}{2}aP$ ((7), (8), (9). Substitution Prop.)   11. $A = \frac{1}{2}aP$ ((1), (10). Post. 18)   41. $\frac{1}{3}$
43. 2 cm   45. $8\sqrt{3}$ cm^2 47. 6a sq. units   49. $\frac{1}{4}$

Page 463   Classroom Exercises   1. 3 : 7   3. 8 : 9

Page 463   Written Exercises   1. $\frac{5}{7}$ 3. $\frac{5}{7}$ 5. $\frac{5}{6}$ 7. $\frac{5}{6}$ 9. $\frac{25}{36}$ 11. 8   13. 117 cm^2 15. 4 : 9 : 49
17. 16 and 24   **19.** 1. $\triangle ABC \sim \triangle DEF$ (Given)   2. Let h be the altitude to $\overline{AB}$ in $\triangle ABC$; let h_1 be the
altitude to $\overline{DE}$ in $\triangle DEF$. ((1). Th. 1-9)   3. Let b and b_1 be the measures of $\overline{AB}$ and $\overline{DE}$, respectively.
((1). Ruler Post.)   4. Area of $\triangle ABC = \frac{1}{2}bh$; area of $\triangle DEF = \frac{1}{2}b_1h_1$ ((1), (2), (3). Th. 10-3)

5. $\dfrac{\text{Area of } \triangle ABC}{\text{Area of } \triangle DEF} = \dfrac{\frac{1}{2}bh}{\frac{1}{2}b_1h_1} = \dfrac{bh}{b_1h_1}$ ((4). Mult. Prop.)   6. $\dfrac{h}{h_1} = \dfrac{b}{b_1}$ ((1), (2), (3). Cor. 6-16)

7. $\dfrac{\text{Area of } \triangle ABC}{\text{Area of } \triangle DEF} = \dfrac{b}{b_1} \cdot \dfrac{b}{b_1} = \dfrac{b^2}{b_1^2}$ ((5), (6). Substitution Prop.)

Page 464   Geometry Review Capsule for Section 10-7   1. 60   2. 50   3. 68   4. 64   5. 14   6. 85

Page 465   Consumer Applications   1. 11; $65.89   3. 8; $55.92   5. 10; $64.90

Page 468   Classroom Exercises   1. 28π cm   3. $\frac{4}{3}\pi$ units

Page 468   Written Exercises   1. 4   3. 24; 48   5. $\frac{15}{16}, \frac{15}{8}$ 7. 1 : 2   9. 16 cm   11. 3π 13. $\frac{12}{5}\pi$ 15. $\frac{8}{5}\pi$
17. 60   19. 45   21. 225   23. 12 cm   25. 2x   27. $\frac{3}{2}a\pi$ 29. $\frac{40}{9}\pi; \frac{20}{3}\pi$ 31. $\pi r(1 - \frac{x}{180})$

Page 472   Classroom Exercises   1. $A = 36\pi$ cm^2 3. 5 units

Page 472   Written Exercises   1. 8   3. 16; 32 cm   5. $\frac{9}{8}, \frac{9}{4}$ 7. $\frac{1}{2} : \frac{1}{4}\pi$ 9. 9 : 25   11. 4 : 1   13. 14π cm
15. $\frac{14}{5}\pi$ m   17. 900π units^2 19. 144π units^2 21. $\frac{25}{2}\pi = \frac{9}{2}\pi + \frac{16}{2}\pi$ 23. 1 : 4   25. $\frac{9}{4}\pi$ 27. 24. $\frac{2}{3}\pi - \sqrt{3}$;
25. $\frac{9}{4}\pi - \frac{9}{2}$;   26. $\frac{16}{3}\pi - 4\sqrt{3}$ 29. 60   31. $A = \frac{\pi}{4}d^2$ 33. $A = \frac{\ell r}{2}$ 35. 3 : 4   37. $3\sqrt{3} - \pi : \pi$ 39. $r^2(\pi - 2)$

Page 474   Applications   1. 306.25π m^2 3. 109.9 m   5. less than   7. 6.25π cm^2 9. $\frac{24}{25}$ 11. 62.5π cm^2
13. $\frac{9}{25}$

Page 476   Review   1. $A = 72\sqrt{3}$ units^2 2. 324 units^2 3. $16\sqrt{3}$ units^2 4. $\frac{243}{2}\sqrt{3}$ units^2
5. 3 : 8   6. 3 : 8   7. 9 : 64   8. $\frac{32}{3}\pi$ 9. 6π 10. $\frac{52}{9}\pi$ 11. m = 135   12. 180   13. 30   14. 48π sq.
units   15. $(48\pi - 36\sqrt{3})$ units^2

Page 477 Chapter Objectives and Review 1. 20 units^2 3. 40 cm^2 5. 6 units 7. 20 units^2 9. 18
11. $4\sqrt{3}$ dm 13. $81\sqrt{3}$ units^2 15. $\frac{2}{5}$ 17. 18 units 19. $\frac{1}{2}$ 21. $\frac{16}{49}$ 23. $(6\pi - 9\sqrt{3})$ units^2 25. 3π cm^2

Page 479 Chapter Test 1. 96 units^2 3. $18\sqrt{3}$ units^2 5. $\frac{9}{4}\sqrt{3}$ units^2 7. 7 cm 9. 30 11. $4\sqrt{3}$ cm
13. 25 : 8 15. 14π m 17. $\frac{28}{45}\pi$ m 19. $\frac{9}{8}\pi$ units^2

CHAPTER 11: SURFACE AREA AND VOLUME

Page 483 Classroom Exercises 1. 48 cm 3. $96\sqrt{3}$ cm^2 5. 17 m

Page 484 Written Exercises 1. 28, 196, 49, 294 3. 10, 400, 100, 600 5. 20, 180 7. 28, 168 9. 30,
210 11. 1500 13. 486 15. $121\frac{1}{2}$ 17. $6e^2$ 19. $T = 6e^2$ 21. 150 cm^2 23. 144 25. $6x^2$
27. $T = 3d^2$ 29. S 31. S 33. A 35. Isosceles right triangle, $\angle A = 90°$ 37. Yes, since $\overline{DH} \perp \overline{HF}$.
39. $5\sqrt{2}$ 41. $3\sqrt{2}, 3\sqrt{6}$ 43. $\triangle ABC$: $\overline{AC}$; $\triangle ABD$: $\overline{AD}$; $\triangle BCD$: $\overline{BC}$; $\triangle ADC$: $\overline{AC}$ 45. $6\sqrt{5}$

Page 486 Geometry Review Capsule for Section 11-2 1. 25 2. $4\sqrt{3}$ 3. $\frac{25\sqrt{3}}{2}$ 4. $216\sqrt{3}$

Page 487 Classroom Exercises 1. 252 m^2 3. $(252 + 36\sqrt{3})$ m^2

Page 488 Written Exercises 1. A 3. A 5. N 7. $3\sqrt{3}$ cm, 18 cm, $27\sqrt{3}$ cm^2 9. $\frac{e}{2}\sqrt{3}, 3e, \frac{3\sqrt{3}}{4}e^2$
11. 84 cm^2 13. 120 cm^2 15. $54\sqrt{3}$ units^2 17. $\sqrt{91}$ 19. $9\sqrt{91}$ 21. 16 cm 23. 81 25. 260 m^2;
360 m^2 27. 24, 24 29. $8\sqrt{6}$ units^2 31. $2\sqrt{15}$ 33. $48 + 8\sqrt{6} + 4\sqrt{15}$ 35. 10 37. 384 39. $450\sqrt{39}$

Page 492 Classroom Exercises 1. $240\pi, 440\pi$ 3. $64\pi, 96\pi$

Page 492 Written Exercises 1. 80π cm^2; 130π cm^2 3. $68\frac{1}{4}\pi$ m^2; $92\frac{3}{4}\pi$ m^2 5. 48π 7. $640\pi, 640\pi$
9. 9 11. $r = \frac{L}{\pi s}$; $s = \frac{L}{\pi r}$ 13. $1\frac{1}{2}$ 15. 10 17. $L = 2\pi h^2$; $T = 4\pi h^2$ 19. $2\pi xy$ 21. 12 m

Page 494 Applications 1. 7104 cm^2 3. 115 m^2 5. 128,154 m^2 7. The Great Pyramid; 109,793 m^2

Page 495 Review 1. 1080 cm^2 2. 1575.4 cm^2 3. 160 cm^2; 342 cm^2 4. 28 5. 140 sq. units
6. 189 sq. units 7. 20π 8. $32\frac{1}{2}\pi$ 9. $5\sqrt{74}\pi$ 10. $5\sqrt{74}\pi + 25\pi$

Page 498 Classroom Exercises 1. 60 cm^3 3. 480 cm^3 5. $151\frac{2}{3}$ mm^3

Page 498 Written Exercises 1. 315 3. $22\frac{11}{24}$ 5. 192 m^3 7. 192 9. 1000 m^3 11. 7 13. $\frac{15}{4}\sqrt{3}$
15. $4\frac{4}{15}$ yd 17. $16\sqrt{3}$ cm 19. $\frac{2}{3}\sqrt{11}$ cm^3 21. $V = \frac{1}{2}a^2 b$

Page 501 Classroom Exercises 1. 6084π mm^3 3. 320π cm^3

Page 501 Written Exercises 1. 360π 3. 135π 5. 28.125π 7. 100π 9. $28\frac{7}{12}\pi$ 11. 90π
13. 640π cm^3 15. $\sqrt{3} : 4\pi$ 17. 6 units 19. The volume is doubled. 21. 20π 23. $\frac{\pi}{4}$ 25. $\sqrt{109}$ in
27. $T = \frac{2V}{r} + \pi r^2$ 29. 6π in^3 31. $\frac{2}{3}$ 33. 72π 35. The ratio of the radii and the ratio of the altitudes are
the same. The ratio of the areas is the square of the ratio of the radii or the ratio of the altitudes. 37. $\frac{8}{27}$
39. $\frac{3}{5}$ 41. $12\pi\sqrt{13} + 36$; $\frac{100}{3}\pi\sqrt{13} + 100$ 43. The ratio of the radii equals the ratio of the slant heights

and the square root of the ratio of the areas.   45. $\frac{27}{125}$ 47. ratio   49. cubes

1. 5760 Btu's   3. 15,300 Btu's

1. $\overline{TR}, \overline{TS},$ or $\overline{TP}$ 2. $\overline{SP}$ 3. Circle T   4. $\angle STR,$ $\angle RTP$ 5. $\overline{SP}$

1. 100π cm^2 3. 288π cm^3 5. $102\frac{17}{48}\pi$ in^3

1. 100π 3. 81π 5. 750π 7. $221\frac{5}{6}\pi$ 9. $\frac{9}{16}\pi$ 11. $\frac{3}{5}$ cm   13. 21 yd   15. 6   17. $r = \sqrt[3]{\frac{3V}{4\pi}}$ 19. 2400   21. $\frac{\pi}{6}$ 23. $\frac{e^3\pi}{6}$ 25. $\frac{1000\sqrt{2}}{3}\pi$ cu. units   27. $1:8$ 29. $\frac{10,976}{3}\pi$ cu. units   31. $\frac{1372}{3}\pi$ mm^3 33. $\frac{2}{3}\pi r^3$ 35. $\frac{4}{3}\pi r^3$ 37. $V = \frac{8\sqrt{3}}{9}r^3$ 39. $\frac{6}{\pi}$ 41. $\frac{3\sqrt{3}}{1}$

1. 0.352 m^3 3. 2500π mm^3 5. 37.5 L   7. 12   9. 737 cm^3 11. 110.1 in^3 13. two times   15. 1,048,576 times

1. 64 cu. units   2. 14.336 cu. units   3. 144 cu. units   4. $V = 30\sqrt{55}$ cu. units   5. $V = 10\sqrt{55}$ cu. units   6. 0.17 m   7. 8192π cu. units   8. 2π cu. units   9. $\frac{686}{3}\pi$ cu. units   10. 24π cu. units   11. 144π sq. units   12. 46.24π sq. units   13. 134.56π sq. units   14. 432π sq. units   15. 448π sq. units   16. $\frac{256}{3}\pi$ cu. units   17. $\approx 14.2\pi$ cu. units   18. 62.208π cu. units   19. $\frac{64}{3}\sqrt{2}\pi$ cu. units   20. $\frac{27}{128}\sqrt{3}\pi$ cu. units

1. 128 cm^2; 158 cm^2 3. 36 cm^2; $(36 + 9\sqrt{3})$ cm^2 5. 140π cm^2; 238π cm^3 7. 54 cm^3 9. 324 cm^3 11. 36π m^2 13. 3925 cm^2

1. T   3. F; def. of altitude and slant height   5. T   7. 350 sq. units   9. 88π sq. units   11. $160\sqrt{3}$ cm^3 13. 1573π cm^3 15. 4500π m^3

1. b   3. b   5. b   7. b   9. b   11. b   13. a   15. c   17. c   19. d

1. c   3. e

1. d   3. d

CHAPTER 12: COORDINATE GEOMETRY

1. III   3. II   5. IV   7. parallel   9. 5 units

1. I   3. II   5. II   7. y axis   9. origin   11. Start at the origin and make the moves given for each point. G: left 4 units; H: up 9 units; J: down $\frac{1}{2}$ unit; K: no move; P: right $5\frac{1}{2}$ units   13. II   15. x axis   17. 6 units   19. 7 units   21. $y = -3$ 23. $y = 0$ 25. A: 2 right, 1 down; B: 2 right, 2 up; C: 3 left, 2 up; D: 3 left, 1 down   27. $x = -3$ 29. 3 units, 5 units   31. $\overleftrightarrow{CD} \perp \overleftrightarrow{DA}$ or $\overleftrightarrow{CB} \perp \overleftrightarrow{CD}$ or $\overleftrightarrow{CB} \perp \overleftrightarrow{BA}$ or $\overleftrightarrow{BA} \perp \overleftrightarrow{DA}$ 33. $x = -2$ 35. $x = 0$ 37. $y = 4$ 39. $y = 2$ 41. $y = -8$ 43. $(5, 6)$

1. $(4, 8)$ 3. $(\frac{1}{2}, -1\frac{1}{2})$

Page 524 Written Exercises 1. $(5, 1\frac{1}{2})$ 3. $(\frac{1}{2}, 3)$ 5. $(\frac{a}{2}, \frac{b}{3})$ 7. $(3, 2)$ 9. $(2, -1)$ 11. $(-3, 4)$ 13. $(4, 6)$

15. $(\frac{5}{2}, \frac{1}{2})$ 17. $(\frac{9}{2}, \frac{7}{2})$ 19. $(\frac{7}{2}, 2)$ 21. 1. $\overline{P_1 P_2}$ has endpoints (x_1, y_1) and (x_2, y_2) and midpoint $M(x_m, y_m)$.

(Given) 2. Draw $\overline{P_1 A}$, $\overline{MC}$, and $\overline{P_2 B}$ perpendicular to the x axis. ((1). Th. 1-9) 3. $\overline{P_1 A} \parallel \overline{MC} \parallel \overline{P_2 B}$ ((2). Th. 4-6) 4. The coordinates of A, C, and B are $(x_1, 0)$, $(x_m, 0)$, and $(x_2, 0)$, respectively. ((1), (2). All of the points on a vertical line in the coordinate plane have the same x coordinate. 5. $P_1 M = MP_2$ ((1). Def. of midpoint) 6. $\overline{P_1 M} \cong \overline{MP_2}$ ((5). Def. of congruent segments) 7. $\overline{AC} \cong \overline{CB}$ ((6). Th. 5-15) 8. $AC = CB$ ((7). Def. of congruent segments) 9. $AC = x_m - x_1$; $CB = x_2 - x_m$ ((4). Def. of distance between points) 10. $x_m - x_1 = x_2 - x_m$ ((8), (9). Substitution Prop.) 11. $2x_m = x_1 + x_2$ ((10). Addition Prop.)

12. $x_m = \frac{x_1 + x_2}{2}$ ((11). Multiplication Prop.) To show that $y_m = \frac{y_1 + y_2}{2}$, construct $\overline{P_1 D}$, $\overline{ME}$, and $\overline{P_2 F}$ perpendicular to the y axis. Then proceed as in steps 3-12. 23. 1; 3 25. $(-\frac{1}{4}, -\frac{1}{4})$

Page 525 Algebra Review Capsule for Section 12-3 1. -10 2. 6 3. 21 4. 7 5. $-2\frac{1}{2}$ 6. $-2\frac{1}{2}$
7. $1\frac{3}{7}$ 8. 2 9. $1\frac{1}{5}$ 10. $1\frac{1}{5}$ 11. -3 12. -3

Page 527 Classroom Exercises 1. 4 3. $\frac{4}{5}$ 5. undefined

Page 527 Written Exercises 1. Negative 3. Undefined 5. 1 7. 3 9. -12 11. $m_{\overline{AB}} = \frac{1}{5}$; $m_{\overline{BC}} = 6$; $m_{\overline{AC}} = -\frac{5}{4}$ 13. $\frac{11}{4}$ 15. $\frac{4b}{a}$ 17. $(4, 0)$; $(1, -3)$; $(-1, 1)$ 19. Yes 21. No

Page 528 Algebra Review Capsule for Section 12-4 2. $y = 4 - 2x$ 3. $y = 2x - 4$ 4. $y = 3x - 1$
5. $y = 3x - 6$ 6. $y = -\frac{3}{7}x + 3$ 7. $y = -2x - 3$ 8. $y = -\frac{4}{3}x + 3$ 9. $y = \frac{-3x + 1}{5}$ 10. $3x - 12$ 11. $-2x + 12$ 12. $-t - 8$ 13. $-16 + 5r$ 14. $\frac{1}{9}x - 1$ 15. $-\frac{5}{7}q - 5$ 16. $d - \frac{33}{15}$ 17. $30r - \frac{100}{3}$

Page 529 Classroom Exercises 1. The line also passes through $(-7, 0)$ and $(1, 4)$. 3. $y - 2 = \frac{3}{5}(x + 3)$ 5. $y = -\frac{1}{2}x + \frac{5}{2}$; $-\frac{1}{2}$, $\frac{5}{2}$ 7. $y = 3x - 5$; 3; -5

Page 529 Written Exercises In Ex. 1-6, two additional points that each line passes through are given in a. Answers may vary in a. 1. a. $(1, 3)$, $(-1, -3)$ b. $y = 3x$ 3. a. $(1, 6)$, $(4, 8)$ b. $y - 4 = \frac{2}{3}(x + 2)$ 5. a. $(1, 1)$, $(3, 2)$ b. $y = \frac{1}{2}(x + 1)$ 7. $y = 3x - 13$ 9. $y = \frac{2}{3}x + 3$ 11. $y = \frac{3}{4}x - \frac{17}{4}$ 13. $y = -2x + 4$; -2; 4 15. $y = -\frac{3}{4}x + 3$; $-\frac{3}{4}$; 3 17. $y = -\frac{2}{3}x + 2$; $-\frac{2}{3}$; 2 19. $y = x + 2$ 21. $y = 2x - 3$ 23. $y = \frac{1}{3}x + 4$ 25. $y = \frac{5}{2}x - \frac{13}{2}$ 27. $y = -\frac{1}{5}x$ 29. The line passes through $(0, -7)$ and $(1, -5)$. 31. The slope of $\overleftrightarrow{PQ}$ is $\frac{y - y_1}{x - x_1}$. Since the slope is given to be m, $\frac{y - y_1}{x - x_1} = m$, and $y - y_1 = m(x - x_1)$. 33. $y = \frac{4}{3}x + \frac{10}{3}$

Page 530 Review 1. F; In the third quadrant, $y < 0$. 2. T 3. T 4. T 5. F; $y = 3$ is parallel to the x axis. 6. T 7. F; For neither set of coordinates does $y = 3$. 8. T 9. $(6, 1)$ 10. $(-\frac{1}{2}, -\frac{1}{2})$ 11. $(1, -2\frac{1}{2})$ 12. $(9, 3)$ 13. 2 14. $\frac{2}{3}$ 15. 0 16. $m_{\overline{AB}}$: $\frac{1}{2}$; $m_{\overline{BC}}$: -5; $m_{\overline{CA}}$: $-\frac{3}{5}$ 17. $y = -\frac{3}{2}x + 3$ 18. $y = -\frac{4}{3}x + \frac{7}{3}$ 19. $y = \frac{3}{2}x + 2$ 20. $y = -3x + \frac{5}{2}$ 21. $y = \frac{3}{2}x + 6$ 22. $y = \frac{3}{4}x + \frac{1}{4}$ 23. $y = -\frac{2}{5}x - 7$

Page 531 Algebra Review Capsule for Section 12-5 2. $-\frac{1}{2}$ 3. $\frac{1}{8}$ 4. $\frac{1}{17}$ 5. 1 6. $-\frac{3}{2}$ 7. $\frac{b}{2}$ 8. $\frac{2t}{3}$
9. -5 10. $\frac{3}{14}$ 11. $\frac{8}{9c}$ 13. $-\frac{4}{3}$ 14. $-\frac{4}{3}$ 15. $\frac{4}{3}$ 16. -8 17. $-\frac{3}{5}$

Page 534 Classroom Exercises 1. $-\frac{2}{3}, \frac{3}{2}$ 3. 3 5. If two nonvertical lines are parallel, then they have the same slope; If two nonvertical lines have the same slope, then they are parallel.

Page 534 Written Exercises 1. $-\frac{1}{5}, -\frac{1}{5}$; parallel 3. $\frac{1}{3}$; -3; perpendicular 5. $\parallel$ 7. $\perp$ 9. $\parallel$
11. Slopes each equal $\frac{3}{5}$. Thus, equation is parallel to the graph of the given equation. 13. $y = -5x + 27$
15. $y = -3$ 17. $y = -3$ 19. $y = 4x - 3$ 21. $\frac{13}{4}$ 23. m of $\overleftrightarrow{AB} = -\frac{2}{3}$; m of $\overleftrightarrow{AC} = \frac{3}{2}$. The slopes are negative reciprocals of each other, so $\overleftrightarrow{AB} \perp \overleftrightarrow{AC}$. **25. Case I:** If two nonvertical lines are perpendicular, then their slopes are negative reciprocals. 1. $\ell_1 \perp \ell_2$ (Given) 2. Let P be the point of intersection of ℓ_1 and ℓ_2; let ℓ_1 and ℓ_2 intersect the x axis in R and S, respectively. ((1). Th. 1-2) 3. Draw $\overline{PQ} \perp$ x axis. ((2). Th. 1-9)
4. $\angle RPS$ is a right angle. ((1), (2). Def. of perpendicular lines) 5. Let PQ = h, QR = a, and QS = b. ((2), (3). Def. of segment measure) 6. In right $\triangle PRS$, $\overline{PQ}$ is the altitude to the hypotenuse. ((3), (4). Def. of right triangle, altitude, and hypotenuse) 7. $\frac{a}{h} = \frac{h}{b}$ ((6). Cor. 7-2) 8. $m_1 = \frac{h}{a}$; $m_2 = -\frac{h}{b}$ ((3). Def. of slope)
9. $\frac{1}{m_1} = \frac{a}{h}$ ((8). Th. 6-1) 10. $-m_2 = \frac{h}{b}$ ((8). Multiplication Prop.) 11. $\frac{1}{m_1} = -m_2$ ((7), (9), (10). Substitution Prop.) 12. $1 = -m_1 m_2$ ((11). Multiplication Prop.) 13. $-1 = m_1 m_2$ ((12). Multiplication Prop.)

Page 536 Geometry Review Capsule for Section 12-6 1. 13 2. 17 3. 5 4. 29 5. $\sqrt{394}$ 6. $\sqrt{689}$

Page 537 Classroom Exercises 1. 5 3. $10\sqrt{2}$ 5. $\sqrt{a^2 + b^2 - 6(a+b) + 18}$

Page 537 Written Exercises 1. $\sqrt{10}$ 3. $\sqrt{26}$ 5. 10 7. $\sqrt{2}$ 9. 9
11. $\sqrt{a^2 + b^2 + c^2 + d^2 - 2(ac + bd)}$ 13. AB = 3; BC = 5; AC = 4; Perimeter = 12 15. DE = $\sqrt{45}$, DF = $\sqrt{45}$, and EF = $\sqrt{90}$. $(DE)^2 + (DF)^2 = (EF)^2$, since $(\sqrt{45})^2 + (\sqrt{45})^2 = (\sqrt{90})^2$ 17. isosceles
19. $\sqrt{106}$ 21. 1. P_1 is at (x_1, y_1) and P_2 is at (x_2, y_2). (Given) 2. Through P_1 draw the horizontal line $\overleftrightarrow{P_1 Z}$; through P_2 draw the vertical line $\overleftrightarrow{P_2 Z}$; let Z be the intersection of the lines. ((1). Th. 1-2) 3. $\overline{P_1 Z} \perp \overline{P_2 Z}$
((2). Def. of horizontal and vertical lines) 4. $\angle P_1 Z P_2$ is a right angle. ((3). Def. of perpendicular lines)
5. In right $\triangle P_1 Z P_2$, $(P_1 P_2)^2 = (P_1 Z)^2 + (P_2 Z)^2$. ((4). Def. of right triangles; Pythagorean Th.) 6. $P_1 Z$
$= |x_2 - x_1|$; $P_2 Z = |y_2 - y_1|$ ((1), (2). Def. of segment measure) 7. $(P_1 P_2)^2 = |x_2 - x_1|^2 - |y_2 - y_1|^2$
((5), (6). Substitution Prop.) 8. $(P_1 P_2)^2 = (x_2 - x_1)^2 - (y_2 - y_1)^2$ ((7). Def. of absolute value)
9. $P_1 P_2 = \sqrt{(x_2 - x_1)^2 - (y_2 - y_1)^2}$ ((8). Def. of square root) 23. AB = $\sqrt{13}$, BC = $\sqrt{13}$, AC = $2\sqrt{13}$,
so AB + BC = AC and by the definition of betweenness of points, B is a point on $\overline{AC}$ between A and C.
25. AC = $\sqrt{a^2 - 2ac + c^2 + b^2}$, BD = $\sqrt{c^2 - 2ac + a^2 + b^2}$ since AC = BD, $\overline{AC} \cong \overline{BD}$. 27. Midpoint of $\overline{AB}$ is
$D(\frac{a}{2}, 0)$, midpoint of $\overline{BC}$ is $E(\frac{a+b}{2}, \frac{c}{2})$, midpoint of $\overline{AC}$ is $F(\frac{b}{2}, \frac{c}{2})$; the slope of $\overline{AB} = 0$; the slope of $\overline{FE} =$
$\dfrac{\frac{c}{2} - \frac{c}{2}}{\frac{a+b}{2} - \frac{b}{2}} = 0 \therefore \overline{AB} \parallel \overline{FE}$. The slope of $\overline{BC} = \dfrac{c}{b - a}$; the slope of $\overline{DF} = \dfrac{\frac{c}{2}}{\frac{b}{2} - \frac{a}{2}} = \dfrac{c}{b - a}$. $\therefore \overline{BC} \parallel \overline{DF}$. The slope of
$\overline{AC} = \frac{c}{b}$, the slope of $\overline{DE} = \dfrac{\frac{c}{2}}{\frac{a+b}{2} - \frac{a}{2}} = \dfrac{c}{b} \therefore \overline{AC} \parallel \overline{DE}$.

Page 538 Calculator Exercises (Answers may vary.) 1. 12.369317 3. 8.0622577 5. 20.248457
7. 32.310989 9. 37.161808

Page 540 Classroom Exercises 1. $x^2 + y^2 = 25$ 3. $x^2 + y^2 = 36$ 5. $(x - 5)^2 + (y + 2)^2 = 49$ 7. C(0, 0);
r = 3 9. C(4, −3); r = 10

Written Exercises 1. $x^2 + y^2 = 121$ 3. $x^2 + y^2 = \frac{1}{9}$ 5. $x^2 + y^2 = \frac{9}{16}$ 7. $(x-6)^2 + (y-3)^2$
$= 169$ 9. $(x+4)^2 + (y+5)^2 = 25$ 11. $(x - \frac{2}{3})^2 + (y-2)^2 = \frac{4}{25}$ 13. $(\frac{1}{2}, -3); 2$ 15. $(7, -8); 3$
17. $(a, -t); p$ 19. $x^2 + y^2 = 49$ 21. $x^2 + y^2 = 4$ 23. $(x-2)^2 + (y-5)^2 = 4$ 25. $(x-9)^2 + (y-1)^2$
$= 81$ 27. $(x-3)^2 + (y + \frac{5}{2})^2 = \frac{49}{4}$ 29. 75π

Page 542 **Classroom Exercises** 1. $A(0, 0); C(k, k); D(0, k)$ 3. $X(0, 0); Y(b, 0)$ 5. $O(0, 0); Y(0, h)$

Page 543 **Written Exercises** 1. $P(-b, 0); R(b, 2b); S(-b, 2b)$ 3. $A(0, 0); C(j - g, h)$ 5. $P(-c, 0); Q(0, -d)$
7. D is at $(-a, b)$; E is at (a, b); $BD = \sqrt{9a^2 + b^2}$; $AE = \sqrt{9a^2 + b^2}$ 9. For D, $x_m = a; y_m = b$; D is at (a, b).
$DB = \sqrt{a^2 + b^2}; DA = \sqrt{a^2 + b^2}; DC = \sqrt{a^2 + b^2}$. Therefore, $DA = DB = DC$, and D is equidistant from A, B,
and C. 11. R: $(2a, 0)$; T: $(2b + 2d, 2c + 2e)$; Midpoint of $\overline{RT}$: $(b + d + a, c + e)$; W: $(2b, 2c)$; S: $(2d + 2a,$
$2e)$; Midpoint of $\overline{WS}$: $(b + d + a, c + e)$. Thus, $\overline{WS}$ and $\overline{TR}$ bisect each other. 13. Let the vertices of the
square be $A(0, 0)$, $B(a, 0)$, $C(a, a)$, and $D(0, a)$. m_1 of $\overline{AC} = \frac{a-0}{a-0} = \frac{a}{a} = 1; m_2$ of $\overline{BD} = \frac{a-0}{0-a} = \frac{a}{-a} = -1$.
Therefore $m_1 \cdot m_2 = -1$. By Th. 12-3, $\overline{AC} \perp \overline{BD}$. 15. Let the vertices of the parallelogram be $A(0, 0)$, $P(a, 0)$,
$C(a + b, c)$ and $D(b, c)$. The midpoint of diagonal AC is $E(\frac{a+b}{2}, \frac{c}{2})$, and the midpoint of diagonal BD is
is $F(\frac{a+b}{2}, \frac{c}{2})$. Therefore, the midpoint of the diagonals is the same point and the diagonals bisect each other.
17. Let the vertices of the rhombus be $A(0, 0)$, $B(a, 0)$, $C(a + b, c)$, and $D(b, c)$. m_1 of $\overline{AC} = \frac{c}{a+b}$, and m_2 of
$BD = \frac{c}{b-a}$. $m_1 \cdot m_2 = (\frac{c}{a+b})(\frac{c}{b-a}) = \frac{c^2}{b^2 - a^2}$. In a rhombus AB = AD so that $(AB)^2 = (AD)^2$ or $a^2 = b^2 +$
c^2. Substituting $m_1 \cdot m_2 = \frac{c^2}{b^2 - a^2} = \frac{c^2}{-c^2} = -1$. $\therefore \overline{AC} \perp \overline{BD}$ by Th. 12-3. 19. Let the vertices of the
parallelogram be $A(0, 0)$, $B(a, 0)$, $C(a + b, c)$, and $D(b, c)$. m_1 of $\overline{AC} = \frac{c}{a+b}$, m_2 of $\overline{BD} = \frac{c}{b-a}$, and $m_1 \cdot m_2$
$= \frac{c^2}{b^2 - a^2}$. Since $\overline{AC} \perp \overline{BD}$, $m_1 \cdot m_2 = -1$ by Th. 12-3. By substituting, $\frac{c^2}{b^2 - a^2} = -1$ or $c^2 = a^2 - b^2$, or
$a^2 = b^2 + c^2$. Now $AD = \sqrt{(b-0)^2 + (c-0)^2}$ and $(AD)^2 = b^2 + c^2 = a^2$. $AB = \sqrt{(a-0)^2 + 0} = a$ and $(AB)^2$
$= a^2$. Therefore, $(AD)^2 = (AB)^2$ or AD = AB and $\overline{AD} \cong \overline{AB}$. Since ABCD is a parallelogram, $\overline{AD} \cong \overline{BC}$ and
$\overline{AB} \cong \overline{CD}$, therefore $\overline{AD} \cong \overline{AB} \cong \overline{BC} \cong \overline{CD}$ and the parallelogram is a rhombus. 21. Let the vertices of the
triangle be $A(0, 0)$, $B(2a, 0)$, $C(2b, 2c)$. By Th. 12-1, the midpoints of $\overline{AB}$, $\overline{AC}$, and $\overline{BC}$ are $D(a, 0)$, $E(b, c)$, and
$F(a + b, c)$ respectively. The equation of $\overleftrightarrow{CD}$ is $(2b - a)y - 2cx = -2ca$. The equation of $\overleftrightarrow{BE}$ is $(b - 2a)y - cx$
$= -2ac$. The equation of $\overleftrightarrow{AF}$ is $(a + b)y - cx = 0$. The intersection of $\overleftrightarrow{CD}$ and $\overleftrightarrow{BE}$ is $G(\frac{2}{3}(a + b), \frac{2}{3}c)$, which also
lies on $\overleftrightarrow{AF}$. $AG = \frac{2}{3}\sqrt{(a + b)^2 + c^2}$, $BG = \frac{2}{3}\sqrt{(-2a + b)^2 + c^2}$, $CG = \frac{2}{3}\sqrt{(-2b + a)^2 + (-2c)^2}$,
$AF = \sqrt{(a + b)^2 + c^2}$, $BE = \sqrt{(b - 2a)^2 + c^2}$, $CD = \sqrt{(2b - a)^2 + (2c)^2}$. Then $AG = \frac{2}{3}AF$, $BG = \frac{2}{3}BE$, and
$CG = \frac{2}{3}CD$. 23. The slope of $ax + by + c = 0$ is $-\frac{a}{b}$. The slope of line $\ell \perp$ line k is $\frac{b}{a}$. Line ℓ passes through $(x_1,$
$y_1)$ so the equation for line ℓ is $y - y_1 = \frac{b}{a}(x - x_1)$ or $bx - ay - bx_1 + ay_1 = 0$; Solving the equations for lines k
and ℓ simultaneously, we find that $x = \frac{b^2 x_1 - aby_1 - ac}{a^2 + b^2}$ and $y = \frac{-abx_1 + a^2 y_1 - bc}{a^2 + b^2}$ $\therefore$ line k and line ℓ intersect at point $P\left(\frac{b^2 x_1 - aby_1 - ac}{a^2 + b^2}, \frac{-abx_1 + a^2 y_1 - bc}{a^2 + b^2}\right)$. The distance d between (x_1, y_1) and P is
$d = \sqrt{\left(x_1 - \frac{b^2 x_1 - aby_1 - ac}{a^2 + b^2}\right)^2 + \left(y_1 - \frac{-abx_1 + a^2 y_1 - bc}{a^2 + b^2}\right)^2} = \frac{|ax_1 + by_1 + c|}{\sqrt{a^2 + b^2}}$.

Page 545 **Review** 1. perpendicular 2. parallel 3. perpendicular 4. neither 5. $y = \frac{1}{4}x + 8$
6. $y = \frac{1}{2}x - \frac{15}{2}$ 7. $\sqrt{26}$ 8. $\sqrt{194}$ 9. $\sqrt{41}$ 10. $2\sqrt{13} + \sqrt{26}$ 11. $2\sqrt{2}; 4\sqrt{2}$ 12. $(0, 0); 7$
13. $(0, 0); 12$

14. $(3, -2); 4$ 15. $(x + 8)^2 + (y - 5)^2 = 36$ 16. Let the vertices of the parallelogram be $A(0, 0)$, $B(a, 0)$, $C(a + b, c)$, and $D(b, c)$. Then $AB = a$, $BC = \sqrt{b^2 + c^2}$, $CD = a$, and $AD = \sqrt{b^2 + c^2}$. Diagonal $AC = \sqrt{(a + b)^2 + c^2}$ and diagonal $BD = \sqrt{(a - b)^2 + c^2}$. The sum of the squares of the sides = $a^2 + (b^2 + c^2) + a^2 + (b^2 + c^2) = 2a^2 + 2b^2 + 2c^2$. The sum of the squares of the diagonals = $(a + b)^2 + c^2 + (a - b)^2 + c^2 = a^2 + 2ab + b^2 + c^2 + a^2 - 2ab + b^2 + c^2 = 2a^2 + 2b^2 + 2c^2$. Therefore, the sums are equal.

Page 546   Chapter Objectives and Review   1. 5 left, 3 up   3. 3 left, 4 down   5. $(1, 6)$ 7. $(-3, \frac{7}{2})$ 9. 0
11. $y = \frac{3}{2}x - 6$ 13. $y = -2x + 7$ 15. $y = 3x - 9$ 17. $12y = -x + 8$ 19. neither   21. 10   23. $x^2 + y^2 = 9$ 25. $(x + 2)^2 + (y - 4) = \frac{1}{4}$ 27. $(1, 0); 5$ 29. Let $A(0, 0)$, $B(a, 0)$, $C(b, c)$ and $D(d, c)$ be the vertices of the trapezoid with bases AB and DC. The midpoint of $\overline{AD}$ is $E(\frac{d}{2}, \frac{c}{2})$, and the midpoint of $\overline{BC}$ is $F(\frac{a + b}{2}, \frac{c}{2})$ so that $\overline{EF}$ is the median of the trapezoid. m of $\overline{AB} = \frac{0 - 0}{a - 0} = 0$, m of $\overline{DC} = \frac{c - c}{b - d} = 0$, m of $\overline{EF} = \dfrac{\frac{c}{2} - \frac{c}{2}}{\frac{a + b}{2} - \frac{d}{2}}$
$= 0$. Therefore by Th. 12-2, $\overline{EF} \parallel \overline{AB}$ and $\overline{EF} \parallel \overline{DC}$.

Page 548   Chapter Test   1. IV   3. $-4; (0, 7)$ 5. $(-1, 4)$ 7. 2   9. $y + 3 = \frac{1}{2}(x - 2)$ 11. perpendicular
13. $(x + 2)^2 + (y - 3)^2 = 16$ 15. Let $A(0, 0)$, $B(a, 0)$, $C(a - b, c)$, and $D(b, c)$ be the vertices. $DB = \sqrt{(a - b)^2 + c^2}$; $AC = \sqrt{(a - b)^2 + c^2}$; $\therefore DB = AC$ and $\overline{DB} \cong \overline{AC}$.

CHAPTER 13: INTRODUCTION TO TRANSFORMATIONS

Page 551   Classroom Exercises
1. a. 2 b. any two points   3. a. 2 b. endpoints   5. a. 3 b. each vertex   7. a. 6 b. each vertex
9. No

Page 551   Written Exercises
1.

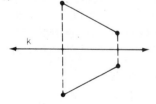

3.

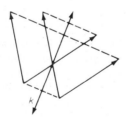

5.

7. Line k is the bisector of the angle formed by the intersection of lines r and s.   9. Let the midpoints be P, Q, and R; $\triangle A'B'C'$ can be determined by using Th. 5-13.   11. They are congruent.   13. Reflect trapezoid ABCD through S to obtain parallelogram C'BCB'. Let h = height of both figures. Area of trapezoid ABCD $= \frac{1}{2}$(Area of parallelogram C'BCB') = (ST)h. This is also the area of a rectangle with base ST and height h.

Page 554   Classroom Exercises   1. None   3. 3   5. 2   7. 1   9. Yes

Page 555   Written Exercises   1. A : 1; B : 1; C : 1; D : 1; E : 1; H : 2; I : 2; J : none   3. None (if it is scalene)
5. 4   7. 3   9. Segment P''Q'' will be parallel to segment PQ.   11. $\triangle$ABC is mapped onto $\triangle$A''B''C'' by a translation over parallel lines and a reflection over k. (Answers will vary.)   13. 9   15. 2a   17. 5 cm
19. $(-5, 1)$ 21. $M(1, 0)$ 23. Draw $\overline{PP'}$ and bisect it. Label the midpoint M. Construct the perpendicular bisectors of segments MP and MP'. These two perpendicular bisectors are the parallel lines.

Page 558 Written Exercises

1.
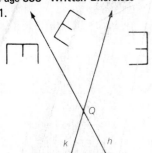

3.
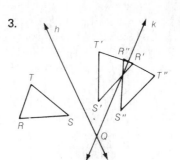

5.
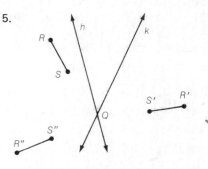

7. 1 cm   9. 94   11. 82   13. Draw segment AB. Construct the perpendicular bisector of $\overline{AB}$. Since B is the image of A, the perpendicular bisector is the line of reflection. Draw segment BC. Construct the perpendicular bisector of $\overline{BC}$. Similarly, since C is the image of B, this bisector is the line of reflection. These two reflecting lines intersect in P.   15.
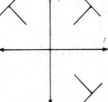
   17. (0, 5) or (0, −5)   19. (1, 3) or (−1, −3)

Page 561   Classroom Exercises   1. ≈ 5 cm; ≈ 3 cm; $\frac{QA'}{QA} \approx \frac{5}{3}$; ≈ 5.5 cm; ≈ 3.3 cm; $\frac{QB'}{QB} \approx \frac{5}{3}$ 3. $\frac{5}{3}$

Page 562   Written Exercises   1. 4   3. $\frac{5}{3}$ 5. 14   7. 5 : 3   9. 94   11. Yes   13. A'B' = 2 cm, A'C' = 4 cm, B'C' = 4 cm   15. ABCD   17. Yes   19. 42 sq. units   21. A'$(-\frac{7}{3}, \frac{8}{3})$, B'(−3, 3), C'$(-\frac{10}{3}, \frac{5}{3})$
23. 9 sq. units

Page 564   Chapter Objectives and Review

1.
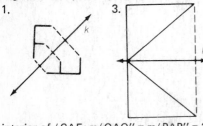

3.

5. 2   7. 4   9. Segment R''S'' will be parallel to segment RS. $\overline{R'S'}$ is the reflection of $\overline{RS}$ over h. $\overline{R''S''}$ is the reflection of $\overline{R'S'}$ over k, or the translation of $\overline{RS}$ over h and k.   11. Answers will vary.   13. Let A be the point of intersection of h and k. Let D be a point on h in the half-plane with edge k which contains $\overline{PQ}$. Let C be a point on k in the half-plane with edge h which does not contain $\overline{PQ}$. Let E be a point on h such that A is between E and D. Then the final image segment P''Q'' is in the interior of ∠CAE; m∠QAQ'' = m∠PAP'' = 2m∠DAC; QA = Q''A and PA = P''A.   15. 27   17. 32

Page 565   Chapter Test   1. P   3. $\overline{PY}$ 5. ∠T   7. 10 cm   9. translation   11. 6   13. 18   15. 8.5

Page 566   Cumulative Review: Chapters 12-13   1. c   3. d   5. c   7. d   9. b   11. b   13. d   15. b
17. a   19. b   21. b

C 5
D 6
E 7
F 8
G 9
H 0
I 1

445 - 2-8 even